The New Certificate Geography Series

ADVANCED LEVEL

EUROPE

excluding the British Isles and U.S.S.R.

The New Certificate Geography Series

ADVANCED LEVEL

EUROPE

excluding the British Isles and U.S.S.R.

J. J. BRANIGAN, M.A., F.R.G.S.

*Formerly Deputy Headmaster and Head of Geography
and Geology Departments, St. Bede's Grammar School, Bradford*

MACDONALD & EVANS LTD
8 John Street, London, W.C.1
1965

First published September 1965
Reprinted October 1966

©

MACDONALD & EVANS LTD
1965

The New Certificate Geography Series

ADVANCED LEVEL

Australasia
Africa
Latin America
North America
The United States
of America
Monsoon Asia

Other volumes in the series
are in the course of preparation on:

The British Isles
The U.S.S.R.

Printed in Great Britain by Richard Clay (The Chaucer Press), Ltd.,
Bungay, Suffolk

GENERAL INTRODUCTION TO THE SERIES

THE study of geography in the Sixth Form has been seriously handicapped in the past through the lack of suitable textbooks. There was no shortage of advanced books at university level, and this meant that pupils who had only just ceased using elementary texts, usually general world geographies, were suddenly introduced to volumes intended for university students. The gap between the two was wide, often too wide for the immature pupil who had only recently passed geography at "O" level. The reading, understanding and digesting of serious studies called for an outlook, comprehension and breadth of knowledge which the average first-year Sixth Former frankly did not possess. Among pupils and teachers there was a felt need for texts which would bridge the gap; for books which were not elementary nor yet abstruse but intermediate in approach, content and style; for books which were clearly arranged and which dealt with ideas and terms new to pupils beginning Sixth Form work. It is a matter of some surprise that such texts have taken so long to appear.

The aim of this new series is to produce such texts, books which are essentially intermediate and more nearly meet the requirements of the Sixth Form student who is beginning to do much work on his own. New ideas and concepts are introduced, facts and figures are as up-to-date as it is possible to make them, maps and diagrams have been kept simple and clear, and a lucid exposition has been aimed at. The authors hope that their efforts will satisfy both students and teachers who are searching for a readily understandable but sufficiently comprehensive text.

While the books in the series have a uniform lay-out and adopt a similar technique in exposition, it has been thought desirable to allow each author to choose his own method of geographical presentation. No attempt has been made to produce stereotyped texts. Flexibility of approach has been considered more desirable. Some continents are more amenable to treatment by regions than others; in some cases it is probably better to follow a description by countries rather than by regions; and in some instances there are special problems that need high-lighting. For these principal reasons each continental area or major world region is afforded differing treatment.

H. ROBINSON
Geographical Editor

AUTHOR'S PREFACE

THE geography of Europe as treated in this book excludes detailed regional study of the British Isles and the U.S.S.R., but both are included in the introductory chapters of Part One. A close examination of the geography of the British Isles at this level warrants a separate volume, and so does an extended study of the U.S.S.R., which involves a large portion of Asia. The remaining area of the continent is often called "peninsular Europe," and this term is used for it throughout the book.

Hitherto, most advanced textbooks on Europe have been written for university rather than grammar or comprehensive school students. The object of this book is specifically to bridge the gap between school and university. It aims at the Advanced Level of the G.C.E. and will also serve students who are preparing for the Special or Scholarship papers in Geography. It is hoped that in addition it will be of interest to the general reader, especially in its treatment of the under-developed countries of Europe and its consideration of the impact of history on present political and economic problems.

Part One deals with the geographical background of the continent as a whole; it includes an introductory account of the physical geography of European seas, and such subjects as river régimes and international frontiers, about which information often has to be sought in separate textbooks. The second—and larger—section of the book considers Europe country by country, which is the method most teachers adopt. The countries are first grouped on a major regional basis, then examined separately as part of the major natural regions. In most cases, each country is further sub-divided on more or less traditional lines and treated thus from both a physical and economic viewpoint. Occasionally some repetition is necessarily involved, when the same subject is looked at from different aspects, but this is felt to be if anything an advantage as it will help the points to sink in.

Great care has been taken to obtain up-to-date information on economic advances, especially for the under-developed countries of Europe. The latest available statistics have been used, but statistical tables have been purposely avoided. For the latest information in this sphere I am indebted to the relevant departments of every European government, and I should like to express my gratitude to the Ambassadors and Foreign Relations staffs of the embassies and legations listed on p. 597, who have also provided most of the photographs.

History is inseparable from a study of European geography, and each chapter has a section on the development of the country as a geographical unit, with emphasis on the political and economic factors which have led to the emergence in this century of several new states.

Maps and diagrams have been specially drawn to illustrate the text, and an effort has been made to include on them every place-name mentioned in the text. Where there are alternative names or where names have been changed, both forms are given at least once. Sample examination questions are appended to each chapter, and a list of more general questions added at the end of the book, which is a summary of the present political and economic position of peninsular Europe. Both Centigrade and Fahrenheit figures are given wherever temperature is mentioned throughout the book.

Among the many works used in connection with the writing of this book, I received valuable help from Gottmann's *Geography of Europe*, Hoffman's *Geography of Europe*, Pounds' *Europe and the Mediterranean*, Monkhouse's *Western Europe*, Dickinson's *Germany*, Sinnhüber's *Germany*, Walker's *Mediterranean Lands* and Robinson's *Mediterranean Lands*, and I acknowledge it gratefully. All these titles are included in a "Short Guide to Further Reading and Study" at the end of the book. I am grateful to the Joint Matriculation Board and the Oxford and Cambridge Schools Examinations Board for their permission to use questions set by them; they are distinguished by "J.M.B." or "O. & C." in the lists of questions. My thanks are due also to Messrs Longmans, Green & Co. (London) and John Wiley and Sons (New York) for the use of the quotation from Monkhouse's *Western Europe* in Chapter XIV. Finally, I must thank Dr Harry Robinson, the editor of this series, who read the manuscript of this book and made useful suggestions, and my wife, who has given constant encouragement and moral support in my search for material.

July 1965

J.J.B.

CONTENTS

LIST OF ILLUSTRATIONS

PART ONE

THE GEOGRAPHICAL FRAMEWORK

Chapter I

STRUCTURE AND RELIEF

INTRODUCTORY

EUROPE is a "peninsula of peninsulas." It projects westwards from the continent of Asia and has a large number of subsidiary peninsulas, the main ones being Scandinavia, Denmark, Iberia, Italy and Greece. The Baltic, Mediterranean, Adriatic and Aegean seas, together with the Arctic and Atlantic oceans, and the Black and Caspian seas to the east, have given Europe a coastline longer in proportion to its area than that of any other continent. Except in eastern Europe, no point is more than 400 miles from the sea, a factor of great significance where climate and transport are concerned. The continent narrows in the west; yet in this more restricted area are the densest populations and it is here that Western civilisation has developed over the past two hundred years.

Except for Australasia, Europe is the smallest continent. With an area of about 3,800,000 square miles, it has less than 7% of the total land surface of the globe; but its great variety of relief and soils, its large proportion of productive agricultural land, its comparative freedom from climatic extremes and its mineral wealth—especially of coal and iron— have been responsible for outstanding cultural and economic development. Within its small area live nearly 600 million people, about a fifth of the world's population, with an average density of almost 150 per square mile, compared with less than 100 for Asia and only 4 for Australasia.

The limits of Europe are well-defined in the north, west and south, where the Arctic and Atlantic oceans, the Mediterranean and Black seas (connected by straits and the Sea of Marmara), form clear-cut boundaries. To the east, however, the division from Asia is not so obvious, for it runs through part of the U.S.S.R. The usually accepted boundary runs along the Ural mountains, the Ural river and the Caucasus mountains; but this ignores a lowland gap of about 200 miles north of the Caspian Sea. Others place the southern part of the boundary along the Manych depression just north of the Caucasus. The division between Europe and Asia recognised by the Russians is a line along the crests of the northern Urals, the western edges of the Soviet republics of Siberia and Kazakhstan, and the crests of the Caucasus; but of course the Soviet Union is not very interested in a continental boundary that splits its territory in two.

Most of Europe lies in temperate latitudes, only a very small area reaching northwards beyond the Arctic Circle, where North Cape in Norway, 71 degrees N., is the most northerly point on the mainland. The most southerly mainland point is Cape Tarifa in Spain, 36 degrees N.

THE STRUCTURAL PATTERN

GENERAL CONSIDERATIONS

The physical map of Europe (*see* Fig. 1) shows marked differences in relief between east and west. In the east is a vast plain stretching from the shores of the Arctic Ocean to the Black and Caspian Seas. To the west lies a complex succession of mountain ranges, plateaus, valleys and plains which look very confused on the map but have in fact a simple geological pattern. They are the result of four periods of *orogenesis* or mountain-building, each accompanied by widespread shattering effects and followed by long periods of erosion. More recently in geological time, most of this western region has been affected by the ice sheets and glaciers of the Quaternary Ice Age. In the north of the western division of Europe is the oldest part of the continent, the mountainous mass of Scandinavia, which slopes gradually to the plain of Finland. South of it lies a plain stretching from the Atlantic coast to Poland, geologically the youngest major region of Europe. Still farther south, a discontinuous belt of hills and plateaus borders the plain, older than the plain itself but younger than the northern mountains. These hills press against the most outstanding and most recently formed mountain ranges, which stretch across the south of Europe from end to end, and are known as the Alpine system.

THE RUSSIAN PLATFORM

The great plain of eastern Europe lies mainly in the U.S.S.R. and is called the Russian platform, because of its flatness. Since early Palaeozoic (Silurian) times there has been only slight epeirogenic (vertical) movement in this area, so that shallow seas have been able to flood it and sediments to cover it with clays, sandstones and conglomerates, from Permian to Tertiary times. A geological section from north to south across the plain shows a very slight dip towards the south, with outcrops of older rocks in the north and younger ones in the south. A small amount of local warping and faulting has scarcely affected the level surface, except to

Fig. 1.—Europe: structure. The Caledonian system is of Siluro-Devonian age; the rocks of the Hercynian and Median blocks are Carbo-Permian. Rocks of Triassic, Rhaetic, Jurassic, Cretaceous and Tertiary age make up the Alps and most of the lowlands, while large areas in the north have superficial deposits of Quaternary age. All the recognised geological systems are found in Europe.

produce undulations which have been accentuated by river erosion. The present surface of the plain is covered with sands, gravels, silts and loess of Quaternary age. The Hercynian orogenesis caused a folding of the rocks in the east of the plain, to produce the Ural mountains; another raised the Donets plateau in the south. Warping, followed by the erosion of the younger rocks near the surface, has left a "window" of pre-Cambrian rocks between the rivers Dnieper and Bug, in the Ukraine.

THE NORTH-WEST MOUNTAINS

These belong to two systems of orogenesis, the Charnian and the Caledonian, roughly 600 and 400 million years ago respectively. All that remains of the Charnian mountain system is a flattish peneplain in eastern Scandinavia and Finland, for the most part less than 600 ft above sea level, known as the Fenno-Scandian or Baltic Shield (because a slight doming of the rocks has produced a shield-like shape). The crystalline granites, gneisses and schists are the oldest surface rocks in Europe—roughly contemporary with the Wrekin, Charnwood Forest and the Malvern Hills in England, and with the Dnieper "window" mentioned above. The Baltic Shield was scraped bare of its soil by the ice sheets of the Quaternary Ice Age; the same glaciers scooped out rock basins to produce thousands of lakes in Finland, whose native name is *Suomi* (Lakeland). To the east and south-east the Shield merges into the Russian platform.

West of the Baltic Shield are the remains of the Caledonian mountain system, lying partly in the west of Scandinavia and partly in the highlands of Scotland and northern Ireland. The mountain folds, dating from Siluro-Devonian times, were worn down to a peneplain, so that the present surface represents the roots of the original mountains. Then, near the end of the Tertiary period, and possibly connected in some way with the uplift of the Alpine system, there was extensive fracturing and subsidence to form the basins of the north Atlantic between Spitzbergen, Europe and Iceland. At the same time the peneplain was faulted, uplifted and tilted, with the highest parts nearer the Atlantic and a more gradual slope eastwards. Along the edges of the subsidence which produced the ocean basins were outflows of basaltic lava and the eruption of volcanic cones. The basalts of Iceland, western Scotland and north-eastern Ireland belong to this period, and so does the volcanic peak of Sulitelma (Sulitjelma) in northern Norway.

The granites, gneisses and schists of which the Caledonian mountains are largely composed have worn away slowly, especially in Scandinavia: the uplifted blocks are like huge platforms cut by deep valleys where faulting weakened them. They are not very high—3000–4000 ft in Scotland (Ben Nevis, 4406 ft) to 6000–7000 ft in Norway (Glittertind, 8140 ft). The highest peaks are of more resistant gneiss or gabbro, which in Norway stood above the ice sheets of the Ice Age, as do some of the *nunataks* of Greenland today.

The whole of the area has been intensively glaciated. It was completely covered by ice sheets in the Quaternary Ice Age; and their movement outwards carried the surface soils to the plains of Russia, Poland, Germany, the Low Countries and England, where they were deposited as sands, gravels and boulder-clays, and in some cases blown as dust to form loess farther south. The high plateaus in many parts of Norway are still almost completely lacking in surface soil, with large stretches of polished rock and rounded knobs. These high areas are called *fjells* (fells). Some of them contain considerable ice sheets, relics of the Quaternary glaciation.

The fault-valleys, often occupied by rivers, were deepened by glaciers, especially in the later stages of the Ice Age, and were given the characteristic U-shape. When the ice finally melted the resultant deepening of the neighbouring seas, helped by slight isostatic movement of the plateau blocks, drowned the valleys near the coasts to form the fiords of Norway and lochs of western Scotland; and the Baltic and North Seas, the Strait of Dover and the English Channel assumed their present shapes.

Another result of the ice movements, already noted in the Baltic Shield, was the formation of lakes. In Scandinavia they were formed on the fjells by the ice scooping basins where the rock was less resistant. Others were formed along the line where the Caledonian mountain system meets the Baltic Shield—the glint-line lakes which are so remarkable a feature in Sweden. These were probably trapped between a retreating, melting ice sheet and the mountain blocks, the formation of basins being helped by rejuvenation of the rivers flowing from a slowly rising land mass. Other lakes were formed by barriers of moraine left across the path of rivers, or the over-deepening of river valleys.

THE CENTRAL MOUNTAIN BLOCKS

In Carbo-Permian times, roughly 200 million years ago, a series of great folds, the Hercynian system, was uplifted across the middle of Europe in a general east–west direction. The name comes from *Hercynia silva*, the Latin term for the forests of the Bohemian block which was part of the system, which has been adopted for all formations of similar geological age. The folds were originally high mountains, but long denudation wore them down to a low peneplain. They subsided and were covered by shallow seas and sediments washed down in Permian, Jurassic and Cretaceous times. Sub-tropical forests flourished on the deltas and coastal swamps formed during the slow subsidence, subsequently to decay into the coal measures scattered along the flanks, especially on the northern side, of the Hercynian system.

When the Alpine system was uplifted in Tertiary times, the resultant pressures from the south fractured the worn-down Hercynian folds, causing some blocks to be forced up and others down. The uplifted portions form block-plateaus rather than mountains; they vary in height from about 2000 to over 6000 ft. Moreover, they were tilted, with their steepest and most elevated slopes on the side nearer the Alpine folds. The uplift of the Hercynian blocks was accompanied by faulting, so that several of the plateaus are cut by long, deep valleys, as in the Central Massif of France and the Rhine highlands. These, with the Ardennes, the Vosges, the Black Forest, the Harz mountains, and the Bohemian "diamond," lie along the north of the Alpine ranges; and encircled by folds of the Alpine system are the Meseta of Spain, the islands of Corsica and Sardinia, the Bihor massif in Transylvania, and the Char and Rhodope blocks in the Balkan peninsula. The German name *horst* has been given to the uplifted blocks, and *graben* to the areas of subsidence, such as the rift valley of the Rhine. Volcanic activity took place along the fracture lines, and extinct volcanoes, very much eroded, are found on the Central Massif of France (there called *puys*), the Eifel in Germany and the Erzgebirge in Czecho-slovakia.

Though the Hercynian blocks—they are also known in the west as Armorican or Variscan "fragments"—are mainly of rocks which break down only very slowly into soil, they are much more favourable to human occupation than their formation would suggest. They are easily pene-trated from the side away from the Alpine ranges; for instance, the Meseta drops to a plain on the Portuguese side, and the Central Massif of France presents little obstacle when approached from the Paris basin or the plain of Aquitaine. Moreover, the younger sedimentaries which have been eroded from the horsts are still to be found in the gaps between the blocks and in the numerous graben, broken down into fertile soils; the volcanic soils are rich; and in the river valleys there are productive silts. The Hercynian blocks are low plateaus which rarely form serious obstacles to communication; and they contain igneous intrusions rich enough in minerals to have encouraged early use of metals in the Meseta, the Erz-gebirge (Ore mountains), the Rhine highlands and elsewhere, with con-sequent population concentrations.

THE ALPINE SYSTEM

The most recent mountain-building movement in Europe originated in Tertiary times, roughly 20 million years ago, and it produced the Alpine system. Before the uplift took place there was an ancient sea, Tethys, far wider than the present Mediterranean, between two land masses which we can think of as "Eurasia" and "Africa," although they were of different shape and area from the present continents. The sea occupied a great geosyncline in which were laid down sedimentary rocks, chiefly limestones. Then, for some reason not yet explained, the continental masses began to move towards each other. The sedimentary rocks on the floor of Tethys buckled into folds, some simple, some complex. The folds

[*Courtesy of Swiss National Tourist Office.*

FIG. 2.—Switzerland: a view in the Pennine Alps. Note the frost-shattered peak, the snow-field in a cirque, an arête, a scree and an alluvial fan.

were forced on to the edges of the continents and in the north pressed against the resistant Hercynian blocks, rising out of the sea to form mountain ranges.

The ranges were in two series, north and south. The northern series has been called the Alpides, the southern one the Dinarides. Between them were enclosed some of the Hercynian blocks or horsts, like the Meseta and the Rhodope; and the graben of the western Mediterranean, the Hungarian (or Pannonian) basin and the Black Sea were consequences of Hercynian subsidence (*see* Fig. 2).

The Alpides consist of the Sierra Nevada (or Betic Cordillera), the Cantabrians and the Pyrenees in Spain; the main ranges of the Alps in

south-east France, Switzerland and Austria; the great curve of the Carpathians, the Transylvanian Alps and the Balkans (Stara Planina); the
Yaila mountains in the Crimea, and the Caucasus. The Alpides continue
far to the east in Asia—to the northern Pamirs and ranges such as the Tien
Shan.

The Dinarides include the Atlas mountains in north-west Africa;
Sicily; the Apennines and southern ranges of the Alps in Italy; the Dinaric
Alps and Pindus mountains in Yugoslavia and Greece; the island of Crete;
and the Taurus mountains in Asia Minor. Asiatic continuations of the
Dinarides appear to include the mighty Himalayas; but as yet the exact
relationship of the Tertiary ranges of Asia to those of Europe has not been
fully established.

The folds of the Alpides and Dinarides are in a series of great arcs,
seen very well in the Carpathians. Where the two series approached each
other closely, as they did in northern Italy, the tremendous pressures
produced a complicated system of folds which were broken and forced
northwards on top of each other in vast overthrusts and nappes, as in
Switzerland (*see* Fig. 70). These have so dislocated the original folds as to
make it extremely difficult to reconstruct the mountain-building in this
area. Nappes are found also in the Betic Cordillera, the Apennines, the
Carpathians and the Dinaric Alps. The vastly more complicated geology
of the Alpides as compared with the Dinarides suggests that the resistance
of the Hercynian system was a major factor in the Alpine orogenesis.
The difficulty of explaining what happened is increased by the presence
of very much older crystalline rocks laid bare by erosion of the predominant limestones in most of the folds. These crystalline rocks are
found in the highest peaks in Switzerland and France (Mont Blanc,
15,681 ft), and in the Caucasus, the highest mountains in Europe (Mt.
Elbruz, 18,467 ft).

As the folds of the Alpine system were rising, sediments were deposited
in shallow seas on their flanks. These deposits became mostly clays and
sandstones, known as *flysch*. They are found on the northern sides of the
Alps proper and in the Apennines. Erosion has been rapid throughout
the system, more in the Alpides than in the Dinarides. It has been suggested that, for the northern ranges to have their present altitude, there
must have been a slow but continuous rising of the whole system after
the first orogenesis or folding. That stability has not yet been reached is
shown by earthquakes and vulcanicity, especially in the Dinarides.
Violent and destructive earth movements have been frequent along the
whole length of the system, and there are active volcanoes in Italy, Sicily
and Asia Minor. During the Ice Age, most of the Alpides were glaciated,
so that the mountains show all the characteristics associated with valley

glaciers. There are today many peaks perpetually covered with snow, and some quite extensive glaciers in the high valleys of the Alps.

One of the results of glaciation was to make the Alpides more open to human penetration and settlement than the Dinarides, by reason of the deep valleys carved out by the ice. Though the actual peaks are higher, numerous passes make the ranges easier to cross, and from very early times the Alps, Pyrenees, Carpathians and Balkans have supported considerable numbers of people. The Dinarides, on the other hand, are less eroded because they are not so faulted and broken and because they are in a drier climate. Their limestones have weathered into rugged and often almost impenetrable masses with precipitous slopes, as in the central Apennines and the ranges east of the Adriatic. All these areas have only a scanty population.

THE EUROPEAN PLAIN

Associated with the orogenic movements which caused the Alpine system was a series of oscillations of the sea floor north of the Hercynian blocks. The floor was already warped and slightly folded by the Hercynian movements. In Tertiary times sediments were washed down on to it from the rising Alpine system. The final result was a plain which extended from the North Sea to the Russian platform, lifted in Tertiary times only a little above sea level. Slight warpings have made it undulating rather than flat, and in Quaternary times—the last 100,000 years— the ice sheets radiating from Scandinavia have deposited on it boulder-clays, gravels, sands and the terminal moraines of the last glacial phase. The relief is low-lying and disorderly, especially in the northern section, where moraines covered with clays run in a broken and criss-crossing pattern of low hills from Denmark to Poland; there are eskers, kames and drumlins rising above the general surface, and lakes, swamps and bogs in the depressions. The effects of the glaciation reached as far south as the Hercynian blocks, but the streams flowing from the front of the melting ice sheets "sorted" their load so as to cover the southern section of the plain with finer and more fertile silts. Post-glacial winds blew great quantities of dust southwards; it accumulated in considerable depth on the flanks of the central mountains or was carried south-eastwards to cover the southern portion of Poland and Russia with fine-grained loess, which has developed into the famous Black Earth of today.

The western end of the European plain shared the movements which caused oscillation of the surface, but in addition it was affected by isostatic sinking during the glacial epoch. The great weight of ice on the north-west corner of Europe pressed the land down several hundred feet. When the ice melted, the seas filled up again and flooded neighbouring lowlands. Thus the North Sea, the Irish Sea and the English Channel were formed and the shape of the Baltic Sea modified. The land, freed from its load of ice, is once more rising, but at a very slow rate. The "raised beaches" in the south-west of England, and on the coasts of Wales, Scotland and Norway, are indications of this slow uplift.

Throughout its length the European plain has been modified by river action and the deposition of alluvium, but fertility varies with the type of glacial detritus laid down on it. In the north the heterogeneous mixture of boulder-clays, gravels and coarse sands is not at all productive and supports only poor agriculture. Much of it remains under coniferous forest. South of the morainic hills there are still sands and gravels which are dry, porous and infertile, and give rise to much heathland. Only in the south, where there are clays or loess, is the plain rich in agricultural produce and capable of supporting a dense population.

STUDY QUESTIONS

1. Divide Europe into major physical regions, and give a reasoned account of *one* of the divisions you indicate.

2. Write short notes on *four* of the following and say where examples of those you select may be found in Europe: nunatak, fjell, horst, nappe, glint-line, puy. Where possible, use diagrams to illustrate your answer.

3. Describe the landscape you might expect to find in *either* the Caledonian mountain region *or* on the Germano–Polish plain.

Chapter II

EUROPEAN SEAS AND RIVERS

COASTS AND NEIGHBOURING SEAS

THE CONTINENTAL COASTLINE

Europe everywhere faces the Atlantic or one of that ocean's great extensions into the land mass, such as the Baltic and Mediterranean Seas. The northern coastline faces the Barents Sea, which is frozen for several months in winter and so reduces possibility of development of the neighbouring land. In the west, however, there is an ice-free passage to Murmansk in the Kola peninsula, and ice-breakers maintain an opening to Archangel in the White Sea. In this area, despite difficulties, the U.S.S.R. is making great economic progress. Nevertheless, the northern coasts and seas must be said to have little value for man.

The western coasts, from North Cape in Norway to Cape St Vincent in Portugal, owe their present shape mainly to the collapse of the Hercynian system in Tertiary times, which produced the North Atlantic basins and created Iceland. From this period date the rectangular shape of Iberia, the Strait of Gibraltar, the Bay of Biscay, and the deep cleft that later became the Skagerrak and Kattegat. Since the beginning of the Quaternary era there have been far-reaching changes along these coasts. Large-scale invasions of the land by melt-waters from the disappearing ice of the glacial epoch have been followed by isostatic oscillations of the land. The North Sea and English Channel were probably extensions of the Rhine and Seine valleys respectively, and were drowned when the ice retreated. The Baltic was originally a shallow lake (the Sea of Yoldia) connected to the Kattegat. When the ice melted, the land rose, breaking the outlet and making a true lake. With a tilting of the Scandinavian massif, the Baltic assumed more or less its present shape. The Irish, North, Norwegian (in part) and Baltic Seas are really submerged portions of the continental shelf. In places they are only a few feet deep at low tide. The numerous shoals in the south of the North Sea, such as the Goodwin Sands, are a constant menace to shipping, and the only easy passage into the Baltic is along the graben mentioned above. The rest of the entry is obstructed by islands and shallow waters. It is interesting to work out on a map of Europe just how much of the sea bed would become dry land if the sea level were reduced by only 300 ft.

The extensive penetration of north-west Europe by shallow seas has had important results. An obvious one is the large number of waterways and inlets far into the land mass, and the opening up to the Atlantic of countries as far east as the U.S.S.R. Fiords, rias and river estuaries provide magnificent harbours; where they are backed by open plains, convenient passes or mountain gaps, some of the largest ports in the world have developed. The tidal range in these shallow seas is great, especially in estuaries like the Thames, the Bristol Channel, the Seine, the Loire, the Gironde and the Tagus, on all of which there are major ports. The intimate relationship between land and sea has made this part of Europe the birthplace of ocean navigation, the starting point of almost all the great voyages of discovery.

The continental shelf off north-west Europe is the home of myriad fish, such as herring, cod, mackerel, pilchards, brisling and halibut. It is one of the four most important fishing grounds in the world, the North Sea for its size producing more fish for food than any other comparable region.

A further effect of this articulated coastline (to be examined more fully later) has been to extend maritime influences far into Europe, giving a climate more favourable to man over a wider longitudinal stretch than in any other continent, and helping the movements and settlement of people.

THE NORWEGIAN SEA

Lying between Norway, the Shetland and Faeroe islands, Iceland, Greenland and Spitzbergen, the Norwegian Sea is a trough let down between the Atlantic and Arctic oceans, separated from them by submarine ridges 1800–2500 ft below the surface. The basin of the Sea is divided by a number of transverse ridges into a series of smaller troughs, some of which are 10,000 ft deep. It is the meeting-place of waters from the Atlantic and Arctic Oceans, as well as from the North and Barents Seas, so that the currents set up are most complicated. Moreover, the moving waters are confined to the upper layers: the submarine ridges prevent the deeper waters passing from one basin to another, and the troughs have peculiarities of salinity, density and marine life not yet fully examined.

THE NORTH SEA

The North Sea, between Great Britain and the European mainland, is merely a drowned part of the continental shelf. It is shallow, ranging from about 50 fathoms deep in the north to less than 17 fathoms in the south. Across its middle latitude the Dogger Bank, a submarine plateau, extends from east to west, with a depth of water less than 10 fathoms near the English coast. The depth increases south of the Dogger in local depressions, known as the "Silver Pit," up to 45 fathoms. To the south, near the English coast, are a number of shoals with only a few feet of water covering them at low tide. In the east of the sea is a deep gully—the "Norwegian Channel"—following the coast of Norway and extending into the Skagerrak. This is a graben where the depth increases to 400 fathoms.

The depression of the North Sea was a consequence of the Alpine orogenesis. During the glacial period there was a general subsidence of the northern part, but the south, between England, Belgium and France, seems to have been little affected, except that a narrow inlet may have been opened where the Strait of Dover now lies. In the northern portion immense quantities of glacial detritus were deposited, possibly to a thickness of 600 ft, and the whole region was subsequently raised above sea level. On this new "plain" a river system developed which continued the course of the Rhine to the north. Some of the present rivers of England, such as the Thames and Humber, may have been tributaries of this great river. Finally the land again subsided, the waters poured in to form the North Sea as it is now, and the narrow opening in the south became the Strait of Dover.

Like most marginal seas which receive much river water, the salinity of the North Sea varies in places from the 35 per thousand parts which is the average for ocean waters. The water flowing from the Baltic reduces salinity to 32 *pro mille*, and for some distance north and south of the Baltic opening the salinity is not more than 34 *pro mille*. Differences in salinity cause movement of the waters: although it is not a very big movement, it further complicates the currents caused by wind or tidal flow. The North Sea lies in the stream of the North Atlantic Drift, a weak current blown by the westerlies. This brings the warmer Atlantic waters to the coast of western Europe. By their movement northwards they keep the western and northern coasts of the continent free from ice as far as the entrance to the White Sea.

Its tides are very complex. The tidal wave of the Atlantic enters partly by the English Channel and partly round the north of the British Isles. The northern part splits in two, one section moving south along the Scottish coast, the other across to the coast of Norway and thence into the deeper waters of the Norwegian Channel and the Skagerrak gully. Both northern waves are retarded by the shallows over the Dogger Bank, and the Scottish wave turns eastwards just south of it. All three waves,

Scottish, Norwegian and English Channel, meet east of the Dogger. The result is such a complex of tidal movements along the continental coast that in some places there is little obvious difference between high and low water. It is this lack of true ebb and flow which has led to the formation of the Rhine delta. On the English side the tides are more normal, the set of the flow being to the south-east and that of the ebb to the north-west.

The waters carried into the North Sea bring with them vast quantities of plankton. This abundance of food supports such numbers of fish as to make the North Sea fisheries the richest in the world. Herring and mackerel are caught by drift-nets; plaice, turbot, sole, etc., which feed near the seafloor, mainly by trawl; in deeper waters hook-and-line fishing is used for halibut, haddock and cod. There is much overlap between hook-and-line and trawling.

THE BALTIC SEA

The Baltic Sea came into existence in glacial times (*see* Fig. 3). A subsidence during the Ice Age allowed an arm of the sea to stretch across Sweden along the line of the lakes Vener, Hjelmar, Mälar and, possibly, Ladoga; it may have had a connection through to the Arctic. This inlet is known to geologists as the Yoldia Sea, from the fossils of a salt-water mollusc, *Yoldia arctica*, found there. A slight upheaval of the land restricted the entrance to a narrow passage north of Denmark, and the waters of the Baltic became less salt, so that some of its marine life (*e.g.* seals) became extinct. A further uplift transformed it into a large fresh water lake, known as the Ancylus Lake, from the fresh-water mollusc *Ancylus fluviatilis*. This lake covered a larger area than the present Baltic, for it submerged part of eastern Sweden, much of Finland, and the Lake Ladoga basin. Another subsidence followed, once more opening the channels to the North Sea and allowing the waters to become salt again. In this sea clays and silts were deposited from the adjacent land areas. A prolonged period of slow elevation ensued, which gave the Baltic its present shape and produced many of the clayey coastal plains on its margins. This gradual uplift is still continuing.

The coasts of the Baltic are thus mainly low-lying, and on them have been left the morainic remains of the last glacial epoch. The south coast is interesting for its variety of coastal features caused by subsidence or by currents and winds. From Schleswig to Lübeck Bay is a series of long, narrow openings, called *förden*, thought to be the drowned valleys of rivers which flowed beneath the ice sheet. East of Lübeck they give place to *bodden*, wider openings with islands which suggest subsidence. The bodden—which have their counterpart in Scania in Sweden, with which

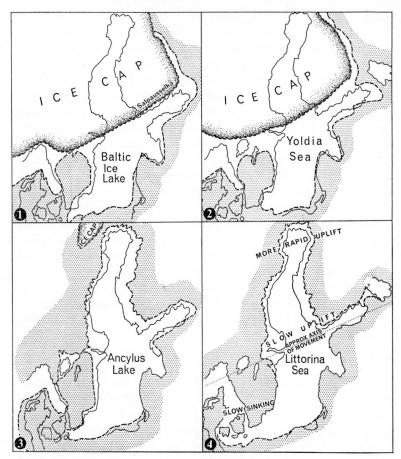

Fig. 3.—Development of the Baltic Sea. The present coastline is shown as a thin continuous line. (1) The ice of the Quaternary Ice Age has retreated, leaving the Salpausselkä moraine in Finland. The trapped ice-melt escapes by a depression in Sweden. (2) Further retreat of the ice, plus sinking of the land, allows salt water from the North Sea to enter the Yoldia Sea. (3) The ice has almost gone, the land in the south-west rises and the Ancylus Lake is formed. (4) Isostatic movement opens a passage in the south-west, where the land sinks, and brings new land to the surface in the east and north, where there is uplift. In the Littorina Sea the present shape of the Baltic is approached. Uplift still continues today north of the approximate axis shown.

they were connected by an isthmus until the last subsidence—extend to the mouth of the river Oder. This river mouth seems to have been the result of a depression formed by the lobe of the retreating ice. East of the Oder is an unbroken, dune-covered coast as far as the Gulf of Danzig. There it is cut by the mouths of the Vistula, Pregel and Memel, all of which are obstructed by long sand-spits, called *nehrungen*. A west-to-east longshore drift, helped by prevailing winds, has piled up these sandy strips and straightened the coastline, trapping numerous lagoons or *haffe*. The largest are the Frisches Haff and the Kurisches Haff.

The Oder, then, divides the south coast of the Baltic into two distinct parts, one with many openings, and one with very few. On the openings west of the Oder grew up several ports such as Lübeck and Rostock, important in the days before large ships but unable to accommodate modern vessels. In the haffs, kept open by dredging or by the construction of artificial harbours, Gdansk (Danzig), Gdynia, Kaliningrad (Königsberg) and Klaipeda (Memel) are important ports. Szczecin (Stettin), at the mouth of the Oder and the nearest port to Berlin, has suffered because of the anomalous position of that city in the present divided Germany.

Navigation is difficult in winter because of ice. The north of the Gulf of Bothnia is closed from November to May, and the Gulf of Finland from December to April. In the latter case, however, navigation is made possible by ice-breakers. The southern part of the Baltic has drifting ice, with compact sea ice only in severe winters. The waters between Stockholm and the Åland islands are blocked every winter, and sometimes the ice is thick enough for special surface motor transport to maintain trade connections.

THE MEDITERRANEAN

The Mediterranean, with its extension into the Black Sea, forms most of the southern boundary of Europe. The present Mediterranean is all that remains of a great ocean—the Tethys—which in early geological times stretched halfway round the globe south of Eurasia. It took the form we know in late Cretaceous and early Tertiary times as the result, apparently, of a movement together of proto-Eurasia and proto-Africa which squeezed the layers of sedimentary rocks on the floor of the Tethys geosynclines and uplifted, crumpled and faulted them into the mountain ranges of the Alpine system. At the same time, other parts of the synclines and main blocks of the proto-continents were forced down to form the several "basins" of the western Mediterranean; yet others, such as Corsica and Sardinia, fragmental portions of the ancient mainland, were left above sea level. The southern side of the eastern Mediterranean basin has no folds: the African table-land descends in a series of faulted terraces to the deeps north of Egypt. The movements that produced the mountains by which most of the Mediterranean is surrounded took place over a period of millions of years, so the ranges differ in age and possibly structure. The Atlas ranges and the Pyrenees are older than the Alps, and the Alps were uplifted before the Apennines and the Dinarics.

The Alpine orogenesis is not yet complete. A settling-down process is still going on, as is shown by extensive and frequent volcanic and earthquake activity in the young mountain folds, especially in the Dinarides region of the Mediterranean basin. Vulcanicity was widespread from Italy eastwards. Many areas are covered by basaltic soils or lava sheets in central Italy, the Cyclades, Crete and Asia Minor. Volcanic cones are at various stages of activity and decadence in these areas and in southern France and Greece. The best-known active volcanoes—Vesuvius, Stromboli, Vulcano and Etna—are all in Italy. The worst earthquake shocks are also experienced in the eastern Mediterranean region, although the west is not immune: great damage was caused at Lisbon in 1735 and at Orléansville in Algeria in 1954. Earthquakes of disaster proportions have occurred in recent years in Sicily, Greece and Turkey; the latest was in 1963 at Skopje, in Yugoslavia, when the town was almost demolished and a thousand people died.

The Mediterranean basin is divided in two by a ridge, the Adventure Bank, running from Sicily to Cape Bon, at a depth of not more than 200 fathoms. At the Strait of Gibraltar another submarine ridge separates the Mediterranean from the Atlantic. The two main basins—east and west—are further sub-divided by other ridges. The deepest part of the sea is in the east. There is a depth of 2110 fathoms near the island of Rhodes, and 65 miles west of Cape Matapan, Greece, a maximum depth of 2800 fathoms has just been discovered. The deepest sounding recorded in the western basin is 2040 fathoms.

Because it is enclosed, the Mediterranean's waters are on average more saline than those of the open ocean. In the west the salinity is about 36·3 *pro mille*, and it increases to 39 *pro mille* or more in the Levant. The more saline waters seem to creep westwards along the African coast.

There are few definite currents in the Mediterranean. In the Strait of Gibraltar and the Dardanelles, at the western and eastern ends respectively, fresher surface waters flow inward to make good the loss by evaporation and in both cases there is a slight outward movement of the deeper and denser waters. In the deepest parts of the basins there can be little movement, and the salinity must be over 40 *pro mille*. It may be that these deep waters have remained unchanged since the sea basins were finally shaped, and they have been stagnant so long that most of the fish food has been exhausted. Consequently the Mediterranean is poor in fish. The sardines, anchovies, tuna and eels which are the chief fishing harvest come in via the surface waters from the Atlantic.

The Mediterranean is almost tideless, and what tides there are may be obliterated by feeble local currents set up by winds or the outflow of rivers. One result of this lack of movement has been the formation of deltas, the most important being those of the Ebro, the Rhône, the Po and the Nile. Another has been to make the Mediterranean a good school for seamen, for it is possible to sail from any part of its shores to another without losing sight of land, and its mountainous littoral provides an abundance of good harbours. Even the violent storms that break the placidity of its surface in winter have had their value in increasing experience and knowledge of navigation. It is noteworthy that each of the

[*Courtesy of Spyros Meletzis, Athens.*]

Fig. 4.—Greece: Parga, on the west coast south of Plataria. Note the village in a small lowland, the monastery on the hilltop and the bare limestone islets. This is "karst" limestone.

three great peninsulas which project southwards played a part in the gradual conquest of the sea. The most broken coastline is that of Greece, where a civilisation developed that was carried by sea to colonies established from Spain on the one hand to southern Russia on the other. The Roman civilisation which followed spread its influence from Italy to yet more distant lands, as far north as the British Isles; and from Spain and Portugal sailed the great adventurers who in the fifteenth century opened up the New World and the Far East.

The Mediterranean coast on its European side presents everywhere a kaleidoscope of mountains, hills, tiny plains and sea; scenes of classic beauty under a clear, blue sky (Fig. 4). A voyage along its shores reveals a succession of villages and farms clinging precariously to steep slopes where agriculture is possible only by terracing and where tree crops are more common than cereals or vegetables. The plains, mainly deltaic, are dwarfed by the ring of mountains behind them, and vary in development. Some had become malarial swamps and are only now being recovered; others show the rectilinear outlines of reclaimed land—smallholdings each with its isolated homestead; and still others have a look of permanence, with irrigation systems and a rich cover of orchard and field crops. More will be said about them later in dealing with the separate countries; and as for the climate which has helped to fashion the Mediterranean landscape and give the area a characteristic unity, *see* Chapter III.

THE BLACK SEA

The Black Sea, also called the Euxine Sea, lies in a basin-like depression between Russia and Turkey, and is connected to the Mediterranean by the straits of the Bosphorus and the Dardanelles and the intervening Sea of Marmara. The basin has a maximum depth of 1030 fathoms near the centre. Water conditions in the Black Sea are very different from those in the Mediterranean, although there is the same stagnancy in its depths. The surface water comes mainly from numerous rivers, the largest of which are the Danube, the Dniester, the Dnieper and the Don. It is much less saline than the larger sea, in fact in the Sea of Azov, an opening in the north with a maximum depth of only six fathoms, the water—mainly from the river Don—is almost fresh. The northern part of the Black Sea freezes readily in winter, and ice-breakers are needed to keep passages open to some of its ports.

Below a depth of 100 fathoms the Black Sea is without life, except for bacteria. It has been suggested that when the opening to the Mediterranean was formed the more saline waters which flowed in through the Bosphorus killed the animal life in the deeper parts and caused the formation and accumulation of sulphuretted hydrogen and an extensive precipitation of calcium carbonate. There is an almost complete absence of oxygen, so that any form of higher organic life is impossible. Such conditions, it is suggested, favour the formation of petroleum. The animal life killed by the incursion of more saline water, plus the dead remains of organisms from the surface layers, would rot differently because of the absence of oxygen. They would be attacked by bacteria, which would absorb any residual or diffused oxygen, and be transformed into fatty or waxy compounds, the beginnings of petroleum. Muds which have been dredged from the deeper parts of the Black Sea are green in colour and contain up to 25% of organic matter, much of which has already been changed into heavy hydro-carbons which behave like

B

petroleum. The green comes from chlorophyll, the colouring matter of plant life rather than of animals; and this gives weight to the theory that plant remains contributed more to the formation of petroleum than animal remains. It is a question about which there is still a great deal of argument.

RIVER SYSTEMS AND DRAINAGE

Almost two-thirds of Europe is less than 650 ft above sea level, and only 15% is above 1600 ft. Consequently, the great majority of its rivers run for most of their course in the plains and basins and they are mainly slow-flowing. But their value must be measured in terms of their *régime*, that is, the rate and amount of water flowing in them at any given place and time; when this is taken in conjunction with obstacles such as sand-banks or too-steep sides, we find that only a few are suitable for navigation. All, at least in their upper courses, are important sources of water-supply. In the mountains, or where the gradient is steep enough at lower levels, they can be used to provide hydro-electric power.

The principal rivers of Europe are shown in Fig. 5.

RIVER SYSTEMS

When considering the *systems* of European rivers they may, broadly speaking, be divided into two main categories: (1) Western and central European river systems; (2) Eastern European systems.

1. *The river systems of western and central Europe*

These have their origin mainly in the mountain ranges. Many of them, as in Norway, peninsular Italy and the Balkan peninsula, are short, swift and broken by falls. Others, such as the Guadalquivir, Po, Ebro, Rhône, and parts of the upper Rhine and upper Danube, flank the mountain folds and collect the waters of numerous tributaries before entering the sea or passing to the plains. The rivers flowing to the north from the Hercynian blocks of central Europe or from the Carpathians—the Weser, Elbe, Oder and Vistula, for instance—show, where they traverse the plains, the influence of the lines of moraines which lie across their paths, causing them to take sudden, right-angled bends, to produce a modified kind of *trellis drainage*. The Seine and part of the Loire occupy a true basin, with drainage tending towards a common centre and leaving by one exit; similarly, the upper Douro and upper Tagus collect the drain-age of basins in the Meseta before leaving it by gorges and entering Portugal. Sweden shows a remarkable number of parallel *consequent* streams which drain a series of glint-lakes, and run into the Baltic. The

Fig. 5.—Europe: chief highlands, seas and rivers. Four-fifths of the surface of Europe
lies at elevations of less than 1500 ft. Consequently, most of its rivers flow across
lowlands, with only small stretches of their courses in the highlands. Note the
major water-parting formed by the Central Highlands and Alpine system.

gradient of these rivers, and the natural reservoirs of the lakes, have made
them valuable as carriers of, and store-places for, timber and as a source
of hydro-electric power for pulping and paper mills.

Two rivers, the Rhine and the Danube, have somewhat complex
courses. The Vorderrhein and Hinterrhein, headstreams of the Rhine,
flow first to the east and then to the north-west to Lake Constance

(Boden See). This part of the course is Alpine. But the river turns once again in a south-westerly direction, crosses the Swiss plateau and breaks through the Jura folds to an *elbow of capture* at Basel: here its upper course was captured by a stream flowing north through the Rhine rift valley. It then breaks by a series of gorges through the Rhine highlands of Hercynian age, and enters the European plain. It empties into the North Sea through an extensive delta.

The Danube rises in the Black Forest, only a few miles from the Rhine rift valley, and flows eastwards. The first part of its course is along the northern flanks of the Alpine folds, from which it receives several tributaries. It cuts across the Alpine system at Vienna and again at the Iron Gate between the Transylvanian Alps and the Balkan mountains (Stara Planina), so draining the Hungarian basin (Pannonian basin), which was at one time a lake. It runs on between the folds of the eastern Alpine system across a wide flood-plain to a delta in the Black Sea. It is the longest river (about 1750 miles) in the west and centre of Europe. Several of its tributaries—the Inn, Drava and Sava from the south side and the Olt, Theiss (Tisza), Sereth and Prut from the north—are longer than most of the major rivers of western Europe.

The Danube and the Rhine are of great human significance. Both are navigable over long distances; together they form a natural passage-way from west to east Europe. They are connected by a canal from Bamberg on the Main, a tributary of the Rhine, to Regensberg (Ratisbon) on the Regen, a Danube tributary, but it is little used. A proposal to construct a large canal which would allow barges of 1500 tons to pass without break of bulk from the North Sea to the Black Sea has been shelved because of ideological differences between eastern and western European countries. In their own basins, however, both the Rhine and the Danube are of outstanding importance as commercial routes.

2. *The rivers of the east European plains*

These differ from those of the west in that, with few exceptions, they do not rise in mountains but in low, morainic heights left by the Quaternary glaciers. The chief exceptions are the Dniester (Dnestr), (865 miles) which has its source in the outer Carpathians, and the Pechora and Ural (900 miles), both of which rise in the Ural mountains. Because of the vast extent of the plains, the rivers are the longest in Europe. The Volga (2325 miles) is the greatest, with two tributaries, the Oka (950 miles) and the Kama (1150 miles), the length of the latter being exceeded in western Europe only by the Danube. Other long rivers of the plain are the Dnieper (Dnepr) (1410 miles) and the Don (1325 miles). All have very meandering courses, as would be expected in a land of very slight relief.

All, too, have long stretches of navigable water, so that they form an essential part of the transport system of Russia. On all of them the differences of water level caused by summer floods have been utilised, by the construction of dams and barrages, for hydro-electric power. In the north-east of the plain are several large lakes, relics of the Ice Age, drained to the Baltic by an indeterminate series of rivers, of which the Neva is the chief outlet.

RIVER RÉGIMES

From the point of view of régime, the rivers of Europe are of four main types, two with maximum flow in winter and two in summer. Those with most flow in winter (1) are associated with cool temperate western marginal climates or (2) are purely Mediterranean rivers. Rivers with a maximum summer flow are those which (3) have their courses entirely within the folds of the Alps or (4) are flowing under cool temperate continental conditions. Some rivers have complicated régimes because they flow from one climatic area to another. Chief among them are the Rhine and the Danube, already noted as having complex physical basins.

1. Rivers with a "western" régime

Where the climate is similar to that of the British Isles, with rain falling at any season but with a greater precipitation in the winter half of the year, rivers have their maximum volume in the cool season. During the summer the rain falls on a heated surface and is either quickly evaporated or absorbed by a dry soil. There is little run-off, and the volume of water in the rivers is reduced. In winter the soil is cold and saturated, there is little evaporation, run-off is great and the rivers become full. The fact that there is seldom a period of drought during the year precludes a too-rapid rise and fall in volume, so that in general the rivers of western Europe are fairly uniform in flow, especially if there are lakes in their courses to act as natural storage reservoirs.

Typical rivers are the Seine, Somme, Meuse and Scheldt, none of which depends except incidentally on snow-melt. Other western rivers have régimes complicated through their headwaters or upper courses being in highlands that are snow-clad in winter, so that a thaw in spring may cause sudden increases in volume. The Elbe and the Oder, for instance, are swollen by the melting snows of the Erzgebirge, the Bohemian plateau and the Sudetes; the Loire, Allier and Dordogne by thaw-water in spring from the French Central Massif. The rivers of Sweden are frozen in winter and have a régime somewhat like those with a continental climate, i.e. with a summer maximum.

2. Mediterranean rivers

The contrast between summer drought and winter rains in the Mediterranean region is seen in the river régimes. During the dry summers there is little water in the rivers: some dry up to mere trickles. In winter the rains may produce raging torrents with two periods of high water, one at the beginning, the other at the end, of the season. The winter rains are heavier near the beginning of the season, but the run-off is reduced because of the dry, porous nature of the surface soils parched during the summer, and so the rise in water level is not as great as might be expected. The end of winter is marked by the "little rains," which again cause the rivers to rise.

This is the typical régime; but as most Mediterranean rivers also receive water from snow melting in spring on the mountains bordering the Sea, their régime is modified and their flow increased in the early summer, thus reducing their period of very low water. Some rivers, like the Rhône, Garonne and Po, may receive so much melt-water that their even flow continues throughout the summer, and their régime is more like the rivers of the west. The Douro, Tagus and Guadiana in Spain, and the short rivers in southern Italy, Sicily and southern Greece are those with the true Mediterranean régime. Steep gradients and wide variations in volume have caused most Mediterranean rivers to incise their beds deeply, reducing their value for navigation and necessitating much bridge-building; and the fact that they are lowest in the hot dry summer means that their usefulness for irrigation is at a minimum then.

3. Alpine rivers

Rivers with their sources in the Alpine ranges have their maximum flow when the snows melt, from April onwards. The highest water is in June and the lowest in February, when most precipitation is in the form of snow. Moreover, the Alps are regions of heavy rain in summer, and so the truly Alpine rivers are in flood in that season. Such rivers are the Isère, Durance and other Rhône tributaries, the Aar, the Inn, and the upper courses of the Rhine, Rhône, Danube, Drava and Sava. Snows on the highlands of central Europe have a similar effect on the régime of the rivers that flow northward from them, giving them an Alpine component, as in the Weser, Elbe, etc.

4. Eastern European rivers

The régimes of the rivers which flow across the plains of eastern Europe are affected not only by the summer rains but also by the frost of winter, and the snow that covers the plains at that time of the year. Rivers start to freeze towards the end of October, and a general thaw does not begin until the following March or April, when a break-up of the ice may cause jams on the rivers. At the same time, melting snows result in floods, so that spring is a season of high water. Rains come in the summer and prolong the maximum flow, but it is easy to over-estimate their effect. They are falling in the hot season onto parched soil and run-off is slight. The rivers, in consequence, gradually diminish in volume towards the autumn, when there is again a slight rise, the result of the thawing of the first snows before the final freeze-up.

Rivers with a régime like this are the Volga and its tributaries, the Dnieper and the Don. The Ural, Pechora, Vistula, and other rivers with their headwaters in mountains, may have their peak volume affected by thaws occurring at different times—later on the higher slopes than on the plains part of the course. The rivers of eastern Sweden, although not plains rivers, may be said to have a régime similar to those in Russia, for they freeze in November and thaw all together about March. Their flow in summer is made more uniform because of the lakes they drain.

5. *The Rhine and the Danube*

The régime of the Rhine as far as Basel is Alpine, with a maximum flow in June and July. In its middle course it receives tributaries, the Neckar, Main, Moselle and Lahn, which have "western" régimes with maximum flow in winter, although all of them are fed, too, by melting snows in spring. Their waters tend to cancel out the summer maximum of the main river, replacing it with a larger winter volume, so that in its plains course in Holland the Rhine has a winter maximum, like most western rivers. Before the final levelling-out, the Rhine may show two peaks of greater volume, a larger one in winter and a lesser in summer. This occurs at places in the Rhine gorge.

The upper course of the Danube, as far as Vienna, also has an Alpine régime with a summer maximum. When it crosses the basin of Hungary, and still more on the plains of Walachia, it has a régime similar to the Russian rivers. As a "Russian" type its maximum flow comes in April and May, that is, earlier than in the "Alpine" section. It freezes in Hungary and Walachia, hence the spring floods. In summer the rains of the eastern end of its basin are only small, and so its volume falls at that season. Its régime in Hungary is complicated by "Alpine" tributaries like the Drava and Sava, and by the "Mediterranean" characteristics of some of the right-bank tributaries of the Sava. "Alpine" tributaries from the Carpathians and Transylvanian Alps cause extensive summer flooding in eastern Hungary and western Rumania.

1. Select *two* European seas, and compare and contrast them from the points of view of (*a*) salinity, (*b*) climatic influence, (*c*) economic value.

2. Compare the Baltic shoreline of Sweden and Finland with that of Denmark, Germany and Poland.

3. Contrast in as many ways as you can *either* the Mediterranean and North seas, *or* the Black and Baltic seas.

4. What do you understand by "river régime"? Show by reference to definite examples in Europe how river régime may influence the activities of man.

5. Select two European rivers, one with a simple and the other with a complex régime, and in each case give an account of the régime.

Chapter III

THE CLIMATES OF EUROPE

CLIMATIC FACTORS

CLIMATE is average weather, and is defined by a careful analysis of the interplay of temperature, barometric pressure, winds and rainfall. Records of sunshine, cloud and humidity are kept and related to rainfall. The analysis shows there are three main controls of climate; latitude, or distance from the equator; altitude, or height above mean sea level; and distance from a sea large enough to be effective. In considering the climate of any place, it is best to examine the three controls and correlate their effects upon the main climatic factors mentioned above, that is, upon the temperature, barometric pressure and winds, and rainfall.

Europe lies between the 35th and 71st parallels north latitude and so, but for a small strip inside the Arctic Circle, is almost entirely in the temperate zone. It is somewhat misleading, however, to think of the climate as truly temperate, for although there are few extremes, continental influences in the east of the continent cause differences between absolute maximum and minimum temperatures of more than 130° F (54·4° C), and many areas have an annual range of 50° F (10° C) or more. Still, generally speaking, it can be said that Europe's annual range of temperature is less and its rainfall greater than on comparable latitudes in other continents. There are two reasons: (i) Europe is on the western side of the huge land mass of Eurasia, in the track of prevailing westerly winds which have crossed the Atlantic, bringing moderating influences, making temperatures higher than in corresponding latitudes east of the continental mass, and carrying moisture far into the interior; (ii) the penetration of the warm, rain-laden winds is assisted by the marginal seas and peninsularity of Europe, and by the absence of any high north–south mountain ranges which would restrict maritime influences.

TEMPERATURE

The distribution of temperature in Europe can be understood best by examining a map showing sea-level isotherms for January and July (Fig. 6).

(a) The isotherms show that in July temperatures are highest in the south and lowest in the north. Some Mediterranean areas have over 80° F (26·7° C), while the shores of the Arctic Ocean are about 50° F

(10° C). In other words, temperature decreases as latitude increases: the height of the sun is the dominant factor. It should be noted, too, that the length of the day increases northwards, and so in higher latitudes the amount of heat in summer is increased by a longer insolation. This means that although the heat of the sun may not be so great in the north, the sun is shining for longer periods during the summer days and the total heat may be sufficient to allow of agricultural activity farther north than one would expect. The growing period is shorter, of course, and so plant life must be adapted in some way. In Russia, as in Canada, special wheat that

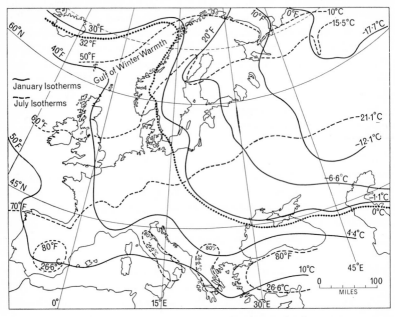

FIG. 6.—Europe: isotherms reduced to sea level.

will complete its life cycle from seed to harvest in ninety days is now grown near the Arctic Circle.

(b) In January the temperatures decrease as one goes from the Atlantic shores eastward. The sun is now south of the equator, the days are short, the mid-day sun is low in the heavens and its influence is reduced. The Atlantic Ocean becomes the dominant factor. Relatively warm air masses are blown across Europe from over the Atlantic, so that in most years the western coasts remain ice-free, even inside the Arctic Circle. Temperatures on the western coasts range in January from over 50° F (10° C) in southern Portugal to 25° F (—3·9° C) at North Cape in Norway. It is interesting to compare the winter temperatures of north-west Europe with those of places on similar latitudes in north-east North America. For instance, Corunna, in north-west Spain, has a January temperature of 47° F (8·3° C), whereas Portland, Maine, has 22° F (−5·6° C); Bergen, in Norway, has an average of 37° F (2·8° C) in January, and is in the same latitude as Hudson Strait, which is frozen from November to March.

Further inland, in central and eastern Europe, winter temperatures fall with increased distance from the Atlantic, and may be well below freezing point for months. The January temperature of Leningrad is 15° F (−9·4° C), of Moscow 12·2° F (−11·1° C), of Kuibyshev, in the middle Volga basin, 9° F (−12·8° C). Not so far east are Prague, 29° F (−1·7° C), Debrecen, in Hungary, 25° F (−3·9° C) and Bucharest, 26° F (−3·3° C). Eastern Europe has the nearest approach to a continental climate, with big annual ranges of temperature. The difference between mean summer and winter temperatures at Moscow, for instance, is 54° F (30° C). Near the Atlantic coast, on the other hand, the range is very small, *e.g.* at Corunna it is 22° F (12·2° C), at Roscoff in Brittany, 17° F (9·4° C), at Valentia in south-west Ireland 15° F (8·2° C); and even at North Cape it is only 24° F (13·3° C).

PRESSURE SYSTEMS AND WINDS

The winds that blow over Europe are related to four major pressure systems, two high and two low, which should be identified on maps of the world showing air pressure and winds in January and July. They are (1) the Azores "High," which varies in extent but is continuous all the year, (2) the Icelandic "Low," which is equally continuous but more extensive in winter, (3) the Asiatic or Siberian "High," which exists only in winter, and (4) the Indian or south-west Asiatic "Low," which develops in summer and affects only a small area of Europe: the eastern Mediterranean. All the pressure systems vary considerably in extent and intensity from year to year and from day to day. In areas affected by Lows the weather is further complicated by *depressions*, with their accompanying *fronts*, which are carried in the air stream of the main wind circulation. The depressions, also called *cyclones* and *lows*, are areas of more intense low pressure. They are separated from each other by *anti-cyclones* or areas of high pressure. Most depressions which affect Europe are born along the "Arctic Front," the line of demarcation between the cold air-cap of arctic regions and the warmer air which has travelled from tropical regions. They seem to be the result of the attempt of these two air masses to mix, modified by the rotation of the earth. A more detailed explanation of their origin will be found in most books of physical geography or meteorology; it is sufficient here to note that a succession of these depressions approaches Europe from the west, more in winter than in summer, and that they are the main reason for the changeable climate and the quick changes of wind and weather which the continent experiences.

1. The Azores high pressure system

This is formed where the trade winds and the westerlies diverge in the north Atlantic. In summer the region of high pressure increases in size to cover the Mediterranean area, and may extend farther north to include the British Isles. It brings calm, sunny weather with cloudless skies to southern Europe in summer; and the same fine conditions are on occasion experienced in the British Isles, northern France, the Low Countries and Germany. In general, high pressure regions tend to be rainless, and so the lands they cover suffer from drought. This is why the Mediterranean countries have little or no rain in summer and why, if there is an extension of the Azores High northwards, western Europe may have "heat waves," periods of sunshine and cloudless skies.

2. The Icelandic low pressure system

This is centred all the year in the northernmost Atlantic. It is a region where polar winds and westerlies converge, warm and cold air, as already mentioned. In summer the area of low pressure is smaller than in winter, when it extends south as far as the coast of Spain and Portugal. The depressions formed in this system move east across Europe, and in winter are more frequent and cover larger areas. They seem to have certain routes—storm tracks—which they tend to follow and along which their influence is greatest, but no part of western Europe escapes their effects. In winter, when the system is larger, one route is along the Mediterranean basin; and so in that season Mediterranean countries have rain and changeable weather. In summer the depressions penetrate across western Europe and affect the lands in the extreme east of the continent.

3. The Asiatic or Siberian high pressure system

In winter the extremely low temperatures of central Asia intensify the normal sub-tropical high pressures, making them extend far to the north to form a great mass of cold air centred over the northern part of the Gobi Desert. This is known as the Asiatic or Siberian High, and its influence is felt westwards in Europe, where it acts as a wind-divide separating the westerlies into two streams that blow north and south of the cushion of cold air. In other words, the rain-bearing cyclonic westerlies so characteristic of western and north-western Europe are separated from the Lows which bring rain to the Mediterranean region in winter by a belt of anti-cyclonic conditions which stretches across Europe like a wedge with its base in Asia. In eastern Europe the anti-cyclones last longer and are more extensive, so that the winter climate of Russia features long periods of calms and intense cold, with a minimum of precipitation. Westwards the High influences affect Poland, Germany (especially East Germany), the countries bordering the Danube, Switzerland and even eastern France, but the anti-cyclonic periods become shorter and are interspersed with periods when the westerlies dominate, bringing cloudy, wet and stormy weather.

One of the results of the belt of cold air which in winter stretches across the centre of Europe is felt in the Mediterranean region. When deep depressions are moving in that season from west to east along the northern coastlands of the Mediterranean Sea, cold air is drawn southwards to form the strong, cold winds that blow down the Rhône corridor and in the north of the Adriatic Sea, where they are known respectively as the *mistral* and the *bora*.

4. The Indian or south-west Asiatic low pressure system

Although, generally speaking, in summer the Mediterranean region lies under an extension of the Azores high pressure system, it may be said that the eastern end of the Mediterranean Sea and its adjoining coastlands fall also within the periphery of the low-pressure system which is centred in north-west India and known as the Indian Low. This is the Low which causes the monsoonal rains in India, where the summer winds blow from the south-west; but in southern Russia, Turkey-in-Europe, and most of the Balkan peninsula, which lie in the north-west quadrant of the Low, the prevailing winds in summer are more from the west and north-west, and are dry. Thus, the south-eastern corner of the European continent has the summer drought and clear, blue skies of the typical "Mediterranean" climate.

RAINFALL

Rainfall can be divided, according to the way it is caused, into three distinct types. They are (i) orographic, (ii) convectional and (iii) cyclonic rains.

(i) *Orographic* rain, as the name suggests, is the result of air which contains moisture being forced upwards and cooled by differences in the height of the land it passes over. High mountain ranges lying athwart the moving air mass are obviously the most effective cause of orographic rain, but even small obstacles such as low hill ranges and plateaus may so reduce temperatures as to result in precipitation. In Europe, the greatest amounts of orographic rainfall are on the western sides of the Scandinavian mountains and throughout the ranges of the Alpine system, for here the air masses moving from the Atlantic are forced up highest. Over most of the continent, however, differences in altitude are too small to produce much orographic rain, except locally; indeed, some parts of the very flat plains found in eastern Europe have no orographic rainfall, and must depend on convectional and cyclonic rains. In this connection it must be noted that every region with orographic rainfall invariably has additional rain due to precipitation resulting from cyclonic or convectional disturbances.

(ii) Local differences in the amount of heat radiated from the earth's surface may cause the air over adjacent areas of land to be heated differently and so set up convection currents rising vertically at different speeds. It may be that one area is lower or more sheltered than adjoining areas, or that because of differences in rocks or the presence of surface water in the form of lakes and rivers, heat radiation is less in other areas, so that the air above it becomes relatively turbulent and unstable. The upward movement of the air causes cooling and, if this is rapid, condensation of the moisture content. This is *convectional* rain. The heavy rains often experienced in thunderstorms are convectional; although convectional rainfall is not necessarily associated with thunder, in Europe most rain of this type comes in thunderstorms. These may occur anywhere in Europe, usually in summer, but they are most frequent in the central and eastern parts of the continent, where convectional rainfall forms the major part of the total annual precipitation.

(iii) *Cyclonic* rain accompanies the passage of depressions or Lows which are carried by the westerlies in a constant succession. All parts of Europe, therefore, which receive the westerlies and their depressions will have cyclonic rains. The whole of western Europe has westerlies all the year round, and so has rain at all seasons. But because the number and the intensity of the Lows are greater in winter than in summer, the winter rainfall nearer to the Atlantic seaboard tends to be greater than during the summer. The Mediterranean region is subject to westerlies and depressions only in winter, so that rainfall there, apart from convectional and small amounts of orographic rain, is confined mainly to that season. Eastwards in Europe, with the Atlantic more distant, rainfall caused by depressions becomes less and less, for the westerlies are being gradually denuded of moisture. Moreover, in summer they are moving in the east of the continent over lands which are hotter, and so the winds pick up, rather than deposit, moisture. In winter, as already noted, the westerlies are prevented from entering eastern Europe, except sporadically, by the Siberian High. Partly for this reason, and partly because convectional rains are more common in summer than in winter, the rainfall of central and eastern Europe is greater in summer (*see* Fig. 7).

In general, Europe is wet in the west and increasingly drier eastwards. This is best seen by looking at the rainfall of several towns which range

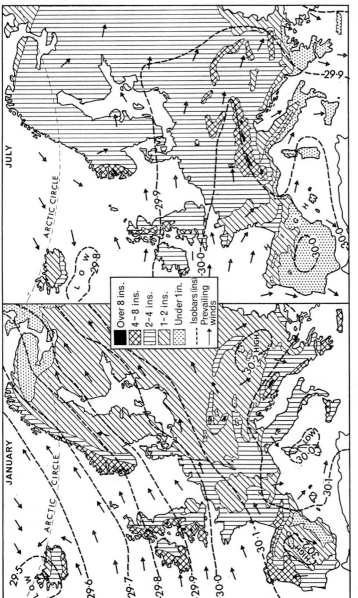

FIG. 7.—Europe: rainfall and isobars for January and July. Note centre of low pressure near Iceland in both winter and summer, and the continuous high pressure in the Iberian peninsula. Relate these maps and Fig. 6 to Figs. 9 and 10, which show climatic divisions and natural vegetation.

from the Atlantic seaboard to the east of European Russia. Brest in north-west France has an annual rainfall of 29 in.; eastwards the amount falls to 22·7 in. in Berlin, 22·1 in. in Warsaw, 21 in. in Moscow and 16 in. in Odessa. Astrakhan, on the delta of the Volga, has only 6·6 in. Where the westerlies cross over uplands and mountains the result is very marked. Bergen, for instance, has an annual rainfall of 84 in., and rain occurs on two days in every three. Most of the west coast of Scandinavia has an annual precipitation of over 100 in. Even when mountains are a long way from the Atlantic their effect is great. The Puy de Dôme in the Central Massif of France has 66 in. annually; Mount Santis, near Appenzell in Switzerland, 95 in.; Dubrovnik, backed by the Dinaric Alps, 59 in.; and part of the Caucasus, next door to the driest part of Europe, 100 in. Places which lie in the lee of highlands, *i.e.* in the rain-shadow, have a much reduced rainfall. Athens, on the sheltered eastern side of Greece, has only 15·4 in., and this in the winter half of the year; Haparanda, at the northern end of the Baltic, in the lee of the Scandinavian plateau, has 19 in. annually.

Rainfall in the Mediterranean lands comes mainly in winter, for it is then that the area is under the influence of the westerlies with depressions. Moreover, the path of the Lows lies more to the north of the Sea, and so the European side of the Mediterranean receives more rain than the African coasts. In addition, the trend of the Apennines and of the Dinaric ranges presents an obstacle to the westerlies, making their western side wetter than their lee. As in northern Europe, the amount of rainfall in low-lying areas decreases as one goes east, but the varied relief and the height of the many mountain ranges cause very heavy rainfall in some areas and a much reduced precipitation in others. The seaward slopes of the Karst plateau in Yugoslavia, with 180 in. annually in places, is one of the wettest districts in Europe, whereas Athens, on the opposite side of the Balkan peninsula, has only 15·4 in. annually. In summer the extreme eastern end of the Mediterranean basin sometimes comes under the influence of the south-west Asiatic or Indian low pressure system, which causes the heavy monsoon rains in India. In the Mediterranean region, however, the winds are from the west or north-west at this season, and are blowing to warm lands. They do not, in consequence, bring rain to the part of Europe they affect.

The coldest part of the world in winter is in north-east Siberia. The intense cold leads to an air mass at very high pressure, the Siberian or Asiatic High, which covers the whole of interior Asia and extends west-ward over the Great European Plain. The cold air holds very little mois-ture, and so in eastern Europe there is a minimum of precipitation in winter. It is in the form of snow, which falls frequently in small amounts, but in total is rarely more than a few inches. Winter days in eastern Europe are usually calm, with clear blue skies and bright sun, although the air temperature is far below freezing point. Moscow, for instance, has an average January temperature of 12·2° F (−11·1° C), with 5·7 in. precipitation in the six winter months out of an annual total of 21 in.; Chkalov, near the southern Urals, averages 3·4° F (−15·8° C) in January, and has 6·5 in. out of 15·2 in. from October to March. In some years the Siberian High extends its influence to the western seaboard of Europe. When this happens, as in the winters of 1947 and 1962 and the spring of 1963, the weather in western Europe is bitterly cold; and where the north-east winds have crossed the Baltic or North Sea, skies are overcast and snowfall heavy, especially in the Low Countries and the British Isles.

CLIMATIC DIVISIONS

Europe may be divided climatically into six areas (Fig. 8), each with its own characteristics yet, with the single exception of the Mediterranean region, not very clearly demarcated from its neighbours. Each climatic area is considered in turn below.

1. *Warm temperate western marginal climate*

This, the Mediterranean region, is the nearest approach to a clear-cut climatic area in Europe. Its general characteristics are winter rains and summer drought, hot summers (over 70° F (21° C)) and mild winters (over 43° F (6° C)), and long periods of sunshine. Lands round the Mediterranean Sea are in a region of transition between the westerlies, which blow during the winter and bring rain, and the north-east trades of summer, which are dry. It may be said that the region has a temperate and changeable climate for the winter half of the year and a more uniform tropical climate during the summer. Yet within the Mediterranean basin there are many variations and departures from what might be considered the normal.

The sea extends 2000 miles from west to east, and in that distance total annual rainfall decreases from 36 in. at Gibraltar to 15·4 in. at Athens. Mountains cause an increase in rainfall, so that the winter totals in some parts of Italy, Greece and Yugoslavia are greater even than the full year's amount in some of the "wet" places in north-west Europe. Then, too, certain areas are so enclosed by mountains or so high as to have climates which are more continental than Mediterranean. Among them are the Meseta of Spain, the Plain of Lombardy and various parts of Yugoslavia and Greece. In these the winter temperatures are lower than the Mediterranean average, Burgos in Spain having a mean in January

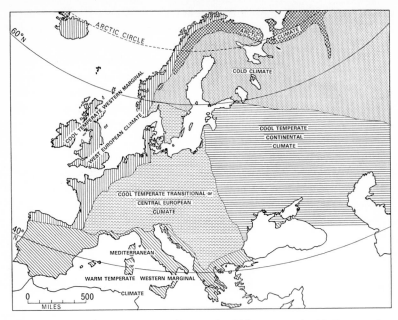

FIG. 8.—Europe: climatic regions. This map should be compared with Figs. 6 and 7.

of 35·5° (1·9° C) and Milan 32·4° F (0·3° C). These areas also have more rain in summer than in winter.

It is these frequent variations from the generally accepted idea of a Mediterranean climate that have led some geographers to discard the title "Mediterranean type," and to substitute something more descriptive, such as the heading given above, which can more accurately be applied to comparable climates in other parts of the world, e.g. in central California and central Chile.

2. Arctic climate

In the extreme north of Scandinavia, with a strip running southwards along the high Kjölen ridge, and in the northern Urals, are small areas with an Arctic climate, where the summer temperatures do not rise above 50° F (10° C), the winters are between 8° F (−13·3° C) and 12° F (−11·1°C), and precipitation, mainly in the form of snow, is less than 15 in. annually.

3. Cold climate

South of the Arctic climatic region, in the lee of the Scandinavian block and shut off from maritime influences, is a cold zone, stretching from the slopes of Sweden across the Baltic Shield to northern Russia. Winter temperatures are less than 20° F (−6·7° C) and decrease eastwards; Oslo has a January mean of 24° F (−4·4°C), Helsinki 20° F (−6·7° C), Leningrad 15° F (−9·4° C). The cold zone widens in Russia. Summer temperatures may rise to over 60° F (15·6° C), Leningrad, for instance, having a mean of 64° F (17·8° C) in July. Rainfall comes more in the summer half of the year, and is rarely more than 20 in. (Leningrad 18·8 in., Archangel 15·3 in.).

4. Cool temperate western marginal climate

The region with this climate includes the west coasts of Scandinavia, the whole of the British Isles, Denmark, Belgium, the western half of France and north-western Spain. Here the influence of the westerlies with their Lows is at its maximum, giving changeable weather conditions. The nearness of the Atlantic with the warm North Atlantic Drift results in a small annual range of temperature, high humidity and a rainfall fairly evenly distributed throughout the year.

Typical figures are those for London, with 39° F (3·9° C) in January, 63° F (17·2° C) in July, annual range 27° F (15° C), and annual rainfall 23·8 in.; Paris, 37° F (2·8° C) January, 65° F (18·3° C) July, range 28° F (15·5° C), rainfall 22·6 in.; Bergen, 34° F (1·1° C) January, 58° F (14·4° C) July, range 24° F, rainfall 84·3 in. In all this area, although no month may be considered dry, there is a slight tendency for more rain to fall in the winter half of the year, for then the Lows are more frequent and more intense.

5. Cool temperate transitional climate

Eastwards from the Atlantic, maritime conditions merge with continental characteristics to produce a cool temperate transitional climate in southern Sweden, central and eastern France, Germany, Switzerland, western Poland and the countries which border the middle Danube. Maritime influences are still present, but progressively less effective; rains may come at any time in the year but tend to have a summer maximum; and though summer temperatures are fairly normal for their latitudes, in winter the thermometer may fall below freezing point throughout January and February, so giving a wide annual range. Berlin, for instance, ranges from 30° F (−1·1° C) in January to 66° F (18·9° C) in July, annual range 36° F (20° C), with 22·7 in. rainfall, of which 12·7 in. falls in summer; Belgrade, 29° F (−1·7° C) January, 72° F (22·2° C) July, range 43° F (24° C), with 24·4 in. rainfall, 14·6 in. in summer. The rainfall in this climatic area is not very great. Its effectiveness is reduced because most of the rain falls in the hot days of summer, when evaporation is greatest.

6. *Cool temperate continental climate*

Farther to the east the transitional conditions merge into the cool temperate continental climate in Rumania, Bulgaria, eastern Poland and Russia. There the summers remain normal for the latitude, but the winters are much colder, and annual ranges of temperature greater. Some figures for winter temperatures in this area have already been given; to them may be added Chkalov, which with means of 4° F (−15·6° C) in January and 70° F (21·1° C) in July, has an annual range of 66° F (36·6° C), perhaps the greatest in Europe. The rains in this climatic division fall mainly in summer, with maxima in June and July, and are mostly convectional in character. The total amount decreases towards the southeast, where the Black and Caspian Seas seem to have little effect on neighbouring lowlands. Rarely, except where there are mountains, is the annual total as much as 20 in.; and the plains north of the Caspian, lying below sea level, have desert conditions with only 6 in. rainfall annually.

STUDY QUESTIONS

1. Attempt an explanatory account of the climatic conditions of western Europe. (O. & C.)

2. Outline and justify a division of Europe into climatic regions. (J.M.B.)

3. Comment on the importance of the Icelandic low pressures and the Azores high pressures in the climate of western Europe. (O. & C.)

4. With reference to Europe, describe the difficulties of defining climatic regions. (O. & C.)

5. Give a reasoned account of the differences between the climates of the localities of Riga, Bergen and Marseille. (J.M.B.)

6. Account for the variations in temperature and rainfall régimes over western Europe. (O. & C.)

7. Describe the rainfall régime of the Mediterranean region. Give reasons for the seasonal variations you mention and discuss the differences in total annual rainfall that are found in stations around the Mediterranean Sea. (O. & C.)

Chapter IV

NATURAL VEGETATION AND SOILS

THE variety of land forms, rock types and climates in Europe has resulted in a remarkable number of different kinds of soil and vegetation. Natural vegetation—that is, what grew before man started to develop and change it—exists in large areas only in the north, but enough remains everywhere to show what the vegetation cover used to be.

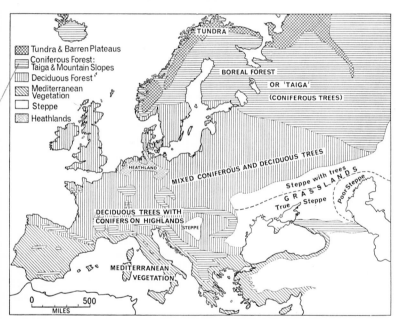

FIG. 9.—Europe: natural vegetation. It should be noted that much of the area near the Atlantic seaboard shown as deciduous forest would be better described as moist grassland. It is doubtful, for instance, whether Ireland was ever completely clothed with forest. Similarly, the steppe shown in the Pannonian basin may be the result of deforestation in historical times. Note, too, that the lines of demarcation between different types of vegetation are purely arbitrary: there are very few such distinctive boundaries in nature.

Soil is a complex mixture of mineral and organic products. The development of soil begins with the physical breakdown of surface rocks into small particles, which are colonised by bacteria and mosses. When

39

these die, mould and humus begin to accumulate; other plants begin to take root, grow and decay; burrowing animals stir up the surface layers; air and water enter and are retained. With the decay of dead plants and animals, organic acids are formed, and these react with the mineral contents of the rocks to form soils. Since all chemical reactions depend on varying amounts of heat and moisture, *i.e.* (in this case) temperature and rainfall, it is clear that the formation of soils depends to a large degree on the climate of the region in which they have developed. This is why there are different types of soil, and why it is possible to associate soil types with the vegetation that grows on them.

In this chapter we shall examine the major regions of natural vegetation in Europe from the point of view of, first, the vegetation cover itself (*see* Fig. 9) and, second, the effects the climate and the plant life have had on the underlying soils. In most areas it must be remembered too that man has taken a hand in the formation of soil, by destroying the natural vegetation, ploughing the land, introducing new plants and using organic manure which is already rich in humus. He has also, by the addition of lime, made unproductive acid soils capable of cultivation and by irrigation has made arid soils fruitful.

1. *Tundra: Arctic soils*

In the "Arctic" and "cold" climatic divisions, natural vegetation has been changed least. North of the Arctic Circle the soils are thin and permanently frozen within a foot or so of the surface. They are mainly the result of the surface rocks being frost-shattered and then acted upon by the climate. Since the heat and moisture necessary for chemical action are here at a minimum, soil formation is slow. The long, cold winters and short summers allow only mosses and lichens, with berry-bearing shrubs such as cranberries, crowberries and bilberries near rivers or in depressions in the surface, to survive. When they die, they rot slowly into a surface layer of peat, which in badly drained areas forms bogs. This type of vegetation is called *tundra*. It is cold desert, a region of privation in which semi-nomadic peoples, such as the Lapps, rear reindeer. Similar peaty soils and scanty vegetation are found at high altitudes in all mountainous regions, as in the length of the Scandinavian peninsula, the Alps and the Caucasus.

2. *Coniferous forest: podsol*

In the southern part of the tundra, stunted trees—willows, birches and occasional firs—are found in the river valleys, and they increase in size and number towards the south, forming the characteristic cover of the cold climatic region, coniferous forest. It stretches almost continuously from Norway to the Urals, widening towards the east, where it is often called the *taiga*, although strictly speaking this name should be reserved for the Siberian part of this extensive forest. The chief trees are spruce, Scots pine and fir; a wide distribution of the hardier deciduous trees—birch, larch, willow and poplar—persists to the northern limit of tree growth. Coniferous forest covers almost two-thirds of Finland and half of Sweden and, with the taiga, constitutes the greatest reserve of timber in Europe. There are not many varieties of tree, which means that lumbering for a single species is made easier. The commonest is the spruce, which is actually increasing in numbers at the expense of other conifers. This is fortunate, since it provides the best source of wood-pulp.

Elsewhere in Europe, coniferous forests are found on mountain slopes and high surfaces where low temperatures prevent the growth of deciduous trees. Such are the forests of the Alps, Pyrenees, Jura, Vosges, Black Forest, Ardennes, Central Massif, Bohemian Forest, Carpathians and Caucasus. Among coniferous forests planted by man are a large one in the Landes of France and smaller areas in Holland, Belgium, western Denmark and north Germany.

Coniferous trees are adapted to their environment by their conical shape and needle-like leaves, both of which can withstand an accumulation of snow, and because they can thrive with as little as 10 in. precipitation. These forests have a minimum of undergrowth: the tough leaves rot only very slowly, and the soil is accordingly deficient in humus. Clearings, often caused by forest fires, may be occupied by peat bogs. Agriculture is carried on only with difficulty, and then mainly for rye, barley and potatoes, in clearings near the south of the forest or where maritime influences are felt more, as in southern Sweden and Finland or more especially at the heads of the fiords in Norway. The main occupations in the coniferous forests are lumbering, mining and fur-trapping, though the last has declined in importance in recent years.

The soil type of the coniferous forest regions is called *podsol*, Russian for "ashy grey soil." A vertical section through any natural soil shows a layered arrangement known as the *soil profile*. This is well developed in the soils under coniferous trees, where the topsoil is covered during the winter by a layer of snow, and chemical and biological action, which produce good soil, are at a standstill. When the snow melts, water drains downwards, and iron hydroxides and the humus from the rotting vegetation near the surface are carried in a colloidal solution to the lower soil layer, thus *leaching* the topsoil or upper *horizon*. This top zone is thus bleached to a predominantly greyish tint, hence the name podsol. The ferro-humus material accumulates at a depth of a few inches where, mixed with particles of clay and silt, it forms a deep brown layer. Occasionally, this becomes a hard, cemented band which prevents further drainage and leads to waterlogging, and so there is a marked tendency for peat bogs to develop.

3. Deciduous forest: brown soils

South of the coniferous forests, in the regions of cool temperature marginal and transitional climates, with an extension eastwards into continental regions, that is, over the greater part of Europe, the land was at one time covered by forest which contained mainly deciduous trees. In the northern part of the zone the forests are mixed conifers and deciduous; elsewhere the broad-leaved deciduous trees predominate, with conifers only at higher altitudes or where man has reforested, as in the Landes. The commonest deciduous trees in Europe are the oak, walnut, chestnut, elm, ash, beech and sycamore, all of which produce excellent hardwood. There are now very few stands of these trees left, for most of the mixed and deciduous forests have been cleared for agriculture.

This is because the soils underlying the mixed and deciduous forests are less acid and contain more humus than the soils under the true coniferous forest, and so are more fertile. They are various shades of brown in colour, the shade depending on the amount of decomposition that has taken place in the surface rocks, and this in turn varies with climatic conditions, as we have seen. In the north of the belt, for instance, the soils are grey-brown, for they are somewhat podsolised. In this northern region the cleared areas produce good crops of rye, oats, potatoes and flax; to the west, where it is wetter, meadows with grasses and clover are important. In the south of the deciduous forest zone, especially in western and central Europe, there are soils which have developed from the loess deposited at the end of the glacial epoch, and these are rich brown in colour and have a high humus content. The forests here have been replaced by fields of wheat, maize and sugar beet; orchards of bush and tree fruits are widespread.

In eastern Europe, the deciduous forests thin out southwards, and the trees, predominantly oak and aspen, are separated by patches of grassland. This is a transition belt known as *wooded steppe* or *woodland steppe*. The grassland has now largely disappeared, giving way to mixed farming. The soils are dark brown, and are also transitional in character between the true brown forest soils of the main deciduous belt and the Black Earth of the steppe lands to the south.

4. Heathland: acid soils

In the west of the deciduous forest belt is a region whose natural vegetation is heathland—stunted gorse, broom and heather. It comprises the

Campine of Belgium, the *geest* of Holland, and the *Heide* (heaths) in the west of West Germany. The soils consist of the sand and gravel outwash of the melting glaciers of the Ice Age. In some parts they rest on the boulder clays of moraines from an earlier phase of the glaciation. Geologically, they are young soils, and under the cool temperate marginal climatic conditions of the region they have been slow to develop. Moreover, because of the impervious subsoil, they tend to become waterlogged and acid in character, and are consequently infertile. This is especially the case in hollows in the surface, where lack of drainage has resulted in the formation of bogs with a considerable layer of peat. Peat, which is dug out and used for fuel, is the imperfectly decomposed remains of sphagnum moss, which is the usual vegetative cover of these boggy areas.

Somewhat similar natural vegetation is found along the coastlands of the Bay of Biscay (the Landes of France), the western half of the Jutland peninsula in Denmark, and the more elevated regions of western Ireland and Scotland. Here the strong winds blowing from the Atlantic are probably a factor inhibiting natural tree growth.

A large proportion of the heathland has been reclaimed, either by afforestation, mostly with conifers, or by removing the surface layers and then, by deep ploughing and the addition of lime and fertilisers, turning it into agricultural land.

5. Steppe: chernozem

South of the forest in eastern Europe, in a belt stretching from the plains of the lower Danube to the borders of Asia and beyond, is the *steppe*, grassy plains with few or no trees. The continental climate in this belt, with soils frozen for months in winter and then moistened by snow-melt in spring and quickly evaporated rains in summer, is inimical to tree growth. On the other hand, it favours grasses which have a short and rapid life cycle, and bulbous plants which can lie dormant during the dry autumn and long, cold winter and resume active growth with the spring thaw. This region, then, sometimes known as the *true steppe* to distinguish it from the *wooded steppe* to the north and the *dry steppe* in some parts to the south, was once naturally covered in spring and early summer by grasses and brightly coloured flowers of bulbous plants, with a few trees near rivers. In late summer and autumn the flowers withered, the grasses were scorched and brown; in winter the steppe was a vast expanse of snow. In its natural state the steppe was a great pasture land, where Cossack and Khirghiz horsemen herded cattle and sheep.

Little of the original vegetative cover now remains, for the soil of the true steppe is the well known black earth or *chernozem*, one of the most fertile in the world. The region has been ploughed and extensively cultivated for wheat, barley, oats, rye, maize, sunflowers (for oil), sugar beet, tobacco and melons. Pastoral activities, except locally for dairy produce, are confined today to areas which have more saline and less fertile soils, or to the desert steppe which occurs around the northern part of the Caspian Sea.

Chernozem occurs almost continuously in a belt extending from the Ukraine eastwards into Asia. Formed in a region which has frequent summer rains, and temperatures which do not evaporate them too quickly, chernozem has two horizons: a topsoil up to 40 in. in depth and black in colour, and a subsoil which is yellowy-brown and rich in lime (calcium carbonate). The black colour of the topsoil is due primarily to the age-long decomposition of grass, but the presence of lime in the parent rock seems also to be essential. Chernozem is formed from loess, and is greatest in depth where this rests on chalk, as in the Ukraine; where the underlying rock is clayey, the black earth is rarely more than 20 in. deep. Its great fertility is due to the high humus content which has accumulated from the decomposition of the grasses, and has been acted upon by calcareous solutions drawn upwards from the subsoil during the dry season. It is this chemical action which produces the black colouring. Humus varies in amount from 6% in the Ukraine to nearly 15% east of the Volga where, however, the depth of black earth is only a few inches.

A vegetation cover similar to that of the true steppe used to be found in the enclosed basin of Hungary (Pannonian basin), where the grassy plains were called *pusztas*. Most of the area has been ploughed for agriculture, but in one small region in north-east Hungary, Magyar herdsmen continue their traditional pastoralism, with sheep and cattle. Steppe occurs, too, in the Walachian Plain in Rumania, and in northern Bulgaria; these have also been transformed into cereal producers. North of the Carpathians, in southern Poland and western U.S.S.R., there is steppe of the wooded type.

6. *Dry steppe: chestnut soils*

South of the true steppe, in a belt commencing to the north of the Crimean peninsula and widening eastwards towards Asia, the natural vegetation is still predominantly of grasses, but they are shorter than in the true steppe, and there are relatively few bulbous plants. This is the dry steppe, distinguished from the true steppe by a lower annual rainfall and higher summer temperatures, with consequent greater evaporation. The soils are chestnut in colour, and may be saline. They range in depth up to 20 in. and have a humus content of about 3%, so they are far less fertile than chernozem. Where irrigation is possible they have been ploughed for cereals, but in the eastern part of the belt, where droughts are frequent, pastoralism is still the chief occupation.

Near the northern shores of the Caspian Sea the greater heat of summer and the smaller amount of rainfall have resulted in a poor soil, light chestnut in colour, deficient in humus (1%), and not very productive even when irrigated. The grass cover is patchy and there is a good deal of bitter, stunted shrub (*artemisia*). Saline areas occur more frequently, especially in depressions in the surface; in them the poor soils, impregnated with alkaline salts of potassium, magnesium and lime, support little more than halophilous (salt-loving) shrubs such as tamarisk.

7. *Mediterranean vegetation: terra rossa*

The region with a Mediterranean climate has a natural vegetation adapted to a rhythm in which rain comes in the cool season and fierce heat is accompanied by drought. The adaptation consists largely in various means of conserving or obtaining moisture, and many of the plants are xerophytic (drought-resisting). The Mediterranean climate is inimical to the growth of grass, except a tussocky type, hard and tough such as esparto, which is found on the Meseta in Spain. Other grassy districts, Thessaly in Greece and the uplands of Sicily, have been ploughed for cereals.

The characteristic vegetation is a thin, open forest of conifers like the Aleppo pine and stone pine, mixed with stunted, broad-leaved, evergreen oaks, beech and sweet chestnut. Some of these, like the cork oak, have a thick, spongy bark; most have small, thick leaves, sometimes coated with wax; others have long, deep roots; and fruits, *e.g.* the pomegranate, may have thick skins. The object in each case is obtaining or keeping moisture. Smaller plants have similar protective features. Small, hard, leathery leaves covered with wax or hair, shrubs with thorny spines, plants which exude aromatic and sticky sap—all are indicative of the fight against drought. Where the trees have been cut down in the past, nature has replaced them with a thick, stunted growth of scrub, known as *maquis* in the south of France and as *macchia* in Italy. Maquis grows on the crystalline soils of Corsica; *garrigue*, a poorer type, is common on soils developed from limestone.

Many plants which today are regarded as typically Mediterranean in character are not native to the region. The orange and lemon, for instance, are comparative newcomers from other climatic regions. Date-palms at Elche in south-east Spain are obvious immigrants, and rice, sugar cane and cotton came originally from tropical countries to the south or east. Their successful cultivation is possible because of the heat of summer, but only if water is available for irrigation. It is even doubtful if the vine is indigenous to the Mediterranean, although it has adapted itself by its long roots and is now found throughout the Mediterranean basin and is regarded as typical. The olive is the only one of the useful so-called "Mediterranean products" which is truly native, although there is a distinct probability that wheat and barley were developed from native grasses somewhere in the Mediterranean basin.

Soils in the Mediterranean region are thickest in the valleys and along the coasts. On the mountain ranges the winter rains wash down the surface cover, which is deposited as alluvium at lower levels. It is often deep and rich, and brown in colour. In areas where vegetation was scanty it is deficient in humus, but, if water can be provided, is rarely so poor as to be infertile.

In some places *terra rossa*, red soil, has developed. This is a rather heavy, clayey type formed from underlying limestones and coloured by iron oxides. Rich in lime but poor in humus, it has limited value and is usually the site of olive groves and vineyards. Outcrops of terra rossa are found in small patches in south-east Spain, the lower Rhône valley, the eastern slopes of the Apennines, Sicily, Corsica, Sardinia and Greece. In eastern Italy and Sicily are small areas of *volcanic soil*, which is rich and extremely valuable.

One of the problems of the Mediterranean region is that of *soil erosion*. Rains in the winter may come in heavy showers, so intense that the soil cover is washed from the steep slopes so common in the region, and deep gullies are carved in the land surface, even in the lowlands; then in the dry summer the powdery soil is blown away by strong winds. The total loss of soil is serious, and has been aggravated by deforestation in the past, which laid bare the surface to erosion. Indiscriminate grazing of goats, which devour young trees and shrubs, produced the same result.

To combat soil erosion, terraces with retaining walls are constructed on slopes, gullies are blocked by walls, wind-breaks are planted or built, quick-growing crops are placed where their roots will prevent the downward movement of soil, reforestation is carefully planned and supervised, and pasture by goats is controlled and restricted.

STUDY QUESTIONS

1. Describe the seasonal temperature conditions of Europe and show how they are reflected in the distribution of types of vegetation. (J.M.B.)

2. Relate the natural vegetation of Europe to the dominant physical controls. (J.M.B.)

3. Write a short essay on "The soils of Europe."

Chapter V

THE PEOPLES OF EUROPE

SETTLEMENT

PREHISTORIC SETTLEMENT

It is possible that man existed in Europe before the Pleistocene Ice Age, but nothing certain is known until the latest phase of the Glacial period. The ice which covered northern Europe limited settlement to the southern half of the continent. In south-west France, the interior of the Iberian peninsula, and the Italian peninsula south of Tuscany, the skeletal remains of Palaeolithic (Old Stone Age) man, which are found extensively, are probably representative of the aboriginal inhabitants of Europe. These people were rather short in stature, but were all dolichocephalic* or long-headed. There is no direct evidence of their colouring, but it is thought they had dark skins and black hair.

As climatic conditions improved in the north of Europe and the ice sheet retreated, northern Africa and south-west Asia became drier, more desert-like and inhospitable to man. New movements of people developed from these areas into Europe, over land bridges which were still in existence at Gibraltar and the Black Sea straits. One of these peoples was distinctly negroid in character, and settled in southern France near the Italian border. Skeletons and statuettes found in graves suggest similarities with the Hottentots of South Africa, but their existence in Europe seems to have been brief, and their distribution was limited to this one small district.

The immigrants to the northern shores of the Mediterranean were all dolichocephalic but varied in stature. Those in the west mixed peacefully with the older palaeolithic inhabitants, and inter-breeding seems to have produced mesocephalic types. Others penetrated the mountains and infiltrated the plains of north-west Europe to become ultimately, it is thought, the long-headed, fair-skinned peoples characteristic of Scandinavia: the ancestors of the so-called Nordic race. The change

---

* Anthropologists use the size and shape of the skull as part of their classification of racial types. By expressing the ratio of maximum breadth to maximum length of the skull as a "cephalic index," two extreme types, *dolichocephalic* (long-headed) and *brachycephalic* (round-headed), were observed. A third type, intermediate between these two and the result of inter-breeding, is known as *mesocephalic*.

from dark skins and black hair was the result of biological mutations which perpetuated themselves in these northern peoples.

During the neolithic (New Stone Age) period large numbers of brachycephalic people moved from the south-east to the west, interposing themselves like a wedge between the long-headed and medium-headed inhabitants of the Mediterranean and those in the north. These broad-headed or round-headed peoples migrated via the Danube valley to the highlands of central Europe and the valleys and lower slopes of the Alpine ranges, penetrating to the Central Massif of France and even to the British Isles.

It would appear, then, that the early inhabitants of Europe were of three main races: the Mediterranean and the Nordic, both long-headed; and the Alpine, broad-headed; and that the dolichocephalic predominated, if we accept the evidence of burial places. Today, however, the bulk of Europe's population is brachycephalic or mesocephalic, even among the fair-skinned, blonde peoples. The reason for the change is a matter of conjecture among biologists, who are of the opinion that further immigration through the ages of broad-headed people from Asia and inter-breeding with the inhabitants already there have caused genetic changes which tended to brachycephalism. Thus almost all the peoples of Russia are broad-headed, and brachycephalics are found in a narrowing wedge westwards in Poland, Germany, the countries of central Europe, the northern Balkans, Switzerland, the Low Countries and eastern and central France. Long-headed people of the Nordic type, with fair skins and hair, are confined mainly to the west and north of a line running south through the Gulf of Bothnia to the Harz mountains and then curving through Holland to Scotland. The dolichocephalics of the Mediterranean are mostly in the Iberian peninsula, the southern part of the Italian peninsula, Corsica, Sardinia and the other islands of the western Mediterranean. People with medium heads, dark skins and hair, and brown eyes, range from northern Italy, southern France, southern Spain, along the Bay of Biscay to Brittany and possibly to south-west Ireland. A tall, dark, brachycephalic people, sometimes called the Dinaric race, is found in the western Balkan peninsula, the Plain of Lombardy and the eastern Alps.

The above classification is based mainly on shape of skull, stature, and colour of skin and hair, but it must be noted that any attempt to distinguish race types must take into account other factors such as blood groups and the influence exerted by dominant and recessive genes and perhaps physical environment, about all of which there remains great uncertainty. Moreover, there has been so much inter-breeding between the original peoples that only rarely can one find in Europe groups with enough homogeneity or uniformity of physical characteristics to justify the division of present-day inhabitants on a racial basis. For this reason language is often given greater importance, indicating (it is suggested) common purpose and tradition, and separating one group of people from another. The latter, however, is not a division according to race, but into nations or cultures.

HISTORICAL SETTLEMENT

In historical times the first noteworthy movements of people in Europe were from the Mediterranean area, where a longer period of settlement and stability had helped a rise to civilisation and a consequent increase in population. This in turn led to emigration and colonisation, first by the Greeks and later by the Romans. Greek colonies and trading posts spread themselves all round the coasts of the Mediterranean and Black Seas; the Romans advanced through Gaul to the British Isles and the Rhineland, or through the Alps and along the Danube to Rumania (*see* Fig. 118). With the breakdown of the Greek and Roman empires, the colonists were withdrawn or submerged in a series of invasions by Nordics or by new peoples, including Slavs, from Asia. The Romans left their language—Latin—in the countries they had colonised, and it was adopted and modified by the native inhabitants or by invaders to make the beginnings of modern Spanish, Portuguese, French and Rumanian, and the Walloon and Provençal dialects.

For some time before the end of Roman supremacy, hordes of barbarians from the north had made sporadic raids towards the south-west of Europe, and by the early Middle Ages these became wholesale migrations of complete tribes. First the Goths and Vandals occupied Italy, France and Spain, the Vandals passing over in A.D. 429 from Spain to Roman Africa, where they established a naval empire in the western Mediterranean and raided the trading posts in Sicily and Italy. The Goth and Vandal empires did not last, but their successors, the Franks and the Saxons, in numerous small bands under military chieftains, settled in the lands they conquered. The Franks gave their name to France but adopted the language already spoken there. The Saxons moved to the eastern coast of the North Sea and into England (*see* Fig. 10).

The movement of all these peoples may have been the result of pressure by other groups advancing across the plains from Asia, for to the same period belongs the migration of the Slavs, who infiltrated from western Russia in two directions, a northern branch passing through Poland to the upper Elbe basin and a southern branch into the northern Balkans, the present Yugoslavia. Another savage Asiatic tribe, the Huns, conquered the lands now called Hungary and Transylvania, and under their great chief, Attila, overran and devastated the whole of the European plain as

far as the Rhine, penetrating into France and Italy. Attila was defeated in
France by a combination of the western tribes and withdrew to Hungary.

Invasion and movement continued throughout the Middle Ages. The
Magyars, savage horsemen from the Asiatic steppes, settled in the Hungarian plain and for upwards of a century from their arrival about A.D.
906 were a scourge to central and western Europe. Their conversion to
Christianity brought an end to their warlike activities, and they became

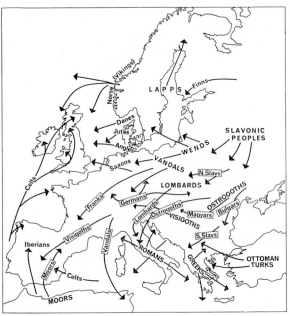

FIG. 10.—Europe: historical movements of peoples. Notice
that, with the exceptions of the Greeks, Romans and Germans, most migrations were to the west. The eastern
movement of the Germans brought them into conflict
with the Slavonic peoples and the Ottoman Turks, and
resulted in several wars.

pastoralists. Magyar is the language of Hungary, and it bears little resemblance to any other European tongue, except possibly Finnish,
Estonian and Lapp, spoken by the descendants of other minor Asiatic
migratory infiltrations into the far north of Europe. Norsemen (Vikings)
sailed from the fiords of Norway to settle in England and France; among
their descendants were the Normans.

In the eighth century, with the rise of Mohammedanism, the north
African coastlands were overrun by fanatical Arab tribes, one of which,
the Moors, crossed into Spain, conquered almost the whole of the Iberian

The Population of Europe

	Area (square miles)	Population ('000)	Density (persons per square mile)
Northern			
Finland	130,082	4,523	34
Sweden	173,630	7,542	43
Norway . . .	125,064	3,626	29
Denmark . . .	16,615	4,617	279
Iceland	39,961	185	4
Western			
Netherlands . . .	12,962	11,745	904
Belgium	11,755	9,229	785
Luxembourg . . .	999	319	319
France	212,919	47,600	223
Monaco	368 *acres*	20	
Central			
West Germany . .	95,744	56,173	592
East Germany . . .	41,802	17,079	408
Poland	120,733	30,483	252
Czechoslovakia . .	49,359	13,868	281
Switzerland . . .	15,941	5,565	349
Austria	32,370	7,074	219
Liechtenstein . . .	64	17	265
South central			
Hungary . . .	35,909	10,054	279
Rumania . . .	91,671	18,750	204
Bulgaria . . .	43,818	8,100	184
Yugoslavia . . .	98,725	19,064	193
Southern			
Portugal	34,831	8,889	255
Spain	194,945	30,430	156
Andorra . . .	190	*c.* 5	26
Italy	116,280	50,464	435
San Marino . . .	24	17	708
Vatican City . . .	109 *acres*	1	
Maltese islands . .	121	329	2,718
Greece	50,534	8,389	166
Albania	11,097	1,665	151
Turkey-in-Europe . .	9,000	2,294	254

peninsula, and advanced into France as far as Narbonne. They were gradually driven back into southern Spain but remained in Europe until their final expulsion in 1494. They had a great influence on the language of Spain, and left their legacy in place-names, architecture, agriculture and irrigation. In the east, too, there were further invasions: Tartar nomads advanced into the steppes of Russia; and later, after the fall of Constantinople in A.D. 1453, the Turks marched into Europe and took possession of the Balkan peninsula.

C

Most of the migratory or invading movements of peoples in Europe, it will be noticed, were from east to west. The result was that the west of the continent became relatively overpopulated; so new movements began to relieve the pressure. Some took the form of looking for new lands across the oceans. From the countries of the west—Spain, Portugal, France and England—voyages of discovery led to the finding of the New World and routes round Africa to the Far East, and opportunities for colonisation. In other cases, peoples turned eastwards again to settle in areas not fully populated. The Swedes, for instance, crossed the Baltic into Finland, where they form a significant admixture in the south-west. German-speaking tribes in central Europe forced their way east along the Danube basin, where they came in conflict with the advancing Slavs. The colonies they established even as far as the shores of the Black Sea, though they never achieved more than local importance, were a source of irritation to the Slavs and helped to maintain the hostility between the two peoples which was still a factor in both world wars. The Iron Curtain is, in effect, a division between the Slavs and non-Slavs, a cultural-linguistic barrier, if an imperfect one.

The Russians, too, turned east. The Slavs who had taken refuge in the mixed forests moved south-east to the steppes which had been devastated by Tartar invaders. The branch known as the Cossacks became the owners of the grasslands as far as the southern Urals. Colonists penetrated into Asia and in small numbers spread to the Pacific shores or skirted the Caspian. In recent years the colonisation of Asiatic U.S.S.R. has become a definite policy of the Soviet government; European peoples have been planted wherever it has seemed possible to plan development. Present-day co-ordinated efforts at colonisation bear little resemblance to the migratory movements of the past, but the apparently haphazard and unplanned spread of peoples in days long gone has resulted in a Western Europe which bred modern civilisation.

LANGUAGE, NATIONALITY AND POLITICAL BOUNDARIES

NATIONAL UNITS

The first inhabitants of Europe were hunters, and their migrations were mainly through open country, avoiding the forests in the moister lowlands. So we find extensive prehistoric settlement in the grasslands of central and eastern Europe. But in the west, movement was along the drier, more porous chalk and limestone ridges or the sandy and *limon* strips which flank their lower slopes. From their upland encampments these primitive peoples made hunting trips into the forests, but not until population increased and agriculture had been introduced did they settle permanently in the wetter areas. This is thought to have happened at the beginning of the Bronze Age, and to coincide with the migration of broad-headed tribes from south-west Asia.

It is certain that agriculture was known along the Mediterranean coastlands for a long time before it was practised in the north-west, but whenever and wherever it was introduced it necessitated a settled life, with fixed homes that could be defended against marauders who were still nomad hunters; and it demanded a different and more complex social organisation. It led to the development of towns, the building of walls to protect them, the storage of surplus food, the possibility of trade or exchange, the division of the people into those who produced the food, those who distributed it, and those who protected all, *i.e.* soldiers. The last were of vital importance, for without them invaders might wipe town-dwellers and farmers out of existence, so their leaders were the chief men in the community.

We have seen how different types of men settled in different parts of Europe and how wave after wave of migration over many centuries resulted in a mixing of the peoples, especially in western Europe, which makes it difficult to distinguish physical characteristics as indicative of race. At the same time, we know that the population of Europe can be divided into groups separated from each other by some difference, the most obvious one being language. What probably happened was that in the distant past communities were isolated from their neighbours over long periods, and from the language spoken by their ancestors developed their own means of communication, modified by time and the geographical surroundings.

A community which spoke a common tongue would be cut off by a linguistic barrier from other communities, but would be unified within itself. Differences in language make it difficult to exchange ideas and knowledge or to conduct commercial or political business, and these differences, helped by a way of life and cultural traditions developed through centuries, are major factors in the growth of nationalities. It is difficult to define the word "nation" adequately. It connotes a number of people larger than a single tribe, living as a community, usually with the same language, ways of thought and life, ideals and purpose. A nation may originally have been several tribes with different languages, but living together and intermixing led to a fusion which produced the result we see in modern times, and which we recognise instinctively, even where we cannot explain it.

For instance, we understand very clearly what is meant by the French nation or the German nation or the Italians; but we usually think in terms of the language they speak, and not of their origin; and although we regard some of their customs and habits as peculiar to each of them, we are apt to regard language as the criterion of distinction. This idea of equating language and nationality is a modern concept. It led to the unification of Italy and Germany from many small states in the nineteenth century, and to the setting up of Holland, Belgium, Greece, Serbia and Rumania as separate nations. In this century Norway, Sweden, Finland, Estonia, Latvia, Lithuania, Czechoslovakia and Yugoslavia claimed sovereign status on the basis of language, although in two cases (Czechoslovakia and Yugoslavia) there was no common tongue. These two countries, however, had languages cognate to each other, Czech and Slovak in one case, Serbo-Croat and Slovene in the other, all of them Slavonic in origin.

There are twenty-nine main languages in Europe which are official spoken and written means of communication. In addition there are several sub-languages, often called *patois*, more dignified than dialect. Such are Maltese, Provençal (southern France), Basque (south-western France and northern Spain), Lappish and Ruthenian, all of which are spoken by considerable numbers of people, but within very limited areas.

NATIONAL BOUNDARIES

The boundaries of countries inhabited by a population speaking a common language have been determined in Europe by history and political negotiation, yet they show the influence of geographical conditions when examined in detail. In this they differ from many boundaries, especially in North America and Australia, which were marked out by lines of latitude or longitude, sometimes in advance of settlement. The general rule in Europe is for frontiers or political boundaries to run through some strip of poorly populated country, such as mountain ranges, bleak uplands with poor soil, or lowland marshes and heathlands. Large rivers are rarely used as boundaries, even of administrative divisions within a country, and for any exceptions there is always a special reason. Where large rivers are navigable, they unify rather than divide; the same people occupies both banks, and river-steamers can touch one side as easily as the other. Small rivers, however, form portions of boundaries if they flow through districts of low population density, for they are obvious lines of demarcation.

Of the larger rivers the Danube shows some departures from the usual. For a few miles below Passau it flows in a deep trench, an effective boundary between Germany and Austria; and from below Bratislava, for about eighty miles, it passes through country liable to inundation and divides Hungary from Czechoslovakia. It is in its lower course, however, that its function as a boundary is most noticeable. East of Belgrade the Danube enters mountainous country thinly peopled, and proceeds by narrow defiles, culminating in the gorge of the Iron Gate, before it emerges on to the plains of Walachia. This cleft through the Alpine folds is a well marked divide between Yugoslavia and Rumania, The river then forms most of the boundary between Bulgaria and Rumania, although it is wide, navigable and flows in a plain. This is because on its left bank the land is low-lying and subject to floods, so has few towns, and on the right bank there is a quick rise to a sparsely peopled limestone plateau. In this part of its course it is a better boundary than the Balkan Mountains, which would appear to be a clearer line of demarcation.

The Rhine is a boundary in its upper course through the mountains between Switzerland, Austria and Germany, where its valley is either liable to flooding or runs through difficult country. The notable departure from the orthodox is in the rift valley, where its navigable section begins. From just below Basel to Lauterbourg, a distance of about 100 miles, the river is the boundary between France and Germany. The reason is historical rather than geographical, both countries claiming the river valley in this stretch. Here, immediately before the Second World War, two powerful lines of fortification faced each other across the river, the Maginot Line in France and the Siegfried Line in Germany. Today the river is internationalised and the principle of free navigation accepted, although grudgingly by the Germans.

At the end of the Second World War the Russians advanced their western boundary to the river Bug at the expense of Poland. The Poles pushed westwards and made the Oder, with its tributary, the Neisse (Nisa), their western boundary. This was a convenient north–south dividing line in an area where physical features gave little help; but although it is well marked, it is not likely to be permanent, for both sides of the river are equally accessible and a river never forms a satisfactory ethnic boundary. In this case, with Teuton on one side and Slav on the other, historic enmities are likely to lead ultimately to trouble.

It is a useful exercise to examine the boundaries of European countries closely, to find why they twist and turn as they do. Where there are mountains the boundary is often obvious; in lowlands their course is not always clear, but can usually be explained. Take the Netherlands, for instance. The eastern boundary starts in the north through a marsh parallel to the river Ems, then winds south and south-west through poorly peopled heathland to the Rhine, which it crosses. It moves to the scarp overlooking the Maas (Meuse) valley, and for some distance runs parallel to the river along comparatively high land with less development and fewer people than the valley. Near Aachen it bends suddenly west to the Meuse, crosses it to enclose Maastricht, then follows the river to the edge of Belgian Limburg. In this "tail" of Holland is the Limburg coalfield, which explains the peculiar shape of the frontier. The boundary then meanders through poor, sandy heaths between the Dutch province of North Brabant and the Belgian districts of Limburg and Antwerp, crossing the river Scheldt near the head of its estuary and skirting the reclaimed polders to the coast. The boundaries of the Netherlands exemplify the typical use of belts of scanty population.

REGIONAL DIVISIONS OF EUROPE

GEOGRAPHICAL DIVISIONS

The countries of Europe may be grouped, according to their position in the continent, into (1) northern, (2) western, (3) central, (4) south central, (5) southern or Mediterranean, and (6) eastern, Europe. By grouping in this way, each division (*see* Fig. 11) contains countries which show marked similarities of relief, climate and natural vegetation, and possibly of human and economic development.

1. Northern Europe

This division includes Finland, Sweden, Norway, Denmark and Iceland. Judged by position, race and language, these countries form a distinct geographical unit, although in detail their geography must differ, affected as they are in varying degree by distance from the Atlantic climatic influences.

2. Western Europe

This comprises the Netherlands, Belgium, Luxembourg, France and the British Isles. The region borders the Atlantic where the tempering effects of the ocean on climate and natural vegetation provide a favoured environment in which man has found great opportunity for development. The British Isles form part of western Europe, but are not examined in this book; however, they are introduced where relevant references or comparisons seem necessary. With regard to France, it should be noted that although its Mediterranean coastlands belong climatically to southern Europe, and some parts in the east of the country show characteristics of structure and climate more like those of central Europe, it is treated here as entirely a western state.

3. Central Europe

This is regarded as the transitional climatic region between the maritime west and the continental east; it contains the countries of Germany, Czechoslovakia, Poland, Switzerland, Liechtenstein and Austria. The last three lie mainly among the Alpine mountain folds; the others occupy

Fig. 11.—Europe: political divisions. The thick lines denote the regional groupings made in this book: Northern, Western, Central, South Central and Southern or Mediterranean Europe. For the area, and the total and density of population for each country, see the table on page 51.

a large part of the Great European Plain and the massifs of the central uplands with their intervening basins.

4. South central Europe

The countries abutting on the middle and lower Danube—Hungary, Yugoslavia, Rumania and Bulgaria—differ from those of central Europe in some aspects of climate and in economic development. With the exception of Yugoslavia, their natural vegetation is largely steppe; and they are all orientated more to the east than to the west. For these reasons they are regarded as a separate unit.

5. Southern Europe

The countries of southern Europe are those with a Mediterranean climate—Portugal, Spain, Italy, Malta and Greece. To these are added Albania and European Turkey, although each of the last has affinities to south central Europe. Northern Italy, too, it must be observed, belongs rather to central than to southern Europe, for it lies outside true Mediterranean influences.

6. Eastern Europe

This area comprises the truly continental, non-peninsular part of the continent. It is all the lands that make up the European section of the U.S.S.R., and in area occupies about half the continent. The study of its regional geography is outside the scope of this book, since it would be incomplete without a comparable treatment of Soviet Asia. Reference to eastern Europe will be confined to those details of its structure, relief and climate which are relevant to a consideration of peninsular Europe as a whole.

GEO-POLITICAL ANOMALIES

The siting of political boundaries has been discussed above, but the fact that some countries—France, Italy, Albania and Yugoslavia, for instance—overlap different climatic regions, and that others—Germany, Poland, Rumania, Hungary and, again, Yugoslavia—have political frontiers that are not physical boundaries, suggests that such frontiers are not always satisfactory limits in dealing with the geography of a continent.

Political boundaries divide one country from another, and may separate widely different cultures; but in many cases, in order to obtain a broad view of the physical environment, they must be disregarded. Considerations of extensive physical divisions such as the Great European Plain, or the Alpine system, or the Baltic Shield–Caledonian region, or the Balkan peninsula, need refer to individual countries only as a means of locating detail. The frontiers of countries are not good guides, however, in a broader examination of the complicated patterns of human, historical and economic development which have been built up on the physical background. In short, political boundaries play a minor role in geography.

In spite of this, it has become traditional to deal with the geography of a continent by examining it country by country, notably so when Europe is being considered. In its small area, history has formed thirty political states, as well as the semi-independent enclaves of Andorra, Monaco and San Marino, and they range in size from the vast expanse of European U.S.S.R. to only a few square miles. There are historical reasons for the existence of every one of them. But it must be remembered that the history of a people is to a great extent its reaction over many centuries to its physical environment, factors of relief, climate and soil formation, and to the occurrence or not of mineral resources. Physical environments, even of adjacent areas, are never exactly the same and may be vastly different. This is especially so in Europe, with its infinite variety of topography and its different climatic types. The reactions of its peoples resulted in a diversity of economies, cultures and ideologies, which early in history were separated from each other probably by mountain divides, rivers, swamps or other physical features. Some of these physical boundaries still form the frontier lines between countries, but throughout history there have been constant shifts of frontiers, based as time went by on human—racial or linguistic—rather than physical factors. This is why we find in Europe countries which overlap physical or climatic divisions, and frontiers for which no satisfactory geographical reason can be given.

STUDY QUESTIONS

1. Discuss the importance of (*a*) language, (*b*) physical features, in the establishment of frontiers. Illustrate the points you make by reference to any *two* frontiers. (O. & C.)

2. "Mountains divide, rivers unite." Discuss and illustrate this statement. (O. & C.)

3. With reference to specific examples in Europe, discuss the advantages and disadvantages of rivers as international frontiers. (J.M.B.)

4. Illustrate from Europe *three* ways in which features of natural geography have been utilised as political frontiers. (O. & C.)

PART TWO

THE REGIONAL GEOGRAPHY OF EUROPE

Chapter VI

NORTHERN EUROPE

Norway and Sweden together form the peninsula of Scandinavia proper, and with Finland are known as Fenno-Scandia. Owing to its similar language and its history, Denmark is sometimes included with Scandinavia. Iceland, a republic since 1944, was up to that date in union with Denmark; because of that and its northern position, it is included in this section. The Faeroe islands, an archipelago 400 miles west of Norway, are an administrative unit of Denmark. Svalbard, a group of islands—Spitzbergen the largest of them—far to the north in the Arctic Ocean, belongs to Norway. Northern Europe, with a total area of nearly 600,000 square miles, stretches from 55 degrees N. in the south of Denmark to 81 degrees N. in Svalbard, *i.e.* well inside the Arctic Circle. It is noteworthy, too, that while the western part of this section is definitely "Atlantic," the line of longitude, 30 degrees E., passes through eastern Finland, the Ukraine and the Black Sea, which are far from oceanic influences.

STRUCTURE

Over most of the mainland of northern Europe are extensive outcrops of granites, gneisses and schists forming a peneplaned shield, the Baltic or Fenno-Scandian Shield. These are among the oldest rocks on the earth's surface, and represent the remnants of a block which extended westwards far into the Atlantic and eastwards into Russia. At various times, parts were folded into mountain ranges, but by the beginning of the Cambrian period they were completely eroded to a peneplain. In Cambrian, Ordovician and Silurian times large areas of this worn-down land mass gradually subsided and were invaded by shallow seas, in which great thicknesses of sedimentary deposits accumulated.

Towards the end of the Silurian period these newly formed sedimentary rocks were squeezed up from the trough or geosyncline to form a mountain range estimated to have stretched from Scotland through Norway and Svalbard and possibly to western Greenland. To the east a more

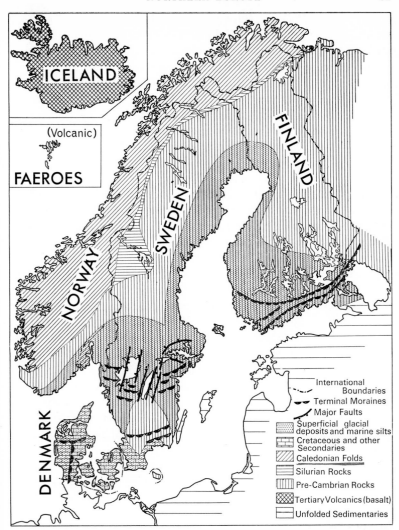

FIG. 12.—Northern Europe: structure (much simplified). The area with Pre-Cambrian (Archaean) rocks at the surface is the Baltic or Fenno-Scandian Shield.
Note (a) the belt of unfolded Silurian rocks widening into the fertile Jämtland
platform, (b) the influence of faulting in the lake district of Sweden, (c) the extent
of glacial deposits and their coincidence with regions of densest population (see
Figs. 14, 17, 20 and 24).

gradual uplift brought unfolded sedimentaries out of the receding waters.
This mountain-building movement, the Caledonian orogenesis, was
followed by a long period of quiescence during which the newer rocks
were eroded from the eastern part of the region, exposing once more the

original shield, which was still further worn down. The mountains, too, weakened by crumpling and faulting, were reduced in height by thousands of feet through prolonged denudation. For the most part, however, northern Europe did not suffer further tectonic disturbance and has remained above sea level at least since Devonian times. There are exceptions in the north and south of the region: in Svalbard are rocks of every age from Cambrian to Tertiary, and the coal measures in Spitzbergen indicate a period in Carboniferous times when the climate there was sub-tropical; in Denmark and the extreme south of Sweden are chalk and limestone of the Cretaceous period.

In Tertiary times, more especially towards the end of the period, there occurred the Alpine orogenesis, with great mountain folds across southern Europe. In northern Europe, connected with it in some way, there was a tremendous fracturing of the western end of the land mass, and large parts sank to form the North Atlantic basin. The worn-down mountains collapsed in places to form ridges on the floor of the sea bed and leave gaps at sea level, such as are found between northern Scotland and Norway or between Norway and Svalbard. Other sections of the mountains, as in Norway, were uplifted and rejuvenated, to form the present Kjölen range and the steep western coast. At the same time, great outpourings of basaltic lavas built up a vast volcanic island in the north Atlantic, fragments of which remain in central Greenland and the islands of Iceland, the Faeroes, Jan Mayen and the Inner Hebrides; and there was considerable volcanic intrusion into the Kjölen mountains and in the rocks of the Shield in southern Finland. To the same period may belong the great depression which extends from the Norway Deep (400 fathoms), via the Skagerrak, the Great Lakes region of Sweden, the Gulf of Finland, lakes Ladoga and Onega, to the White Sea. The break-up of the volcanic island was caused by further tectonic movements in the Pliocene, the last system in the Tertiary period, and the Scandinavian peninsula was further uplifted.

GLACIATION

In the early part of the Quaternary, the period in which we live, Fenno-Scandia was the centre of a continental ice sheet. In the so-called Ice Age, snow accumulated in the mountains to form glaciers which coalesced into one vast sheet and began to move outwards, wearing down the peaks and planing the rock surface, deepening fault-valleys and carving rock basins. There were several major advances of the ice, separated by warm interglacial phases and retreating movements; there is evidence that the earlier ice-cover was thicker and more prolonged, and that some of the mountain peaks in the later part of the Ice Age were left above the ice as nunataks. In its last advance the ice built a terminal moraine across western Denmark and southern Sweden. In its retreat it remained stationary for some time in central Sweden and southern Finland, where there are low morainic ridges, known in Finland as the Salpausselkä (ridge).

The glaciation of Fenno-Scandia had several important results. The advancing ice stripped all loose material and soil from the surface, so that over much of the area there is only thin bare rock; in some places there exists a shallow, superficial layer of new rocks, including recently-formed alluvium. In the final stages of retreat, eskers and drumlins were deposited on the eroded surface, slowing down or blocking the outflow of melt-water and facilitating the formation of lakes, the accumulation of clays and the development of bogs.

The glacial melt-waters caused a rise in sea level in the Baltic, on the floor of which were laid down the clays which today constitute the coastal plains of east and south Sweden and south Finland. Only in Denmark and the southern tip of Sweden was there any extensive deposition of surface outwash of gravels and boulder clays, but minor deposits are associated with moraines and other glacial features like drumlins, kames and eskers. This deposition, and the formation of hollows in the rock surface by the differential erosion of the ice sheet or the over-deepening of valleys by residual glaciers, have so obstructed drainage as to produce the numerous lakes of western Sweden, and in Finland have resulted in upwards of 60,000 lakes covering one-eighth of the country and giving it its native name, Suomi (lakeland).

One of the effects of the widespread glaciation was to depress the land mass under the great weight of ice. With the final melting of the glaciers the land began to rise again to restore the isostatic balance. The movement, quick at first, caused rejuvenation of the drainage. Along the fractured coastline of Norway the combined action of ice, running water and isostatic uplift resulted in fiords and a marginal archipelago called the skerry-gard (skjaergård). The uplift is not yet complete; the land is still rising throughout much of Scandinavia. In the past, the emergent process was greatest in Atlantic Norway, as shown by the series of "raised beaches"; today the most significant changes are measured in the northern half of the Baltic basin.

It has been calculated that the present rate of uplift per century along the south coast of Finland is about 15 in., and at the northern end of the Gulf of Bothnia it amounts to nearly 3 ft. The rise has important human consequences. In the first place, it increases the land area available for settlement; one Finnish author, for instance, has pointed out that the area lost to Russia in the east would be compensated in less than 6000 years by uplift of the sea bed in the west. But the restoration of isostatic balance presents problems. Ports and harbours will have difficulties in keeping open their facilities; the builders of railways and roads may find their gradients have altered; and rivers may change their courses or lakes their outlets, causing flood damage or affecting hydro-electric development.

The Ice Age covered volcanic Iceland, the Faeroes and Greenland with its glaciers, with striking results. Most of Greenland is still covered with a thick ice sheet, estimated to be at least half a mile thick in the north of the country; Iceland has glaciers over one-eighth of its surface. The Vatnajökull, some 3200 square miles in area, is Europe's largest glacier. Iceland, too, continues to have volcanic activity, from both cones and fissures. Some of the craters have a thick ice cover, and when there is an eruption in such places, a tremendous glacial "burst" occurs, flooding the land and causing great damage. The Faeroes were originally a single basaltic block which has been eroded by glaciers and marine action along fault-lines so as to disintegrate into an archipelago, with eighteen large islands and a number of smaller islets and stacks.

CLIMATE

The climatic description in Chapter III shows northern Europe to have an essentially maritime régime, modified east of the "keel" (Kjölen range) by continental influence and complicated by its position in high latitudes. Nearly a third of the mainland lies inside the Arctic Circle and for a period in winter does not see the sun. In this season, mining and fishing activities in the north must be carried on under floodlighting; in the south the peak of unemployment comes in late winter, for it must be noted that four of the five capital cities are within a few degrees of the Arctic Circle. At mid-summer there is a corresponding short period of constant daylight north of $66\frac{1}{2}$ degrees N. when the sun dips towards the northern horizon but does not sink completely.

Winter temperatures in northern Europe (see Fig. 13) are far higher than one would expect, except in Finland. Even here, where continental influences are greatest, the average January temperature of the northern interior is $10°$ F ($-12°$ C), a high figure for the latitude. The Atlantic seaboard, from Denmark northwards as far as the Lofoten islands, has an average temperature in January above freezing point. Iceland, whose south and west coasts are washed by a branch of the North Atlantic Drift, averages $30°$ F ($-0·6°$ C) in that month in Reykjavik. Nowhere else in the world are such high winter temperatures found so near the poles. Summer temperatures are more normal, averaging from $65°$ F ($18°$ C) in Denmark to $50°$ F ($10°$ C) along the north coast of Norway, in the Scandinavian mountains, and in the Faeroes and Iceland. Maximum temperatures of well over 70° F (21° C) are common in summer, but only rarely does the thermometer rise above 80° F (26° C).

The amount of precipitation varies widely. West of the Scandinavian mountain axis the amounts, though well distributed through the year,

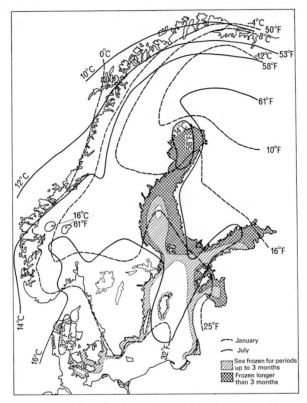

FIG. 13.—Northern Europe: January and July isotherms. Compare this map with Fig. 6 and note the influence of the "Gulf of winter warmth" on the temperatures of the western and northern coasts. The entrance to the Baltic Sea and the approaches to the ports of south-east Sweden and south-west Finland are kept open in winter by icebreakers.

vary from less than 20 in. annually in northern Iceland to over 200 in. in the Kjölen range, with an average of over 40 in. everywhere along the west and south coasts of Norway and the west coast of Sweden. The lowlying lands of Denmark and south Sweden, and most of the area east of the mountain axis, have less than 40 in. annually. The total falls to less than 20 in. in sheltered parts of northern Sweden and eastern Finland. Snow falls over most of northern Europe in winter, but a deep and lasting cover is confined to the mountains of Norway, the whole of Sweden except the southern lowlands, all Finland and the north of Iceland, the depth decreasing eastwards. The amount of snow is vital to the lumbering industry and to the northern farmer, but may dislocate land transport.

The brackish waters of the inner Baltic freeze every winter; the Gulfs of Bothnia and Finland may have at their heads solid ice more than five feet thick and are blocked to navigation for four to six months. Even where the sea is not closed by fast-ice, drifting pack-ice banded by wave action is a serious obstacle, preventing steamer traffic in the two gulfs and hampering the work of ice-breakers in other parts. It is only with difficulty that the ports of Stockholm and Hangö are kept open through the winter. The southern Baltic and, except in severe winters, the passages to the North Sea remain open all the year.

STUDY QUESTIONS

1. Relate the structure of Scandinavia to the present relief.
2. Give a reasoned account of the various climatic types found in northern Europe.

Chapter VII

FINLAND

PHYSICAL ASPECTS

STRUCTURAL DIVISIONS

Finland is essentially a low-lying country, rising gradually from newly emerged land in the south and west to the pre-Cambrian peneplain in the north and east. Structurally, its rocks range from some of the youngest to the oldest on the earth's surface. It may be divided into six main regions (*see* Fig. 14).

1. The lake plateau

The whole of central Finland, apart from a coastal plain, is a low plateau, never more than 650 ft in height and characterised by the large number of lakes—estimated at 60,000—which fill hollows in its surface. The surface of the plateau is covered with morainic deposits left by glaciers of the Ice Age, but they are usually so thin that the topography is determined essentially by the underlying and greatly eroded Archaean rocks of the Baltic Shield. Most of the lakes are in rock basins carved in this ancient peneplain. The plateau is crossed by some of the longest and most elevated eskers in Europe, and where these traverse the lakes they provide routes for roads and railways. Occasionally, even a village is found straggling along one of the narrow ridges. The drainage of the central plateau is indeterminate: there are no well-marked watersheds and sometimes there is more than one outlet to a lake. The greater number of the lakes are drained by the rivers Oulu, Kokemäki, Kymi and Vuoksi. The Vuoksi drains Saimaa, Finland's largest lake complex, to Lake Ladoga, in the U.S.S.R.

2. The coastal plain

In the south and west of Finland is a coastal plain, 20 to 80 miles wide. It is a plain of emergence rising slowly out of the waters of the Gulfs of Bothnia and Finland. The isostatic uplift is greatest in the north, where it amounts to about 40 in. a century. The south coast is rising at about half that rate. Near the sea the coastal plain is composed of marine silts; further inland it has a thin cover of ground moraine and boulder clay. The inner boundary of the coastal plain in the south, along the Gulf of

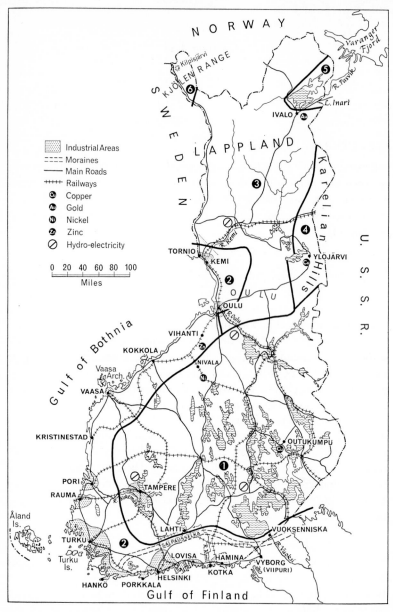

FIG. 14.—Finland: physical and economic divisions. (1) Lake Plateau   (2) Coastal Plain, (3) Northern Plateau, (4) Karelian Hills, (5) Inari Lowlands, (6) Kjölen Range. Note the concentration of economic development along the south and south-west coastal plain.

Finland, is a series of morainic ridges, the Salpausselkä, which rise to 660 ft. The sandy peninsula of Hankö (Hangö) is a seaward prolongation of this moraine. Off the coast is an almost continuous belt of islands, with two main concentrations in the Turku–Åland archipelago and the Vaasa group.

3. The northern plateau

Most of northern Finland is a low plateau, rarely exceeding 1200 ft in height. The northern portion of the plateau is part of the Caledonian mountain system, worn down to a peneplain, with granites and gneisses similar to those of nearby Norway and Sweden. The south of the plateau has surface outcrops of pre-Cambrian rocks which belong to the Fenno-Scandian or Baltic Shield. The boundary between the two parts is roughly along an east–west watershed which can be identified in an atlas. Flowing southwards from the watershed is the Kemijoki system (*joki*, river), which has been harnessed for hydro-electricity. Except in the south, the plateau is very sparsely peopled.

4. The Karelian hills

To the north-east of the lake plateau the land rises to the Karelian hills (Maan Selka), which vary in height from 1200 to 2100 ft. The hills are the highest part of the Baltic Shield. Their worn-down slopes and bare, rounded summits are reminiscent of the Norwegian fells, though very much less in altitude. It is a harsh and uninviting region, more or less isolated from the rest of Finland. Through it passes part of the Finno-Russian frontier, which in this area has been described as the boundary not only of Finland, but of "Western" Europe.

5. The Inari lowlands

In the extreme north-east of Finland is Lake Inari, which is drained to Varanger Fiord by the river Pasvik (Patsjoki), which leaves Finland to form the boundary between Norway and the U.S.S.R. Lake Inari lies at the eastern end of the watershed mentioned above, and is at the junction of two geological regions. The lowland belt which surrounds the lake and stretches into Norway and the U.S.S.R., although composed of glacio-fluvial silts, has little economic value, except as grazing ground for reindeer, which are herded by Lapps. The area is connected to southern Finland by a road constructed from Kemi on the Gulf of Bothnia during the 1920s to tap the nickel-producing district around Petsamo, which at that time belonged to Finland. Petsamo was ceded to the U.S.S.R. in 1947, after Finland's defeat in the Second World War, during which the country was allied to Germany.

FIG. 15.—Finland: view in Lappland. The low, rounded hills of bare rock, and
the scanty, stunted vegetation at lower levels are typical.

6. The Kjölen range

Finland's highest altitudes are in the north-west, where its boundaries
include a small portion of the Kjölen range, with Kilpisjärvi (3300 ft)
the highest point. The region consists of inhospitable high fells and is
virtually uninhabited. On its edge is the meeting place of the boundaries
of Norway, Sweden and Finland.

CLIMATE AND NATURAL VEGETATION

Finland, lying as it does in what has been designated the cold climate
zone, is characterised by warm, rainy summers and cold, snowbound
winters. The country lies between the 60th and 70th parallels of north
latitude, and about a quarter of its area is within the Arctic Circle, so
that temperatures both in summer and winter decrease northwards. In
general, the coldest month in most of the country is January, but in north
and east Finland it is February; July is the hottest month everywhere.
Helsinki, on the south coast, ranges from an average of 22° F (−4° C)
in January to 63° F (17° C) in July; Kuopio, in the middle of the lake
plateau, has a range for the same months from 15° F (−10° C) to 61° F
(16° C), Sodankylä, on the northern plateau, inside the Arctic Circle, has

a February temperature of 8° F (−14° C) and in July averages 57° F (14° C). On the whole, these temperatures are higher than any found at corresponding latitudes and distance from the ocean in other continents, owing to the tempering influences of the Gulf Stream and its overlying air currents.

Temperatures in northern latitudes are affected by the length of the day. In southern Finland the length of the day around midsummer is 19 hours. In the north, starting slightly below the Arctic Circle, there is constant daylight, which lasts, on the 70th parallel of latitude for instance, for 73 days. It is this constant insolation which accounts for the high summer temperatures, in spite of the low altitude of the sun. In midwinter, on the other hand, there is an uninterrupted night, lasting on the 70th parallel for 51 days, during which there is continuous loss of heat by radiation.

Precipitation, in the form of rain and snowfall, is greatest on average in south-west Finland and decreases northwards to the Inari lowlands. Most of it falls in heavy showers in the summer half of the year, especially in August. A lasting but not very thick snow layer covers the ground from late October to May in north Finland, and from December to April in the rest of the country. The average annual precipitation varies from 27 in. in south-west Finland to less than 16 in. in the Inari region.

The natural vegetation of Finland is coniferous forest, which covers over 56% of its surface. In the south-west and along the south coast there are mixed forests in which the oak predominates. In Lappland, farther north, the trees begin to thin out, but with the exception of a few small patches in the extreme north-east there is no real tundra in Finland. Even in the north of Lappland there are birch trees, and enough ground vegetation to support large herds of reindeer. In the forest and on swamps near some of the lakes are berry-bearing bushes; cranberries, blueberries and cloudberries are of economic value. Fur-bearing animals such as the fox, squirrel, muskrat and pine-marten are found in the forest, and the occasional bear or wolf may be encountered in the Karelian hills or the remote parts of Lappland.

HUMAN GEOGRAPHY

PEOPLE AND HISTORY

The Finns, together with the Estonians, Hungarians and Lapps, belong to a linguistic group, Finno-Ugrian, which is quite different from other European languages. The Finns' remote ancestors are thought to have come from the bend of the river Volga, and to have settled in southern Finland prior to A.D. 800. For four centuries after that date, Swedes moved into Finland, pushing many of the native inhabitants into the lake plateau, from which in turn the Lapps were driven to the far north, to become nomads. Sweden's right to Finland was agreed after she defeated Russia in 1323. By 1362 Finland was a separate entity known as Eastland, and took part in the election of the king of Sweden. The original Finnish settlers were probably hunters and fishers, with little knowledge of agriculture, but the Swedes brought with them a Christian culture and new ideas of farming and settlement. The first towns began to develop in the fourteenth century. The oldest is Turku (Abo), already mentioned in records in 1198 but not definitely a town till 1229. Helsinki, the present capital, was not founded until 1550.

For three hundred years from 1495 Sweden, with whom Finland was incorporated, fought a succession of wars with Russia. Encouraged by Sweden, Finland's economy expanded, mainly in its forests, and the Swedish language was adopted by educated Finns. The Finnish War of 1808–9 between Sweden and Russia led to the annexation of Finland by Russia and until 1917 Finland remained an autonomous grand duchy in the Russian Empire; the Finnish language was restored in 1863 to an equality with Swedish. In 1917 Finland declared her independence and in 1920 was recognised as a republic.

Shortly after the outbreak of the Second World War, Finland, with the other northern countries, announced that she would remain neutral; but her hope of avoiding war was dashed when the Soviet Union invaded and crushed her in the Winter War of November 1939–March 1940. She was forced to cede the city of Viipuri and a long strip of Karelia, and to lease the Hankö peninsula to the U.S.S.R. for thirty years. In June 1941 the Finns joined the Germans in attacking Russia but had to capitulate in September 1944. By a peace treaty signed in Paris in 1947 her earlier cessions were confirmed. In addition she lost the Petsamo area in the north, had to lease the Porkkala peninsula to the Soviet Union for fifty years and pay indemnities of 300 million dollars in commodities, mainly metal. Her payment of reparations, which gave a great impetus to her metal industries, was completed in 1952; and by a renewal of a friendship pact with the Soviet Union in 1955, Porkkala was restored to Finland. In the same year she was admitted to the United Nations.

POPULATION

The population of Finland totals 4,523,000 (1963), with an average density of 34 per square mile. Since nearly 35% of her people live in towns, mostly in the south and south-west, the density figure is deceptive; some areas in the north and east have a population density of less than 1 per square mile. The vast majority (91·2%) are Finnish-speaking, but there remains a small (8·6%) Swedish-speaking minority, living in two areas:

along the south coast from Lovisa (Loviisa) to the Åland islands, and on the west coast from Kristinestad (Kristiinankaupunki) northwards to Kokkola (Gamlakarleby). Finland is a country which, since achieving independence in 1917, has only slowly shown signs of emergence as a fully-developed Western state; many of her people who could not be absorbed into her infant industries have emigrated. Emigration was greatest in the years after 1945, when large numbers of Finns left southern Karelia (including Viipuri) and the Petsamo district, which had been taken by the U.S.S.R. By 1954, 80,000 Finns had settled abroad, about 58,000 of them in Sweden and 19,000 in Norway.

In northern Finland are upwards of 2000 Lapps, a semi-nomadic people, of whom a fuller description is given in Chapter IX.

THE ECONOMY

FOREST INDUSTRIES

Of the total area of Finland, 71% (55 million acres) is forested; about 45% of the woods are pine (redwood), 35% spruce (whitewood) and 20% non-coniferous, mainly birch. In consequence, it may be said that Finland's national economy is based on timber industries, for they constitute 39% of the country's exports and are an integral part of most farmers' lives. Forest-farms, combining farm and forest husbandry, are characteristic. The climate makes farming difficult, and the farmers for the most part own a piece of forest which provides them with fuel and building material. Surplus timber is sold to obtain fertilisers, farm machinery and improved seed and stock. Almost as much timber is used by the rural population or by industry as fuel as the amount which enters the pulp and paper mills, the processing works, or is exported as raw timber. About a third of the forests are State-owned, these are mainly in the northern provinces of Oulu and Lappland. They are remotely situated and still largely unexploited.

Upwards of 70,000 workers are employed regularly in the forest industries, but the number is more than doubled in winter, when felling and transport are chiefly carried out. Most of the extra workers are small-scale farmers, who have little to do on the land in that season. Many of them take their horses to drag lumber short distances, but the tendency is towards an increased use of tractor and motor transport.

The numerous lakes and rivers make long-distance timber-floating (Fig. 16) relatively easy, with discharge mainly into the Gulfs of Bothnia and Finland. In the coastal plains and the lake plateau the lumber-camps are well distributed, but most of the forest industry works are on the coast at the mouths of rivers. Many of the timber and wood products are carried by rail, but as more of the special forest roads are constructed motor transport will take a greatly increased share.

The forest industry is divided into the "wood industry" and the "paper industry." The former covers sawmills and planing mills, plywood factories, furniture and joinery works, and the making of prefabricated houses and boxes. The paper industry includes mechanical pulp mills, board mills, the making of sulphite and sulphate cellulose and paper.

[*Courtesy of Finnish Embassy.*

FIG. 16.—Finland: floating timber in the lake plateau. One of many methods of transporting timber on the lakes. These logs are pit-props which have been debarked at the logging camp.

There are upwards of 2000 sawmills, large and small, scattered along the coast, with Helsinki their commercial centre. At present 24 plywood mills are responsible for about a quarter of the world's production of plywoods—made almost exclusively of birch—and of veneers, for which timbers from other parts of the world are sometimes used. Helsinki is also the centre for prefabricated house manufacture, which includes schools and hospitals as well as dwelling houses. Finnish wooden houses are found all over the world. About half the furniture is made in Lahti (72,245), Finland's fourth city. The spool industry, for which Finland was once famous, is now insignificant; but the production of particle boards (chipboard), begun in 1956, is making headway. The wood industry also includes the manufacture of vast quantities of match splints or match-stalks.

The mechanical pulp mills require a great deal of power and are usually near rapids, which provide sources of hydro-electricity, and work in conjunction with paper and board mills. The bulk of the raw material is spruce, though in making hardboard the waste from all sawmills and plywood factories can be utilised. Cellulose, used in the manufacture of rayon, is made by "cooking" timber either with calcium bi-sulphite or sodium sulphate. The sulphite process is applied to spruce, birch and aspen; the sulphate method to pine. In 1958, the total production of cellulose was 2,080,000 tons, of which 1,201,000 tons were exported. Among the by-products of the industry are crude alcohol and turpentine.

The chief forest industry towns are Helsinki (477,062), Turku (130,844), Lahti, Oulu (63,607), Pori (57,229) and Vaasa (44,436), all on the coast. Tampere (133,406), though well inland, shares in the pulp and paper trade. Kotka (31,158), though only a small port, is rapidly becoming the most important timber exporter, taking the place of Viipuri (lost to the U.S.S.R.) as the outlet of the Lake Saimaa forest region.

AGRICULTURE AND FISHING

If a line be drawn from the northern end of the Gulf of Bothnia to the south-east corner of Finland, the country is divided into "cultural" and "natural" sections. Yet in the cultural division, south of this line, man's efforts have been exerted mainly in clearing the forest for agriculture rather than building towns and developing manufacturing industries and the cultural landscape still contains much of the original natural features. Away from the coast the only obvious industrial concentration is in Tampere. The main occupation is agriculture in the coastal belt, the towns of the interior being chiefly route centres, local markets or communities based on a single forest factory. In "Natural Finland" land has been claimed for cultivation by burning out clearings in the forest; farms are widely scattered and isolated; but most of it remains still untouched virgin forest.

Finland is the world's most northerly farming country, and its climate and meagre soil-cover limit both the type and the yield of crops. Most of the farms are small, the majority less than 35 acres, part of which may be forest. The total cultivated area amounts to 7% of the country, and farming occupies a third of the population. In the south, where the farms are larger, sometimes up to 250 acres, the emphasis is on cereal crops. Elsewhere, cattle farming predominates.

The most important crops at present are wheat and rye, the area under wheat increasing year by year. Barley and oats are grown for fodder, but hay is a principal crop everywhere away from the cereal belt of the south-west. Finland aims at self-sufficiency in cereals, and more land is being brought under cultivation. However, the stony nature of new land hampers mechanisation, and at present Finland produces only about 65% of her requirements in wheat and rye, although she grows enough oats and barley to be able to export in some years. The loss of the productive region in the south-east, in the hinterland of Viipuri, and the need to accommodate the farmer-refugees from that area, accentuated the country's agricultural difficulties.

Potatoes, which form a main part of the diet, are grown on all farms. Root crops, including sugar beet, are important in the south and west. There are sugar factories in Helsinki; margarine, based partly on oleaginous plants grown on the southern farms, is made there and in Tampere. Both these industries, however, are still in their infancy.

Cattle rearing is not hampered by climatic factors to the same degree as arable farming and, even in the most northern districts on the edges of Lappland, cattle are kept for dairy produce. The growth of the dairying industry may be measured by the increase in the number of milking machines from a negligible pre-war figure to nearly 30,000 in 1963. Butter and cheese are exported in large quantities. Other surplus livestock products include condensed and dried milk, eggs, pork and reindeer meat.

All the rivers and lakes of Finland are rich in fish, which are consumed in the domestic market. Sea fishing is confined to the Baltic, where the most important catch is herring. The total industry, including some seal catching in the Gulf of Bothnia and in Lake Saimaa is, however, of small account in the national economy.

POWER AND METALLURGICAL INDUSTRIES

Finland has no coal, and must look to its forests and waterways for sources of power. Upwards of one-twelfth of the annual timber output is used as fuel by industry, but the development of water power is vital to the expansion of its economic life. The country is rich in lakes and rivers, but its water power resources are reduced in value by the generally low elevation of the land and the relatively small rainfall. Of the theoretical estimate of 30,000 million kWh only one-third can be harnessed; and half of this lies in northern Finland, away from the centres of industry. The chief hydro-electric schemes in the south are at the Imatra falls on the Vuoksi river, and at Tampere on the Kokemäki. There are many smaller power plants built primarily for the forest industries but passing surplus electricity into the national grid. All the power produced in the south is insufficient to satisfy the regional demand, so electric power is fed there from two stations on the Oulu river and another on the Kemi river, both in the north. The provision of electricity now amounts to 70% of the possible total, and has been a boon to the rural community as well as to manufacturing industry.

Although practically every metallic ore is present in the crystalline shield of Finland, only rarely is there any concentration of economic value; there are fewer mineworkers than any other major industrial group. At present there are copper mines at Outukumpu and Ylöjärvi, iron mines at Otanmäki and Kärväsvaara, zinc at Vihanti, nickel at Kotalahti and gold at Haveri. The most important of these minerals is copper pyrites from Outukumpu; with a 3% copper content, there is sufficient for Finland's own needs. A sulphur by-product from the smelting is used in the making of cellulose. Finland must import all other minerals.

In spite of its low output of mineral ores, Finland's metal industry employs more workers than any other. There are currently about 55,000 people engaged in smelting mineral ores, the manufacture of pig iron, and engineering, as compared with 50,000 in the forestry and furniture trades. If the 32,000 employees in the paper and cellulose industries are included with the latter, however, the forests are seen to be the main source of work.

The Finnish iron smelting industry was started in the seventeenth century by the Swedes, who used charcoal from the forests as fuel. But it was not until the so-called "Winter War" against the Soviet Union (November 1939–March 1940) that any great advance was made. The engineering industry was harnessed to armament production and expanded at once, but it was mainly because of the indemnity Finland had to pay the U.S.S.R. after 1947 that the metal industry gained momentum, for reparations had to be paid mostly in pig-iron and engineering products. Copper is smelted by electric furnaces at Outukumpu, and iron by the same method at Vuoksenniska, near Imatra (34,363), which makes machinery for the paper and pulp industries. The raw material for the iron industry is, however, imported scrap. It is turned into pig iron and steel at Helsinki, Tampere and near Turku. Tampere makes railway rolling stock, electrical apparatus and wire. It is also the country's textile centre, manufacturing woollens and cottons (also produced at Turku). The making of rayon staple fibre is an outcome of the cellulose industry.

As the engineering industry grows, it will supply machinery for the chemical, footwear, food and printing undertakings, all of which are at present geared to home demands. Agriculture, for instance, requires extensive mechanisation, if only to release labour for the growing industrial centres on the coast.

COMMUNICATIONS AND TRANSPORT

In a country like Finland, the maintenance of communications presents difficulties due to the climate, with its frost-bound winters. Although there is a network of lakes and rivers, navigability is restricted to comparatively short stretches, and there are few places where it is possible for river traffic to reach the coast. The Saimaa Canal, linking the eastern lake plateau to the Gulf of Finland, was lost to the Soviet Union in 1947, and a projected canal to join the area to the Kymi river would in the present state of the economy be too costly. The main transport value of the waterways is to float timber; and this is restricted to the summer months.

In 1938, Finland had 5100 miles of railway, mainly in the south and west, with extensions in the north to open up new timber areas. After 1947, the network was reduced by treaty losses to 4300 miles; and since then fewer than 500 miles have been added. An increase in motor transport seems likely, as in other countries, to reduce the value of railways, which are not as flexible in remote areas nor as suitable for light goods as motor lorries. The present road network totals approximately 40,000 miles, but a large proportion is unmetalled, especially in the interior and north. There are major airports at Helsinki and Turku.

Finland's railway system uses the broad gauge of the Soviet railways, for it was first constructed by the Russians. As a result, through running into Sweden is not possible, and foreign rail traffic is confined to the U.S.S.R. All foreign trade other than to the east must be waterborne, and in this respect Finland is less favoured than any other country because its coastal waters freeze in winter. There are shipbuilding yards at Helsinki and Turku, but Finland's merchant fleet is small. Exports are mostly bulky in character—forest products, iron and steel goods—and are carried in foreign ships. Her best customers are the United Kingdom, the Soviet Union and West Germany, in that order, taking altogether nearly 60% of Finland's exports and providing about the same amount of her imports. There is a noteworthy difference between the importing and exporting ports, based on volume of trade. The five ports with the biggest percentage of imports are Helsinki (34·8), Turku (20·5), Kotka (11·6), Hamina (5·2) and Hauma (4·7); the export ports are Kotka (24·2), Oulu (12·0), Pori (9·6), Helsinki (6·3) and Turku (5·7). Here the influence of the timber exports can be seen.

REGIONAL ECONOMY

1. The Coastal plain

As might be expected, because of its proximity to the sea, its better climate and soils, and the fact that it has a long history of habitation, the coastal plain of Finland is the most fully developed region in the country. Yet its economy is more agricultural than industrial, for manufactures are still limited in growth. Just over 40% of all the people of Finland obtain their livelihood primarily from agriculture and, although the percentage on the coastal plain is lower because there are more people in the towns, it is still over 30%. Dairying is of great importance, as already noted, and fodder crops, such as hay, oats, mangolds and turnips are grown to support it. Production of wheat, sugar beet and potatoes is increasing, but their cultivation is confined largely to the south-west of the plain, where the growing conditions are best. The northern limit of cultivation for these three crops more or less coincides in Finland with the northern edge of the southern coastal plain. The rearing of dairy cattle is not hampered as much by climatic factors, and dairying is carried on to the northern limits of the western coastal plain. Throughout Finland, cattle are housed indoors during the long winter.

Most of Finland's population lives in the coastal plain, and with one or two exceptions the largest towns are situated there. Nearly all of them are ports, handling the products of the forests, and those along the south coast have furniture and food-processing industries too. Around Helsinki and Turku there are thriving industrial areas, specialising in the making of pig iron, textile manufacture (mainly of woollens, cottons and rayon), clothing, leather goods, engineering and shipbuilding.

2. The lake plateau

The economy of the lake plateau is concerned almost entirely with the forest industries and the extraction of mineral ores. Most of the small settlements are either dependent on saw-milling, pulp and paper and ancillary industries, or are mining communities. The towns connected with forest industries are at the junction or crossing points of timber-roads, or where roads and railways cross the lakes. In this connection, many of the eskers which are so numerous in the lake plateau form natural platforms across the lakes.

The only towns of any size in the plateau are Tampere and Lahti. Tampere, helped by hydro-electricity developed on the river Kokemäki, was the first town in Finland to become an industrial centre. Today it is the chief textile town, and has also pulp and paper industries, and engineering, especially railway rolling stock. Lahti is the centre of the furniture industry.

3. The rest of Finland

The remainder of Finland is too far north and as yet too undeveloped to have much economic significance. The northern plateau and the lower slopes of the Karelian hills have forests still untouched, but they are being surveyed and supervised as future sources of timber. An important asset of the northern plateau is the hydro-electricity station on the river Kemi, current from which is fed to southern Finland. The north of the plateau and the Inari lowlands are the home of Finland's Lapps, with their reindeer. Efforts are being made to encourage the use of reindeer meat, and small quantities are exported from Kemi, Oulu, Turku and Helsinki.

STUDY QUESTIONS

1. Show how geographical position and glaciation have affected human activities in Finland. (O. & C.)

2. Examine the relative importance of the forest and mining industries of Finland.

Chapter VIII

SWEDEN

PHYSICAL ASPECTS

STRUCTURAL DIVISIONS

Sweden, the largest and most central of the countries of northern Europe, occupies the eastern side of the Scandinavian peninsula. The Swedes speak of it as "a long drawn-out land," for it stretches 978 miles from south to north, as compared with 310 miles from west to east at its widest point. Its relief is intermediate between the low shield of Finland and the dissected plateau of Norway, which means that it has a much more varied type of landscape than Finland.

The country can be divided morphologically into four regions of very unequal size (*see* Fig. 17). (1) The largest is Norrland, usually taken to be the whole of Sweden north of the Dal Älv (*älv*, river), and comprises 60% of the total surface. (2) Central Sweden is a "shatter zone" of lakes and plains, the latter rarely more than 300 ft in elevation, except where remnants of the Archaean shield rise in low hills to a maximum of 600 ft. (3) South of the central lowland is an upland region, the South Swedish Highlands, a plateau whose highest altitude is 1235 ft. (4) This is followed by the Scanian (Skåne) lowland, which is similar in formation to Denmark's island of Zealand (Sjaelland). The four divisions, which follow each other from north to south, are distinct physical regions.

1. Norrland

This region may be sub-divided into (*a*) a narrow strip of the Caledonian mountains in the west, (*b*) the Swedish portion of the Baltic Shield, with which may be included the Jämtland depression, and (*c*) the Baltic coastal plain. Overall, it covers 100,000 square miles.

(*a*) In the west of Norrland part of the Caledonian orogeny extends into Sweden. Massive overthrusts during the mountain-building period forced relatively younger rocks to the eastern side of the main ridge, where they form a steep scarp. Prolonged denudation has reduced much of the surface to a peneplain roughly 3000 ft in height, but in the north the land rises to the Kjölen range, in which there are several peaks over 5500 ft. The highest mountain in Sweden, Kobnekaise (6957 ft), lies near the north of

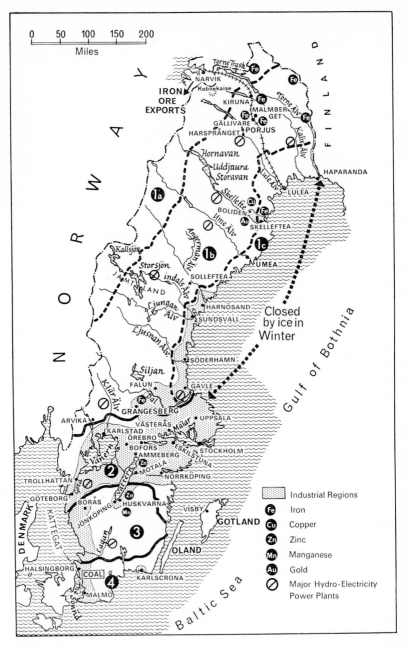

FIG. 17.—Sweden: physical and economic divisions. The numbers correspond with the regional divisions used in the text.

the range. Most of the area north of 60 degrees N. is fjeld, with bare rock or tundra vegetation, and contains a number of small ice fields.

(b) Sloping gently eastwards from the Kjölen range and the region of Caledonian rocks, from an elevation of about 1500 ft down to 300 ft, is the Swedish portion of the Baltic Shield, composed for the most part of Archaean rocks. Where the two types of structure meet is known as the "glint line," which may be recognised on the map by a series of lakes near the Swedish border. The Quaternary ice sheet appears to have lasted longer on the slope of the Shield than on the lower parts of the mountain belt, and it blocked the upper courses of rivers, thus forming lakes. Some of them were drained to the Atlantic, as the presence of overflow channels in that direction demonstrates. When the ice sheet finally disappeared, the lakes became smaller or were drained completely. In the latter case, high alluvial flats were left and, in the former, terraces of silt formed the reduced shore lines. The chief glint-lakes in Sweden are Torne Träsk (122 square miles), Virihaura, Frostviken and Kallsjön.

A large number of rivers flow in parallel courses across the Baltic Shield. They have all experienced rejuvenation as a result of isostatic uplift, and have cut deep valleys in the Shield. Most of the courses have been blocked by morainic debris left by the retreating glaciers, thus forming the numerous "ribbon lakes" characteristic of this part of Sweden. The most important rivers are the Torne, Lule, Skellefte, Ume and Dal. The last is usually taken to form the southern boundary of Norrland. The largest of the valley lakes are the interconnected Lule Träsk and Langas (85 square miles) and the complex of Hornavan, Uddjaura and Storavan (255 square miles), the former group drained by the Lule, the latter by the Skellefte. All the rivers are broken by falls and rapids, and the interfluves have stretches of peat and the most extensive forests in Sweden. In the rocks of the Shield, covered by a layer of boulder clay, are rich deposits of iron and copper ores and other minerals.

Towards the south of the Shield the Archaean rocks have been down-faulted, and Cambro-Silurian sandstones, limestones and schists preserved on the surface of the Jämtland depression, to give relatively better soils and support a belt of agricultural settlement. The value of this depression is increased by the fact that the Kjölen range to the west is also lower, thus providing one of the few routes across the Scandinavian mountain mass. The route through the Jämtland depression leads to the Trondheim low-lands in Norway. In the middle of the depression is the large lake, Storsjön. A smaller depression farther south contains Lake Siljan.

(c) The third sub-division of Norrland is the Baltic coastal plain, similar to, but of lesser extent than, that of Finland. It is composed of the marine silts of the newly-emergent sea bed (which is rising here at the same rate

D

as on the Finnish side of the Gulf of Bothnia) and of alluvium washed down by the rivers in early summer. Where the rivers leave the Shield to flow across the very much younger coastal plain there are waterfalls; this "fall line" marks the western margin of the plain.

The Norrland coast of Sweden is broken by a great number of indentations which are crowded with tiny, low-lying islands. The openings are called *fjards* or *fiards*, and are distinguished from fiords by their origin and because they are enclosed by lowlands instead of cliffs. They are thought to have been formed by the action of sub-glacial streams whose valleys were subsequently drowned by the post-glacial increase in volume of the Baltic Sea, helped possibly by the subsidence of the land. Now that the sea bed is slowly emerging again, many of the fiards will become dry land and the islands will be joined to the mainland, as has already happened in the extreme north of the Gulf of Bothnia, both in Sweden and in Finland.

2. The central lowlands

South of the river Dal, a broad belt across Sweden consists of extensive plains and large lakes. The region contains many major faults, and is known as a "shatter zone." The two largest lakes, Vänern (2140 square miles) and Vättern (735 square miles), lie in north–south fault valleys, and lakes Hjälmar and Mälar were caused by east–west faulting. The whole region is a zone of subsidence, which allowed the waters of the ancient Yoldian Sea to submerge it and form a strait between the inner sea basin and the North Sea. With the melting of the Quaternary ice cap, the land rose again, and the clays deposited in the waters appeared on its surface, to develop into the rich soils of central Sweden. Lake Vänern is drained to the west by the Göta river, on which are the Trollhätten Falls, among the first in the world to be used for hydro-electric power. Lake Vättern drains to the east coast, and Hjälmar into Lake Mälar. Lake Mälar is more like an extended opening from the Baltic Sea than a lake, for its exit is wide and its surface only 2 ft above sea level. The lake itself contains many islands of pre-Cambrian rocks, fragmented portions of the Shield, and its outlet is crowded with similar islets. These latter form part of the Stockholm skerry, an archipelago of some 25,000 islands lying off the coast, all composed of crystalline rocks and quite different from the silty islands of the fiards.

The most extensive plains of central Sweden are around lakes Mälar and Hjälmar, in the provinces of Uppsala, Västmanland, Stockholm, Södermanland and East Gotland. Together with the Scanian lowland (*see* below), they are the best agricultural lands in Sweden. As in the Finnish lake plateau, eskers wind their way across the plains; on them, and on crystalline outcrops of the Shield, there are coniferous forests. In the outcrops, too, are numerous important deposits of mineral ores.

3. The South Swedish Highlands

South of the central lowlands the land rises to the barren highlands of Småland, a peneplaned dome of pre-Cambrian granites and gneisses, with an average height of nearly 1000 ft. The entire plateau is an infertile region, with small lake basins, morainic remains and peat bogs, reminiscent of the Shield area of Norrland. Being at a lower latitude and altitude, however, it is more suited to habitation. On its eastern and western flanks there are coastal plains of marine silts and clays, fertile and well developed. The fault valley of Lake Vättern penetrates the northern portion of the Småland plateau, and the southern third of the lake is encompassed by steep, rocky slopes.

4. The lowlands of Scania

The southernmost division of Sweden is Scania (Skåne), an area which has been depressed between north-west—south-east faults to form lowlands. The sinking of the land preserved the younger rocks which were deposited on the Archaean foundation and in some places, where they have been exposed by faulting, successions of Silurian strata may be seen, overlain by Jurassic limestones and Cretaceous chalk and marls. Here and there, the faulting resulted in horst ridges of granite or gneiss, some of them 600 ft high. Most of the surface of Scania is covered by glacial clays deposited before its submergence during the Ice Age or by marine silts laid down in Yoldian times and exposed by the later isostatic uplift. The clays and silts, mixed with the underlying chalk, have produced a very fertile soil.

CLIMATE AND NATURAL VEGETATION

The highland barrier which fills the west of the Scandinavian peninsula causes a rapid change from maritime to continental climatic conditions; and the climate of Sweden, which, but for a small portion, lies in the lee of the highlands, shows more seasonal contrasts than are found in Norway, which is open to Atlantic influences. The south of Sweden is more exposed and has temperatures little different from those of Denmark. Göteborg, for instance, has mean temperatures in February (the coldest month) of 30·4° F (−0·8° C) and in July of 62·2° F (16·8° C). This region, too, has a higher precipitation, fairly evenly distributed throughout the year: the western slopes of the Småland highlands have 50 in. annually, the heaviest rainfall in Sweden.

From the Great Lakes region of the central lowlands northwards,

January mean temperatures fall rapidly, from 26° F (−3·3° C) in Stockholm and 25° F (−3·9° C) in Karlstad (on Lake Vänern) to 11° F (−12·8° C) in Haparanda (on the northern coast of the Gulf of Bothnia) and 5° F (−15° C) in Karesuando (nearly 150 miles inside the Arctic Circle). It might be noted that the Lofoten islands, in the same latitude as Karesuando but on the Atlantic side of the Scandinavian barrier, have a January mean

[*Courtesy of the Swedish Tourish Traffic Association.*

FIG. 18.—Sweden: A wintry scene in Norrbotten. This is the northernmost province of Sweden. A village may be seen in the background, on the right, and there are scattered farms in clearings in the coniferous forest. This may be called the "pioneer fringe" of Sweden.

temperature of 31° F (—0·6° C)—which illustrates the powerful climatic effect of the mountains. Mean July temperatures are much more even: both Stockholm and Karlstad average 62° F (16·7° C), Haparanda 59° F (15° C) and Karesuando 54° F (12·2° C). The length of daylight in summer and darkness in winter increases from south to north, as in Finland. One consequence of the long period of midsummer sunshine is that high afternoon temperatures, occasionally over 80° F. (27° C), are registered well inside the Arctic Circle.

The annual precipitation in that part of Sweden which lies in the rain-shadow of the Scandinavian highlands—and this comprises most of the country—amounts to 20–30 in., according to height and aspect. Sheltered valleys may have less than 20 in., and in the north, in Lappland, there may be no more than 10 in. Maximum rainfall is during the summer half of the year; in winter there is a thick carpet of snow. The rivers and lakes of Sweden are frozen in winter, and the coast north of the island of Öland is blocked by ice and the passage to Stockholm has to be kept open by ice-breakers. Luleå, in the north of the Gulf of Bothnia, is closed completely for over five months (*see* Fig. 13).

The climate of northern Europe seems to furnish optimum conditions for the growth of coniferous trees, especially spruce and pine. In Sweden these softwood trees cover more than half the surface, and at one time were even more widespread. The amount of forest cover varies from 80% in the north to less than 5% in the south, where it has been largely cleared for agriculture. The coniferous forests of Sweden are eminently accessible; the parallel lakes and rivers of the Shield and coastal plain help the transport and storage of the felled trees; the numerous falls and rapids provide power for sawmills; and the winter freeze, although it closes rivers and sea, assists in felling operations and in haulage.

On the slopes of the Kjölen range and near the Arctic Circle, coniferous trees give place to the hardy birch, which at higher altitudes and latitudes is replaced by mosses and lichens, soft grasses or bare rock. Around some of the glint-line lakes and on the Småland plateau there are stretches of peat bog. In southern Sweden, where the climate is more maritime, deciduous trees, especially beech, are found mixed with the conifers.

HUMAN GEOGRAPHY

PEOPLE AND HISTORY

Remains of prehistoric people of the Neolithic, Bronze and Iron ages have been found along the south coast and in the Lake Mälar district; and by the sixth century A.D. there were Goths in the south and Swedes in the central lowlands, probably descended from the earliest inhabitants, for there is no clear evidence of the advent of any new race. Uppsala, the present ecclesiastical capital of Sweden, dates from these early days. So does Lund, a university town in Scania, which was started by the Danes who invaded and occupied the south of the peninsula.

In the Viking period, which is dated A.D. 800–1100, Danes and Norsemen began to move westward, but the people of Sweden looked to the north and east. The Goths and Swedes united under the king of Sweden, and first pushed against the Danes and the Norsemen, thus widening their boundaries, then crossed into Finland. Visby, a port on the island of Gotland, later to become the chief trading post of the Hanseatic League, was built at this time. This commercial league originated in northern Germany. By the end of the fourteenth century it commanded the trade in dried fish and in the iron exported from Dannemora via Stockholm. Late in the fourteenth century Sweden was brought unwillingly under the domination of Denmark, which already ruled Norway; but after sporadic warfare over many years it became independent again in 1523. The struggle with Denmark continued for another hundred years, each country striving to control the Baltic. Sweden was the more successful, driving the Danes from Scania and the Norwegians from the lands north of the river Dal, which until then had been counted part of Norway. By the time of Gustavus II (1594–1632), peace was concluded with Denmark, and the Baltic became in effect a Swedish lake. Gustavus penetrated into western Russia, strengthening his hold on Finland, taking possession of Estonia and Latvia, and subjugating Brandenburg and Saxony. His power was felt as far afield as the Rhine and the Danube, and Sweden's empire could match that of the Holy Roman Emperor.

With the advent of Peter the Great in Russia, Sweden was driven from all her conquests except Finland and since 1720 has shown little extra-territorial ambition. She was expelled from Finland by Russia in 1809. At the end of the Napoleonic wars she was given Norway, which was taken from Denmark, but the two countries separated amicably in 1905. Sweden then adopted a policy of neutrality and has maintained it through two world wars, refusing to align herself with any military grouping such as the North Atlantic Treaty Organisation. She is, however, a member of the European Free Trade Area (EFTA), in co-operation with Great Britain, Norway, Denmark, Austria, Switzerland and Portugal, the object of which is to increase commerce between its members.

POPULATION

Sweden has a population of 7,542,000, 60% of whom live in the central lowlands and Scania. The average density of population is 43 per square mile, well below the average for the whole of Europe (110 per square mile). The greatest density is in Scania (270 per square mile), the least in Norrland (less than 2 per square mile). Density is directly related to industrial development and soil fertility, the densely peopled districts with 100–200 per square mile constituting only 7% of Sweden's total area. In recent years the most populous districts, round Stockholm and Göteborg, because of their greater social amenities, have attracted many people from the farmlands and forests. The general drift to industrial areas has so depleted the rural economy as to present a major problem in this country of small farms and long, dark winters. The fact that so much recent industrial development is in the "pioneer fringe" of the north, and that on its successful achievement depends a great deal of Sweden's future prosperity, is another difficult problem, for here the severe climate makes farming conditions difficult and urban life unattractive.

In the north of Sweden there are roughly 10,000 Lapps, of whom about 3000 are transhumant reindeer herders. The remainder are subsistence farmers, who also hunt and fish or are absorbed into the towns which have sprung up to exploit the mineral resources of the far north (*see* Chapter IX for a fuller account of the Lapps). The population of Sweden was augmented after the Second World War by thousands of refugees, Finnish and Lapp, displaced from the territories taken by the U.S.S.R. from Finland.

THE ECONOMY

AGRICULTURE AND FORESTRY

The best soils in Sweden are found where there are young sedimentary rocks or where isostatic uplift has raised marine silts and clays above sea level, or caused drainage of lakes, exposing lacustrine silts. The most fertile area is the Scanian lowland, with over 70% of the land under cultivation. The central lowland, with extensions along the intermittent limestones round Lake Siljan and the river Dal, has up to 50% farmland. The percentage of cultivable land falls rapidly where the underlying crystalline rocks are covered by a shallow layer of glacial clays, so that there is only a thin, poor soil; in the South Swedish Highlands less than one-fifth is cultivated, and in the interior of Norrland, a mere 0·5%. It must be remembered, too, that the growing season is shorter farther north, where all farming operations must be concentrated between the melting of the snows in May and the onset of winter and rapidly shortening days in October.

The bulk of Sweden's agricultural land is in holdings of from 25 to 150 acres, the largest arable farms being in Scania. The average farm in the south is about 35 acres, in Norrland 10 acres, and nearly one-seventh of the working population of Sweden is engaged in agriculture. The country is self-supporting in essential foodstuffs. The chief crop, as in all northern Europe, is cultivated grasses, including clover, for hay. This is followed by wheat, which has replaced rye in the national diet; it is the main crop in eastern Scania, and new varieties enable it to be grown as far north as the Siljan region of central Sweden. Rye can be grown up to the Arctic Circle, and Sweden is noted for its rye bread, much of which is exported. Oats and barley are produced for fodder, often in mixed-grain fields. Potatoes are a principal crop, more in the north than the south; while sugar beet is confined to the southern third of the country. Oilseeds, especially flax (linseed) and rapeseed, are grown in Scania and on the plains of central Sweden.

A very large proportion of Sweden's crop is fed to cattle and pigs, of which there are respectively $2\frac{1}{2}$ and 2 million, with the biggest concentrations in the south. As in Denmark, co-operative dairying is the general rule, and butter, cheese, bacon, eggs and canned pork are exported. Dairy cattle are reared everywhere, their grazing lands being adjacent to the farm buildings, whereas beef cattle may be allowed to graze in forest glades at some distance. Sheep are of declining importance, except in the island of Gotland, where wool is exported from Visby.

As in Finland, forestry is inseparable from farming over large areas of Sweden. Even in Scania, which is predominantly agricultural, most farms include some woodland; farther north the amount of forest to be found on farmsteads increases. The forest provides the farmer with timber for houses, farm buildings and fences. Where cattle have to be kept indoors in winter, cheap and readily available material for housing them is a great advantage. Large amounts of fuel come from the forests, which are also grazing grounds, as mentioned; any surplus timber is sold to augment the farmer's income. In Norrland, as in Finland, farmers are employed in the lumber camps and sawmills in winter, when agricultural activities outdoors are suspended.

Much of the prosperity of Sweden depends on its forests. As noted above, more than 50% of the surface is forested, mainly with coniferous spruce and pine. There are stands of beech in Scania, and of birch in the east of the central lowlands, and these are exploited for the furniture industry. Spruce is the chief raw material for pulp and paper. Extensive birch forests on the slopes of the mountains in western Norrland are still virtually untouched. The exploitation of the coniferous forests began more than two centuries ago, chiefly for domestic use and the making of charcoal, and was confined to the centre and south of the country. With the demand for timber in the growing industrial countries of western

Europe, this supply became inadequate and early in the nineteenth century Sweden began to "colonise" the virgin forests of Norrland. These are now the chief lumbering area.

The forests of Sweden are eminently accessible. The distribution of coniferous trees coincides roughly with that of glacial deposits which, in the centre and south, have been the cause of a network of immature drainage and lakes. In Norrland drainage is more orthodox but even more effective. An enormous number of consequent rivers flow in parallel courses from the slopes of the Caledonian mountains, so close together that few parts of the forests in the interfluves are more than 4 miles from running water. The availability of rivers has been increased by the construction of artificial tributary channels, reducing the haulage distance in large areas to an average of two miles. In total, Sweden has more than 20,000 miles of natural floatways.

Floatage is still the most efficient way of transporting logs, although carriage by lorry, train and tractor is common in the older lumbering areas, and is increasing in Norrland. The felling of the trees is mainly a winter occupation, for then the frozen surface of the land facilitates haulage to the ice-bound rivers and lakes, and the minimum of sap in the trees allows the timber to season more rapidly. There is a considerable amount of summer cutting, the seasoning being speeded by artificial means. The logs are de-barked before being allowed to float down the rivers to the saw-mills. A feature of the coniferous forests is the large stands of one type of tree, spruce and pine rarely being found mixed in the same area. This makes the organising of lumber camps and the siting of pulp-mills easier and more economical. Moreover, the absence of undergrowth is an advantage to the hauliers.

"Raw" water power was used at the first saw-mills, which were situated up the rivers at falls or rapids. It was followed by steam power, using waste timber or coal imported from England and Germany, and the mills moved to the mouths of the rivers. Today, hydro-electric power stations built at selected falls have enabled mills to be sited in the most convenient places, sometimes on the coast, sometimes miles up the river. In addition, surplus current may be carried farther afield, to new mining towns in the north or to the older industrial regions of the centre of the country.

Lumbering in Norrland has two further advantages. First, the rivers begin to thaw in spring from the mouths, so that there is a gradual disappearance of the ice upstream. Logs which are stored on the rivers during the winter begin to float to the coast over a protracted period, enabling saw-mills to deal with their arrival more easily and avoid congestion. Secondly, the numerous rivers of Norrland, flowing parallel to each other into fiords along the Baltic coast, ensure a wide distribution of and good storage space for the millions of logs which float down them in the spring thaw.

As in Finland (*see* Chapter VI), the forest industry is divided into the sawn timber, plywood, furniture and hardboard branches on the one hand, and the pulping and paper-making on the other. Pulp, paper and cellulose make up more than a quarter of Sweden's exports, and timber about a fifth. A minor, though still important, forest industry is the making of charcoal to be used in iron-smelting and the manufacture of high class steels. By-products of the pulp mills and charcoal retorts include ethyl alcohol, paints, varnishes and plastics. About 5% of Swedish pig iron is produced in charcoal-fired furnaces.

There is careful Governmental supervision of the forests to ensure (*a*) that cutting does not outstrip the growth of new trees, (*b*) the collection of seed, propagation in nurseries, and planting of new stock, (*c*) control of fire hazards (Sweden has more than 1,000 forest fires a year), (*d*) control of open-range grazing by farmer-foresters' cattle or Lapps' reindeer, (*e*) the establishment of forest schools parallel in function to the farm schools of Scania. The supervision extends to the three-quarters of the forests owned by companies or individuals, as well as to the State-owned quarter. For countries like Sweden and Finland, whose economies rely so much on the output of their forests, it is imperative that over-cutting should be avoided and replacement ensured. Regeneration of softwoods is relatively speedy, but it still takes upwards of twenty years. In much of central and south Sweden, the timber cut consists of trees of second growth.

HYDRO-ELECTRICITY

Although Sweden has less potential than Norway, it leads the way in northern Europe in the development and use of its hydro-electric power resources. Its hydro-stations have a capacity of 7 million kW, and an annual production of 39 million kWh. These resources are in three areas: (i) There are numerous streams flowing from the South Swedish Highlands which were easily harnessed when hydro-electric power was first introduced. The largest stations were built on the river Lagan. (ii) All along the Great Lakes axis are major and minor plants. In the west, the first and biggest was at the Trollhätten Falls on the Göta river; in the centre the Klär and in the east the Dal rivers have large power plants. (3) Northern Sweden's resources are in two groups, one centring on Storsjön and the river Indals, the other the succession of roughly parallel streams in the north, from the river Kalix near the Finnish border to the river Ume.

These rivers, which include the Lule and northern Skellefte, have a lake reservoir near the foot of the mountains and descend to the coastal plain by an entrenched course with falls and rapids. In this remote area is located four-fifths of Sweden's power resources. Because of the distance from the industrial regions of the centre and south, the emphasis in northern Sweden has been on large stations which can "export" power. The largest exporting plant is at Harsprånget, on the Lule, a few miles below Porjus, where there is another major station. When completed, Harsprånget will supply a tenth of Sweden's requirements. For the moment, the largest single power concentration is along the Indals.

It may be mentioned that although Sweden has less than 5% development of thermal electricity she has large reserves of peat and oil shale, which could be used. Most of the peat is in the north, but the oil shales are readily available round Närke in the central lowland. Most thermal power is generated near Sweden's only coalfield, a poor one in north-west Scania outside Hälsingborg, or by using waste timber and sawdust as fuel in the centre and north of the country.

MINERALS AND SMELTING

Sweden's only coalfield is a small deposit in north-west Scania outside Hälsingborg. The coal is poor and of no value for smelting; it is used for household purposes and to generate thermal electricity. Less than 5% of Sweden's generated power comes from thermal stations, but large reserves of peat and oil shale could be used to increase this total. Most of the peat is in the north and west of the country, where it is not readily available. The oil shales occur around Närke in the central lowlands, and from the shale 50,000 tons of oil a year are distilled at Kvarntorp. Thermal stations in the centre and north of Sweden use waste timber and sawdust as fuel.

Sweden is richer in useful minerals than the other countries of northern Europe. Outstanding is the high grade phosphorus-free iron ore which for centuries has been mined in the Bergslagen district in the north-east of the central lowlands. The same area at one time produced copper ore, but the deposits are now almost exhausted and little mining is done. The presence of iron ore in northern Sweden has been known for at least two centuries, but not until the 1880s was it exploited commercially. Today the mines of Gällivara and Kiruna, in Lappland, and the coastal strip of Västerbotten produce 8% of the world's iron ore. The main ores are magnetite, with a high iron content (60%); lower-grade ores interspersed with the magnetite are carefully sorted from it and smelted separately. Apatite, which is used in the manufacture of fertilisers, occurs in association with the magnetite.

The lower basin of the river Skellefte, in Västerbotten, has Sweden's largest deposits of copper and lead ores, and iron pyrites are found further inland in the same region. Zinc occurs at Ammeberg, to the north of Lake Vättern, and manganese near Huskvarna, south of it.

The smelting of iron is still carried on for the most part in coke-fed blast furnaces, using imported coal. Sweden has only the one small coal-field in north-west Scania mentioned above, and the coal is of no value for smelting. For certain special steels, the smelting is done with charcoal, but the process is expensive. A new smelting method, utilising carbon monoxide and hydrogen in the furnace shaft, obviates the direct use of solid fuel, and is producing steel more cheaply; but the most noteworthy development in the industry is the growing use of hydro-electric power. Hydro-electricity is of greatest value in the remoter areas, and fortunately sources for its generation can be found there; but the electric furnace uses so much power that Sweden is already looking to the time when its hydro-electric resources, large though they are, will be insufficient and must be supplemented by atomic energy.

REGIONAL ECONOMY

1. Norrland

The most widespread occupation in Norrland is lumbering, together with the industries dependent on it. As already noted, coniferous forests cover most of the area and are readily accessible. The chief logging rivers, the Skellefte, Ume, Angerman, Indals, Ljungan, Ljusnan and Dal, flow in parallel courses and with their tributaries provide in winter well-distri-buted storage space on their frozen surfaces. With the spring or early summer thaw the logs are floated to the coast, where again the ample accommodation in the numerous river mouths of the Gulf of Bothnia prevents delay in delivery and facilitates the sorting necessary for later processing.

Sawmills may be found on almost every river in Norrland. Some are still worked by raw water power; many use sawdust and waste timber as fuel to drive their machinery, but the most important sawmills and pro-cessing works use hydro-electricity generated in a number of stations on the rivers mentioned above. There are smaller stations on the river Kalix, near the Finnish border. The largest sawmills are at Skellefteå (22,760), Umeå (22,542), Sollefteå (18,000), Härnösand (19,000), Sundsvall (29,355), Söderhamn (31,014) and Gävle (54,618). All these towns are engaged in both branches of the forest industries, exporting sawn timber, plywood, furniture, wood-pulp and paper. In addition, Gävle has an important porcelain industry. The towns mentioned grew originally at the mouths of rivers, but with the uplift of the coastal belt some of them, especially in the north, are now miles upstream and are served by new ports on the coast. Ursviken, for instance, is an outport for Skellefteå, and Holmsund for Umeå.

Agriculture in Norrland is usually of the subsistence type. Rye and potatoes are the main crops, but farmers are concerned mainly with cattle pasture, making use of grasses which grow among the widely spaced trees of the forest. The cattle are sold with the advent of winter, only a few for milk being retained in sheds near the farmhouses. Most farmers own a stretch of forest and depend on surplus timber to supplement their income. Many have part-time jobs in lumber camps and saw-mills. Farmers in the Jämtland depression are slightly better placed, because of the more fertile soils, but the adverse climate inhibits any approach to intensive farming. Dairying, however, is more prosperous than in the rest of Norrland.

Under the heading of pasture must be included the large herds of reindeer kept by Lapps. In Sweden the ownership of reindeer is, with few exceptions, reserved to people of Lappish descent. The reindeer pastures are in the extreme north of Sweden and on the higher parts of the Shield as far south as Jämtland. The nomad Lapps pay little regard to international boundaries, except that of the U.S.S.R., which is closed to them, and wander with their herds into Finland and Norway. Trade in venison is increasing, and much is sent to southern Sweden.

Norrland has important mineral resources, the chief being iron ore. There are two principal centres of production, Malmberget-Gällivara and Kiruna (26,703). Outside these are many other less concentrated or continuous bodies of ore (see Fig. 17). The Malmberget-Gällivara deposits were the first to be exploited, and a settlement of 3400 inhabitants developed there. Today the much larger mass of ore of Kiruna produces the major part of the output, and a planned township of 12,000 people has grown on the slopes of the ore mountain of Luossavaara. In both areas mining began in open-cast workings, but at Gällivara underground operations are now more common, and at Kiruna will commence in the near future. Work continues during the long, dark winter, lighting being supplied by hydro-electric stations on the rivers Kalix and Lule. The principal outlet for the ore is Narvik, at the head of the Ofoten Fjord, in Norway, which remains ice-free throughout the year. Luleå, the Swedish port in the Gulf of Bothnia, is used in summer, but is closed by ice for several months in winter. Moreover, Narvik is only 100 miles from Kiruna, whereas Luleå necessitates a journey of nearly 190 miles. The two ports are connected by an electric railway, which traverses the iron producing areas. Luleå (30,488) has new iron smelting and steel works, which use hydro-electric power.

The copper and lead of Västerbotten are smelted at Boliden, where improved processes in the reduction of the ores yield gold, bismuth and arsenic as by-products. The iron pyrites mined in this region are sent to Falun, in the central lowlands, for the extraction of sulphur.

2. Central lowlands

The lowlands which stretch across the middle of Sweden from the Skagerrak to the Baltic are the economic heart of the country and contain the largest proportion of the population. The name "lowlands" applied to this region is somewhat misleading, for its surface was disrupted by faulting, and there are many low-lying basins separated by low, uplifted horst ridges of crystalline rock. Most of the basins are cultivable, but in many there are waterlogged swamps. The only extensive plains are north and south of lakes Mälar and Hjälmar. The low ridges and the eskers which run through the region are covered with coniferous forests.

About one-third of the surface of the central lowlands is suitable for agriculture, which is carried on in small farms of 150–250 acres. The principal crops are hay and fodder, the latter including oats, root crops, potatoes and mixed grains. Among the cereals, oats are grown over the largest area; wheat comes next, having overtaken rye, which used to be the chief food grain. The largest single food crop is potatoes. The rearing of livestock is the most important agricultural occupation, cattle being bred for meat and milk, and pigs for bacon. Sweden exports large quantities of butter, cheese, tinned and dried milk, and bacon from Göteborg and Stockholm.

In the north-east, the lower basin of the river Dal forms a transition between the central lowlands and Norrland. Here, the Bergslagen district has rich deposits of both phosphorus-free and phosphoric iron ore. Dannemora is the centre for the phosphorus-free ore, which makes the best steels. It has large steelworks, and exports much of this high grade ore, mainly to Sheffield. The chief mining town for phosphoric iron ore is Grangesberg, whose blast furnaces, using improvements on Thomas and Gilchrist's basic process of smelting which enable this type of iron ore to be smelted effectively, produce larger quantities of pig iron and steel than Dannemora. Falun, in the north of the area, at one time a copper-mining town, extracts sulphur from iron pyrites brought from Västerbotten.

Sweden's steel products have a high reputation, and metal-working industries are widely distributed in the central lowlands, nearly half the working population there being engaged in the production of special steels for ball-bearings, drills, razor blades and springs. Outstanding among other metal-using industries are electrical and agricultural engineering, which include the manufacture of generators, cables, telephones, milking machines, dairy equipment and combine harvesters. The lack of coal and the use of hydro-electric power have led to a wider and more scattered distribution of industry and manufacture in Sweden than is found in Great Britain, France, Belgium or West Germany. Only rarely are towns grouped into concentrations or conurbations similar to those in the industrial countries of western Europe.

The largest industrial centre is Stockholm (808,484; over 1,000,000 with suburbs), the capital and second port of Sweden (*see* Fig. 19). The city grew on a partly submerged esker which formed a crossing-place at the eastern end of Lake Mälar. Its island site has made it "the Venice of the north," and its position commanding the north–south route along the

[*Courtesy of Bror Karlsson, Stockholm.*]

Fig. 19.—Sweden: Stockholm. View of the Old Town at night, showing the "Slussen" traffic clover leaf.

coast increased its commercial advantage. When Sweden's Baltic empire was at its greatest—in the seventeenth century—Stockholm was centrally placed, but its economic significance as a port declined with the orientation of roads, railways and commercial traffic towards the south-west of the country, where Göteborg and neighbouring ports are more open to the North Sea and are more easily kept free from ice in winter. Nevertheless, Stockholm remains Sweden's focus of industry, with a range of engineering products which includes cables and telephones (L. M. Ericsson), agricultural machinery (De Laval) and domestic stoves (AGA). It also has large shipbuilding yards.

North of Stockholm, motor cycles (NV) are made at Uppsala (77,397), the ecclesiastical capital of the country; west of it, Västerås (77,788) is the chief copper-manufacturing town and is noted for electrical generators

(ASEA) and locomotives. Eskiltuna (58,793), south of Lake Mälar, is the "Swedish Sheffield," specialising in knives, scissors, razor blades and surgical instruments. Örebro (75,379), at the western end of Lake Hjälmar, has a leather industry and makes boots and shoes. Motala (27,170), on Lake Vättern, produces vacuum cleaners and household appliances (Elektrolux). Nearer the coast, Linköping makes locomotives and Norrköping (90,680) is the centre of the wool textile manufacture. Norrköping has large fertiliser works, using hydro-electric power. Bofors has armament and anti-aircraft gun factories.

In the south-west of the lowlands is Göteborg (Gothenburg) (404,349), Sweden's second city and chief port. Situated at the mouth of the Göta river, it is a terminal of the Göta Canal which connects the lakes and gives a through waterway to Stockholm and the Baltic. This route, built (by Telford) for ships smaller than those of today, is of minor importance; but the land traffic to and from Göteborg is immense, especially in winter, when Stockholm's harbour freezes and is not readily available to ocean-going vessels. Göteborg's harbour remains ice-free all the year. Large shipbuilding yards along the Göta river make Göteborg the chief exporter of ships in the country, and it is the headquarters of one of the world's largest ball-bearing manufacturers (SKF). The city has also cotton, rayon and automobile (Volvo) industries. There are similar textile manufactures in the hinterland of Göteborg, especially at Borås (67,272); Trollhättan (31,901), near the falls of the same name, has large hydro-electricity power stations and makes motors (Saab).

In view of the numerous towns of the central lowlands, it is not surprising that two-thirds of Sweden's industrial workers live there, and that about a quarter of them are occupied in the metal-working trades.

3. The South Swedish Highlands

South of the central lowlands are the barren highlands of Småland, a broad plateau of granite and gneiss, dotted with lakes and peat bogs, and very similar to the Shield area of Norrland. It is largely forested, and its timber, mostly pine, is sent to the small towns around Lake Vättern, where it is used in the sawmills, furniture factories, and paper, pulp and cellulose works. Power is provided by numerous hydro-electric stations built on the rivers flowing from the highlands, whose lakes have been adapted as reservoirs. The plateau has poor soils and can support only a scanty farming population. On its eastern and western flanks are narrow coastal plains of marine clays, with a few towns such as Kalmar (30,802), a fishing port, and Karlskrona (33,010), a naval dockyard, on the eastern side, and Varberg and Falkenberg, fishing ports, on the west. The islands of Oland and Gotland are similar in structure to the highlands, but at a lower elevation. Sheep are reared in Gotland; the wool is exported from Visby, its chief town, and another fishing port.

In the north of Småland, on the southern shores of Lake Vättern, is Jönköping (50,522), the home of safety matches. The use of red or amorphous phosphorus, which is innocuous, for the making of matches was patented in 1844 by G. E. Pasch, and in 1852 J. E. Lundström, another Swede, set up the first match factory in his home town of Jönköping. By the end of the century Sweden had a virtual world monopoly in the manufacture of safety matches. The Svänska Tändsticks trust, with its headquarters in Jönköping, has more than twenty match factories scattered throughout central Sweden. Although output has declined since the death of Krueger, the "match king," in 1932, Sweden exports annually about 16 million tons of matches. The wood used for the splints is aspen, a type of poplar. Jönköping also has hardware and bicycle industries. Huskvarna, nearby, manufactures furniture and paper.

4. The lowlands of Scania

The small rectangular peninsula of Scania, attached to the south-west of Småland, has a cover of glacial clay, which has mixed with the underlying chalk to produce a very fertile soil. The region is a lowland, let down along north-west–south-east faults, but here and there slight warpings of the Jurassic and Cretaceous strata form low hills. Climatically, Scania is the most favoured part of Sweden, the summers being warm enough to ripen peaches in the open, the winters short, and the rainfall (20–25 in.) more evenly distributed through the year than in the rest of the country. Scania is in consequence the richest agricultural region in Sweden, over 60% of its surface being cultivated. Its natural vegetation of mixed forest has almost entirely disappeared.

The chief crops are wheat, barley, sugar beet and fodder. Large quantities of vegetables are grown, and rape and flax (linseed) are cultivated for their oils. Dairying is of greatest importance and, as in Denmark, is on a co-operative basis, butter, cheese, tinned milk, casein, bacon and eggs being exported.

Scania has the highest population density in Sweden, about 800,000 people living on its surface, which is only one-fortieth of the country's area. Malmö (228,878), its largest city and chief port, commands the southern entrance to the Sound. It has butter and bacon factories, makes flour-milling machinery, manufactures cotton and rayon, and has shipbuilding yards. It is also a train ferry port for Denmark. Hälsingborg, at the northern end of the Sound, has a rubber industry. Behind it is a small field of poor, Jurassic coal which supplies fuel for thermal electric stations.

Trälleborg has train ferry connection to Sassnitz, in West Germany. Lund, in the interior of Scania, is a university town.

STUDY QUESTIONS

1. Discuss the importance of forest products in the economy of Sweden. (J.M.B.)
2. Divide Sweden into major physical regions and give a reasoned account of *one* of the divisions. Illustrate by a sketch-map.
3. Discuss the importance to Sweden of (*a*) mining, (*b*) hydro-electric power.

Chapter IX

NORWAY

PHYSICAL ASPECTS

NORWAY stretches 1089 miles from North Cape to Lindesnes, on the western side of the Scandinavian peninsula—a long, attenuated country whose width varies from 267 miles in the latitude of the Sogne Fjord to only 4 miles behind Narvik.

STRUCTURAL DIVISIONS

The surface of Norway is almost entirely highland, the average elevation being over 1600 ft. With few minor exceptions it is composed of ancient rocks. In the south there is an extension into Norway of the Fenno-Scandian Shield, separated from similar structures in the South Swedish Highlands by the Oslo depression, one of the few low-lying parts of the country. The pre-Cambrian or Archaean land mass, of which Norway forms a part, subsided in Cambrian times and sediments laid down in the resultant geosyncline were folded at the end of the Silurian period into the so-called Caledonian mountains. The schists and limestones of the folds were subjected to sub-aerial denudation during the tens of millions of years since the beginning of the Devonian period, and there seems little doubt that but for the "Alpine Storm" of the Tertiary period, the whole surface would now resemble much of the Shield region of Finland.

The folds were highest in the south and lowest in the centre and extreme north. When the Alpine system was uplifted in the Tertiary period, Scandinavia, along with the British Isles and the floor of the north Atlantic Ocean, was on the edge of the mountain-building "storm" and was affected by its "ripples." The Archaean platform was faulted, dislocated and, together with the overlying eroded folds, uplifted into great plateau massifs in the south. To this period belong also the faults of central and southern Sweden, and those which caused the Oslo depression. The uplift was less farther north, and so the Kjölen range, north of the Trondelag lowlands behind Trondheim, is still a true folded ridge (*see* Fig. 12). But in the south, the Caledonian mountains were almost completely eroded, and the plateaus show large areas of Archaean granites and gneiss, interspersed with the "roots" of the worn-down sandstone,

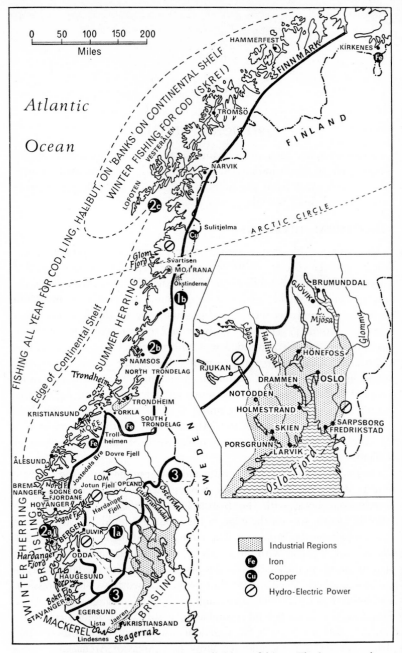

FIG. 20.—Norway: physical and economic divisions; fishing. The inset map shows the Oslo industrial region to a larger scale; numbering is explained in the text.

limestone and schistous folds of Cambrian age. The floor of the Atlantic also subsided, fracturing the Caledonian system and creating as a result the steep, cliff-lined seaward face of Norway.

During the Ice Age, Norway, according to Ahlmann, was subjected to two periods of glaciation. In the first the whole of the surface was covered by ice and in the following warm, inter-glacial period there was vigorous river erosion which resulted in much of the peneplaned landscape and deep valleys seen today. The second and final glaciation was not so complete, and many of the higher and more resistant mountains projected through the ice as nunataks. Land forms characteristic of mountain glaciation, such as roches moutonnées, perched blocks, screes, precipices, etc., seen in most parts of Norway, date from the second glacial period, but the major peneplanation and the carving of the deep, steep valleys which became fiords belong to the inter-glacial period. The length of time which has elapsed since the last glaciation maximum, calculated by de Geer to be 14,000 years, would allow only slight erosion of the land surface. The only parts of Norway where the glaciers left moraines and boulder-clays are in Lista and Jaeren in the south-west. Jaeren has been described as a piece of Denmark clinging to Norway.

Viewed from the air, Norway presents a vast, high, peneplaned landscape, with rounded monadnocks and steep-faced nunataks rising above the general surface. It is possible to divide its surface physically into: (1) the Caledonian plateaus and mountains, (2) the west coastal zone, which is really the western edge of the plateaus and mountains, but because of its great significance in the economy of Norway is here treated as a separate region, and (3) the south-eastern lowlands or Oslo depression (*see* Fig. 20).

1. *The Caledonian plateaus and mountains*

There are two main sections in the Caledonian system: (*a*) the southern plateaus, and (*b*) the Kjölen range, separated from each other by the Trondelag lowlands.

(*a*) The most extensive of the plateaus of Archaean rocks is Hardanger Vidda, at an average height of over 3000 ft, and cut by gorge-like valleys where it was faulted. To the north are the higher plateaus of Hardanger Fjell, Jotun Fjell, Jostedals Bre, Dovre Fjell and Trollheimen, which range up to 5000 ft in height, with rocks of Cambrian and Silurian age resting on an Archaean base. Here and there nunataks, such as Galdhöpiggen (8100 ft), Norway's highest mountain, project through an ice sheet.

Indeed, ice fields cover about 1200 square miles of the *fells* (fjell, fjellene), as the high plateaus are called. The most extensive of the ice sheets is on Jostedals Bre (315 square miles). None of them, with the exception of that on Svartisen in the Kjölen highlands, sends valley glaciers down to sea level. The ice on the plateaus has incised deep troughs and valleys. Some of them contain lakes and others, nearer the sea coast, have been drowned, to form fiords. Away from the ice sheets there are occasional *monadnocks*, residual mountains composed of resistant knobs of gabbro and other pre-Cambrian rocks.

(*b*) North of Trondelag, Norway becomes very narrow and is mainly the western slopes of the Kjölen range. Most of its peaks are less than 5000 ft high (the highest are in Sweden) but Sulitjelma rises to 6282 ft and Okstinderne to 6274 ft. Near the coast is Svartisen Fjell, from which projects Snotind (5200 ft), the birthplace of the only glacier in Norway which reaches the sea. The mountainous islands of the Lofoten and Vesterålen groups are fragmented portions of the northern ranges. In the extreme north, in Finnmark, the mountains become lower and lower, and finally the relief is indistinguishable from that of the Baltic Shield, which stretches to the south. In this region, Norway widens to about 80 miles.

2. *The west coastal zone*

This region may be taken as comprising a zone bounded by the inner ends of the fiords which characterise the Norwegian coast, including any lowlands which may be found around these openings from the sea. This narrow strip, extending from Lindesnes in the south to the Soviet border in the north, may be divided into (*a*) the Great Fiords in the south, (*b*) the Trondheim lowlands or Trondelag in the centre, and (*c*) the northern fiords (*see* Fig. 20). South of the Lofoten islands, all three subdivisions are skirted by about 150,000 islands, known as the skerry-gard (skjaergård), different in origin from the islands farther north, which are broken from the Kjölen range.

(*a*) The fiords (fjords) are long, winding, branching, steep-sided inlets from the sea. In some areas there is a marked rectilinear appearance in the fiord pattern, which gives rise to a theory that intersecting faults of Tertiary age had some part in their formation. Fault-valleys, branching from each other, would be deepened by the vigorous erosive action of the melting glaciers of the Ice Age, more active on the western side of the mountain mass, because there the ice sheet was thickest. It is probable, too, that many of the valleys were along the strike of some of the rocks or followed the line of schistosity of others.

The whole mountain system suffered isostatic depression as a result of the weight of the ice cap, and the ends of the glaciated valleys were drowned, to give the present inlets which so often branch at right angles. It must be remembered, however, that with the disappearance of the ice cap the land is slowly rising again. Before its first submergence the land mass stretched farther west than it does today; the glaciers over-deepened their valleys, especially in their lower courses where the gradient would be greater. This over-deepening would cease not far beyond the ancient coast, and the glaciers would proceed seawards up a reversed slope. This explains why the inner basins of most fiords are deeper than their thresholds. Sognefjord, for instance, the longest of them (114 miles), has an inner depth of 4000 ft, while its threshold is only 500 ft deep. Hardanger Fjord (105 miles long) is 2900 ft deep, and its entrance is of the same order as that of the Sogne. It must be remembered, too, that iso-static depression alone would not have a sufficient drowning effect. The amount of water released by the melting of the ice cap raised the level of the oceans by an estimated 200–300 ft and so augmented the invasion by the sea. At the heads of the fiords there are deltaic lowlands, built up by torrents falling into the quiet waters; and pauses in the isostatic uplift have resulted in raised beaches above the fiords: platforms or shoulders with a covering of fluvio-glacial debris.

From Trondheim southwards, the inlets are known as the Great Fiords. Hardanger and Sogne are the most extensive of a large number of major fiords around which the people of Norway first settled.

(b) The Trondheim lowlands or Trondelag are a relatively low region north of the Great Fiords where the Caledonian mountains did not rise very high and were composed of softer rocks which have been eroded to give a hilly topography, with deltaic flats on its seaward margin. Inland, the "Trondheim Saddle" leads across the mountains to the Swedish low-lands of Jämtland.

(c) North of Trondheim the fiords which penetrate the coastlands of the Kjölen range are shorter, shallower and have lower cliff margins. In Finnmark, where the rocks are softer and the land lower, they have wide mouths and the land around them slopes gently to the plateau above.

The origin of the skerry-gard which lies off the coast has not yet been explained satisfactorily. There are two belts of islands: the outer ones rise to less than 100 ft in height from comparatively shallow waters, but the inner series are up to 1000 ft high and in deeper waters. Neither is there a completely satisfactory explanation for the *strand-flat*, a series of low, flat rock-terraces, often backed by a steep scarp, found in the island zone and along the adjacent mainland. It varies in width up to 37 miles (in the islands of Fröya and Hitra, outside Trondheim Fjord) and averages 100 ft above sea level. It is explained variously as a pre-glacial or inter-glacial wave-cut platform, an Ice Age product of marine action and iceberg abrasion, or a phenomenon of combined glacial and sub-aerial erosion. The argument against marine erosion alone as a cause is strengthened by the occurrence of the strand-flat in some of the sheltered fiords, where wave action is minimal. Nansen proposes three strand-flat levels, originating in three inter-glacial periods, and attributes the uniformity of the surface to variations of sea level and isostatic adjustments.

3. South-east Norway

This lowland, the most extensive in the country, is caused by the convergence of several broad, open river valleys, the chief being Österdal, Gudbrandsdal and Hallingdal; these are collectively known as the Oslo depression. Southwards the lowlands are continued in a narrow coastal plain. Both Österdal and Gudbrandsdal provide routes—the latter the easier and more important—from Oslo to Trondheim and the main route across the southern massif from Oslo to Bergen is via Hallingdal. The rivers, the largest of which is the Glomma (380 miles), drain into Oslo Fjord, which is wider and more open than the western fiords, and is carved into the predominantly Cambro-Silurian rocks which underlie the surface. The basal geological structure is similar to that of Sweden north of the river Dal but it has been extensively down-faulted, so preserving later rocks on the original Archaean platform. Coastal sediments deposited in post-glacial times and then uplifted have helped to make these lowlands the best for agriculture in Norway.

CLIMATE AND VEGETATION

Some of the characteristics of Norway's climate have already been given in Chapter III. The country is affected all the year by the westerlies, which bring warm air and moisture from the Atlantic; but the sharp rise to the fells, the large number of longitudinal valleys shut off by high land from marine influences, and the deep penetration of the coastal region by the fiords, produce marked differences of climate in localities separated by only a couple of miles. Norway lies in the "gulf of winter warmth"; the main stream of the North Atlantic Drift skirts its shores; and so its temperatures are higher than in comparable latitudes elsewhere. This is especially notable in the Lofoten islands, 150 miles inside the Arctic Circle, with a January average temperature of 31° F (−0·6° C). This might be contrasted with Oslo's January temperature of 25° F (−4·1° C), where maritime influences are shut off by the block of southern Norway and cold continental winds blow from the east. Because of the altitude, temperatures on the fells are low even in summer, as the extensive ice fields show; in spring and summer the drainage of cold air into the valleys of the south-east (temperature inversion) often creates problems for the farmers.

The rainfall of Norway varies as widely as the temperature. The westward-facing coast of southern Norway is one of the rainiest and most humid in the world, the annual average precipitation amounting to 80–120 in. On the mountains round the Nordfjord it rises to more than 240 in. Northwards, however, rainfall diminishes to 25 in. at North Cape; there is a rapid diminution, too, eastwards in the fiords. Bergen, facing the open sea, has 84 in. annually, whereas in the interior of the Hardanger Fjord, not far away, the annual total diminishes to 50 in. The south-eastern valleys and lowlands, in the rain-shadow of the high fells, have 20 in. annual average, but some of the more sheltered districts may have as little as 12 in. In some places, such as Lom and Otta, in a valley tributary to Gudbrandsdal, in the lee of Jotun Fjell and Jostedals Bre, the farmers have to resort to irrigation, using snow-melt waters. The high humidity and the tendency for a thick cloud cover to form along the west coast, with a consequent lowering of summer temperatures, make farming operations more hazardous there than in the drier south-east, in spite of the long, cold winters of the latter.

Norway is the "land of the midnight sun." At North Cape the sun remains continuously above the horizon from mid-May to the end of July. At the other end of the year it remains hidden for over two months. In December, the sun rises at Trondheim at 10 a.m. and sinks at 2.30 p.m. In Oslo, midsummer day has only one hour of darkness. These wide variations in the length of day and night, *i.e.* in the amount of insolation, have affected both plant and animal, including human, life in all north European countries, but more so in Norway, which extends farthest north.

The country has very little useful soil, only 4% of its surface being counted as arable land. This is a legacy of the Ice Age, when glaciers stripped the soil cover, leaving bare rock, except in the peninsulas of Jaeren and Lista, which have boulder clays overlying Tertiaries. The best soils, in the Trondheim and Oslo lowlands, in alluvial deposits scattered along river valleys, and in the deltaic flats at the heads of the fiords, are post-glacial deposits.

The natural vegetation of Norway is coniferous forest, which covers 24% of the country. The limit of tree growth varies from over 3000 ft in the south to sea level in the extreme north, although in Finnmark pines and birch may be found up to 1000 ft on sheltered slopes. These two, with spruce, are the chief species everywhere, with the beginnings of mixed forest in the Oslo lowlands and along the south coast, where there are oak, ash, elm and other deciduous trees. Vegetation above the tree-line is scanty. Alpine plants, mosses, lichens and hardy berry-bearing bushes predominate, and in ill-drained hollows there are peat bogs.

HUMAN GEOGRAPHY

HISTORY AND PEOPLE

After the Ice Age, Neolithic people settled on the west coast of Norway, fishing, hunting and tilling along the fiords. They were followed after 1500 B.C. by Bronze Age men, and they in turn, about 600 B.C., by immigrants from the Great European Plain; tall, fair haired, long headed people of the Iron Age. These last were the ancestors of most of the Norwegians of today, although in the last three centuries incursions of Lapps, Finns and Danes have brought new blood and some modification of hair colour, especially in the south, where many Norwegians are dark haired.

About the end of the eighth century, possibly because of over-population, possibly because of political and tribal rivalries, the men of the fiords, the Vikings, began to sail out on voyages of piracy and ultimately of conquest and settlement. Norsemen settled in the Faeroes, northern Britain, Iceland, northern France and Greenland. They landed in North America about A.D. 1000. At home, trading towns grew up at Bergen, Trondheim (then called Nidaros), Oslo, Stavanger and Sarpsborg (originally Borg). In 1380, Norway was joined to Denmark and remained a dependency until the end of the Napoleonic wars in 1815, when she was taken from Denmark and joined to Sweden. Denmark retained sovereignty over the Faeroes, Iceland and Greenland. In the early Danish period, the Hanseatic League made Bergen the leading trading town in northern Europe, an exchange port for fish, butter, grain and salt.

In 1905, Norway separated peacefully from Sweden to become a sovereign state. During the First World War she remained neutral. In 1925 (by a treaty signed in 1920) she added Svalbard to her possessions, then annexed the Arctic islands of Jan Mayen and Björnöya (Bear Island). She maintains weather research stations in all three, and has coal mining and sealing settlements on Spitzbergen, in Svalbard. Norway's interest in the Antarctic whaling industry led to her annexation of the islands of Bouvet in 1930 and Peter I in 1931. She also claims Queen Maud Land, on the Antarctic continent.

POPULATION

The population of Norway was 3,626,000 in 1962 (of whom 20,000 were Lapps) with an average density of 29 per square mile. Many of the Lapps have abandoned their semi-nomadic reindeer herding and found employment in Kirkenes, Tromsö, Narvik and other industrial settlements in Finnmark and Norrland. More than half Norway's population is in the south-eastern region, and another quarter in the west, round the

Sogne, Hardanger and Bokna fiords. The Trondheim lowlands have another tenth, and the whole of the rest of Norway north of this depression less than an eighth. The pressure on the small amount of cultivable land is very great; although the growing electro-industries (*i.e.* based on supplies of hydro-electric power) can absorb some of the surplus rural population, many Norwegians emigrate, generally to Canada and the United States.

THE LAPPS

There are roughly 34,000 Lapps in northern Europe, 20,000 in Norway, 10,000 in Sweden, 2500 in Finland and 1500 in the U.S.S.R. The origin of the Lapp people is not known. It has been suggested that they are descended from a Stone Age people who moved north with the retreat of the glaciers of the Ice Age. They are short in stature—rarely more than 5 ft tall—and have dark hair and swarthy skins. They are the most brachycephalic (round-headed) people in Europe. The area in which they live is called Lappland, and ranges without definite boundaries from Norway to the U.S.S.R., mainly north of 65 degrees N. Linguistically the Lapps belong to the Finno-Ugrian group and their language bears a great resemblance to Finnish, but with considerable borrowings from Swedish and Norwegian.

The popular picture of Lapps is of nomads wandering with their herds of reindeer across the tundra of northern Europe. This is true of only a small proportion—at the most just over 5000 of the total Lapp population, of which about 3000 are in Sweden and 1500 in Norway. It is better, too, to regard even these as transhumant people rather than nomads, for they follow definite grazing routes and usually have a permanent camping site on the northern edges of the forest, returning to it for the winter months. Their migration routes are determined by the available supplies of reindeer moss (*Cladonia rangiferina*), but within limits set by tradition for each group of wandering Lapps. When the reindeer moss is too deeply covered by snow or ice layers, the herds find tree mosses growing on the spruce and pines in the forest. The food of the migrating Lapps in winter is almost entirely reindeer meat, milk and cheese. In summer these are supplemented by rye flour, sugar, salt and coffee, which are bartered in the mining and fishing settlements of the north. The reindeer supply skins for tents and clothing, bones for implements, and serve as transport animals, besides being a source of food.

The non-migratory Lapps fall into several classes: the sea Lapps and river Lapps of Norway; the mountain Lapps and forest Lapps of Sweden; the fishing Lapps of Finland and the Murmansk coast of the U.S.S.R. The sea Lapps have their homes on the mainland, and build boats and hunt

wild reindeer during the winter. In summer they visit the skerries for
fishing, sealing and whaling. River, mountain and forest Lapps are subsistence farmers and own small reindeer herds which feed locally. The
fishing Lapps live around Lake Inari, in Finland, and the rivers and lakes of
Murmansk. These own only a few reindeer. Some of the Lapp communities near towns such as Narvik and Tromsö in Norway, and Kiruna
and Malmberget in Sweden, find occasional employment there but in
general the Lapps confine themselves to their own economy, which is
based on the products of the reindeer. There is an increasing sale of reindeer flesh, fresh and dried, throughout northern Europe.

The growth of fishing and mining towns, and the advance of Finnish
and Swedish farmers and lumberers into the traditional grazing lands of
the Lapps, have had several effects on this northern people. Legislation has
been introduced into all the countries of northern Europe to protect their
rights of migration and reindeer herding. At the same time, reindeer
fences to keep the animals out of cultivated farmlands have been legalised.
More significantly, the boundary lines of countries have been regularised,
and the completely free movement of transhumants from one country to
another allowed formerly has been restricted. The U.S.S.R. territory is
completely fenced off, and a fence between Norway and Finland is being
considered. On the whole, however, such laws as affect the Lapps have
been enacted to safeguard the welfare of this minority people and bring
them more into the economies of the countries in which they live.

THE ECONOMY

AGRICULTURE

The amount of land actually cultivated in Norway is very small, less
than 2 million acres, or 3·2% of the surface; most of the farms are less than
5 acres. Over half the forests in the country, however, belong to the
farmers, and provide a welcome addition to their income. The chief farming areas are in the lowlands around Oslo Fjord, in Jaeren and Lista, and in
Trondelag, where soil and climatic conditions are best, and mechanisation
and co-operation highly developed. Away from these lowlands, farms are
scattered in deep valleys on whose precipitous slopes mechanised farming
is well-nigh impossible, and methods of cultivation, measured by modern
standards, somewhat primitive.

Hay is the most important field crop in all areas. In the wetter west, it is
hung on wire racks or wooden fences to dry. The growing season is too
short and the rainfall too great, except in the south-east, for large-scale
cereal cultivation, but oats, barley and rye are grown, mainly for fodder.
Artificial fertilisers, for which Norway is famous, and the researches of the

Agricultural College at Ås have increased the yields enormously. The acreage under wheat is growing in the Oslo region, but Norway can provide only a small proportion (7%) of her cereal requirements. She must also import up to 50% of her fodder grains. Potatoes, a quick-growing crop, are produced everywhere in the farmlands.

Pastoralism is by far the most important part of Norway's agricultural life, but the numbers of cattle are limited by the amount of fodder available for the winter, when stall-feeding is necessary. Over most of the country the season for outdoor pasture lasts only four months. Milk, cheese and butter are the chief products and co-operative dairies deal with 98% of the output, much of it being exported. There are roughly 1,100,000 cattle in Norway, and about one-tenth that number of goats, the latter mainly in the valley farms and the north. The chief dairying regions are the lowlands, where the fodder crops are most plentiful.

Some mention must be made of the saeter system and transhumance in Norway. *Saeters* are summer pastures lying for the most part above the timber-line, although many are "forest-pastures," where the trees are spaced more widely. They may be compared with the "alps" or mountain pastures of Switzerland. During the summer, cattle and goats are taken to the saeters while the fields of the home farm are growing fodder crops. Sheep, too, are carried by lorries as far as possible, then driven to the highest pastures. The saeters are at varying distances from the home farms: in the fiord belt, usually about 7 or 8 miles, but in the interior—as for instance in Gudbrandsdal—possibly 20 miles away. With modern transport, distance is not very important, but steep slopes, rough tracks and the inaccessibility of some of the saeters have led to a marked decline in their use. On the saeters are chalets and dairies, and the milch cattle are herded near by for milking. Beef cattle are grazed farther away. There are about 20,000 saeter sites, nearly half of them in Oppland and near the Sogne Fjord in Sogn og Fjordane, but this is only half the numbers 50 years ago. Saeter pastures are not as rich as those in the valleys, and the quality and yield of milk may be too low to justify their use in many cases. Nor can the labour lost to the home farms through transhumance be spared today, when so many of the rural population are moving into the towns or emigrating. The numbers engaged in agriculture have declined in the past 100 years from 70% to 15% of the population. Yet at the same time so much grazing land cannot be allowed to go completely to waste. It is the concern of Norway's agricultural experts to find new and more effective means of using the saeters efficiently.

Norway has more sheep (1,800,000) than cattle, the main concentrations being in Jaeren and on the strand-flat in the island zone. In the latter area are silver-fox farms, and Norway is a leading producer of their furs.

Mink farms, however, give the greatest financial return. Pigs (475,000) are reared for bacon in the dairying part of Jaeren, but are not important in Norway's economy. Horses (116,800), although far fewer in number than formerly, are used extensively on farms where the gradients are too steep for tractors, and for hauling timber in the forests. Reindeer herds, once confined to the northernmost parts of the country, are now also found in the mountains of the south. Income derives principally from the sale of their meat and hides in the southern grazing lands; in the north they are the sustenance of the Lapps.

FORESTRY

The forests of Norway are an important source of income to the farmers. They own most of the total exploitable area (at present about 14,800,000 acres) and, as in Sweden and Finland, many of them are engaged in lumbering during the winter months. The forest industries, like those in all modern lumbering areas in the coniferous zone, are divided into the wood manufacturing and chemical branches. Most of the productive forest area is in south-east Norway and Trondelag, while the west and north of the country are relatively unforested.

About 40% of the timber produced for sale is taken by the wood manufacturing industry, but the former export trade in sawn and planed timber has almost disappeared, domestic requirements are so great. Wooden houses are everywhere the rule and a large-scale housing programme since the Second World War in addition to the bigger demand for timber for the pulp mills and other purposes has left little for export.

The paper and pulp industry, on the other hand, is based mainly on exports. It employs about 20,000 people, roughly an eighth of Norway's industrial labour force, and accounts for a fifth in value of all exports. The pulp mills are of two types, mechanical and chemical. Norway's mechanical pulp mills have an aggregate production capacity of between 650,000 and 700,000 tons (calculated dry) and most is exported, mainly to Great Britain. The production of chemical pulp is nearly as great and is increasing. Sulphite pulp, extracted from spruce, is the raw material for high-grade papers and rayon, while sulphate pulp, from pine, makes coarser papers and cardboard. Chemical pulp is largely exported, but Norway is also an important manufacturer and exporter of finished paper, much more so than Sweden or Finland. Alcohol is produced from chemical pulp waste and used in the manufacture of plastics.

FISHING AND WHALING

Norwegian fishermen take more fish out of the sea than any other country in Europe. The fisheries are almost entirely coastal, in the shallow waters between the islands and over the continental shelf, and in the deeper but more sheltered fiords. The average annual haul is over 1,300,000 tons, about 70% herring and brisling, and 15 to 20% cod. Haddock, saithe, mackerel and flatfish make up most of the rest. In 1961, Norway had 61,000 registered fishermen, of whom 28,000 had fishing as their sole occupation; the remainder were engaged in farming or other pursuits while awaiting the arrival of the seasonal shoals of fish.

The great majority of fishermen in Norway are sole or part owners of their boats, and this has tended to keep down the size of the vessels. Moreover, the coastal character of the fishing requires small boats, and they are cheaper to buy and maintain. Norway's fishermen are generally opposed to large trawlers partly on the grounds that they are inefficient because indiscriminate in their catch, but more because large and expensive trawlers would lead to less part-ownership and upset the traditional economy. The number of large trawlers is limited by legislation, and in recent years small trawlers have become more numerous. On the other hand, there is an increasing amount of deep-sea fishing off Greenland and Iceland, and this demands larger vessels.

Herring fishing begins in the north in January, when the shoals appear off the coast, and start to move southwards. The catch is variable, but in the spring months vast numbers are caught in purse-seine nets which can trap a hundred tons of herring in a single cast. Later in the year the main catch is off the coast south of Trondheim, and small trawlers move out into the middle of the North Sea. Cod migrate from deep waters to spawn; they reach the coast of Finnmark in November, move south to the Lofoten islands area from then until April, and in June return to ocean waters via Finnmark again. The most important catch and the best fish are off the Lofoten islands and along the coast southwards to Trondheim. There has been a considerable amount of over-fishing of young cod in recent years, and an international committee was set up in 1965 to discuss the restrictions necessary to safeguard the future of the industry.

A considerable portion of the total catch is processed industrially. Fish processing includes canning, herring-oil and fish-meal manufacture, liver-oil plants and refrigeration. These occupy nearly 13,000 people; fish and fish products account for over a fifth of Norway's exports, and have roughly the same value as her forestry total.

The tiny herring called brisling and sild, often wrongly called sardines, are the basis of the canning industry. Most of the cod is salted (klipfish) or dried (stockfish), and sent to Mediterranean countries and the tropics, where there is a large demand; a growing amount is taken by cold storage plants for conversion into frozen fillets. The production of cod liver oil and halibut liver oil is concentrated close to the cod fishing grounds in north Norway and round the Trondheim Fjord.

An important seasonal occupation is sealing, carried on chiefly off Newfoundland and round the Jan Mayen island. There is a good demand for sealskin (used for fishermen's thigh-boots) and seal-oil.

Much more valuable to Norway is the whaling industry. About 3000 to 4000 whales are caught annually off the northern coast, but the main whaling grounds are in the Antarctic Ocean (12,504 whales in 1961), with a land station at Husvik harbour on South Georgia. It was a Norwegian, Svend Foyn, who invented the shell harpoon and used it successfully; and Norway introduced the first factory ship with hauling slipway, an invention which made whaling expeditions independent of shore stations. Today Norway has nine floating factories in the Antarctic and accounts for about half the world's annual catch of whales. She has, too, taken the initiative in restricting the numbers caught, to avoid the total extinction of the species. A conference of Norway, the U.S.S.R. and Japan—the chief whaling countries—has decided that the total catch of blue whales shall not exceed 4500 in 1965–66. Whale oil is sold direct from the factories to foreign countries, but much is brought home to Bergen and other oil-processing towns, for the manufacture of margarine and soap.

MINERALS AND POWER

The ancient metamorphosed rocks of Norway have numerous and varied mineral deposits, but usually they are of small extent. The exceptions are in iron ore, pyrites and copper pyrites, which make up 70% of the total mining value. The largest iron ore deposit worked at present is behind Kirkenes, in eastern Finnmark. This deposit, estimated to have a reserve of 50 million tons, is largely magnetite, with an iron content of about 35% and a low phosphorus and sulphur content. It is partly smelted at Kirkenes, and exported as a concentrate with 65% purity, mainly to Great Britain and West Germany, although an increasing proportion is now sent to Mo i Rana, on Norway's west coast. Small iron ore deposits are worked in the counties of North Trondelag, More and Telemark. Exploitation has just commenced of an iron field in Dunderland, near Mo i Rana (*see* Fig. 21), which is said to be as big as that at Kirkenes.

Pyrites and copper pyrites are widely distributed; they are processed mainly for their sulphur content. Copper, zinc, iron and silver are by-products of their reduction. Norway is one of the largest producers of sulphur in Europe. Granite is exported from the quarries of Telemark; it was used in the construction of the Kiel Canal, and of the docks at Chatham, Dover and Devonport.

FIG. 21.—Norway: Mo I Rana. The town, visible in the middle distance on the edge of the fiord, is the site of Norway's largest steelworks. The smelting is by hydro-electric power, but in the near future coke is to be brought from Svalbard (Spitzbergen). The iron ore comes mainly from Kirkenes.

The mainland of Norway is lacking in coal and mineral oil. There are coal deposits in Spitzbergen, in the Svalbard archipelago, but they could not be exploited until 1920, when Svalbard became a Norwegian possession. The output is small, only 362,000 tons in 1961.

In contrast, Norway has more water power than any other European country and, relative to its population, is the most hydro-electrified nation on earth (*see* Fig. 22). Its generating capacity today is over 4 million kw, with an annual output of more than 34,000 million kWh, yet less than half its available resources have so far been harnessed. It is estimated that the country has over 600 falls with a head of water exceeding 900 ft, a much more favourable position than that of Sweden or Finland, where the heads are lower.

The hydro-electric power stations lie in three main groups, (*a*) in the highlands on both sides of Oslo Fjord, (*b*) on the west coast around the Sogne and Hardanger fiords, and (*c*) in the fiord belt from Namsos to North Cape. In addition, there are many smaller hydro-electric stations in Trondelag, along Gudbrandsdal (river Lågen) and Österdal (river

E

Glomma), in Hallingdal and near Kirkenes; but although in total their generating power is substantial and they support widely scattered mills and factories, they play only a minor role in Norway's industrial economy. Four-fifths of the county's developed water power lies south of the latitude of Trondheim, which contrasts with the northerly position of Sweden's and Finland's major resources.

The forest and fishing industries of Norway have benefited greatly from the introduction of hydro-electricity, but the greatest impact of cheap and plentiful current has been on the electro-chemical and electro-metallurgical industries, which use about 45% of the total generated

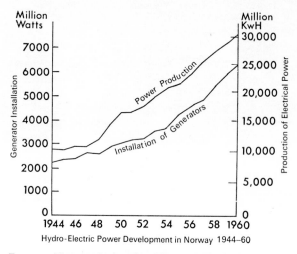

Hydro-Electric Power Development in Norway 1944–60

FIG. 22.—Norway: hydro-electricity. 99·3% of the country's electricity is generated by water.

power. The electro-chemical industry began in 1899 with the production of calcium carbide at Notodden, in the south-east. Carbide is used in the manufacture of cyanamide (for fertilisers) and acetylene, an inflammable gas which is a raw material in the making of polyvinyl plastics. Since 1905 nitrogen has been fixed by electric power from the atmosphere, and a large range of nitrogenous products, chiefly fertilisers, now constitutes an important part of Norway's exports, more than a million tons being sent out annually. Other products of the electro-chemical industry are ammonia, magnesium from sea water, PVC for plastic goods, heavy water for atomic reactors, and argon for welding. The electro-metallurgical industry is concerned principally with the production and export of ferro-alloys, such as ferro-manganese, ferro-silicon, and ferro-chrome, for which the raw materials, including iron, are imported.

REGIONAL ECONOMY

1. *The Caledonian plateaus and mountains*

The high fells of the south are mainly uninhabited waste land. They are crossed by railways built with difficulty from Oslo to Bergen, Åndalsnes and Trondheim, and by a few mountain roads. Hotels have been built along the main roads for summer tourists and winter sports enthusiasts. In the deep valleys are poor farms, often with saeter grazing on the steep slopes. Many of the farmers now own reindeer herds and supply meat to the south-eastern lowlands. In some of the deep, sheltered valleys the rainfall is small and irrigation is necessary. This is most noticeable in the tributary valleys of Gudbrandsdal. In the upper Glomma valley (Österdal) is the small smelting town of Röros, specialising in the extraction of sulphur from pyrites (iron disulphide) and copper pyrites. Local deposits of copper are now exhausted, and the raw material is brought from fields farther north. The Glomma valley provides the easiest route from Oslo to Trondheim.

The Kjölen mountains are equally barren, except around Sulitjelma and in the far north. Near Sulitjelma are deposits of copper pyrites and sulphur, and these are sent to Röros for reduction. On the lower slopes of the northern Kjölen range live the mountain Lapps of Norway, who are transhumant—unlike the mountain Lapps of Sweden, who live by subsistence farming.

2. *The west coastal zone*

This was the first region in Norway to be settled and developed. The sheltered waters of the fiords and inside the skerry-guard formed an excellent nursery for seamen; the deltaic flats at the heads of the fiords encouraged settlement and cultivation; the raised beaches provided saeter grazing or hay for fodder; the forests which occur at lower levels offered timber for boat building, houses and fuel; and the shallow waters near the coast teemed with fish. In this environment grew up the fisherman-farmer culture of the Vikings, whose name means "men of the deep inlets."

The main occupation throughout the coastal belt is fishing. Herring fishing goes on throughout the year; cod fishing mainly from November to June, when the fish move in from deep ocean waters to spawn. The greater part of the herring catch is converted into fish meal and oil in about 70 factories scattered along the coast from Egersund in the south to Trondheim. The meal is used as cattle and poultry food, the oil processed into margarine and other products. Much herring is, of course, sold fresh, salted or frozen. The chief herring fishing and processing

ports are Bergen (the centre of the industry), Stavanger, Ålesund,
Kristiansund and Trondheim. The small herring known as brisling or
sild are canned in upwards of 300 factories, spread along the extensive
coast, with the chief establishments at Stavanger. The principal cod
fishing town is Trondheim. Here, and at many small ports on the
northern coast, there are factories for the production of cod liver and
halibut liver oils. Larger works are at Tromsö and Svolvaer, the latter in
the Lofoten Islands. No part of the cod is wasted; even the scales are made
into a paste used in the manufacture of artificial pearls.

In all the fiords there are patches of agricultural land. For the most part
they are small, with crops of hay, rye, potatoes and vegetables. Cattle are
taken to the saeters in summer and brought down to sheds in winter.
Behind Bergen and Trondheim, however, the lowland is more extensive
and farming operations easier. In the Trondheim lowlands, which are part
of Trondelag, hay is the chief crop, followed by oats, barley and wheat.
Much of the grain is in mixed fields, and is cut and stored as silage, to be
fed in winter to cattle. The Bergen lowlands, further south, have the
nearest approach to mixed farming in western Norway, including fruit
orchards which export apples. In the extreme south the lowlands of
Jaeren and Lista, with the port of Stavanger at their western end, have a
farming economy very similar to that of west Denmark, and concentrate
on dairying. In all the coastal lowlands the farmers share in the fishing
and perpetuate the culture of their Viking ancestors.

The excellence of the fiord harbours and the development of hydro-
electric power has caused a revolution in the industrial growth of the
coastal zone. There were already industries based on imported fuel and
raw materials in the larger towns, such as Bergen, Trondheim and
Stavanger but, with the advent of water-driven turbines, industrial plants
have grown in places previously considered inaccessible or unsuitable.
This is especially the case in the inner reaches of the Great Fiords, and
along the more northerly coasts. Power stations based on low falls have
existed in the south for nearly fifty years, providing electricity for the
industries of Bergen and other towns. Today, up to twenty large installations are designed to utilise more distant and more elevated sources, with
greater potential. Sited near deep, navigable water, they are leading to
the growth of heavy industry, such as electro-metallurgy at Ulvik and
Odda, near the head of Hardanger Fjord. Ammonia is produced at Odda
and at Glomfjord, north of the Arctic Circle. The liquid is shipped in bulk
to the Oslo lowlands, where it is converted into nitrogenous fertilisers.
Aluminium is produced from imported bauxite at Höyanger, on Sogne
Fjord, and zinc at several smelters along Hardanger Fjord.

There are old-established steelworks at Stavanger and Bremnanger, the latter on Nordfjord, using power from local hydro-electric stations. The largest plant, a combined smelting and steel rolling works, is at Mo i Rana, just south of the Arctic Circle. The iron ore is brought from Kirkenes near the Russian border, and power from major hydro-electric stations along Glomfjord and its tributary valley of Rossaga. Small iron ore deposits in Trondelag have led to hydro-electric smelting and steel-works in Trondheim.

Norway has one of the world's largest merchant fleets and a long sea-faring tradition, yet it is not a great shipbuilding nation. In fact, ships rank high in its list of imports. Shipbuilding yards are found in large numbers along the coast from Oslo Fjord to Finnmark, but they are concerned principally in making small wooden vessels for the fishing industry. In this branch of shipbuilding Norway enjoys a high reputation. Large steel ships of a special kind, such as tankers, whaling ships, ocean factories and refrigeration ships, are built on the west coast at Bergen and Trondheim, and also at Oslo.

The textile and clothing industries, food processing, and the manufacture of hardware, machinery, railway equipment, electrical goods, motors and cycles, are all grouped round the same three towns.

The largest town on the west coast is Bergen (115,914), the centre of the herring fishing industry, and the second city in Norway. Situated near the exit of several converging fiords, and with an excellent harbour, it was already an important trading port in the days of the Hanseatic League, from the fifteenth to the eighteenth centuries. Until the development of the Oslo region, it was the focus of the most thriving part of the country, and the largest city. Trondheim (59,300) was once the capital and is still the ecclesiastical centre. Besides the industries already enumerated, it has a large transit trade with Sweden, especially in winter, making use of the low saddle across the mountains which connects the Trondelag region with Jämtland. Stavanger (52,800) is the canning headquarters; Kristian-sund (27,800) and Ålesund (19,000) have fish-meal factories. Narvik (13,300), a small port in the far north, is concerned mainly with the export of iron ore from the fields of northern Sweden.

3. The south-eastern lowlands

Sometimes known as the Oslo depression, these are made up of the lower valleys of several rivers, chiefly those flowing in Österdal, Gut-brandsdal and Hallingdal, which converge on Oslo Fjord. As an economic region, it includes the surrounding slopes of the highlands. The soils are mainly of marine origin and are fertile, producing the usual crops of hay, oats, potatoes, root crops, barley and a small but increasing amount of wheat. A larger proportion of vegetables is grown here than elsewhere in

Norway, to supply the demands of a population which amounts to more than half the country's total. Norwegian agriculture is based everywhere on the holding of livestock and the production of fodder: these lowlands have the largest dairy farms and the most complete system of co-operation

[*Courtesy of the Norwegian Embassy.*

FIG. 23.—Norway: a stave church. These churches are many centuries old. They are built entirely of wood, in a style peculiar to Norway.

in Norway. Forests cover large areas, especially on the mountain slopes, and the farmers supplement their incomes by selling surplus timber or working part-time in lumber camps or other branches of the timber industry. Some of them, too, engage in fur-farming. Sheep are reared in the less fertile parts or on hills.

The greatest development of hydro-electric power is in the Oslo depression. To the east, there are major stations on the lower river Glomma. To the west, around Rjukan in Telemark, five great plants have been built deep inside the mountains. Water is brought from remote lakes through miles of tunnels blasted through the rock to turbines in subterranean chambers, safe even from hydrogen bombs. The timber, electro-chemical, and electro-metallurgical industries of the lowlands have all grown enormously because of this readily available power.

The chief concentration of the sawn timber, pulp and paper industries is in Drammen (31,000), Skien (15,500), Fredrikstad (13,700), Sarpsborg (13,300) and Larvik, which lie around Oslo Fjord, in Gjøvik and Brumunddal on Lake Mjösa, and in Hönefoss, a few miles north-west of Oslo. The headquarters of the electro-chemical industry are at Notodden, where it had its birth, and there are other works at Skien and Larvik. The chief centres of the electro-metallurgical industry are Notodden, Porsgrunn and Oslo. Electrolytic copper and nickel are produced at Kristiansand, and aluminiumware at Holmestrand.

Oslo (477,121), the capital and easily the largest city, lies at the head of Oslo Fjord, at a point where several rivers converge, 62 miles from the open sea. It is a sprawling city, coming fifth in the world in area. Its nodal position in the south-eastern lowlands has made it their natural outlet, and industry has crowded to it. The city shares in almost every branch of Norway's industries and manufactures, and in its environs live a quarter of the country's industrial workers. The port handles about half the country's imports. Its proportion of exports is smaller (one-seventh) for the products of the timber, fishing, and electricity-based industries of the west coast are shipped directly from the ports there. Oslo is increasing in size, largely because of the disconcerting drift of the rural population to the more attractive social and working conditions in the capital. In this respect it resembles Helsinki and Copenhagen.

STUDY QUESTIONS

1. Attempt a comparative study of the economic development of Norway and Finland. (J.M.B.)

2. Describe the factors which have favoured the development of hydro-electric power in Norway. (J.M.B.)

3. The percentage of the total area of Norway and Sweden under cultivation is respectively 3·5 and 9. Comment on these figures in relation to geographical conditions in each country. (J.M.B.)

4. Describe the physical landscape of Norway. Show the extent to which it has influenced agricultural development. (O. & C.)

5. Describe the distribution of population and settlements in the Scandinavian peninsula and analyse the chief factors upon which this distribution depends. (O. & C.)

6. What are the chief characteristics of the climate of Norway and Sweden? Explain their influence on the agriculture practised in these countries. (O. & C.)

7. "Mining and forestry are the mainstays of Norway and Sweden." How far do you agree with this statement? (O. & C.)

8. Illustrate how the geographical position, climate and relief each contribute to divergences between the internal economies of Norway, Sweden and Finland. (J.M.B.)

Chapter X

DENMARK; ICELAND

DENMARK

DENMARK consists of the Jutland peninsula, the large islands of Zealand (Sjaelland), Fünen (Fyn), Lolland, Falster and Bornholm, and about 500 smaller islands, 100 of which are inhabited. In total, the area is twice that of Wales. Fünen is separated from Jutland by the Little Belt, and from Zealand by the Great Belt. The passage between Zealand and Sweden, the Sound, is the deepest channel from the North Sea to the Baltic.

PHYSICAL ASPECTS

STRUCTURAL DIVISIONS

With the exception of the island of Bornholm, which is an outlier of the Baltic Shield and composed mainly of granite, Denmark is a rolling plain of Quaternary morainic remains and post-glacial outwash super-imposed on a Tertiary chalk platform. A line drawn from north to south through the middle of Jutland divides the country into two contrasting halves (*see* Fig. 24). The line marks roughly the position of the terminal moraines of the last ice advances, unsorted masses of debris worn into low, rounded hills rarely above 300 ft high.

1. *Western Jutland*

Western Jutland was not covered by the later glaciations of the Ice Age. The moraines left by earlier ice sheets were worn down and in part covered by sand and gravel outwash. The surface is a broad plain, broken by slight hills, and resembles the Geest in Holland and the Campine in Belgium. Like them, too, this podsolised, naturally unproductive land is being re-claimed by deep ploughing, draining and the addition of vast quantities of marl.

Near the coast, the plain is invaded by sand dunes, which form a ram-part six miles wide in places. The North Sea coast is marked by tongues of this line of dunes forming lagoons, *e.g.* Ringköbing, and preventing the development of harbours. Esbjerg, the only port of any size on Denmark's west coast, has an artificial harbour.

Fig. 24.—Denmark: general features. The underlying chalk outcrops only here and there along the coasts, for the topography of the country is almost entirely the result of superficial deposits.

2. *East Jutland and islands*

The eastern half of Jutland and all the neighbouring islands have more varied relief than the west, with younger morainic hills and a cover of clays containing lime, yielding fertile soils. Here are some good examples of how a morainic landscape may develop. Advance and retreat of the glaciers in their final stages have resulted in a large number of rounded hills, none very high. The highest is Ejer Bavnehöj, only 567 ft above sea level. Between the hills are clay-covered depressions, often with lakes, and there are drumlins and eskers, the latter mainly in Funen and Zealand. Eastern Jutland is extensively cut by "dry valleys," carved by streams blocked by ice in the closing stages of glaciation. The "fiords" (*förden*) along the east coast are probably the drowned valleys of sub-glacial streams.

The northernmost part of Jutland, Vendyssel-Thy, is separated from the rest by narrow, shallow waters, known as Lim Fjord. This is really one of the morainic lakes mentioned above, and has no connection except in name with the fiords of Norway.

The chalk platform which underlies the surface cover of the whole of Denmark can be seen in low cliffs in south Zealand and the nearby island of Mön.

CLIMATE, NATURAL VEGETATION AND SOILS

A small, low-lying, maritime country like Denmark has little regional differences in climate and is reasonably equable for its latitude. Temperatures range from 32° F (0° C) in February to 61° F (16° C) in July—that is, it is colder in winter than eastern England. It is more open at that season to the cold winds from the North European Plain; and the Baltic, which freezes, has a reduced tempering effect. The annual precipitation averages 25·4 in. with more near the west coast than the east. There is a slight summer maximum, the result of thunderstorms which are common in August.

The soils of Denmark are post-glacial and bear little resemblance to the parent chalk which underlies them. The best soils are in the east of the mainland and on the islands, where it is clay loam. West of the morainic belt are sandy soils, leached by rain and deficient in lime.

The natural vegetation cover in the eastern half of the country was deciduous forest, with oak and ash predominating. This was cleared for agriculture; today beech trees are the chief species in the small areas of woodland that remain. Near some of the lakes in Jutland are peat bogs which are dug for fuel and the land reclaimed. The sandy soils of the west were covered with heath, but most of it has been reclaimed for agriculture or forestry, trees being planted in shelter-belts to prevent soil erosion. The dunes near the coast, which tended to spread inland, have been fixed by planting marram grass. The work of reclamation continues, not only in the heathland, but in the shallow fiords and along the coasts, using dams and drainage channels. Over 95% of the total area of the country is now in productive use. It must be noted, however, that the agricultural area has diminished in the past 25 years, the amount gained by reclamation being inadequate to offset the diversion of farmland to such uses as building sites, roads, military establishments, etc.

HUMAN GEOGRAPHY

HISTORY AND PEOPLE

Archaeologists have established the existence of Neolithic man in Denmark round Lim Fjord, and prehistoric implements found there indicate that some agriculture was practised about 3000 B.C. Knowledge of bronze came about 1500 B.C., and of iron about 400 B.C. The present Aarhus, Viborg, Odense and Ringsted are built on the sites of prehistoric settlements.

A Danish people with a history of its own seems to emerge about A.D. 800, and Christianity was introduced by the monk Ansgar in 826. Even then the Danes were farmers; a considerable growth in population appears to have forced many of them overseas. In the ninth and tenth centuries, along with Norwegians and Swedes, they ravaged and plundered large parts of Europe; many Danish warriors settled in eastern England and Normandy. King Sven (Swein, *d.* 1014) succeeded in conquering England, and bequeathed a great North Sea empire to his son Knud (Canute). King Knud the Great added southern Norway to his possessions, but when he died in 1035 his empire fell to pieces.

Denmark prospered as a trading nation because of its position at the entrance to the Baltic. For 400 years its kings dreamed of a Baltic Sea empire. Norway was joined to Denmark in 1380, and nine years later Sweden was forced to ally itself to the Danish Kalmar Union. It broke away from this alliance in 1523, and for a hundred years there followed a bitter struggle between Denmark and Sweden for mastery in the Baltic, with Sweden the more successful. On its defeat in 1658 at the hands of the Swedish king Karl X (Charles X), Denmark ceased to be a great power.

In the Great Northern War (1700–20), Denmark was allied with Russia, Poland and Prussia against Sweden, and as a result of the victory of the alliance was given the duchy of Slesvig (Schleswig) in the south of Jutland. The Industrial Revolution from 1750 onwards made Britain a wheat-importing country, and Denmark was one of the suppliers. Economic expansion led Denmark to adopt a policy of neutrality in the second half of the eighteenth century, and its shipping carried considerable cargoes to the Mediterranean, where only neutral vessels could proceed. In particular, Copenhagen flourished, marketing goods from the Baltic, China and the East and West Indies.

In the Napoleonic wars, Britain forced Denmark to abandon the convoying of merchant ships to French-controlled ports by attacking the Danish fleet at Copenhagen in 1801; and in 1807 forestalled Napoleon's demand that Denmark should enter the war on his side by bombarding Copenhagen. Denmark, however, joined France and as a consequence, by the Peace of Kiel in 1814, had to cede Norway to the Swedish king. For thirty years Denmark suffered depressed conditions, and Copenhagen stagnated. Hamburg became the chief northern port. The growth to prosperity began again with the peaceful change in 1848 from an absolute to a constitutional monarchy, based on general franchise.

The German-speaking people of southern Slesvig resented being included in the new constitution. In 1848–50, and again in 1864, Prussia attacked Denmark on their behalf. In the second war, the whole of Slesvig and Holstein became part of Prussia. Denmark remained neutral in the First World War. In 1918, Iceland became a sovereign kingdom in personal union with Denmark. Two years later, northern Slesvig, mainly Danish-speaking, voted by plebiscite to return to Denmark, but southern Slesvig decided to remain German. In the Second World War Denmark was occupied by the Germans in 1940 and liberated by the Allies in 1945. In the same year the personal union between Denmark and Iceland was dissolved. In 1949, Denmark joined the North Atlantic Treaty Organisation (NATO), and it is also a member of the European Free Trade Association (EFTA) in conjunction with the United Kingdom, Norway, Sweden, Austria, Switzerland and Portugal.

POPULATION

The population of Denmark is over 4,600,000, almost half in towns. The density averages 279 persons per square mile, the highest among the northern countries. The greatest density is in the islands of Zealand and Fünen. Western and northern Jutland have the least densities because the soils are poor and there are fewer towns. There is considerable emigration, mainly to Norway and Sweden.

THE ECONOMY

AGRICULTURE AND THE CO-OPERATIVE MOVEMENT

The mineral wealth of Denmark is negligible. There is no coal, no mineral ores, no oil and no rivers to provide power. Yet despite these handicaps it has the biggest external trade per head of population in the world, because of the use it has made of its soil.

Agriculture is the largest industry, occupying over a quarter of the people. Half the farms, occupying about 70% of the agricultural area, range from 25 to 150 acres. Those with less than 25 acres are given extra land from the largest farms, to ensure they are capable of supporting a family. The average farm grows a small amount of wheat and rye for bread. But the great emphasis is on grass, barley, oats, potatoes and turnips for fodder, for the main products are butter, cheese, eggs and meat products, depending on large numbers of cattle (3,593,000 in 1963, half of them dairy cows), pigs (7,095,000) and poultry. Sheep-rearing has declined in recent years (47,000 in 1963). Danish agriculture used to be heavily dependent on imported feeding stuffs, like coarse grain and oil cake. Large scale soil improvements, such as draining and marling, the use of improved seeds, the control of plant diseases, the application of insecticides, weed killers and artificial fertilisers, have so increased the yield that only half the former imports are required for a much increased output of dairy products. Only in fertilisers, mainly from Norway, are there more imports than previously.

The story of Denmark's pre-eminence in the export of "breakfast table products" begins about 1870. At that time Danish agriculture was mainly grain-producing but, like most countries in western Europe, it could not compete with the vast new wheatlands of Canada and the United States, which could sell grain at lower prices. Some countries protected themselves by tariffs on imported grain, but Denmark, as a country exporting wheat, could not do this. Instead, she reorganised her whole production so as to concentrate on livestock foods, including potatoes and root crops. Special to her new development was the introduction of the agricultural co-operative movement.

The first co-operative enterprise was established in 1882 at Hjedding, in Jutland, with the object of improving the quality of the butter its members produced. It was so successful that the movement spread, and gradually its activities increased. The first co-operative bacon factory was founded at Horsens, also in Jutland, in 1887, followed by co-operatives dealing with eggs, poultry, cattle buying and selling, seed supplies, and even engineering and cement works. Today, there are about 1250 co-operative dairies, dealing with 90% of the country's milk and producing annually about 166,000 tons of butter and 85,000 tons of cheese. Most of it is exported, mainly to the United Kingdom and West Germany. The co-operative bacon factories number more than 60 and, as part of their services, support research stations to increase the quality of bacon pigs for their members.

The co-operatives are financed in the first place by the farmers, according to the size of their farms; but in the running of the enterprise no member has more than one vote, whatever the size of his subscription. The profits are distributed in proportion to the amount of milk, pigs, eggs, etc., delivered, but a farm which belongs to a co-operative must guarantee to send all its produce to it, except what is required for its own use; subject always to quality tests, which are strict. The advantages to the small farmer are great. He gets the same prices as the large farmer; he shares in the economies secured by bulk purchases of feeding stuffs, oil cake and fertilisers; he can call freely on advice and assistance; and he can benefit by the use of technical equipment and the loan of machinery he could not afford to buy himself.

By keeping a close eye on quality, the co-operatives have made Denmark the world's most prosperous farming community, largely because every phase of production is under the personal control of small proprietors. Economic co-operation on a voluntary and democratic basis has been so successful in Denmark that it has been copied in many countries throughout the world; but in none is it so all-pervading as in the country of its origin.

REGIONAL ECONOMY

A study of Denmark's economy may be conveniently based on the physical divisions outlined above.

1. *Western Jutland*

This is the poorest part of Denmark, and has the least population. The reclaimed lands are mainly given over to cultivated grasses; cattle rearing, favoured by the milder winters, is the dominant occupation. The centres of population are very small towns which have grown as road and railway junctions and have butter factories. The largest are Viborg (22,800) and Herning (22,000). On the west coast is Esbjerg (55,171), the most valuable North Sea port. Its harbour was built in 1874 to provide an exit for the dairy produce sent to the United Kingdom, but an equally important result was to help the country's fishing industry. Denmark has important plaice and eel fishing grounds in the shallow waters along the west coast. Esbjerg, in the shelter of the island of Fanö, is today the chief fishing port in western Jutland.

2. *Eastern Jutland and the islands*

In eastern Jutland the more fertile soils allow a greater proportion of arable farming, the chief crops being wheat and potatoes; there is also more woodland. Most of the land, however, is used for grazing, and market towns and dairies and bacon factories become more frequent. The biggest town is Aarhus (119,568), Denmark's second largest urban unit, a port with an improved harbour and the focus of a fertile farming area. It has a light engineering industry. In the north is Aalborg (85,800), at a crossing point of Lim Fjord, the second commercial port of Denmark although far behind Copenhagen. Here the underlying chalk is quarried for a cement manufacture. Horsens (37,261), Kolding (33,200), Randers (42,438) and Vejle (30,700) are combined market towns and ports, situated at the heads of förden. Fredericia (27,900), a similar town, was a rail-ferry port until 1935, when a bridge was built to connect Jutland with Fünen.

The area north of Lim Fjord is less well developed than the rest of eastern Jutland. The soils are poorer, and there are more sandy or marshy stretches; but reclamation is fast improving the land, and crops of oats, barley and rye are grown for fodder. Cattle rearing is the main occupation. At the northernmost tip is The Skaw (Skagen), the centre for

[*Courtesy of British European Airways.*]

FIG. 25.—Denmark: Copenhagen, the city centre. With its suburbs, Copenhagen contains more than a quarter of Denmark's population.

Denmark's Skagerrak fisheries, which are chiefly concerned with plaice, herring and cod.

The islands lying off the east coast of Jutland have the richest soils and the densest population in Denmark. Here are the main wheat and sugar beet lands; the proximity of Copenhagen has encouraged a large market-gardening industry. The islands of Lolland and Falster are almost entirely agricultural, and the largest proportion of dairying and bacon manufacture is on the islands of Fünen and Zealand. Odense (111,145) is the major town of Fünen, and is a market connected to the Great Belt by a canal.

The largest island, Zealand, is dominated by Copenhagen (923,974;

with suburbs 1,300,000), the capital and by far the biggest city. Copenhagen (Köbenhavn), on a good harbour adjacent to a deep channel in the Kattegat, controls the passage to the Baltic (Fig. 25). It has been one of the most important ports in northern Europe since the early Middle Ages. The position of a capital on the borders of a country is unusual, but in the case of Copenhagen its situation may be explained partly by the fact that for centuries before 1814 Norway was part of the Danish kingdom, and for a period south Sweden was included also; hence Copenhagen was central in the combined territories. The modern supremacy of Copenhagen as a port is due to the ease with which its harbour and docks have been extended, and to the creation of a "free port" area which has encouraged a large entrepôt trade and the growth of manufactures. Copenhagen can be said to be the only really significant industrial centre in the country, with about a quarter of the total population of Denmark. It has shipbuilding, engineering, chemical, textile, porcelain and food industries. Among the last is the canning of milk, meat and fish for export. Almost all the raw materials have to be imported.

Away to the east is the island of Bornholm, a horst of pre-Cambrian granites, with younger sedimentaries in the south-west and south. There are quarries for granite, and kaolin is produced and sent to Copenhagen for the porcelain and pottery industry. There is a poor agriculture in the south, and the tiny ports are engaged in herring fishing in the Baltic.

ASSOCIATED TERRITORIES

THE FAEROE ISLANDS

The Faeroes are a group of eighteen islands in the North Atlantic, about halfway between the northern tip of Scotland and Iceland (Fig. 26). The archipelago is an upstanding portion of the submarine Wyville–Thomson ridge which runs from Scotland to Iceland, and rises abruptly to a much-dissected plateau about 1000 ft in elevation, with several peaks above this up to 2000 ft. The islands are all that is left of a vast plateau stretching at least from Scotland to Greenland, built by the outpouring of lavas in Tertiary times, and later fractured and fragmented. The present landscape is the result of the rapid erosion of the basalts and volcanic tuffs along fault lines, through glacial, marine and sub-aerial action. The glaciers were probably local, coeval with but separate from the ice sheets of Norway. The coasts are cliff-lined, except for a few small landing places where settlements have grown and farming may be possible, though difficult.

The Faeroes lie near the northern edge of the North Atlantic Drift, that is, near the "Arctic Front," where cold Arctic air is in contact with the

warm, moist air of the Atlantic. Temperatures at sea level range from
37·8° F (3·2° C) in January to 51·6° F (10·8° C) in July, a very equable
annual range of only 13·8° F (7·6° C). The annual precipitation amounts to
about 60 in., evenly distributed throughout the year, with large snowfalls
in winter. The snow, however, melts quickly, except on the mountain
peaks. Lying all the time so near the meeting place of warm and cold air,
the Faeroes are subject to rapid changes of weather, with a great tendency

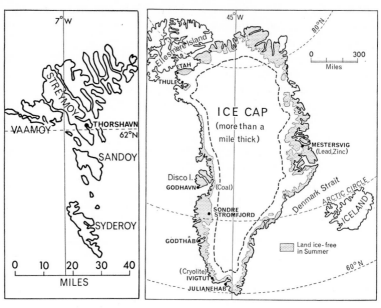

FIG. 26.—The Faeroes   FIG. 27.—Greenland
Both territories form part of the Danish kingdom, and each sends two members
to the *Folketing* (Parliament) in Copenhagen.

to fog, especially in summer. On an average, there is fog on 40 days in the
months from May to September. In winter, fogs are caused—though to a
much less extent—by air from the warmer sea (mean temperature in
January, 42·2° F (5·6° C)) passing over the cold land.

Farms are small and produce is scanty. The fields are tiny and narrow,
and often the soil has been gathered from near rivers and carried to the
fields in buckets and barrows. The chief crops are hay and potatoes,
mainly for winter feed for the few cattle. Sheep are more important, and
wool is exported to Denmark; yet its total, less than 50 tons yearly, is not
impressive. The islands depend mainly on fishing, and 36% of the population of 33,000 get their living from it. The principal catch is cod, which

in 1955 accounted for 85,000 tons out of a total for all fish of 105,000 tons. The capital of the Faeroes is Thorshavn on Streymoy, the largest island.

Since 1948, the Faeroes have constituted a self-governing part of the Danish kingdom, with their own parliament, the Lagting. They send two members to the Danish parliament. By agreement Denmark assists in marketing Faroese fishery products and gives other financial help.

GREENLAND

Though structurally and ethnographically Greenland is a part of North America and not of Europe, it is included here because it is administered by Denmark. Its treatment will be limited to a consideration of Danish enterprise there.

Greenland (Fig. 27) is the world's largest island, 840,000 square miles, of which 708,100 square miles are ice cap. The coastal tracts, 114,600 square miles in area, are widest in the south-west, and this is where most of the 26,192 (1954 census) inhabitants live. Many of them are Eskimo, but there has been a large admixture of European blood, especially from Denmark. The Eskimo of pure blood, still occupied in his traditional hunting and fishing, is now to be found mainly in the hinterland of Julianehab, in the south, or in the far north at Thule and Etah. The largest settlement is Godthåb, with 1000 inhabitants.

Many of the inhabitants are engaged in the fishing industry, which includes sealing and whaling. Almost all its products go to Denmark. An increasing number of people are being employed in the mining industry, which is developing steadily with Danish advice, supervision and finance, and often Danish labour. The chief mineral export is cryolite, a sodium-aluminium fluoride used in the production of aluminium and in enamelling, mined at Ivigtut. Lead and zinc occur at Mestersvig, and coal, enough for Greenland's needs, on the west coast near Disco Island.

Denmark's claim to Greenland was conceded internationally in 1933. It has since given Greenland self-government and two seats in the Danish parliament. It maintains a meteorological service of great value to North Atlantic and trans-Polar flying, and an airfield at Sondre Stromfjord.

ICELAND

Iceland is a large island in the North Atlantic, 63° 24'–66° 32' N. and 13° 30'–24° 32' W. Since 17th June 1944, after a plebiscite, Iceland has been a republic. Before then it was in union with Denmark, under the same king.

PHYSICAL ASPECTS

STRUCTURE AND RELIEF

Four-fifths of Iceland is a plateau 2250–2600 ft in height, with higher mountain ranges or single mountains rising from it. The highest range runs across the middle from west to east, the loftiest peak being Öraefa-jökull (6890 ft), at the eastern end. A large area of the highlands above 5000 ft is covered by glaciers. The most extensive is Vatnajökull (3140 square miles) in the south-east. North-west of Vatnajökull is Hofsjökull

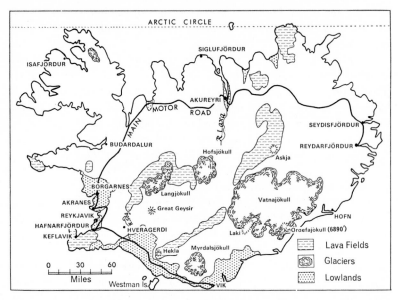

FIG. 28.—Iceland: general features. Most of Iceland has little or no economic value.

(375 square miles) and, farther west, Langjökull (390 square miles). There are many smaller ice sheets, the total covering roughly one-eighth of the country. Continuous lowland areas are to be found only in a few places along the coast, mostly in the south-west; elsewhere, the lowlands are deltaic flats at the heads of fiords. The south-western plains have been caused by faulting and subsidence. The coasts are much indented, except in the south, where they are sandy, with few harbour sites. In the numerous fiords and off the coasts are a multitude of islands, most of them too small for habitation. The chief are the Westman islands to the south, with about 4000 inhabitants (*see* Fig. 28).

Iceland is composed in the main of basalt layers of Tertiary age, poured out by volcanoes in the Eocene period, and again in the Pliocene. Over the basalt are layers of dolerite, baked glacial clays and heaps of tuff, which accumulated during the time of the Ice Age in northern Europe. On top of all are younger lavas, loose stones, basaltic clays and alluvium, the last two in valleys and at fiord heads. Iceland is a part of the vast plateau built by volcanic action in Tertiary times, and was affected by earth movements which fractured the plateau and caused large portions to subside. Parts of the original island remained elevated as horsts, other areas subsided to form the lowlands and islands. Faulting resulted in lines of weakness, which were made use of by later volcanic action. Basalt is not a very resistant rock, and the work of glaciers, wind, rain, rivers and sea has produced a peneplaned surface broken by valleys with cliff-like sides and containing many screes. Recent volcanic eruptions have spread lavas which have not had much time to weather, except into broken rocky platforms; but volcanic ash has been distributed by the wind in such amounts as sometimes to fill valleys and cover pastures to a depth of several inches. The interior of Iceland is country inimical to man, and is entirely devoid of human settlement.

VULCANICITY IN ICELAND

In few places on the earth are there so many volcanoes, active, dormant and extinct, in an area as small as Iceland. There are two well-marked series of fissures along which are many active volcanoes. Since Iceland was settled in the ninth century, twenty of them have erupted, some more than once. In total there have been more than a hundred eruptions. The best-known volcano is Hekla (see Fig. 29), which has erupted on 23 reported occasions; the last eruption, in 1947–48, went on for a year, covering the nearby countryside with volcanic ash and pumice. A great cleft in Myrdalsjökull, called Katla, in the south, has erupted on several occasions, the latest in 1918. The last volcano to erupt was Askja, in north-east Iceland, in the autumn of 1961.

Some of the eruptions have caused great damage, both on account of the lava flow and of the vast quantities of ash deposited. The greatest eruption was in 1783 from the Laki, a series of nearly one hundred craters along a fissure south-west of Vatnajökull. It resulted in a lava field over 220 square miles in extent, the largest flow from a single eruption in historical times. Flourishing districts were laid waste: the ash fall affected the whole of the island, destroying crops and pastures either by burying them or by making them poisonous. More than half the cows, three-quarters of the horses and over four-fifths of the sheep perished. 9500 of the people, a fifth of the total, died of starvation.

Some of the volcanic craters are covered by thick glacier, and when

FIG. 29.—Iceland: Mount Hekla. An active volcano (4875 ft) which has erupted
twenty times since Iceland was discovered in the ninth century. The last
eruption (shown here) began in March 1947 and continued without interruption for a year, covering the surrounding district with ashes and pumice.

there is an eruption in these places, great volumes of muddy waters from
the rapid ice melt pour down the mountain sides. These glacier-bursts (as
they are called) help to build up the lowland plains, but they may cause
devastation in settled districts and have been known to sweep farmhouses,
with their inhabitants and livestock, into the sea. Floods occurred after
the beginning of the eruption of Hekla in 1947.

A feature of Iceland's vulcanicity is the large number of thermal springs,
whose waters may be at boiling point at the surface. Some of them are
continuous, others are *geysers* and spout at definite intervals, hurling
water and steam high into the air. The best known is the Great Geysir,
which has given its name to all such springs. In the middle of Iceland are
steam vents, with no liquid water. Altogether there are about 1500 thermal springs, mainly in the west. Where they are near enough to inhabited districts, their hot waters are being used to heat houses. Most of
the buildings in Reykjavik have heating systems based on neighbouring
hot springs, and many greenhouses have been built on sites where hot
water is available. New villages have grown near hot water; Hveragerdi,
29 miles east of Reykjavik, is one of them.

Earthquakes, often a concomitant of volcanic activity, are common, but only on rare occasions have they caused much damage. In 1896, however, an earthquake destroyed many farmhouses in the plains along the south coast.

CLIMATE

Notwithstanding its name and the fact that the island lies just outside the Arctic Circle, Iceland has a warmer climate than might be expected. This is because the North Atlantic Drift flows along the western and southern coasts, bringing relatively warm waters. A cold Arctic current affects the eastern part of the north coast and a portion of the east coast, making temperatures there lower by up to 9° F (5° C) in winter, and occasionally bringing drift ice to the shores. The ocean currents make the south-west the best part of the country. The average temperatures in Reykjavik range from 30° F (−1° C) in January to 52° F (11° C) in July. The annual rainfall varies with position and height. In Reykjavik it amounts to 34 in. with a winter maximum, but in the north, Akureyri has only 18 in. In the mountains, precipitation is about 80 in.

HUMAN GEOGRAPHY

HISTORY AND PEOPLE

According to tradition, Iceland was discovered by monks from Ireland early in the ninth century, but they did not stay there. The first settlers are reputed to be Ingolfur Arnarson, a Norseman, and his family and dependants, in 870. Iceland was, therefore, the last country in Europe to be inhabited. By 930 the country was fully settled, largely by Norwegians who like Arnarson were fleeing from political persecution and possible execution. In 982, Greenland was discovered from Iceland by Eric the Red; in 1000, America was reached by Leifur Eiriksson. In 1262, Iceland came under the Norwegian crown, but in 1380 its rule was taken over by Denmark. For centuries Iceland was linked politically and commercially with Denmark, but because it was regarded merely as an object of exploitation and all overseas commerce had to be carried on via Denmark, its prosperity declined more and more as time passed. Its population was ravaged by the Black Death in 1402; famine and starvation followed the volcanic eruptions of 1783–90; and the interruption of sea communication in the Napoleonic Wars in 1807–14 led to further loss of life through starvation. The wave of libertarian feeling which passed over western Europe in the early nineteenth century had its effect on Iceland: in 1854 the island received complete freedom in its foreign trade and twenty years later was given a constitution and control of its own internal finances. Home rule came in 1904 and independence in 1918, although Iceland remained united with Denmark under the Danish crown. In 1940, during the Second World War, Iceland was occupied by British forces and the following year U.S. troops took over its defence. In 1944 the people of Iceland decided to sever their political ties with Denmark and the country became a republic. In 1949 it joined NATO.

POPULATION; ICELAND'S FUTURE

The people of Iceland are descended in the main from Norwegians, whom they resemble in features and build, but have darker hair. The population, which had fallen to 47,000 by 1800, now numbers about 185,000, of whom 78% live in towns or villages. Because so much of the island is uninhabitable, the average density is only 4 persons per square mile.

The young republic of Iceland has arisen out of a difficult past. If its future is to be successful, it must find some way of improving industrial output by an extended use of its water-power. The fishing industry, on which its economic prosperity at present depends, suffers wide fluctuations, especially in the herring catch. In 1952, for instance, the total herring catch amounted to only 32,001 tons, as compared with 182,887 tons in 1959. These big variations make Iceland's financial system unstable, for they interfere with the smooth inflow of necessary foodstuffs, manufactured goods and raw materials to a country woefully lacking in other natural resources. However, the country lies in an important strategic position, and since 1951 the United States has maintained a military air base at Keflavik. Iceland is a member of NATO but, without any defensive forces of its own, must depend on foreign aid and use its location as a bargaining point.

THE ECONOMY

FARMING AND FISHING

With the exception of the rich fishing grounds which surround Iceland, and the abundant water-power from its numerous rivers, the country is poor in natural resources. Large stretches of the interior are rough, lava deserts and completely uninhabitable. Of the habitable land only a small proportion is fit for cultivation. Arable land amounts only to 1% of the country's total area. The average size of a farm is 1250 acres, but only a tiny piece of it is cultivated; the rest is used for grazing sheep (840,000 in 1962), cattle (about 50,000) and horses (30,000). Agriculture is concerned mainly with the cultivation of grass for fodder. Practically no cereals are grown because of unfavourable climatic conditions, but potatoes and turnips are found on every farm. Market-gardening is carried on in greenhouses in the hot-spring areas. Iceland is self-sufficient in meat, milk, butter and eggs; it exports wool, hides and mutton.

Almost every settlement in Iceland is on the coast, and all are engaged in the fishing industry, which accounts for about 95% of exports. The chief catch is cod and herring. The cod is carried in ice to British and German ports, or is exported dried, salted or as frozen fillets. Herring are salted in barrels for export, or processed for oil and fish meal. Fishing and fish processing, the chief industries, occupy 17% of the population. To safeguard the fishermen's interests, Iceland in 1958 extended its fishing limits from 4 to 12 miles from its coasts.

HYDRO-ELECTRICITY AND INDUSTRY

Iceland, in proportion to its size has a potential in hydro-electric power as great as any country in Europe. So far, it has been utilised only to a small extent. Stations on the rivers Ellidaar and Sog, in the south-west, supply current to Reykjavik and on the Laxa, in the north, to Akureyri. An increasing percentage of the population is employed in industries based on this power, such as textiles (at Reykjavik and Akureyri), cement (made from shell-sand at Akranes), and fertiliser (at Reykjavik). The most important industry is fishing, which uses hydro-electric power for canning and processing. The biggest processing plants are in Siglu-fjördur, in the extreme north; and canning has its headquarters in Reykjavik. Reykjavik (75,000) is the capital, chief port and industrial centre, and the only large town; it has 40% of the people of Iceland. The next towns in size are Akureyri (9000) and Hafnarfjördur (7300), a fishing port.

There is no real mining in Iceland. Iceland spar, used in optical work, occurs at Reydarfjördur in the east, and small amounts of sulphur are obtained in the north-east. Pumice is worked in a few places and used for insulating material. Peat is plentiful, and before the development of water-power was dug for fuel.

STUDY QUESTIONS

1. Describe the physical landscape of Denmark. Show the extent to which it has influenced agricultural development. (O. & C.)

2. Make a comparison of the coast of Denmark with the west coast of Norway. To what extent have these coastal features influenced the settlement and development of these countries? (O. & C.)

3. Show, with the aid of a sketch-map, how the Quaternary glaciation has influenced the geography of Denmark. (O. & C.)

4. Account for regional contrasts in the economic development of Denmark. (J.M.B.)

5. Discuss the reasons underlying the contrasts indicated by the following data:

	Percentage of total area	
	Arable	Woods and forests
Denmark	62·0	28·0
Finland	7·3	90·2 (J.M.B.)

6. "Iceland completely belies its name." Write a short commentary on this statement.

7. How far is it true to say that the economy of Iceland is based on the fishing industry?

Chapter XI

WESTERN EUROPE

WESTERN EUROPE comprises the countries of the Netherlands, Belgium, Luxembourg and France. Taking this as a separate division of the continent is more a matter of convenience, however, than of creating a distinct physical or climatic region. These countries lie along the western seaboard of Europe between latitudes 43 degrees and 53 degrees N. and so fall within the zone of westerlies at all seasons. They therefore experience a cool temperate marginal climate, and may be considered together. But this type of climate is also found in the countries north and south of the region; and within western Europe itself there are variations from it. In structure, too, "western Europe" must be regarded in many ways as merely a western extension of features found in countries to the east, not as a physical or structural region in its own right. Nevertheless, within western Europe as we have defined it there are so many resemblances in agricultural and industrial development, in cultures, and in economic and political ambitions, as to justify treating it as a separate division. It was this recognition of common economic and political interests that brought about the association of the Netherlands, Belgium and Luxembourg under the name of Benelux, and later helped to give birth to the European Economic Community (the "Common Market"), of which they are all members.

STRUCTURE AND RELIEF

Western Europe differs widely from northern Europe in that its relief is extremely varied, ranging rapidly from high mountains and plateaus to plains and wide river valleys, and with some of its lowlands actually below sea level. Structurally, most of the region shows the effects of the Carbo-Permian (Hercynian) mountain-building movements and of their dislocation and rejuvenation by the Alpine orogenesis in Tertiary times. At the end of the Primary period a great mountain system stretched its western folds across the middle of the region. Prolonged denudation reduced it to a peneplain, which later subsided and was submerged by invading waters. Silts from the eroded land mass were deposited on the floor of the sea, and covered by limestones and chalk. During the Tertiary period, tectonic movements in the south built up the folds of the Pyrenees and Alps. The same forces which were pressing the newly rising mountains against the resistant stumps of the Hercynian system broke the remains of the older mountains into blocks and lifted some above sea level. The blocks nearer to the Alpine system were raised higher than those farther away, so that the Central Massif of France and the Vosges are more elevated than the Armorican massif or the Ardennes. Other blocks either were not lifted so high or were actually depressed; these constitute the lowlands or rift valleys between and around the massifs or horsts.

The rejuvenated Hercynian horsts were denuded of their limestone cover, and some were penetrated by volcanoes, as in the Central Massif. All these are now extinct, and remain as plugs or cones, with basaltic soils around them. The denuded Hercynian fragments are not very high, and their resistant rocks have weathered into thin, poor soils. The lowlands around them have a foundation of limestone, on much of which Tertiary sedimentaries have been preserved.

The sea bed to the north of the Hercynian system was uplifted and thrown into slight folds. This is now the southern part of the western end of the Great European Plain, but is better designated a low limestone plateau. The lower parts are the plains of north France and Belgium; the folds have worn into the scarps which encircle the Paris basin or flank the western Central Massif. Across the northern plateau flowed many headstreams of a great river which ran to the north, incorporating the present Rhine, with the Thames as a tributary. This river may be imagined as having a valley along the present North Sea and a mouth somewhere between Norway and Scotland.

The enormous mass of ice accumulated in northern Europe during the Ice Age caused an isostatic subsidence of north-west Europe; when the ice melted and raised the level of the sea, much of the subsided land was submerged. In this way the British Isles were cut off from the mainland; the North Sea was deepened; the tributaries of the great north-flowing river became independent streams flowing into the North Sea and English Channel; and a delta began to form at the mouths of the Rhine, Meuse and Scheldt. This now constitutes a large proportion of the present Netherlands and a small piece of Belgium. With the disappearance of the ice, the land of north-west Europe began to rise again, and this movement is still going on. One of the effects of the isostatic uplift was to change the drainage to its present shape. Another result of the Ice Age was the cover of sands, gravels and worn-down moraines to be found in the north of the Netherlands. These mark the furthest advance in western Europe of the Quaternary glaciers.

The ranges of the Pyrenees and Alps are described in Chapters I, XIV, XV and XX. Here it is sufficient to note that they form an almost continuous barrier along the south and south-eastern margins of western Europe, acting to a large degree as a physical boundary, but more note-worthy as political, ethnic and cultural frontiers. Along their flanks there are low plateaus of fluvio-glacial debris brought down from the slopes during and since the Ice Age; and they are the only parts of western Europe high enough to have snow resting permanently throughout the year.

[Courtesy of the Luxembourg Embassy.

Fig. 30.—Luxembourg: Esch-sur-Sûre. The town is situated within a loop of the river Sûre, which has formed entrenched
meanders in the Ardennes. The forests are of oak, beech and
birch; in the clearings, fields of cereals may be seen. Note
the remains of castles, which dominate the site of the town,
and the steeply pitched roofs—a sign of heavy snowfall.

The geological history of western Europe has produced a landscape that offers constant variety when the region is crossed in almost any direction. In a journey from the north of the Netherlands to the eastern end of the Pyrenees, for example, we should pass first over plains, some below sea level and dyked against inundation. These are followed by the austere

forest-clad scenery of the Belgian Ardennes and by the rolling plains and
scarps of the eastern Paris basin, a "champagne" landscape of wide fields
with no hedges. Southwards, we climb over limestone scarps and cross
the Central Massif, with its *puys* and craters, relics of an ancient vulcanicity, and looking east we may see in the distance the towering peaks of the
French Alps. Continuing our journey, we traverse the granitic south of
the Central Massif, ascending its uptilted south-eastern edge to cross the
Cevennes. A sudden descent to low limestone foothills is followed by a
glimpse of the Mediterranean Sea across a narrow coastal plain; and a short
ʲourney along the lagoon-girt coast brings us to the foot of the Pyrenees,
which rise before us like a wall.

    The variety of landscape found in this journey can be matched on a tour
from the shores of the Bay of Biscay to Lake Geneva, or from Strasbourg
to Bordeaux. A similar lack of homogeneity characterises the soils and
the agricultural development, for although the climate is designated a
warm temperate maritime type, there are numerous variations. From
north to south, and more particularly from west to east, there are the
contrasts of dyked farmlands, wheatfields, apple orchards, sheep pastures,
river meadows, vineyards, olive groves, thick forests, mountain pastures
and tiny farms dependent on subsistence agriculture. Western Europe is
a mosaic of physical features, presenting a highly diversified picture; yet
in the way that man has managed to achieve control over this many-sided
environment we can detect a surprising unity, as will be seen in the following chapters.

CLIMATE

    Western Europe lies more open to Atlantic climatic influences than
northern or Mediterranean Europe. Moisture-laden westerlies can penetrate further inland and bring their warm air to temper both summer heat
and winter cold. Consequently, precipitation over the entire region,
except for a small area near the Mediterranean, is abundant all the year
round, with a slightly greater fall in the winter months near the western
seaboard. Temperatures, too, are reasonably uniform in the lowlands.
Nevertheless, it must be noted that France, with a greater west–east
extent, tends in the east to have continental climatic characteristics with
higher summer and lower winter temperatures, a greater summer
precipitation, and less cloud cover than in the west (*see* Chapter XIV).
These variations from the typical marginal climate are found also in the
Central Massif and French Alps, so that the climate in the east of western
Europe, having both marginal and continental characteristics, is best
regarded as "transitional." More detail is given in Chapter III and in the
treatment of individual countries.

Along the south coast of France, the influence of the warm Mediterranean Sea is felt, for its surface waters in summer may reach 75° F (24° C) and sea breezes have little cooling effect. Winter temperatures may fall to 40°–45° F (4°–7° C) or slightly lower when the cold mistral is blowing, but are usually around 50° F (10° C). The skies are predominantly blue and cloudless in summer, although in winter, when centres of low pressure develop and depressions are passing along the Mediterranean basin, moisture-laden westerlies bring rain and a humid atmosphere. The climate of the Mediterranean coastlands of western Europe, as we have defined the region, presents a contrast to that farther north in its hot, dry summers and warm, wet winters (*see also* Chapters III and XIV).

HUMAN GEOGRAPHY

Each of the following chapters contains a historical summary of one of the countries which go to make up western Europe. Here, in seeing how the region was peopled and developed economically, it is treated as a whole rather than as a number of separate political units. Politics and political history cannot be completely excluded, for they may have profound effects on economic development. In this book, however, they are introduced only in so far as they help to give a clearer geographical picture.

The history of western Europe may be said to begin when the Romans, in the second century B.C., entered southern France and advanced by the Rhône corridor and the Gate of Carcassonne to occupy the lowlands as far north as Lake Geneva and west to Toulouse (Tolosa). In the following century they extended their conquest over the whole of western Europe as far as the Rhine. Only the northern part of the Netherlands lay outside the Romans' dominion, and even there they exerted some influence. The peoples they conquered, the Aedui, Averni, Senones, Bituriges, Treveri and Nervii had in many cases entered the region in prehistoric times, mainly along the plains to the north. The culture of these tribes, founded on customs and traditions their ancestors had brought with them, bore no resemblance to the way of life the Romans introduced. In the following centuries, the marks of Roman civilisation appeared everywhere. Roads and aqueducts were constructed, towns built and in some cases fortified. Agriculture was systematised and new crops were introduced. Christianity eventually replaced pagan nature worship. The Romans, whose own civilisation in its turn had been transformed by contact with that of Greece, imposed new ideas, new knowledge and new ways of life on western Europe. The culture which emerged was to have a profound effect in later centuries on the whole of European history, especially in its concepts of law, administration and political unity.

In the fourth century, the pressure of advancing Tuetonic peoples from the northern plain began to make itself felt on the frontiers of the Roman Empire. Eventually it forced the removal, in A.D. 330, of the capital from Rome to Byzantium (Constantinople) and in 395 the division into western and eastern empires with capitals at Rome and Byzantium. This was the beginning of the break-up of the Roman Empire, and of the divergence which remains even today between the religion and culture of western and eastern Europe.

In western Europe, barbarian infiltration had already occurred in the north while the Romans were still in power. Roman troops had been recalled and colonists repatriated. Teutonic immigrants took their place, so that the northern part of the region was "barbarised." But the shadow of Roman civilisation and the Christian religion still remained, and was to take substance again after the full-scale barbarian invasions of the next two centuries.

These invasions were of two types, (i) migrations of whole peoples with a German patriarchal organisation, and (ii) small or large bands of emigrants searching for land to settle on, without tribal cohesion but led by military chieftains. To the former type belonged the first invaders, the Goths (Ostrogoths and Visigoths), Vandals, Burgundians and Lombards; to the latter, the Franks and Saxons (*see* Fig. 11). The first type conquered and occupied large territories, even into north Africa, but they never took root and in time they all disappeared. The Franks and Saxons, however, displaced the Roman organisation and established themselves in a number of territorial units, each governed by its own chieftain or "king." Ultimately, the system formed the basis of medieval feudalism. The Franks pressed on into Gaul and the Saxons and Frisians moved west to occupy the Netherlands. From 449 onwards the Saxons, Angles and Jutes invaded and occupied England.

Up to a point, the westward movement of these peoples was caused by the advance of Asiatic hordes yet farther east and their retreat before them; but the defeat in 451 of Attila, king of the Huns, at the decisive battle of Châlons by a combined army of Franks, Goths and Romans brought to an end the fear of Asiatic domination. It is noteworthy that western Europe, in common with most of the rest of the continent, was now unified in spirit by the Christian religion. Although Roman political influences were fading, the Roman Church was transforming western civilisation. To it we owe the preservation of Greek and Roman literature during the Middle Ages and at least part of the creative achievement of the Renaissance.

The southern part of Gaul was still ruled by the Goths, but by the end of the sixth century their power had been broken and the Franks under their king, Clovis, and his successors extended their territory to cover the

whole of present-day France and most of Germany, Switzerland and
Austria. The next hundred years were to see a new threat to western
Europe. After the death of Mahomet in 632 the Arabs, inspired by their
religion, overran Asia Minor, Egypt and the whole of northern Africa.
One branch, the Moors, crossed into the Iberian peninsula. They pene-
trated southern France, conquered Narbonne and marched northwards
until in 732 they were stopped and defeated at Tours by Charles Martel.
Within a few years the Moors were driven out of Gaul and Charles,
though not of royal blood, became the uncrowned ruler of the Franks.
After his death, his son Pippin was elected king, and so commenced the
Carolingian line, as it came to be called, of which Charlemagne was the
most illustrious member.

When Charlemagne died in 814, his empire stretched from the Pyrenees
to Denmark, from the Atlantic to the middle Danube, including Spain as
far as the Ebro and a large part of Italy. This vast territory was split into
three by the Treaty of Verdun (843) and most of western Europe became
the Kingdom of the West Franks, under Charles the Bald. Burgundy,
Alsace, Lorraine, eastern Belgium and the Netherlands formed part of the
long, narrow kingdom of Lotharingia, a buffer state between the West
Frankish kingdom and that of Louis the German in the east. Since that
time the lands allotted to Lotharingius have been a bone of contention
between France and Germany. The most recent of several wars were those
of 1870, 1914–18 and 1939–45.

The later history of western Europe is outlined in succeeding chapters.
What is obvious from the foregoing is that the patchwork of relief in
western Europe was filled by a heterogeneous collection of peoples, often
in groups which had their own community interests and differed from
each other in details of language and daily life, but gradually knitting together to give a unity in diversity. France is a wonderful example of the
mixing of different peoples and the merging of civilisations; although
credit must be given to the native genius of the Franks as a unifying factor,
and to the way they absorbed the Roman tradition they found in Gaul, the
country's own varied relief and natural resources contributed towards the
development of modern France.

From the thirteenth century, western Europe has been something of
a laboratory in which man has experimented with his physical environment as well as with political institutions. Six hundred years ago the
Flemings, in western Belgium, inaugurated a new type of agriculture,
from which stemmed an agrarian revolution in Britain and, later, in
France. Old systems of grazing on common land and strip-cultivation
were largely replaced by enclosures and crop rotation; animal manures
were conserved and used to greater advantage; and the foundations were

F

laid for modern scientific farming. Side by side with the revolution in agriculture came rapid developments in the use of coal and iron, and impetus was given to textile industries by the discovery of the steam engine and the invention of steam-driven machinery. This industrial revolution, which had its birth in England, spread quickly to western Europe, to France and Belgium, the countries which for a hundred years monopolised the new industries on the continental mainland. The Ruhr, for instance, did not develop industrially until after 1850, and Lorraine and Luxembourg only within the past century.

It was from Britain, France, Belgium and the Netherlands that enormous stretches of the world were opened up and colonised; and in western Europe were born the concepts of the individual sovereign state, constitutional government and modern democracy. The impact of western Europe on the rest of the world has had consequences of immeasurable importance. For three centuries prior to the war of 1914–18, western Europe to all intents and purposes ruled the world politically and economically and became rich in the process.

The present century has seen a partial fall from this position of pre-eminence. Two world wars have witnessed the emergence of the United States and the Soviet Union as great powers, and the break-up of the colonial empires of Britain, France, Holland and Belgium. The concept of nationalism and independence, which was so important in the growth of western Europe, has spread to almost all their former possessions. These have cut themselves off from their previous rulers, opting to rule themselves and develop their own resources, though in most cases they still lean heavily on financial and economic support from western Europe or from the new great powers. But although western Europe may have lost its economic and political supremacy, it remains the cultural model in government, and many of its traditional ways of living are being copied in the new countries, even where the environments would seem to be unsuitable.

The transformation of colonial possessions into independent sovereign states was encouraged by Britain, France, Belgium and the Netherlands, and was imposed on Germany and Italy after their defeat in 1945. But as the new countries developed industries and began to use their agricultural and mineral resources themselves, the former colonial powers had to reconsider their own economies. No longer able to regard their empires as unfailing sources of raw materials, and faced by the competition of the U.S.A., U.S.S.R., and the newly emerged countries, they had to examine more closely how to use their own resources and experience to greater advantage.

In 1944, Belgium, the Netherlands and Luxembourg decided to enter into a joint customs union, which they called Benelux, using the first letters of each country's name. Under the Benelux Treaty, which became effective on January 1st, 1948, no duties are levied on goods circulating within the area of the three countries. Ultimately, it is hoped to extend the customs union to a complete economic union, in which each country will concentrate on the production of the goods for which it is best suited, marketing them jointly, to the benefit of all the partners.

This agreement was followed in 1952 by the European Coal and Steel Community, in which the members were France, Benelux, West Germany and Italy. This co-ordinating community controlled the selling prices of coal and steel. It demanded some surrender of national sovereignty, but was so successful that in 1959 it changed its name to the European Economic Community. The new authority (known in Britain as the Common Market) extended the agreement of "the Six," as the group of countries became known, to cover all trade between them. This powerful trading *bloc*, in which the dominant partners comprise western Europe, seems to have a bright future but it is dependent on a partial relaxation of political frontiers and sacrifice of national sovereignty. Possibly it is a foretaste of what may happen in other parts of the world. Western Europe may once more, as in the past, be a model for economic and political development.

Chapter XII

THE NETHERLANDS

THE country usually known as Holland is officially called the Netherlands. The name Holland belongs to two of its provinces, North Holland and South Holland, but was popularly extended to the whole country. The people are called Dutchmen or, simply, Dutch.

PHYSICAL ASPECTS

The Netherlands are at the western end of the Great European Plain, where the rivers Rhine, Maas (Meuse) and Scheldt have built an immense delta. In the east the delta was reinforced by glacial clays, sands and gravel, bringing it above sea level; in the west frequent oscillations of the land and inundations by the sea resulted in a large marshy area separated from the North Sea by a chain of dunes. A very large percentage of modern Holland has been built by man, so that the Dutch, more than any other people, can claim to have made their country, winning it from the sea. The process of reclamation and accretion still continues, as will be seen later in the chapter.

STRUCTURE AND RELIEF

Geologically, the Netherlands date from Tertiary times, when the Alpine earth movements caused dislocations in the worn-down Hercynian system and the horst of the Ardennes was uplifted. The Maas, rising in scarps born in the same period as the Rhine, pierced the Ardennes by a deep cleft and became a tributary of the Rhine, which flowed from the Alps to the north, traversing the Hercynian barrier by a rift valley. The Rhine was of far greater volume than it is today, and flowed to a deltaic mouth farther north than its present outlet. The advance of the ice sheets of the Quaternary age blocked this outlet, forcing the river to take a bend to the west, and the ground moraines which were left in the northern part of the Netherlands after the retreat of the ice perpetuated this new course. In the last stages of glaciation, the low morainic ridges were buried under thick layers of sand and gravel carried by melt-waters, and through the area the Rhine and Maas cut shallow valleys.

During the Ice Age, north-western Europe subsided, and the North Sea invaded the coastal areas of the Netherlands and north Belgium, laying down clays and silts. A slight upward movement of the land brought these layers near enough to the surface for a line of sand dunes to form a barrier against the sea, except in periods of very high tides. Behind the dunes the shallow waters were filled by the silts of the outflowing rivers, and the resultant marshes formed the basis of the *polders* or reclaimed land of present-day Holland. The dune barrier was breached by violent storms between the eleventh and fifteenth centuries, and the marshes in the north were inundated to form the shallow Wadden Zee and Zuyder Zee, and the festoon of the Frisian islands. Much of this flooded land has been reclaimed, the latest projects being concerned with the struggle to make the Zuyder Zee dry land once more; and the muddy islands deposited by the Rhine and Maas at their mouths have been dyked and drained.

The relief of the Netherlands is simple and monotonous. The whole country, except a small piece in southern Limburg in the extreme southeast, lies below 300 ft; the reclaimed area in the west is mostly below sea level. A notice at Schiphol, the airport near Amsterdam, says, for instance, AERODROME LEVEL 13 FT BELOW SEA LEVEL. South Limburg lies in the coal measures which flank the northern side of the Ardennes; its highest point is 1000 ft in elevation. The Netherlands are criss-crossed by a network of distributaries of the Rhine, Maas and Scheldt rivers, and by interconnecting canals, giving a total of 3500 miles of navigable waterway.

CLIMATE AND NATURAL VEGETATION

The Netherlands are too small and the surface too low-lying for much regional variation in climate. The winters are slightly colder than in eastern England, because the land at that season is often affected by the continental high-pressure system. Even so, the average January temperature is above freezing point (Utrecht, 34·2° F, 1·4° C), although the canals may freeze for a couple of weeks. July temperatures are normal for the latitude, ranging in July from 63° F (17° C) in the south to 61° F (16° C) in the north. Rainfall, which is distributed through the year but with slightly greater falls in late summer and autumn, amounts to less than 30 in. (Utrecht, 29·1 in.; Den Helder, 26·8 in.). Snow falls frequently in January and February.

Natural vegetation is almost non-existent. The shifting sands of the dune belt supported hardly any until, to prevent them from migrating, they were planted with deep-rooted marram grasses and pines. The marshes, reclaimed to form polders, had rushes and other aquatic plants, but these disappeared with drainage. Only in the east, on the higher lands, can a real natural vegetation cover be seen. Where glacial sands formed the surface, heathland and moors developed, with occasional copses of deciduous trees. In badly drained hollows, with a "hard-pan" subsoil, were peat bogs. This eastern region, with infertile soils, is the *Geest*, or

barren land, and continues into Germany (the *Heide*) on the one side and
Belgium (the *Campine*) on the other. Much of this heathland has been
reclaimed.

LAND RECLAMATION

THE ZUYDER ZEE

Prior to the tenth century, the inhabitants of what is now western
Holland built their houses on the dunes which rose above sea level or on

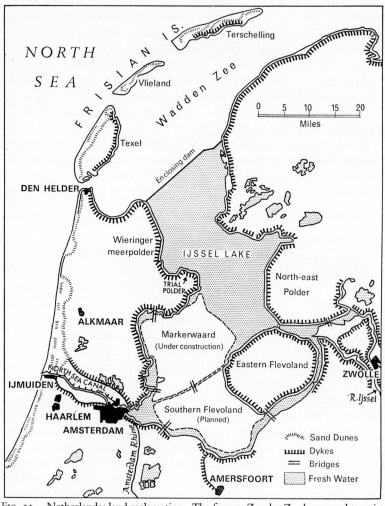

Fig. 31.—Netherlands: land reclamation. The former Zuyder Zee has ceased to exist
and has been replaced by the fresh-water Ijssel Lake, which serves as a reservoir.
As a result of the enclosure, the coast line which had to be protected against the
sea by sea-walls, has been shortened by 185 miles.

artificial hills in the marshes. Some of these mounds (*terpen, werden*) may be seen in Zealand and Friesland. About A.D. 1000, dykes began to be erected and marshes and shallow ponds drained by mills, driven first by hand, later by horses. Windmills were developed in the fifteenth century, their superior power enabling the waters within the surrounding dykes to be lowered still farther. Gradually the country was covered with thousands of windmills, several hundred of which are still in existence, though

[*Courtesy of KLM Aerocarto.*

FIG. 32.—Netherlands: aerial view of the north-east polder. Note the sub-division into rectangular fields, in contrast to the field pattern of the former island of Schokland, which is conspicuous in the middle of the new land. When the whole Zuyder Zee reclamation is complete, the Netherlands will have increased its agricultural land by one-tenth.

rarely used for pumping today. By the seventeenth century it was found possible to drain extensive lakes in the North Holland province after dykes had been built round them. The greater power of the steam pump, introduced in 1840, made possible the draining of the Haarlem Lake, a large stretch of water between Haarlem, Amsterdam and Leiden. It took twelve years, and 46,500 acres of fertile land were reclaimed. With the twentieth century came diesel and electric pumps, and it became feasible to tackle the greatest project of all up to then, the reclamation of the Zuyder Zee. This was an arm of the sea with an area of more than 1350 square miles, which separated northern from western Holland (*see* Fig. 31).

A start was made in 1923 with a great dyke, 27 miles long, across the entrance to this sea. It was completed in 1932, and changed the Zuyder Zee into the IJssel Lake, so called after the river flowing into it. Simultaneously with the erection of the enclosing dam, a start was made on draining the first polder, the Wieringen Lake polder, an area of 50,000 acres. This was finished in 1930, and followed by the north-east polder (119,000 acres) in 1937-42 (Fig. 32), and the Eastern Flevoland polder (133,000 acres) in 1950-57. A further two polders are in process of reclamation, Markerwaard (150,000 acres) and Southern Flevoland (110,000 acres). It is estimated they will be dry land by 1980. Holland will then have acquired 546,000 acres, increasing its total agricultural land by a tenth—enough for 250,000 people. The new IJssel Lake (310,000 acres), in the middle of the polders, will not be drained, but will serve as a fresh water reservoir. Important results of the building of the enclosing dam are the shortening by 185 miles of the length of coast which had to be protected against the sea by massive walls, and the consequent saving in time, labour and money.

DIFFICULTIES OF LAND RECLAMATION

Reclamation of land on a large scale presents immense and far-reaching engineering problems. Once reclaimed and settled on, the polders still have to be watched and controlled, especially with regard to their water-table, i.e. the level of permanent saturation by underground waters. In her fight against the sea, Holland must (i) strengthen the dune barrier and reinforce it by sea walls, (ii) control outflowing river waters by building dykes and regulating their flow by pumping stations and sluices, (iii) keep the surfaces of the polders dry by pumping, but with a close eye on the water-table, where a difference of only an inch or two might be critical, and (iv) prevent the salt sea water entering through open connections with the sea and making the land salty and useless for agriculture and stock rearing. The fight is never-ending. In February 1953, for instance, a spring tide of unprecedented height was blown by a gale against the defences of south-west Holland. The dykes were breached in hundreds of places in the delta area, with the loss of 1800 lives and the inundation of more than 375,000 acres. Reconstructing the dykes and draining the land again took many months.

The problem of salt water is more constant and insidious. The waters of the North Sea can permeate the lower levels of the sedimentary rocks which underlie the surface layers and may, after a journey of centuries, come to the surface in the polders. Of greater immediate importance, however, is the salt water which enters every time a ship passes through locks from the sea. The North Sea Canal, connecting Amsterdam to the open sea, is shut off at IJmuiden by an enormous sluice. Every time a ship passes through the barrier in either direction, enough salt is admitted to fill 150 railway trucks if it were in its solid state. This is washed out again by using the fresh water of the IJssel retaining lake. In South Holland, however, there is as yet no such remedy. The New Waterway, a channel connecting Rotterdam to the North Sea, is vital to Holland's ocean transport and prosperity, but through it and the river mouths farther south the sea water can enter freely. The river water is not fast enough to keep out the salt water, which is heavier and penetrates at each high tide, creeping along the floors of the river valleys.

A disturbing feature is that the salt "boundary" is moving further inland along the New Waterway, and gaining about 250 yards every year. One of the causes is the deepening of harbours near Rotterdam, increasing the volume of tides and bringing more salt. The waters of the Rhine passing down the Waterway are used for Rotterdam's water supply, and for agriculture deeper inland. The presence of salt is inimical to both: salt water poisons the soil, destroying crops and causing cattle-sickness. To obviate the creep of the salt via the rivers, Dutch engineers have

[Courtesy of the Netherlands Embassy.

FIG. 33.—Netherlands: deep ploughing on the Wieringermeer polder. The reclaimed land is ploughed to a depth of 5½ ft, so as to mix the sand which was dumped during drainage operations with the underlying compressed layers of silt, and so allow air to penetrate. It takes some years before the reclaimed land is fully productive.

evolved a plan to shut the river mouths completely, with the exception of the New Waterway, and to direct their waters into the Waterway in such volume and with such force as to act as a barrier against the sea waters. This is part of the Delta Plan.

The preparation of a polder, such as those of the Zuyder Zee, takes years. When the dykes are complete and pumping has revealed the sea bottom, the desolate expanse of slippery clay is still like a sodden sponge. At the first opportunity special wide-tracked machines dig ditches to drain off the surplus water (*see* Fig. 33). Broad channels are excavated and filled with sand to become roads, for without this procedure the ground would be too soft to support traffic. The sites of villages or farmhouses are dug out similarly to remove the weak layer, and the cavities filled with sand; then the whole area is covered by a network of porous drainpipes. Seeds are dropped from planes and helicopters—reeds in the hollows, peas and beans in the better-drained parts—but the ground is still sterile and without bacterial life. Micro-organisms by the million are supplied by the Reclamation Service and mixed with the seed, to give "life" to the soil. At length the polder becomes productive and comes under cultivation, with villages, farms, roads and canals. The problem now is to keep it supplied with fresh water and to prevent the re-entrance of the sea, which is at a higher level. The giant sea walls and the IJssel Lake are the solution in the northern Netherlands.

THE DELTA PLAN

Once the polder is complete, it begins to sink, to shrink. It has been estimated that the Zuyder Zee polders, with their villages and everything on them, will subside as much as three or four feet in the next eighty years. This sinking happens to all polders, however small or old, and of course the dykes sink with them, reducing the height of the barriers against the sea. The lowest polder, near Rotterdam, is some thirty feet below storm-flood sea level. The subsidence of the land is accompanied by a rise in sea level near the coasts of six to eight inches a century, the result of the melting of the northern ice caps. It is not sufficient, therefore, just to build dykes and keep them in repair: it may become necessary to replace them with even more massive constructions. Obviously, the best solution would be to enclose the whole coastline with a giant sea wall, high enough and strong enough to resist the most violent gales; and to make it short and straight by reducing the length of the coastline.

This is the plan worked out by the Delta Commission, to close the estuaries in the south (*see* Fig. 34). This area, where the Rhine, Maas and Scheldt flow out through breaks in the sand dune barrier, is the weakest in the country, for the sea has free entry and floods and salt water are a constant menace. The Delta Plan, as the scheme is known, would close all the funnel-shaped openings except two, those which lead directly to the ports of Antwerp (in Belgium) and Rotterdam. The difficulties are much greater than in the Zuyder Zee, since the inlets are deeper, the currents stronger, and the tidal ebb and flow twice as powerful. The knowledge gained in the construction of the enclosing dam and in the closing of the dykes after the 1953 disaster, however, enabled a start to be made on the

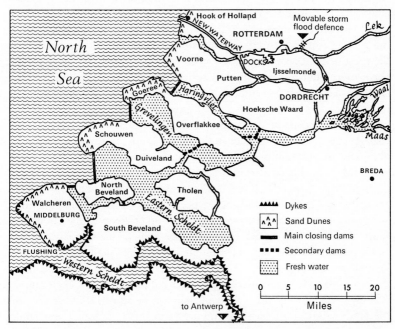

FIG. 34.—Netherlands: the delta plan. Unlike the Zuyder Zee scheme, the primary object here is not to reclaim land, although this will eventuate, but to shorten the coastline which has to be protected by sea-walls, to acquire fresh-water reservoirs and to prevent the salting-up of the land. It is hoped the scheme will be completed by 1990.

gigantic scheme in 1956. By 1961 the first dam was completed across the Haringvliet estuary, and although this is the smallest of the openings that are to be dammed it was still the greatest engineering project attempted in Holland.

The Delta Plan will be completed in about 25 years, and will make the Netherlands watertight. It will reduce the length of the coastland by some 450 miles and keep out the salt water. But it will provide very little, if any, new land; its effect will be to trap vast quantities of fresh water round the islands in the estuaries, to the great advantage of the south

Netherlands. For, strange to say, fresh water is urgently needed in the south of the country. The retaining lake which will come into being will make North Brabant and the islands of Zealand much more productive and free from the droughts which affect them at present.

FUTURE PLANS

A much more ambitious scheme is already being considered by Dutch engineers. This is to join Den Helder (at the northern tip of the mainland) and the Frisian islands in a continuous line, and reclaim the Wadden Zee. This Herculean task may have to be commenced before the end of this century, for the growth of population is rapid, and Holland is already the most densely peopled country in the world. Moreover, more people mean more built-up areas and less agricultural space, so that much of the land so laboriously reclaimed becomes non-productive and more is required.

While the reclamation of land from the sea is more spectacular, the changes which are taking place in the higher sandy heaths and peaty areas in the east are very significant. The sandy areas are easily reclaimed. They are ploughed, artificial fertilisers applied, and grasses planted. Cattle and sheep provide manure and, as the soil texture improves, root crops and rye are grown. The sandy lands never become very fertile, and sometimes are given over to plantations of pine and other trees, as the country is short of timber. The peaty cover in other parts of the Geest is dug out and some of it used as fuel. The soil underneath is ploughed to a depth of several feet to break the hard-pan which restricts drainage, and some of the peat, mixed with fertilisers, is replaced and ploughed in. The resultant soil, especially if river silt is available and can be added, is richer than on the sandy lands. Pig rearing is important in these reclaimed peat-lands, and sugar beet is grown where the soils contain more clay.

HUMAN GEOGRAPHY

HISTORY AND PEOPLE

On the hills to the east, and on mounds amid the original vast marshes, lived the early few inhabitants of the Netherlands. Many of these mounds, known as *terpen* or *werden*, were artificial. Using them as centres from which to operate, the natives as early as the first century A.D. learned to protect themselves against the encroachment of the sea. By the seventh century they had begin to build dykes and reclaim the marshlands, and in the sixteenth century the draining of lakes began. During the Middle Ages, Holland was a group of autonomous counties, duchies and cities, known as the Nether (Low) Lands. Up till 1482 they were the property of the House of Burgundy, and then by inheritance passed to the House of Austria (the Hapsburgs). In the sixteenth century the Netherlands provinces rose against the Hapsburg Philip II, a tyrant and a despot who had succeeded to the throne of Spain and the overlordship of the Low Countries, proclaiming themselves a republic. The struggle for independence continued from 1568 to 1648, and ended in victory for the Republic of the United Netherlands.

During the war with Spain the Netherlands became one of Europe's most powerful countries, especially through its navy and its world-wide commerce. Its ships and traders were active in South Africa and the East Indies, and colonies were settled in North America and the West Indies. It will be remembered that in the first half of the seventeenth century the Dutch charted for the first time some of the coastline of Australia, and Tasman discovered Van Diemen's Land (Tasmania) and Staaten Land (New Zealand). In North America, New York until 1674 was called New Amsterdam.

The Netherlands remained a republic until 1795, when they were occupied by Napoleon. They were freed in 1813, and in 1815 their Stadtholder (President), a member of the House of Orange, was invited to become king of the United Netherlands, which until 1831 included Belgium. The country was overrun in 1940 by the Germans, and liberated again in 1945.

Prominent in the history and development of the Netherlands is the role played by the towns. The population of Holland at present is over 11,700,000, and about one-third lives in towns of more than 100,000 inhabitants. This proportion existed in the Middle Ages, though of course both the total population and the towns were then much smaller. Even at the birth of the independent republic with the conclusion of the Treaty of Utrecht in 1579, the towns overshadowed the nobility in importance; and when an attempt was made by the Spanish king to impose a culture derived from his own person and his court, it seemed natural that it should be opposed by the concerted action of the Dutch towns. It was the hesitation of Amsterdam to join this confederation which led to the initial growth of Rotterdam as a great city. Through the influence of the towns, Holland developed peacefully into the parliamentary democracy with a sovereign at its head that we know today.

POPULATION PROBLEMS

The Netherlands are in danger of becoming over-populated. With an average density of population of 904 per square mile, they are the most thickly peopled country in the world. More than 40% of the total lives in the two western provinces of North and South Holland, which include the three largest cities. About 42% of the employed population works in industry, as compared with less than 11% in agriculture. The Dutch are therefore *not* predominantly a farming people, as is so often thought; indeed, the arable area in the country will not accommodate more agricultural workers than it does now. That is why it is so vital that every branch of industry must produce optimum yields, and why further land must be reclaimed. For the population will continue to grow; without emigration, it is estimated that it will be 14,500,000 in 1980, which would give a density in large areas of over 2000 per square mile.

Emigration provides a way of easing this increasing pressure. Since 1952 the Netherlands have actively encouraged their surplus people to seek homes in other lands. In the period 1946–60, 350,000 Dutchmen left their country for good, the majority to Australia, Canada and the U.S.A. On the other hand, the same years saw the immigration into the Netherlands of about 300,000 Indonesians, who presented the authorities with a problem of integration.

THE ECONOMY

AGRICULTURE AND FISHING

Roughly 11% of the working population is employed in agriculture and fishing. Most of the farms are small, the majority between 2 and 12 acres, yet by intensive management the average yields are among the highest in the world and the country has a large export of excess agricultural products, amounting to a quarter of the total exports. The eastern Netherlands, mainly on the reclaimed peat-lands, produce large crops of potatoes, rye and oats. The potatoes are the basis of an important starch industry centred on Groningen (147,000), the chief market in the north.

The polder-lands have a very fertile soil and versatile agriculture. The islands of Zeeland are mainly arable, with wheat, sugar beet, root crops for fodder, and vegetables. Most of the Netherlands, however, is pastoral, and cattle are kept for dairy purposes: among exporting countries, the Netherlands are first for condensed milk, second for cheese and third for butter and powdered milk. The Westland, south of The Hague, is a region of hothouses, growing tomatoes, lettuce and cucumbers; southwest of Amsterdam, centred on Aalsmeer, another hothouse area cultivates flowers and plants for export. Exports of bulbs from the sandy district between Haarlem (170,000) and Leiden (97,500) in North Holland were worth £25 million in 1963. Holland is also the world's largest exporter of eggs (3000 million in 1963). All the agricultural and processing enterprises are helped by co-operatives organised on similar lines to those in

Denmark, and deal with such derived industries as the making of potato flour and strawboard. A co-operative factory for the manufacture of superphosphate, a fertiliser, is located at Vlaardingen in South Holland.

The fishing industry is concerned more with the home market than with exports, contributing less than 1% to the national income. The chief catch is herrings, which in the sixteenth and seventeenth centuries were a major factor in the country's growing prosperity. Today, however, only small amounts of salted herring are exported. The chief fishing ports are IJmuiden, Scheveningen, Vlaardingen, Den Helder and Oudes-child. The IJssel Lake is noted for eels, and the rivers of Zeeland for mussels and oysters.

POWER AND INDUSTRIES

Holland has many rivers, but none of any value for hydro-electric development. Its small coalfield in the south-eastern province of Limburg produces about 12·5 million tons annually, and Maastricht (83,000), the mining centre, has coke ovens and glassworks; but Holland has to import coal from the Ruhr. Oil is found at Schoonebeck in Drenthe and near The Hague, and refined at Pernis, near Rotterdam. The annual output, nearly 2 million tons in 1960, is only 30% of requirements. The refineries at Pernis, however, deal with large imports and re-export petrol and petroleum products. An oil pipeline is in use between Rotterdam and the West German Rhine.

In 1962, large deposits of natural gas were discovered around Slochteren, in Groningen. They are now estimated to contain 1,100,000 million cubic metres of gas, which makes the Netherlands second only to the U.S.A. in this valuable resource. The discovery of oil and natural gas in the Netherlands has encouraged the search for similar deposits under the floor of the North Sea near the British Isles. In 1963, the North Sea was divided into "blocks" for exploration and exploitation, and preparations for borings in the sea bed are already well advanced. They are taking place in the western half of the North Sea, and not near the Dutch coast.

Holland has no mineral ores and, apart from coal, petroleum and natural gas, no natural resources except clay and salt. These have given rise to the widespread manufacture of bricks and to the more specialised production of tiles at Delft and ornamental pottery at Gouda. Brine in the east and north-east is processed into table salt or utilised by a soda factory at Delfzijl. About 270,000 tons of table salt are exported annually.

In spite of a shortage of fuel for power and of minerals, the Netherlands have become an important industrial country. Increasing industrialisation has necessitated the importing of electric power, current being transmitted from stations in Belgium, West Germany and Switzerland. The growth of industry was the result of Holland's geographical position in the North Sea, the busiest sea-lane in the world, at a point where it is joined by the Rhine, Maas and Scheldt, the main arteries of western Europe. To its ports and along its rivers came shipping from all parts of the world, with

Fig. 35.—Netherlands: general features. The Netherlands may be divided into (*a*) the dune-lined coast, (*b*) the polders and dyked lands, (*c*) the Geest. The numerous rivers which intersect the country are controlled by dykes, behind which the water-level is regulated by pumping stations and sluices. There are about 1170 miles of dunes and dykes in the Netherlands.

raw materials; many of them were processed and re-exported as finished goods. Industry was, in a sense, an offshoot of the country's trading services, the manufactured goods being taken for sale by the traders. In the sixteenth and seventeenth centuries Holland was a world power, with extensive colonial possessions. Her ships carried tropical spices, cotton, sugar cane, cocoa, coffee and diamonds to Europe, to be processed for sale and export. Later, raw materials passed along the Rhine to the industrial districts of Germany, whose exports returned by the same route, with Rotterdam the exchange or warehouse port.

Industries connected with ocean and river transport grew at the same time. The building of ships and barges, rope works, sail making, biscuit works, etc., are distributed along all the main rivers; breweries, flour mills and sugar refineries use both domestic and foreign supplies of raw materials. The home industries of the Netherlands, if we except those connected with dairying and horticulture, are insignificant; but those which import raw materials and process them are of world-wide importance.

Iron ore, brought mainly from Sweden and Algeria, is smelted at IJmuiden (Ymuiden), where there are steel works. Holland exports annually about 200,000 tons of pig iron. Tin is smelted at Arnhem (126,000), where there is one of the largest tin smelters in the world, turning out one-sixth of the world's production. Near Rotterdam and Amsterdam are smelters for zinc and lead; and copper and aluminium concentrates are imported and refined. The metal industries account for roughly 34% of Holland's industrial exports. Engineering naturally includes all forms of pumps and machinery used for land reclamation: Dutch engineers are called on wherever there may be drainage problems. Exports of internal combustion (including diesel) engines, dairying machinery, cranes and bridge parts are large; and electrical engineering includes radio and television sets and light bulbs from the Philips factories at Eindhoven (172,388). Textile machinery is made at Enschede (128,780) and Tilburg (140,261), mainly for the home market.

The chemical industry is located in the north-east, as mentioned earlier, on the coalfield and near Rotterdam. In Limburg, near Maastricht, it is based on the by-products of coal and concentrates on nitrogen fertilisers. Ancillary to the oil refineries at Pernis, near Rotterdam, are plants for detergents, synthetic rubber, glycerine, sulphur and insecticides. Half the chemical industry's products are exported and make up about one-fifth of the total exports of the country.

Holland produces only a small proportion of its textile raw materials, from sheep reared principally on the sand-hills along the coast and on the Frisian islands, and in the heathlands to the south-east. The country is nearly self-sufficient in cotton and wool textiles, and has a large export trade in rayon yarns. Cotton goods are manufactured in the province of Drenthe, with Enschede the centre. Tilburg, in the south, is the chief wool textile town. Clothing manufacture is centred in Amsterdam.

"Colonial" manufactures are an important branch of Holland's industry. Chief among them are the making of cocoa and chocolate, vegetable oils and margarine, and the cutting and polishing of diamonds. Based on the trade between Holland and its former colonies, they are located round the chief ports, Amsterdam and Rotterdam. Here, and at Dordrecht (84,807) and Flushing (29,000), are the chief shipbuilding and marine engineering works.

MAJOR TOWNS

The seat of government is *The Hague* ('sGravenhage) (607,000), with the usual administrative departments and foreign representatives; like Washington and Canberra, it has no industries of national importance. The economic and commercial capital is Amsterdam (873,000), but many of the head offices of the nation's industries are situated at The Hague, so as to be in close touch with the Government. Here, too, is the International Court of Justice.

Amsterdam was an important merchant city before the sixteenth century. When the Dutch East India Company, a powerful commercial enterprise whose activities extended from the Cape of Good Hope to the Far East, established its headquarters in the city, Amsterdam became the richest and most influential centre of the time. Its prosperity declined with the silting of the Zuyder Zee, but the North Sea Canal, opened in 1876, restored much of its former eminence. Wider and deeper than the Suez Canal, this joins Amsterdam directly with the North Sea, cutting through the sand dunes to IJmuiden, on the coast. The city regained its position as a market for tea, tobacco, rubber, sugar, coffee, skins, leather, diamonds and timber; its shipbuilding industry increased; and manufactures based on the processing of imports developed. Amsterdam is not, however, a good transit port and, although the city is connected to the Rhine by the Amsterdam–Rhine Canal, there is little through traffic. Its industries are concerned mainly with importing and exporting via the North Sea.

Rotterdam (731,000) is situated on the Lek estuary of the Rhine. Originally a small fishing port, it started to develop as a harbour for larger vessels when Amsterdam did not join immediately in the resistance against Spain. Shipping avoided the Zuyder Zee port, and in this period, between 1570 and 1625, Rotterdam prospered. Like Amsterdam, it was first a market for colonial produce. Later it became the base of the powerful Dutch fleet. Its rise as the most important transit port in western Europe dates from the opening of the New Waterway in 1870. One of the arms of the Rhine was deepened and widened to compete with Amsterdam's sea-going traffic and in the following years, which saw the phenomenal rise of Germany's industrial regions along the Rhine, Rotterdam became the main entrance and exit for the whole of western Europe. The city has important shipbuilding, chemical and oil refining industries, but its chief function is as an entrepôt (warehouse) port, whence goods brought by ocean-going vessels are carried by inland shipping along the rivers and canals, and vice versa. Each year more than 20,000 ocean-going ships and 200,000 inland vessels exchange their cargoes. Rotterdam as a harbour is still growing. In 1957, a plan known as "Europoort" was developed, providing for new and bigger harbours near the entrance of the New Waterway. Holland has an eye on the greater trade anticipated in the European Economic Community (the "Common Market"), to which she belongs in association with Germany, France, Italy and the other two Benelux countries. Rotterdam was badly damaged by the Germans in 1940, but it has been rebuilt and its harbour equipment completely modernised.

Utrecht (258,000) is the fourth city of Holland. It is an old regional capital, but much of its trade has moved to the larger cities. It has a university, railway engineering, sugar and fertiliser factories, and milk-processing works.

STUDY QUESTIONS

1. Examine the problems associated with the reclamation of land for agriculture from the sea. (O. & C.)

2. Account for the importance of the principal ports of the Netherlands despite the small size of the country and its dearth of natural resources. (O. & C.)

3. Write an account of the physical geography of the delta of the river Rhine. What are the main problems associated with the land of the delta region? How have the people of the Netherlands met these problems? (O. & C.)

4. Describe the natural regions of the Netherlands. (O. & C.)

5. Discuss the geographical aspects of land reclamation in the Netherlands. (J.M.B.)

Chapter XIII

BELGIUM; LUXEMBOURG

BELGIUM

BELGIUM is smaller than the Netherlands. It is situated south of the Rhine–Meuse delta, occupying most of the Scheldt (Escaut) basin, although the mouth of this river is in Holland; and the middle Meuse basin is inside its boundaries. Belgium is a "buffer" state, lying at the western end of the Germanic world, and to the south in contact with the "Mediterranean" civilisation of France. It has been an age-long area of conflict between the two cultures, and its numerous battlefields have earned for it the title of "Cock-pit of Europe."

PHYSICAL ASPECTS

STRUCTURE AND RELIEF

Belgium has had a much more complex geological history than the Netherlands, and in consequence has a more varied relief.

In the south-east of the country are the Ardennes, the western end of a group of uplands known as the Middle Rhine Highlands. Most of the Ardennes are in Belgium; a small area reaches into France, and a fragment comprises the northern third of Luxembourg. The Ardennes belong to the Hercynian orogeny of late Carbo-Permian times. The ancient folds, mainly along east–west axes, were worn down to a peneplain during a long period of denudation, lasting to Cretaceous times, possibly a hundred million years. During this time the Carboniferous and Permian rocks disappeared from the surface, except in the north near Dinant and in the long trench extending from Mons to Liège, where limestones and coal measures are preserved in discontinuous basins. Limestones appear also in Luxembourg on the southern flanks of the Ardennes. The rocks of the highlands are mainly sandstones of Devonian age, with limestones and shales of the same period in places. The core of the mountains is exposed across the centre, where Lower Palaeozoic rocks, mainly Cambrian and Silurian slates and quartzites, outcrop in the north-east and south-west, in the latter extending into France.

In the Cretaceous period the whole of the worn-down peneplain sank and was covered by the Chalk Sea. In this sea, which covered most of western, and reached into central, Europe, chalk was deposited; as a result of oscillations between land and sea levels, during subsequent periods of the Tertiary newer rocks were laid down. Oligocene marine clays may be found overlying chalk in some places, Silurian metamorphics in others, showing that there must have been long denudation of the surface before they were deposited. This was the time of the Alpine mountain-building, and much of the movement in the Hercynian region was probably connected with it. No doubt, too, the Brabant massif—a branch of Hercynian rocks stretching westwards from the Ardennes, but at a great depth below the present surface—belongs to this period of uplift, fracture and subsidence.

The net result of the latest movements is the formation in the southeast of the country of a deeply dissected plateau, tilted towards the northwest, easily divisible into two distinct parts: the High Ardennes, of intensely metamorphosed slates and quartzites, rising to over 2000 ft and occupying most of the area; and the Low Ardennes, usually below 1000 ft, on the northern edges. These are low plateaus with ridge-like outcrops of shales, sandstones and limestones, ranging from Silurian to Carboniferous age. The High Ardennes (highest point, the Botrange, 2277 ft) often have peat bogs in hollows between the rounded peaks; the soils are thin, acid and infertile. Rainfall is heavy (over 45 in.), and snow lies in some places for nearly three months. Only in the deeper hollows and in the valleys is farming possible, and the area as a whole is one of forests, mostly spruce and Scots pine. The Low Ardennes, the plateaus of the Condroz and Entre-Sambre-et-Meuse, have more fertile soils, for the rocks are less resistant; but they are not very good, and are used more for pasture than for arable farming. The whole of the Ardennes is thinly peopled, presenting a great contrast to the dense population of the Sambre–Meuse trench which lies parallel to the massif on its northern flanks.

The marine transgression of Cretaceous times resulted in layers of chalk over a vast basin in western Europe. In Belgium the chalk cover was worn away or covered by newer deposits. Chalk underlies much of the Flanders plain, but not Brabant; it reappears in the Campine, where the shafts of coalmines pass through the chalk before arriving at the coal measures. Outcrops of chalk are found near Mons and in the Herve and Hesbaye regions, east of the Campine. At various times in the Tertiary, transgressions by the sea resulted in the deposit of sands and clays, and the rocks found in different parts of the basin vary according to the type and time of transgression. In Belgium, for instance, the earlier deposits include the clays of Flanders and the sands of Brabant and Hesbaye. These were covered by vast amounts of sand in late Tertiary times, and there followed a tilted uplift, during which deposit of sand and clay continued, but in amounts which differed greatly from north to south.

The land seems to have risen and tilted at the same time, the axis of movement running along a line a little south of the Belgian–Netherlands frontier. The south of Belgium became a plain which rose to 500 ft in the south; to the north of the axis lay a deeper area in which the silts of the Rhine–Meuse–Scheldt were deposited, to build the delta which later became the polders of the Netherlands and coastal Belgium. As the uplift was taking place, rivers began to flow from the higher southern edges, wearing wide valleys and carrying most of the surface deposits to the sea. The newer sandy layers were denuded from the whole of the south, except for a few hills in Flanders, but were left in the Campine in the north; and the earlier Tertiary sands and clays were once more exposed on the surface in central and western Belgium. The ice sheets of the Quaternary glaciation did not reach Belgium, but in the north the outwash of sands and gravels reached the Campine from the melting ice front; the Scheldt and its tributaries would have contained much more water than at present. Alluvium was spread widely across their flood-plains.

One part of the central plain is covered with *limon*, very similar to loess. This was fine dust blown in either inter-glacial or immediate post-glacial times by drying winds from high-pressure centres over the ice. It was deposited in thick sheets across Europe, from France to Poland, and apparently trapped against the Hercynian uplands or the Alpine folds. In Belgium it covered the Tertiary layers in Brabant and Hainaut, and the chalk in Hesbaye. It is so fertile that it constitutes a distinct soil division in the otherwise sandy plain.

STRUCTURAL DIVISIONS

It is possible, then, to distinguish in Belgium eight regions, based on the geological structure (*see* Fig. 36):

1. *The Belgian Lorraine*

In the extreme south-east of Belgium is a tiny region belonging to the Jurassic scarplands of Lorraine. It lies south of the Ardennes, and is made up of parallel outcrops of Jurassic limestones, sandstones and marls.

2. *The Ardennes*

In the south-east are the Ardennes, a highland mass which falls in the south to a tiny area of limestone scarps. The Ardennes themselves may be sub-divided into (*a*) the High Ardennes and (*b*) the Low Ardennes, the Famenne depression forming the line of separation.

3. The Sambre–Meuse valley

North of the Low Ardennes is a deep long trench, the Sambre–Meuse valley, with a narrow coalfield. The valley of the Meuse, before receiving the Sambre, cuts through the Ardennes from south to north. The drainage is *antecedent*, *i.e.* the river was flowing before the Ardennes were uplifted to their present position, and it maintained its course and deepened its valley throughout the slow uplift.

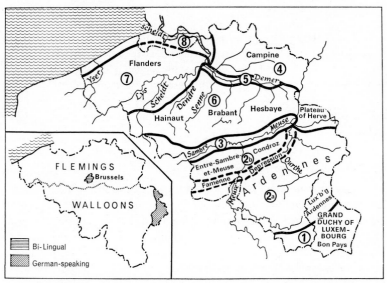

FIG. 36.—Belgium and Luxembourg: physical divisions. The numbers refer to Belgium and are explained in the text. The inset map shows the linguistic regions defined by law in 1963, reproduced here by courtesy of H. van der Haegen.

4. The Campine

The rest of Belgium is a plain, sub-divided according to its soils. In the north is the Campine (Kempenland), a sandy heath-land similar to the Geest of Holland, of which it is a continuation. It stretches from the Scheldt estuary to Limburg, and contains the Campine (Kempen) coalfield.

5. The région mixte

Immediately to the south of the Campine is a transition belt between the sands of the Campine and the loams of Brabant. This is known as the "Région Mixte." It coincides more or less with the Demer valley and the lower Dyle valley.

6. *The central plains*

South again is the limon-covered plain of Brabant and Hainaut, with an extension into Hesbaye. This is really a series of low plateaus, rising in the south of the Brabant–Hainaut area to nearly 600 ft, but with such gradual slopes as not to detract from their plain character. They include the richest farming lands of Belgium. This area is also taken to include the Plateau of Herve, to the east.

7. *Interior Flanders*

This is a triangular-shaped plain west of the limon regions, with the base of the triangle in northern France and its apex near Antwerp. In the south there is a cover of clay, with a gradual change northwards to sands. The rivers Scheldt, Lys and Dendre have spread their alluvial silts over most of the region. It is not naturally as fertile as the limon, but careful cultivation over many centuries has resulted in prosperous intensive farming.

8. *Coastal or maritime Flanders*

This is a broad sandy beach backed by a line of dunes which, as in the Netherlands, have been strengthened in places against the sea. The coast is straight and unbroken throughout its length of just under 42 miles. Inside the belt of dunes is the low-lying reclaimed plain of Belgian polders, varying in width up to 10 miles. The polders of Flanders are not below sea level, except at high tide, and so there is not the same danger of floods as in the Netherlands; nevertheless, there is the same need to get rid of surplus water, and the area is covered with a network of drainage channels, with exit sluices at Ostend, Nieuwpoort, Zeebrugge and elsewhere.

CLIMATE

The climate of Belgium is definitely maritime over most of the country. The only approach to continental conditions is in the Ardennes, which have a harsh, wet winter with much snow. Temperatures in the lowlands are similar to those of south-east England, ranging from 34° F (1·5° C) in January to 63° F (18° C) in July. Rainfall near the coast is about 26 in. annually, increasing inland to 30 in. at the foot of the Ardennes. In the Ardennes, 50 in. annually is common. The rains come mainly in the winter half of the year, but thunderstorms may make August the wettest month in most years.

HUMAN GEOGRAPHY

HISTORY AND PEOPLE

On the death of Charlemagne, his empire was split by the Treaty of Verdun, 843, into three kingdoms, and the land now occupied by Belgium was divided between two of them. Flanders, west of the river Scheldt, was given to the Capet king of western France; all east of the river formed the northern part of a new state, Lotharingia, carved out of the empire as a buffer between France and Germany. Because of the inept rule of the Lotharingian kings, eastern Belgium broke up into a number of virtually independent duchies and ecclesiastic states.

The period from the ninth to the fourteenth century witnessed an unprecedented growth of industry and commerce throughout Belgium. Flanders manufactured both woollen and worsted cloth and sold it abroad, especially in England, which supplied most of the raw wool. Coppersmiths and iron workers established themselves in the Meuse valley, and trade fairs were held in Brabant. At the same time, farming was being revolutionised in Flanders, by the process of heavy manuring and the abolition of the fallow. To this period, too, belongs the rise of most of Belgium's towns. Though not unified, the country was rich and well developed.

Unification came in the fourteenth century, when most of the Belgian area passed by marriage to the rule of Burgundy, and later, in 1515, of Spain, as part of the Netherlands. When the northern Netherlands became independent, Belgium continued under Spanish or—after the Treaty of Utrecht in 1713—Austrian rule. This was brought to an end in 1795, when Napoleon added Belgium to his First Republic.

After his defeat, it was decided by the Treaty of Vienna in 1815 to create a Kingdom of the United Netherlands, which would include the northern Netherlands, all the possessions held by Austria, the ancient bishopric of Liège and most of Flanders, so bringing Belgium and Holland together as one unit. The union lasted only fifteen years, for in 1831 Belgium was recognised as a separate sovereign state, with Leopold I as king. In 1914, and again in 1940, Belgium was overrun by the Germans. In the First World War the country suffered far more material damage than in the Second, when the Germans needed the products of the coalfields and the iron industry, and conserved them then as much as possible. In consequence, Belgium was more fitted to face the economic difficulties of the immediate post-war years than her neighbours to the north and south.

WALLOONS AND FLEMINGS

The position of Belgium as the meeting point of Germanic and Frankish peoples—a legacy of Charlemagne's days—has resulted in two separate, and sometimes conflicting, cultures. The Romans, who invaded southern Belgium from Gaul in 57 B.C., colonised the area for nearly 500 years. The result was that the people of the south spoke a dialect of French known as Walloon, which they later abandoned for orthodox French, and their way of life derived from France. The north is occupied by people descended from Germanic tribes, speaking Flemish, a Low German dialect. Belgium, then, is bi-lingual, the line dividing the two languages and the two peoples, Walloons and Flemings, running roughly west to east from Hazebrouck (France) to Aachen (Germany), slightly south of latitude 51 degrees N. Brussels, though on the Flemish side of the line, speaks predominantly French (*see* inset, Fig. 36). In the Eupen–Malmedy districts, acquired from Germany in 1919, a large proportion of the inhabitants speaks German. The Flemings are Catholic in religion and conservative in politics; the Walloons, though mainly Catholic, are far more liberal and socialist, and their republican ideals are in opposition to the staunch loyalty of the Flemings to the reigning monarchy. Mutual interdependence in industry and commerce has up to the present enabled the two peoples to live in peace, if not always in harmony, but there are signs of discord and possible conflict ahead.

Until just over 100 years ago the Walloons were in the majority. They considered themselves superior in education and social standing to the uncouth Flemings; French was the official language of the schools and Government. The Sambre-Meuse coalfield and the major heavy industries were in Walloon territory, and the industries of the Flemings depended on Walloon coal. The ports, however, were Flemish, so successful overseas trade necessitated agreement between the two peoples.

Gradually, the proportion of Flemings increased. By 1864 Flemish became a teaching language, and later an official language recognised equally with French. Today, Belgium's population is over 9,200,000, of whom 5,064,000 are Flemish-speaking, 3,046,000 French-speaking and 1,023,000 bilingual. There are also nearly 58,000 German-speaking people in the east of the province of Liège, around Eupen and Malmedy. As the birth rate among the Flemings is higher than among the Walloons, their majority is likely to grow. Moreover, the opening of the Campine coalfield and the development of modern industries nearer to Antwerp (*see below*) have had a most important economic result, changing completely the balance of productive power. The future of the older Sambre-Meuse coalfield and its associated industries is uncertain, for many of the seams are already worked out, and much of the coke required in the steelworks there has to be brought from the Campine. There has been much emigration of the Walloon workers, not to the new coalfield, but into the cities of Brussels and Antwerp.

The Walloons, supreme in the not too distant past, are today restive and dissatisfied, economically and politically, when they see the prosperity of the north, with its supplies of good coal and its much easier access to imports of raw material via Antwerp and the Albert Canal, to which they have no counterpart. Many of their leaders advocate a separation from Belgium and a unification with France; others desire some kind of federalism, similar to that in Switzerland, also a multi-lingual country, but one without racial problems. Whatever the solution of this cultural, political and economic problem may be, it appears that before it is found Belgium will pass through a period of uncertainty and unrest.

POPULATION

After the Netherlands, Belgium is the most densely peopled country in the world, with an average of 785 per square mile. The population is not evenly distributed, the area south of the Meuse valley, in the Ardennes, contrasting sharply with the rest of the country. Occupying roughly a quarter of the total area, it has less than one-tenth of the people, with a density of 100–200 per square mile. Central Belgium, including the Sambre-Meuse coalfield, has over 950 per square mile and Flanders about 850. Flanders, with its high birth rate and limited resources, is over-populated, despite its intensive use of the land and its industries; throughout history, thousands of Flemings have had to emigrate. Many of them went to northern France, others to England, where they introduced their knowledge of manufacturing fine worsteds. Today, large numbers are going to the Campine coalfield, and there is a seasonal migration to the farms of the Paris basin.

THE ECONOMY

Belgium, far more than the Netherlands, is an industrial country. Yet she must import almost all the raw materials used in her manufactures, and pay for them with manufactured goods. Forty per cent of her total production is exported, and she has to obtain one-fifth of her food-stuffs from abroad. Of her total working population, over 55% are engaged in industry. All this demands a first-rate transport system. For its size, Belgium has the densest railway network in the world, and a canal and river navigation system second in Europe only to the Netherlands'.

MINERALS

Belgium's only mineral resource of importance is coal. At one time, iron ore and zinc were found in the foothills of the Ardennes, near Liège, but the mines are no longer in production. Their output was never great, and Belgium's activity in the early days of the Industrial Revolution soon exhausted them, so the country now has to depend on imports of metallic raw materials.

Coal is found in two areas (*see* Fig. 37). The first of these is the Sambre-

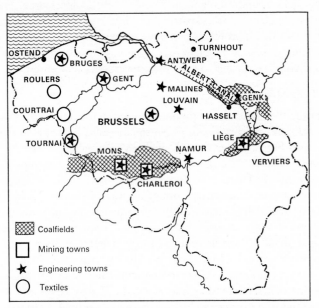

Fig. 37.—Belgium: minerals and industries. All the towns shown have food processing and brewing industries; the Sambre-Meuse coalfield specialises in heavy engineering; the textile towns in the west deal mainly with linen and cotton, in the east with wool. The zone of the Albert Canal is a new and rapidly developing industrial region (*see* text).

Meuse or southern coalfield, the Belgian part of coal measures which extend from the departments of Pas-de-Calais and Nord in France to Liège, though not continuously in Belgium. In the west is a productive series of measures round Mons, in the area known as the Borinage (3,987,000 tons yearly). The chief producing area is round Charleroi, with an extension northwards to La Louvière (10,569,000 tons). The district round Liège, farther east, (4,531,000 tons) is second in importance. The seams in the Namur district, important once, are now exhausted.

The Sambre-Meuse coalfield is not an easy one to work. It suffered from the later earth movements of the Hercynian massifs along whose flanks it is situated. Faulting and overthrusting broke the seams, making the basins discontinuous and the seams dip steeply. Most of the thicker seams have been worked out, and thin seams are uneconomic, for they are difficult to mechanise and expensive to exploit. Yet in spite of difficulties, the coalfield produces two-thirds of Belgium's coal, and is still at present the chief factor in the country's industrial output. The coal in the Mons area is mainly bituminous, used for household purposes and to produce gas; in the Charleroi mines are the chief supplies of coking coal, suitable for smelting; and round Liège is anthracite. The blast furnaces and steelworks of Liège depend largely on coke brought from Charleroi and from the newer Campine coalfield.

The discovery of coal in the Limburg district of the Netherlands led Belgian geologists to think it might exist in the Kempenland, although the surface rock strata gave no promise. Deep borings were made, and early in this century coal was reached at Zuiden, just north of Genk, at a depth of 1775 ft. Further borings proved the existence of a field stretching westwards for 50 miles in Belgian Limburg, at depths varying from 1600 ft to nearly 6000 ft. This is truly a "concealed" field, covering an area of about 500 square miles, under deep layers of Tertiary clays and sands and Cretaceous chalk. The exploitation of coal at such depths presents great difficulties, especially of drainage and ventilation. But the work has gone on apace, and today the annual output of the Campine (Kempen) coalfield is over 10 million tons of coal, including large quantities of the types used for metallurgical coke. The development of a coalfield in a region as unpromising as the Belgian Campine was another problem. It was a heathland almost without population, and so, along with the opening of the mines, there grew up villages and towns for the miners. Labour, too, was scarce and had to be imported, and this process continues. Genk, which was only a small village when coal was first discovered, now has a population of 48,345, of whom about 15,000 are foreigners, largely from Italy. The development of the Campine coalfield is leading to the growth of a new industrial region in Belgium between Liège and Antwerp, and to the breakdown of the monopoly previously held by the Sambre-Meuse, with consequent industrial, commercial and indeed political repercussions, as we have seen.

REGIONAL ECONOMY

In making a more detailed study of the economic geography of Belgium it would seem wise not to examine it under the separate headings of agriculture, manufacturing industry and commerce; for although some of its regions are more important for one type of economic development than for others, over most of the country there is a close connection between rural and urban activities. In much of Flanders, for instance, there is a constant movement from town to country: many of the farmers are small-holders in their own time, but travel daily to regular employment in the towns.

1. *The Belgian Lorraine*

In this tiny region the low hills are forested with conifers, and the valleys given over to pasture and fodder crops. Cattle rearing for meat and dairy products is the chief occupation. Population is small, averaging about 200 per square mile, as compared with a density of 785 for Belgium as a whole. There is only one town of any size, Arlon (12,400), a market town and frontier route centre. Athus (6200), just north of the border, has a steelworks, which uses iron ore from Lorraine.

2. *The Ardennes*

The High Ardennes are a region of bleak moors and rough pasture, with extensive coniferous forests over about half the surface. The scanty population is engaged in farming in the valleys for potatoes and hardy cereals like rye and oats, and in cattle rearing for meat. Quarrying for building stone is widespread, the stone being transported via the Meuse. The river cuts its way across the western end of the High Ardennes in a deep, narrow valley, but, except for the last couple of miles, this part of its course lies in France.

To the north of the High Ardennes is a long trough, the Famenne depression, followed by the low plateaus of Entre-Sambre-et-Meuse, the Condroz and Herve. These are collectively known as the Low Ardennes; but the Herve is covered with limon and so is usually included with the plateaus of central Belgium. The Low Ardennes, especially in the Famenne depression, where there are loams and clays derived from the Devonian rocks, have better soils than the region to the south, but in general the farming activities are similar to those in the rest of the Ardennes. There is a bigger proportion of arable land, however, and a larger output of oats, barley, rye and potatoes. Cattle are reared, mainly for milk, which is sent to the towns of the neighbouring coalfield. The scenic beauty of the Low Ardennes and the Meuse valley has given rise to a tourist industry, and many of the small towns cater for visitors. The chief of them is Dinant (6900) at a crossing place on the Meuse (*see* Fig. 38). The Meuse becomes navigable after it enters Belgium, and the navigable stretch continues almost to the border of the Netherlands. On it are carried large cargoes of coal, iron ore and building stone.

[*Courtesy of the Belgian Embassy.*

FIG. 38.—Belgium: Dinant. An important tourist centre and holiday
resort in the Namur province and on the edge of the Ardennes.
In the picture may be seen the bridge over the river Meuse and
the thirteenth century church of Notre Dame, with its bulbous
baroque tower.

3. *The Sambre–Meuse coalfield*

This long, narrow coalfield, extending 100 miles along the northern
flanks of the Ardennes and rarely more than 6 miles wide, is the most
highly industrialised region of Belgium, with a population of over
2,000,000—a quarter of the country's total. As we have seen, production
is concentrated in three areas, round Mons, Charleroi and Liège, but
Namur, although no longer coal-producing, must be included as a fourth
industrial area. Each of the main towns is surrounded by numerous

smaller ones, all contributing to the main industries of their centres, iron and steel, zinc, chemicals and glass.

Mons (26,136) and its satellite towns, at the western end of the coalfield, are concerned more with coal and coal products than with metallurgical industries. This area, the Borinage, has coke ovens, chemical works and a small cotton textile industry. The last is a kind of overflow from the textile region of France, south of the border.

Charleroi (25,666) would seem from this nominal figure to be the same size as Mons, but it is the centre of a conurbation with a population of about 270,000, making it the fourth largest agglomeration in Belgium. It is an area of steelworks, which are spread along the banks of the Sambre, of engineering plants producing girders, bridge parts, railway rolling stock and engines; there are large chemical and glass works. A large proportion of the mining population comes from foreign countries.

Namur (32,860) is at the confluence of the Sambre and Meuse, and grew originally as a fortress town commanding the route through the Ardennes. It has engineering industries which developed during its coal-producing period, and is also a market town and tourist centre.

Liège (156,728), the largest city of the coalfield, has a conurbation of about 380,000 people, the third largest concentration in Belgium. It is situated on the Meuse, at the meeting point of routes from Paris, Brussels, the north and the Rhineland. It had an ancient iron industry based on ore from the Low Ardennes smelted with charcoal. In 1823, John Cockerill, an immigrant from England, built the first blast furnace with coke as a fuel; from that date Liège became Belgium's chief smelting and steel-making centre. Iron ore is no longer available locally, and supplies are imported from Sweden, Luxembourg and Lorraine. Besides the many steelworks, there is a large zinc smelting and refining industry, using imported raw material. This, too, had its origin in deposits found locally but now exhausted. Heavy and light engineering is widespread, and there are chemical, glass and rubber works. The making of armaments is an old speciality of Liège. The Sambre and Meuse, both navigable, have been of great advantage to the growth of industry in the coalfield; but there was no good through water route to the coast until the opening in 1940 of the Albert Canal, connecting Liège to Antwerp. This canal, together with the development of the new Campine coalfield in the north, has increased the importance of the Liège district, extending the city's sphere of influence well to the west.

East of Liège, in a valley leading from the Low Ardennes, is Verviers (35,350), the centre of a district which since the fifteenth century has been noted for wool textiles, based on soft water and local supplies of wool from the Ardennes. Today most of the raw material is imported. It is interesting to note that the first spinning frame was introduced in 1798 by William Cockerill, father of John, who built the first blast furnace in Liège.

4. The Campine

Westwards from the boundary with Dutch Limburg stretches a belt of heathland, known as the Kempenland or Campine. It is a region of varied development. Over most of its area the sandy soils support meagre agriculture and a poor population, but here and there, where the soils have been improved, are richer communities with dairying and crops of wheat, barley, potatoes and market produce. This is especially the case in the west, nearer Antwerp, where Turnhout (36,334) is a regional centre and market, with agricultural engineering, flour mills and paper manufacture. The largest town in the east of the Campine is Hasselt (36,630), with flour milling and distilling. Both towns have brickworks to supply the growing needs of the new communities of the Campine coalfield.

Along the line of the coalfield, industrial establishments are growing rapidly. At the two ends, the industries of Liège and Antwerp are expanding, mainly in the manufacture of chemicals and glass. In the centre are brickworks and engineering shops concerned with the opening up of the mines. There are as yet no large towns; Genk, with 43,345 inhabitants, is the biggest. South of the coalfield, near the borders of the Campine, is the Albert Canal, constructed specifically to give an all-Belgian passage between the Meuse and the port of Antwerp, and to help in the transport of coal from the Campine field.

5. The région mixte

This narrow belt between the central plains and the Campine has some of the characteristics of both regions, its soils being a mixture of sands and loams, enriched with alluvium from the river Demer. Deposits of clay are the basis of an extensive brick-making industry. It is the most important market-gardening region in Belgium, specialising in early vegetables and chicory. The market is Mechelen (Malines) (64,701), where there are also cotton and foodstuffs manufacturing.

6. The central plains

The provinces of Brabant, Hainaut and the district of Hesbaye, centred on Brussels, are plains or low plateaus covered with limon and river-silts; with them is included the Herve plateau. Here are the most naturally fertile soils, and agriculture is of great importance. The chief crops are wheat and sugar beet, but farming is intensive, and there are many market

G

gardens and orchards. Dairying is important, especially near Brussels. To the north-west of the city, horticulture in hothouses has led to exports of plants and flowers; but in general Belgium is not an exporter of agricultural produce and must import large quantities of wheat and animal fodder.

Manufactures in the central plains are scattered through the many small towns, with concentrations round Brussels and towards the Borinage part of the Sambre-Meuse coalfield in the south. Many of them are connected with the farming products, and flour mills, sugar refineries, distilleries, breweries, canneries and starch works are widespread. Leuven (Louvain) (33,088), in north Brabant, is the largest town outside the capital, and has agricultural engineering and chemical works. The small towns in the south, the Borinage, share in the cotton industry.

Brussels (Bruxelles) (180,771; with suburbs, 1,019,543) is the capital, centrally situated and with easy access to all parts of the country. Besides the administrative and commercial functions usually associated with a capital, it has become the chief industrial city of Belgium. It is a railway and road focus, and is connected by canals to the Scheldt estuary and to Charleroi. Its industries include all types of engineering, chemicals, textiles and clothing, foodstuffs and furniture.

7. Interior Flanders

Flanders occupies the whole of western Belgium, and can be divided into an undulating plain drained by the Scheldt and its tributaries, and the marshes, polders and dunes which border the coast; that is, into "interior" and "maritime" Flanders. The surface cover in the south of the interior plains is of clay, and there is a gradual change northwards to sands; but by heavy manuring the sandy soils have been made as productive as the clay loams, and the whole area has an intensive agriculture.

Early in history the Flemings took advantage of the position of their country at the outlets of the Scheldt, Meuse and Rhine, and became the merchants and manufacturers of the time, trading with England and northern France. Bruges, Ypres and Gent (Gand) were important textile towns in the thirteenth and fourteenth centuries, using wool from local sheep or imported from England. Agriculture was developed to feed the growing population in the towns, and the addition of manure enabled the farmers to abandon the fallow-field system, and obtain the maximum return from their land. The intensive use of the soil continues today, but the industries in the towns, though still important, no longer dominate Belgium's economy as they did in the past.

Throughout interior Flanders there are high yields of wheat, sugar beet, potatoes, hops, chicory and market produce. In the north the farms are small and often worked entirely by hand; in the south they are larger, and there is more mechanised farming. Flax is a specialised crop in the valley of the Lys, whose waters are admirably suited to retting, a preliminary process in the extraction of the fibre from the stalks. Tobacco, too, is grown on most farms in the south. Cattle rearing is relatively unimportant, as there are few meadows, but almost every farm has a few dairy cows which are stall-fed, and there are one or two co-operative dairies.

Because of the silting up of the canal outlets to the sea from Ypres, Gent and Bruges, the wool textile industry of Flanders decayed and its centre moved to Verviers, near the coalfield. There remains, however, a small wool textile industry, specialising in worsteds, at Gent (Gand) and Kortrijk (Courtrai). Gent (158,414; with suburbs, 225,000), situated at the confluence of the Scheldt and Lys, is the chief industrial city of interior Flanders, and the fifth largest conurbation in the country. It is the centre of the linen industry, based originally on local flax. Today four-fifths of the raw material is imported. Round Gent, too, is the greatest concentration of cotton manufacture; the city has textile engineering. Cottons are made also at Oudenaarde (6530), Aalst (Alost) (45,593) and Dendermonde (Termonde). Tournai (33,383) has engineering and very old porcelain and tapestry industries.

8. *Maritime Flanders*

This is a narrow belt of polders protected from the sea by a line of dunes, broken only by canal exits at Nieuwpoort, Ostend, Blankenberge and Zeebrugge. In the dunelands is a succession of holiday resorts, Ostend and Blankenberge the chief of them. Ostend (56,747) is Belgium's main fishing port, and has packet steamer connections with England. The fishing has led to canning and the building of trawlers. Nieuwpoort is a minor port serving the south of Flanders, and has a small chemical industry. Zeebrugge is an artificial harbour, built so that the canal from Bruges to the sea might be reopened and widened.

The Belgian polders are mostly under grass, and the chief occupation is dairying, associated with the rearing of pigs. Vegetables are grown for the towns along the coast, and for Bruges, the largest town of the interior. Brugge (Bruges) (52,167) is on the edge of the polders, and is one of the old worsted towns. Today it has lace-making and embroidery (Fig. 39), mainly for sale to tourists; but far more important than these craft industries are the engineering works and shipyards near the canal which connects the city to Zeebrugge.

The northern part of the polders, bordering on the Scheldt estuary, is intensively cultivated to supply the large population of Antwerp. Antwerp (261,405; with suburbs, 525,000) is Belgium's chief port, built at the

[*Courtesy of the Belgian Embassy.*

FIG. 39.—Belgium: a lace maker at work. The photograph was taken
in Bruges, which for centuries has been noted for lace. Bruges
claims to be the best-preserved medieval city in Europe.

lowest bridging point of the Scheldt, and where ocean-going vessels can
reach its extensive docks. Inland, it has barge traffic via the Albert Canal
to Liège, the coalfields and Luxembourg, and via the Scheldt and a connecting canal to Brussels. It handles Belgium's main imports of mineral
ores, textile raw materials, petroleum, timber and foodstuffs, and exports
principally steel, chemicals and glass. It has shipbuilding yards and oil
refineries, engineering and food processing industries; and its diamond
cutting and polishing rivals that of Amsterdam. It is much more a city of
miscellaneous industries than most large ports, since it is the only major
port in Belgium.

LUXEMBOURG

REGIONAL GEOGRAPHY

The Grand Duchy of Luxembourg, one of the smallest sovereign states in Europe, lies south-east of Belgium. Physically, it may be divided into (1) the Ardennes plateau, sometimes called the "Oesling," in the north, and (2) a low, rolling plain, the "Gutland" or "Bon Pays" in the south. In the south-west, the Bon Pays rises to an extension into Luxembourg of the Lorraine plateau (*see* Fig. 40).

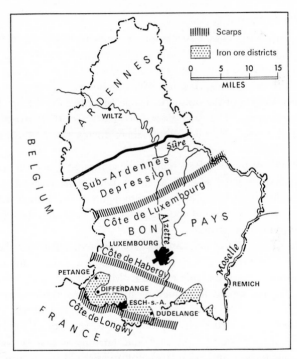

FIG. 40.—Luxembourg: general features. The Ardennes region is also known as the Oesling, and the Bon Pays as the Gutland. Part of the Sûre basin is called "Petite Suisse" ("Little Switzerland").

1. *The Luxembourg Ardennes*

These are similar in structure to Belgium's High Ardennes, of which they are outrunners. They are composed mainly of slates, quartzites and hard sandstones. They are not as high as the Belgian ranges, rising from

1300 to 1835 ft, but they are more deeply dissected by narrow valleys. The climate is not as harsh as in the High Ardennes, but the soils are just as poor. The valley sides are thickly forested with conifers and beech, and there is some lumbering. Part of the region has been called "Petite Suisse" ("Little Switzerland") because of its picturesque scenery, and an attempt is being made to develop a tourist industry.

The scanty population grows potatoes, oats and rye, but the main occupation is dairying, mainly for butter, which is made in co-operative dairies. The largest town, Wiltz, with fewer than 5000 inhabitants, is little more than a village. The whole region occupies 32% of the Duchy's area, but has less than a fifth of its inhabitants.

2. *Southern Luxembourg*

South of the Ardennes, a succession of outcrops of Jurassic and Triassic sandstones, chalk, marls and clays have broken down to form a plain crossed by ranges of low hills. This is the Bon Pays or Gutland ("Good Land"), with soils of varying fertility, but on the whole good. In the south-west, fingers of the oolitic Côtes de Moselle extend from Lorraine into Luxembourg. The Bon Pays falls gently south-eastwards to the valley of the river Moselle, which there forms the boundary of the Duchy.

The climate of the Bon Pays tends to be continental, and the scarplands in the south-west have actually as much rain as the Ardennes, but the Moselle valley is sheltered and has mild winters (35° F; 1·6° C), warm summers (65° F; 18° C), and about 25 in. of rain annually. On the south-east slopes, vines are grown.

The Bon Pays was at one time largely forested, but today the lower-lying areas are cleared. The clay lands are used for pasture, and the marls and sandstone areas for arable farming. Much of the timber was burnt to make charcoal for the iron smelting industry. As in northern Luxembourg, dairying is the most important branch of agriculture, the chief product being raw milk, which is supplied to the city of Luxembourg and to the iron-working towns. Arable farming is mainly for wheat, potatoes, sugar beet and root crops for fodder. Wine is produced at Remich and other villages in the Moselle valley.

INDUSTRY AND TOWNS

The chief product of Luxembourg is iron ore. The *minette* field of Lorraine extends for 14 square miles into the Duchy; and although it is of such small area, it is estimated to have reserves of over 300 million tons of iron ore. The ore is not rich, the iron content being usually less than 30%; but three-fifths of the total is calcareous and self-fluxing, and can be mixed with the remaining more difficult siliceous ore. The main smelting town is Esch, and there are blast furnaces at Pétange, Differdange and Dudelange; all the towns have converters and steelworks. The capacity of the Duchy's blast furnaces is greater than its actual output of ore, and large amounts of iron ore are imported from Lorraine and Sweden.

[*Courtesy of the Luxembourg Embassy.*

FIG. 41.—Luxembourg: Esch-sur-Alzette. This is the centre of the steel industry in the Grand Duchy. The deposits of *minette* iron ore are extensions of the Lorraine iron-field of France.

By agreement, some ore is sent raw to Liège and Charleroi, in return for coke. Steel accounts for nearly 90% of Luxembourg's total exports.

The largest town in the Duchy is Luxembourg (72,000), the capital, built at a bend in the river Alzette, in the middle of the Bon Pays and in the lee of the Ardennes. Its name was originally Lützelburg (little fortress) for it grew first on the top of steep cliffs overlooking the winding river. The modern town lies in the valley at their feet. It is in the centre of a good farming region and has miscellaneous industries such as glove-making, tanning, woollen manufacture, brewing, paper-making and sugar refining. It has also the largest steel-using works in the Duchy, making bridge parts, cranes, boilers and agricultural machinery.

The only towns of any size away from the capital are those already mentioned on the iron field, Esch-sur-Alzette (27,954), Differdange (17,600), Dudelange (15,000) and Pétange (12,000) (*see* Fig. 41).

HUMAN GEOGRAPHY

HISTORY AND PEOPLE

The county of Luxemburg (note the different spelling), of which the present Duchy forms a part, was originally in the empire of Charlemagne, and passed into the hands of the Luxemburg family about 1060. In the following centuries it belonged at different times to Germany, Burgundy, Spain and France. At the end of the Napoleonic wars it was assigned to the Netherlands, but in 1830, when the Belgian provinces separated from Holland, Luxemburg became part of the new kingdom, although there was a demand that the eastern portion should remain in Dutch hands. The partition was enforced in 1838 and Luxemburg, within its present boundaries, came into existence, still as a Grand Duchy but under the Netherlands crown, and remained so until 1890. In that year it passed to the Nassau family, to whom it still belongs.

As part of the Treaty of Vienna (1815), Germany was empowered to garrison the fortress of Luxemburg, and Prussian troops were stationed in the Grand Duchy from 1815 to 1872, when, by the terms of the Treaty of London (1867) they were withdrawn. By the same treaty the great powers guaranteed the neutrality of the Grand Duchy, and although it was still ruled by the king of the Netherlands it became a sovereign and independent state, with the Dutch king as Grand Duke.

BENELUX

In the original Grand Duchy, the people nearer to France and Belgium were French-speaking, and those in the east spoke a German patois. When the Duchy was partitioned, the "French" portion was given to Belgium; the present Grand Duchy is mostly German-speaking. The population is about 319,000, with a density of 316 persons per square mile. Prior to 1914, Luxembourg formed part of the German *Zollverein* (customs union) and economically was largely dependent on Germany. In 1922 it abandoned its German trade treaty and entered into a customs union with Belgium. In 1944 it joined Belgium and the Netherlands to form the commercial and industrial union of Benelux. The change in the spelling of its name became general after 1922, and the new spelling—Luxembourg—has been adopted also for the Belgian province.

1. Explain why Belgium has one of the highest population densities of western Europe and yet is relatively poorly endowed with natural resources. (O. & C.)

2. Give a reasoned account of the economic geography of Belgium. (J.M.B.)

3. Compare Belgium with Norway in respect of their external trade. (J.M.B.)

4. What is there in the geography of Belgium, the Netherlands and Luxembourg to suggest that they could form a single economic and political unit? (O. & C.)

Chapter XIV

FRANCE: PHYSICAL

FRANCE, after the U.S.S.R., is the largest country in Europe, with an area twice that of the United Kingdom. It is a very compact country, the distance from the middle of its eastern frontier to any of its coasts varying little from 300 miles. France has coastlines along the Atlantic and the Mediterranean so that, although it is boxed in by mountains on its eastern side, its coasts provide easy access to the interior, the more so as they are backed by wide lowland gaps. Through these gateways in the north, west and south entered from earliest times a succession of colonising and civilising peoples, so that France became a meeting place of varying cultures which gradually fused to produce the present-day unity. In other ways, too—in the diverse characteristics of its structure, relief, climate, soils, use of the land and ways of life—France shows how the most varied factors can harmonise to engender a culture which has had profound influence not only on its own people but on the civilisation of the world at large. To choose just one example: the French language was for centuries the common means of communication in diplomatic circles and the tongue of all educated people. As the largest and potentially the most important country in peninsular Europe, France is given more extended and detailed treatment in this book than other countries.

STRUCTURE IN GENERAL

Geologically, the most ancient parts of France are the uplands of the Armorican and Central massifs, the Ardennes, and the Vosges. These belong to the Carbo-Permian period, when widespread earth movements caused folded mountain chains to rise from south Russia to southern Ireland. These chains, known as the Hercynian system, were denuded for millions of years and worn down to peneplains. In subsequent repeated and prolonged periods of marine transgression they were covered by limestones, sandstones and clays. At times when the seas retreated, these sedimentaries were washed from them by rivers, so that long, low ridges of older rocks remained, surrounded by still lower plains of younger rocks (*see* Fig. 42).

During the Alpine mountain-building movements of Tertiary times, the worn-down Hercynian ranges acted as buffers against the folding forces from the south and influenced the size and trend of the newly rising ridges considerably. At the same time they were affected themselves. The ancient, worn-down ranges were faulted and fractured into numerous blocks, some of which were uplifted and tilted, some depressed. Here and there the dislocation was accompanied by volcanic activity. The uplift of the blocks (horsts) was followed by renewed

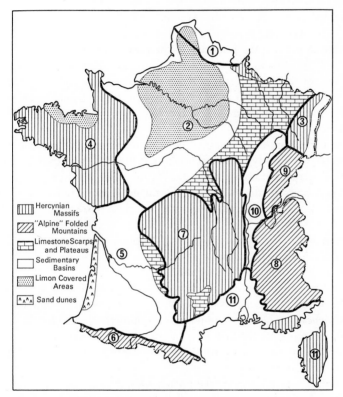

Fig. 42.—France: chief structural divisions. The numbers refer to the physical and economic regions treated in the text.

denudation, exposing in each of them some of the pre-Cambrian and Palaeozoic rocks which existed before the Hercynian movements, or bringing to the surface intrusive rocks such as granite. All the Hercynian horsts contain metamorphic rocks too—schists, slates—and older sedimentaries—limestones, sandstones. Some have lavas and volcanic ash.

The effects of the Alpine orogenesis on the Hercynian structures were unequal. The horsts further away from the new folding were not so broken and uplifted. The greatest effect was felt in the Central Massif, the eastern edge of which was uptilted to form the Cevennes. The western side of the Massif falls more gently to the basin of Aquitaine. The Central Massif is the largest of the horsts, occupying one-sixth of the surface of France.

The Vosges mountains lie along the western side of the Rhine rift valley. They rise gradually from the Paris basin, but on the east they present a steep face to the valley. Only a small portion of the Ardennes is situated within France; the Ardennes Massif is part of the fractured plateaus which interrupt the middle or gorge tract of the Rhine. The Armorican plateau, the peninsula in the north-west of the country, projects into the Atlantic; it was the least affected of the Hercynian horsts and, but for the fact that it is made up of rocks of an earlier age, it would be hard to distinguish in relief from neighbouring regions. It has in fact a lower average elevation (300 ft) than any other major structural division of France.

The formation of the Alpine fold-system in the south and south-east of France has already been outlined in Chapter I. The Pyrenees, which form a barrier between France and Spain, were uplifted earlier than the main body of the Alps, though still in Tertiary times. They rise abruptly from the plains in the south, and their narrow ranges contain fragmented blocks of Hercynian rocks which were carried up in the folded sedimentaries. The Pyrenees are more continuous and have fewer passes than later Alpine ranges, but they are not as high as some of the Alps in south-eastern France or Switzerland.

The Jura mountains are hills rather than heights. They run in a great arc from the southern end of the Rhine rift valley to a point south of Lake Geneva. They are composed of symmetrically folded limestone ridges and represent the first onset of later Alpine movement, which was not affected by the vast overthrusting and nappe formation found in the more southerly ranges.

South of Lake Geneva are the French Alps, divisible into northern and southern sections by the valleys of the rivers Drac and lower Isère (*see* Fig. 67). The northern French Alps are further divided by the middle Isère valley—the "Alpine furrow"—into the High Alps and the pre-Alps. The southern French Alps, or Basses Alpes, have a more east–west trend than the northern ranges. The folds are in the line of the Pyrenees, but in the confused topography it is not easy to distinguish them.

South of the Alpine folds, in Provence, are the ancient massifs of Maures and Estérel, bordering the Mediterranean. They are fragments of an old Mediterranean land mass, of which the mountainous island of Corsica also formed a part. They are probably of Hercynian origin.

The lowlands of France are best located by relating their positions to the adjacent massifs and mountains. In the north of the country, lying between the Vosges, Ardennes, Armorican massif, and the Central Massif, is a great basin filled with sedimentary rocks of Secondary and later times. The Alpine movement was responsible for the basin shape, for it tilted the original horizontal strata upwards along the edges of the Hercynian blocks. Erosion has resulted in a series of curved escarpments, best seen in the eastern portion of the basin, in the Côtes de Meuse and Côtes de Moselle. The basin formation is not so obvious in the west, where, as already remarked, it is difficult to distinguish a definite boundary between the sedimentary plains and Armorica. The basin centres on Paris and so is usually called the Paris basin.

To the north of the Paris basin is the plain of French Flanders, separated from the basin by the hills of Artois. These are anticlinal ridges folded on a buried Hercynian platform, and form a structural boundary between the plains of Belgium and France.

Between the Central Massif and the Armorican block is the Gate of Poitou, a broad gap which leads from the Paris basin to an undulating plain drained principally by the rivers Dordogne, Garonne and their tributaries. This is the basin of Aquitaine, bounded on the east by the Central Massif, on the west by the Bay of Biscay and on the south by the Pyrenees.

Along the Mediterranean coast is a triangular plain, bounded by the Alps and Central Massif. The apex of the plain, which is known as the Midi, is in the lower Rhône valley near the confluence of the Drôme. Northwards, the lowland continues in the narrow Rhône valley to the low plateaus of Bas-Dauphiné and Dombes, beyond which there is a widening to the plains of the river Saône. The lowlands of the passage from the delta of the Rhône in the south to the foot of the Vosges in the north are the Rhône–Saône "corridor," an apt name for the most important entrance from the Mediterranean to the north of France. The Mediterranean plain is connected to the basin of Aquitaine by the Gate of Carcassonne, between the Pyrenees and the Central Massif. The Rhône–Saône Corridor marks the close juxtaposition of the Alps and the Central Massif.

The last, and smallest, of the French lowlands is the plain of Alsace. It lies between the Vosges and the river Rhine, forming the western half of the floor of the Rhine rift valley.

STRUCTURAL REGIONS

From the outline of the structure of France given above, it is seen that the country may be divided into convenient regions for more detailed study. Since these regional divisions are distinguished from each other not only by their structure and physical features but also by their human and economic geography, they will be adopted also as economic regions. They will be considered in the following order (*see* Fig. 42):

(1) the industrial north-east, (2) the Paris basin, (3) the Vosges and the plain of Alsace, (4) the Armorican Massif, (5) the basin of Aquitaine, (6) the Pyrenees, (7) the Central Massif, (8) the French Alps, (9) the Jura mountains, (10) the Rhône–Saône corridor, (11) the Mediterranean region. These regions are the usual basis for the regional study of France, but some geographers prefer to treat the scarplands of Lorraine as a separate region, or to include the industrial north-east, *i.e.* the plain of French Flanders, with the Paris basin, or to deal with the plain of the Midi as part of the Rhône–Saône corridor. There is something to be said for all these alternatives, but in this book the only departures from the structural divisions are the inclusion of the southern portion of Armorica (the Vendée) with the Paris basin, and the treatment of the Vosges and the plain of Alsace in the same section.

1. *The industrial north-east*

Although the structural name for the northernmost region is the plain of French Flanders, it is often referred to as the industrial north-east, since that aspect of its geography is predominant. The plain lies north of the hills of Artois, a chalk ridge never more than 600 ft in elevation. The plain of French Flanders resembles its Belgian counterpart in having maritime and interior sections. The maritime area has dunes near the coast, and these are backed by polders reclaimed from marshland. Interior French Flanders is a clay-covered plain, crossed by the upper Lys and Escaut (Scheldt) rivers, and their tributaries Lawe and Scarpe. Running roughly east–west under the chalk of the Artois ridge is the concealed Nord and Pas-de-Calais coalfield. It is a continuation of the Belgian field, and was similarly broken and disrupted by Hercynian earth movements, so that mining is difficult.

2. *The Paris basin*

This is the largest and most important plain in the west of Europe. In a depression surrounded by Hercynian formations, strata ranging from Triassic to late Tertiary (Pliocene, Miocene) times were laid down on a slowly sinking sea bed. Alpine earth movements caused an uplift and slight wrinkling of the strata; the corresponding Hercynian rejuvenation allowed the rocks of the depression to sag, so as to give the appearance of a dish, lower in the centre and with upturned edges. Prolonged erosion, especially rapid in post-Glacial times, stripped the newer rocks from the up-tilted rims of the basin, exposing the older rocks and producing a succession of escarpments or *cuestas*, with intervening valleys floored by young rocks.

The Paris basin in consequence resembles a series of saucers stacked on top of each other, each one smaller than the last, their rims represented

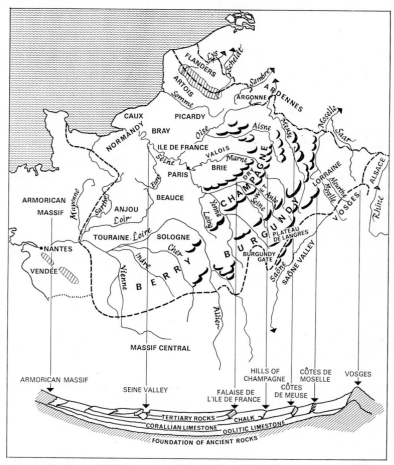

FIG. 43.—France: Paris basin. Showing surface features, rivers, and chief districts. *See also* Figs. 59 and 60.

by concentric rings of sandstone, limestone and chalk hills (*see* Fig. 43). Since the strata all dip towards the centre, there is a corresponding series of scarps facing outwards. Most of the area of the basin is under 600 ft in height, but some of the eastern limestone escarpments, *e.g.* in Lorraine, rise to more than 1200 ft. The "saucer" formation is best seen in the east. Near the Vosges is a zone of Triassic rocks, which is followed by the

Jurassic escarpments of the Côtes de Moselle, the Plateau de Langres and the Côtes de Meuse. The first two are composed of Oolitic limestone, the last of Corallian limestone. Between the two limestone types is a vale floored with Oxford clay, through which flows the river Meuse. Westwards, the Jurassic rocks are overlain in "wet" Champagne by Gault clay, and this is succeeded by the chalk escarpment of "dry" Champagne. The dip-slopes of the chalk hills fall to the valley of the river Seine, on the other side of which there is a quick rise to the Falaise de l'Ile de France, the edge of the innermost "saucer," which is composed of Tertiary limestones, sandstones, marls and clays.

The rims of the "saucers" cannot be traced so readily on the north, west and south of the Paris basin as on the east. In the north, the chalk escarpments are interrupted at the English Channel, and the Jurassic rocks occur only in small outcrops at Cape Gris Nez and from Honfleur to Trouville, where there are cliffs. In the west, where earth movements were least, there was minimum scarp formation, and erosion has so worn the surface as to make the relief more or less continuous with the pene-plained Armorican massif. In the south the escarpments are masked by later deposits of residual clays, gravels and alluvium.

Large areas of the centre and north of the Paris basin are covered by a super-ficial layer of *limon* (*see* pp. 168, 212); as mentioned above, the limestones and chalk often have overlying residual clays (clays-with-flints), gravels and—in the valleys—river alluvium. All these hold moisture, and where they cover porous or permeable strata they give more scope for arable and pastoral farming than where the limestone or the chalk is at the surface.

The drainage of the Paris basin, with the exception of Lorraine and the south (middle Loire), is towards the north-west. The Jurassic scarplands of Lorraine, although structurally a part of it, are often treated as a separate region, largely because their drainage (via the rivers Meuse and Moselle) is away from the main basin. In the south, the middle Loire is included with the Paris basin; and the lower Loire, although it forms a part of the Armorican massif, is added too, mainly as a matter of economic conven-ience.

Drainage in the remainder of the basin is controlled by the arc shape of the eastern scarplands, which throw the flow of their streams to a meeting-point near Paris, where they are gathered by the river Seine. The chief tributaries—Oise, Marne, Aube and Yonne—cut through the escarpments by wide gaps, making communications easy. All the rivers are navigable for river traffic, or have been canalised, and by means of a system of linking canals the whole of the Paris basin has been covered by a network of water communications. This in turn has been joined by canals to the rivers Meuse, Moselle, Rhine, Rhône and Somme. The

Somme, which flows independently to the sea north of the Seine, is connected also to the Scheldt (Escaut) and thus to the canal and river system of Belgium and the Netherlands. The waterways of the Paris basin are a very important part of the water network which covers so much of western Europe.

The Seine basin is an excellent study for physical geographers. Many of the streams present examples of antecedent drainage; there are many wind-gaps and dry valleys in the chalk escarpments; river capture has been frequent. One of the outstanding cases of river capture is that of the Loire. The Loire originally joined the Seine via the valley of the present Loing. Its upper course was captured by a swift stream flowing to the Bay of Biscay. The elbow of capture is easily discernible. It seems to be the case, too, that the Yonne and lower Seine were originally a consequent stream flowing from the Plateau de Langres; and that a vigorous right-bank tributary at the foot of the Falaise de l'Ile de France captured first the upper Seine and then the Aube. The incised meanders between Paris and the sea should also be noted. In this part of the river a tidal bore (the *mascaret*) penetrates beyond Rouen.

The diverse rock structure, relief and soils of the Paris basin have led to a great variety of landscapes and land utilisation. "There are rolling expanses of arable lands with fertile loamy soils growing wheat and sugar beet; extensive tracts of poor grazing on bare chalk and limestone; heavy, well watered clay lands with prosperous dairy farms; dense plantations of conifers on sandstone ridges; market gardens along the valley floors and serried rows of vines on south-facing slopes" (Monkhouse, *Western Europe*, p. 186).

3. *The Vosges and Plain of Alsace*

The Vosges form part of the Hercynian orogeny, rising like a wall along the western side of the Rhine rift valley. The ridge is divided in two by the Saverne Gate, the only easy passage through the mountains. North of the gap are the Low Vosges, mainly of sandstones, at an average elevation of 1300 ft (Wintersberg, 1906 ft, the highest point). The sandstones have weathered into difficult terrain, and the extensive forests which cover them support a very scanty population. The High Vosges, south of the Saverne Gate, average 3000 ft and rise in some rounded peaks to over 4500 ft (Ballon de Guebwiller, 4679 ft, is the highest). The High Vosges are composed of crystalline gneisses, schists and granite, with some sandstones in the north.

The Plain of Alsace, on the western side of the Rhine, varies in width from 10 to 25 miles. It descends from the foot of the Vosges, first by wide, loess-covered terraces, then by stretches of sandy gravels and finally to

ill-drained alluvial clays near the river. The Rhine in the southern part
is swift and unnavigable, but canals constructed parallel to its course give
water communication from Strasbourg to Basel and to the Rhône. The
Rhine below Basel has been harnessed for hydro-electric power. North
of Strasbourg it is navigable.

4. *The Armorican massif*

Often the peninsular mass which projects westwards into the Atlantic
is referred to simply as Brittany or the Breton peninsula, but the ancient
rocks of which the region is composed extend eastward and southward
beyond the limits of the province, and are known as the Armorican
massif (*Ar Mor*, "land of the sea"). Armorica shows many outcrops of
pre-Cambrian rocks, and possibly these were folded in Caledonian times.
The main movements belong to the Hercynian (Carbo-Permian) period,
when complex folding, with trends in a general east–west or south-east–
north-west direction, raised high mountains. In Secondary times these
were worn down to a peneplain, and prolonged marine transgression
covered the resultant low plateau with Secondary and Tertiary sedimentaries, such as are found in the Paris basin.

Armorica was far from the centre of the "Alpine storm" of the mid-
Tertiary, and the earth movements were felt merely as ripples. The whole
mass was uplifted and tilted slightly to the south but there was no major
faulting. The uplift led to further denudation, and the Secondary and
Tertiary rocks were stripped from its surface, except along the eastern
edges and, where they were preserved in a very few hollows, in the south.
River drainage was developed on the Tertiary surface; as the newer rocks
were eroded, its pattern was *superimposed* on the older rocks laid bare
on the surface. The resultant relief is a series of low plateaus of resistant
granites and crystalline schists, separated by slightly lower depressions
floored by weaker Silurian, Devonian and Lower Carboniferous slates
and shales, and the clays derived from them.

The plateaus follow the ancient trend-lines. In the north the rounded
Montagnes d'Arrée (1283 ft) can be traced eastwards to the Montagnes
d'Alençon in Normandy; across the centre of Brittany are the Montagnes
Noires (1069 ft); along the south coast, continuing to the Hautures de
Gâtine in the Vendée, is a still lower (600 ft) line of plateaus, broken by
several lowland gaps, prominently in the lower Loire valley. Between
the series are the depressions of the Châteaulin basin, which opens to the
west coast, and the much more extensive Rennes basin in the east. A
broken Hercynian ridge can be traced in the north, in the Cotentin peninsula and the Channel Islands.

Armorica has a rugged coastline, especially in the west, where it is

[*Courtesy of the French Embassy.*

FIG. 44.—France: Dinan. A small market town and tourist centre in northern Brittany. Note (*a*) the "bocage" landscape, (*b*) the roads following both banks of the river Rance, (*c*) passenger vessels on the river, which is navigable from Dinard, a port at its mouth. Dinan is at the limit of navigation.

subjected to the marine erosion of the Atlantic. A slight post-Glacial (Quaternary) inundation by the sea drowned the lower valleys of rivers and formed rias where the coast cuts across the grain of the land. In the inlets caused by constant pounding of ocean waves against rocks of varying resistance are deposits of marine clays, sands and fragmented shells, covered frequently by thick masses of seaweed, which is collected and used as fertiliser or for the extraction of iodine.

5. *The basin of Aquitaine*

Between Armorica and the Central Massif is a broad gap 40 miles wide: the Gate of Poitou, connecting the Paris basin to the large, triangular plain of Aquitaine, which extends southwards to the Pyrenees between the Central Massif and the Bay of Biscay. As in the Paris basin, the underlying basal rocks are Jurassic limestones, which outcrop here along the edges of the Central Massif. These were covered by Cretaceous chalks and limestones which today form the surface of most of the area north of the Gironde, and of a belt near the Pyrenees. Tertiary clays and sands are the cover south of the Gironde. They extend eastward in the basin of the Garonne, between the Central Massif and the Pyrenees.

The Alpine movements of Tertiary times caused very slight folding in the Aquitaine basin; but the uplift and tilting of the Central Massif gave it a slant to the west. The glaciers of the Quaternary period deposited boulder-clay, gravels and drift in a thick band on the Pyrenean piedmont, and the post-glacial rivers cut wide valleys and spread alluvium in the rapidly eroded lowlands. Slight transgression by the sea in more recent Quaternary times resulted in the laying down of marine sands in the west, and these have helped to build the line of dunes—the Landes—along the coasts of the Bay of Biscay.

The whole basin has worn to a gently undulating plain, with more prominent ridges and valleys in the limestones to the east. The limestone and chalk areas are dry and only moderately fertile. The Tertiary soils south of the Gironde are richer, but the sands of the Landes and the glacial deposits in the Lannemezan area on the flanks of the Pyrenees—fan-shaped screes from which the finer materials have been washed to leave thick layers of gravel—are poor and support only a very small population. The best areas are the valleys of the Garonne and the Adour.

6. The Pyrenees

The Pyrenees are a complex system of fold-mountains, forming a barrier more than 250 miles long between France and Spain, from the Bay of Biscay to the Mediterranean. They belong to the Tertiary earth movements but are older than the main Alpine uplift. They may be divided into the western Pyrenees, averaging about 3000 ft in height and composed of limestones; the central Pyrenees, where intense folding brought to the surface pre-Cambrian and older Primary rocks with intrusive granites, in the highest part of the ranges; and the eastern section, where the trend-lines become more east–west, the ranges are lower again and there are outliers of the Hercynian Central Massif mixed with the Alpine folds. The highest peak in the Pyrenees is the Pic d'Aneto (11,169 ft) in the Maladetta massif in the central section; but this, and indeed most of the Pyrenean mountain complex, is in Spain. In both the central and eastern sections the crystalline core is flanked on the north and south sides by limestones, mainly of Jurassic age. The Pyrenees are a remarkably continuous system, with few passes; the best are the Pass of Roncesvalles in the west, and the Col de la Perche, east of Andorra (see Fig. 64). The Somport Pass, near the Pic du Midi d'Ossau, is crossed by a railway which rises to 3973 ft. Other passes are little more than mule tracks in their upper portions. One of them, the Envalira, climbs to nearly 8000 ft and links the little mountain state of Andorra to the outside world.

The chief rivers rising in the French Pyrenees are the Adour and its tributary, the Gave de Pau, the Ariège which flows to the Garonne, and the Aude. The Garonne has its source south of the international boundary. In their upper courses they flow through limestone country, with intermittent surface drainage, underground streams and caves, and massive gorges, reminiscent of the Causses in the Central Massif. On the French side the Pyrenees in many places rise like a wall; valleys running into the range terminate in cirques or in narrow passages leading upwards to cols. One of the best known cirques is that of Gavarnie, a great amphitheatre 2 miles across, with cliff walls rising in terraces to over 5000 ft. Much of the land-sculpture is due to glaciers in the past, although today permanent snow is found only in the central Pyrenees above 10,000 ft.

7. The Central Massif

The Central Plateau or Massif (Massif Central) is the largest of the ancient blocks in France, occupying about one-sixth of the country, at an average elevation of 3000 ft, with a maximum height of 6188 ft in the Puy de Sancy. Ancient crystalline rocks predominate in its structure: granites, gneisses and schists, as well as Silurian sedimentaries, form the surface over large areas. Its development was extremely complex. Beginning in Hercynian (Carbo-Permian) times, folding took place along two lines, north-east to south-west and north-west to south-east, meeting as a V in the south of the region. This period of mountain-building was followed by long denudation during which the ranges were worn down. The peneplanation removed most of the Carboniferous and Permian rocks, leaving coal measures in only a few small and scattered basins.

Slow subsidence and marine transgression allowed the deposition of Triassic and Jurassic rocks, mainly limestones, which, in a deep syncline in the south, reached a thickness of well over 4000 ft. The limestones were later eroded from the Massif, but remained in this southern area between the Cevennes and the Montagnes Noires, known as the Grandes Causses, and round the margins of the Massif. In early Tertiary times, new tectonic movements allowed the formation of Eocene and Oligocene clays and sands, which remain in the Limousin and the upper Loire and Allier valleys; but the present outline of the Central Massif was determined mainly by the Alpine orogeny of the mid-Tertiary.

First of all, the Pyrenean uplift must have caused severe faulting in the south and south-east. Then the main Alpine movements exerted forces from the south-east, which were resisted by the rigid horst. The whole block was uplifted and tilted from east to west, and south to north; great faults occurred along the eastern edges, and rift valleys in the middle. The Limagne, for instance, traversed by the river Allier, is a rift valley. The faulting was accompanied by extensive vulcanicity in the centre of the Massif, and this volcanic action continued until comparatively recently.

Most of the volcanic rocks are in the Auvergne, with a smaller area in the Plateau du Velay, south-east of it. In the south of the Auvergne is the Aubrac plateau, composed of basaltic lava outflows and rising to over

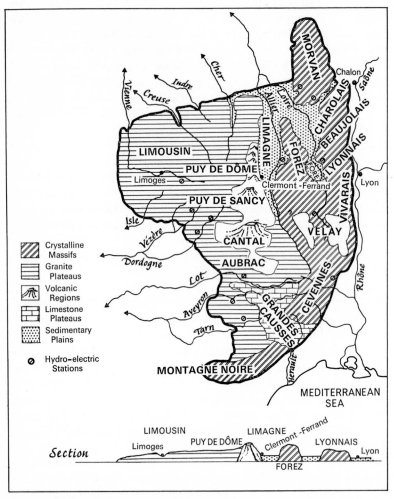

FIG. 45.—France: Central Massif, structure. The map should be studied in conjunction with the text and with Fig. 65. Note how the river drainage gives a clue to the tilting and faulting of the Massif.

4250 ft. This plateau has an undulating and unbroken surface, but the Velay plateau, separated from it by the granite mass of Margeride, is eroded by the headstreams of the Loire into a larger number of isolated rock-pinnacles, separated by deep valleys. In other places are more pinnacles, volcanic plugs from which the surrounding cones have been eroded. On the tops of many of these eminences are churches or monuments; and on the lower slopes of one of them stands the little town of Le Puys.

North of the Aubrac is the Cantal, a huge crater 50 miles in diameter, in which differential erosion has left parts sticking up as peaks, the highest being the rounded basalt dome of Plomb du Cantal (6096 ft). Northwards is the much dissected cone of Mont Dore (6188 ft), followed by the remarkable Chaîne des Puys or Monts Dôme, a group of about 70 cones large and small rising from the plateau and known generally as *puys*. Most are composed of cinders or volcanic ash, but some are the plugs of highly acid lavas, and project upwards in pillars of Peléan type. The finest example is the Puy de Dôme, which reaches a height of 4806 ft.

The Central Massif, then, is a peneplaned horst with large areas of flat or rounded platforms away from the volcanic region, sloping to the west and north-west from the high Cevennes, which form its south-eastern boundary. It is cut by deep and in some cases wide valleys, made deeper and wider by the rejuvenation of Alpine times and by post-Glacial floodwaters. In the north are the tectonic basins of the Loire and Allier, which were lakes in early Tertiary times and are floored in places by Eocene and Oligocene deposits. In the west and south are the dry, limestone Causses; and in Limousin the hills have the same general trend as those of Armorica. The Morvan, in the north-east, is very like the Vosges in its structure and forest cover.

8. *The French Alps*

The Alps in France form a great curve from Lake Geneva to the Mediterranean. Within their ranges the frontiers of France, Italy and Switzerland meet at a point north-east of Mont Blanc (15,782 ft), the highest peak in the system. The French Alps are penetrated by only two railways, a northern line using the Mont Cenis tunnel ($8\frac{1}{2}$ miles long; also called the Fréjus tunnel) *en route* to Turin, and a southern line northwards from Nice via the Col de Tende, also to Turin.

As we have already indicated, the Alps in France are divided into northern and southern sections by the valleys of the Drac and lower Isère; the northern portion is further sub-divided by the middle Isère valley into the pre-Alps and the High Alps. The pre-Alps are of simple limestone folds, like the Jura, but the High Alps are the result of intense folding. Great blocks of the existing Hercynian land mass were caught up in the folded sedimentaries and are found as crystalline masses in the Grandes Rousses and Mont Blanc. *Nappes*—recumbent folds torn by overthrusts and carried bodily forwards away from their original position—add to the complexity of the High Alps. In addition to the ancient crystalline rocks, there is a variety of Carboniferous, Permian, Secondary and Tertiary sedimentaries, many of them metamorphosed into schists. The Great St Bernard nappe is mainly in Switzerland, but there is a small portion of it—the Graian Alps—in France.

To the west of the High Alps is a mass of Tertiary sands, shales, breccias and marls, collectively known as *Flysch*; it occurs also along the edges of the southern French Alps. These are composed of limestone, like the

[*Courtesy of the French Embassy.*]

FIG. 46.—France: Valgaudemar, in the High Alps. Note (*a*) the shape of the valley, (*b*) the extensive screes and absence of vegetation on the left of the river, (*c*) the cultivation of the valley flats, (*d*) the "alps" on the right of the picture, (*e*) the sheltered site of the village, helped further by a wind-break of trees.

pre-Alps, but the ranges are less simple in structure. In the south, the north–south folds of the Alps were in conflict with the eastern end of the Pyrenean east–west folds, and the result is a confused region of broken ranges, difficult to penetrate. The limestone Alps, which include the pre-Alps and the southern French Alps, and run from Lake Geneva to the Alpes de Provence, are sometimes referred to as the fore-Alps.

The Alps were heavily glaciated during the Quaternary Ice Age, and there are still permanent snow-fields in the Mont Blanc and neighbouring massifs. Most of the usual glacial features are present—cirques, cols, benches, hanging valleys, etc.—and many of the lower valleys are U shaped and floored with boulder clay or blocked by moraines.

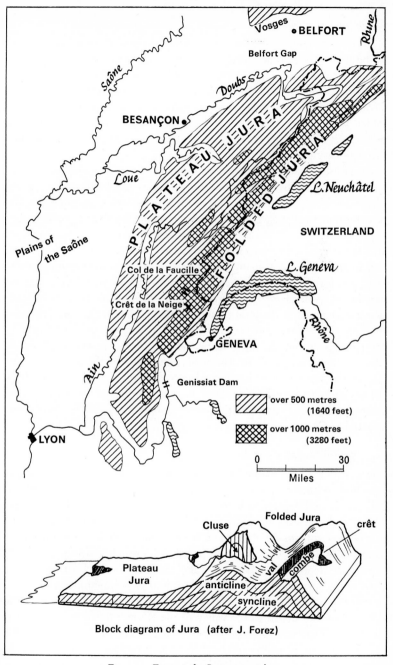

FIG. 47.—France: the Jura mountains.

9. *The Jura mountains*

The Jura mountains stretch northwards in a crescent from Lake Geneva to the Belfort Gap. The surface rocks are mainly Oolitic and marly lime-stones of Jurassic age, folded into parallel ranges on the inner or eastern side of the crescent but remaining as plateaus which descend in step-like terraces to the Saône valley in the west. Only a small portion of the folded Jura, as they are called, is in France but it contains the highest point, Crêt de la Neige (5600 ft). Near this peak is the Col de la Faucille, the only easy pass across the mountains.

An unusual feature for Alpine mountains is that the anticlines of the Jura folds form the ridges and the synclines the longitudinal valleys (Fre. *vaux*, sing. *val*). Rivers, such as the Doubs, pass from one val to the next by transverse valleys (*cluses*) and the whole drainage system, as well as being antecedent, assumes a trellis pattern. The highland blocks separated from each other by cluses are known as *monts*. The crests of the anticlinal folds have in many places been worn by torrents into depressions (*combes*) from which the fast-flowing streams make their exit by narrow, steep-sided gaps (*crêts*) (*see* Fig. 47). There is an absence of surface water over much of the Jura, though rainfall is heavy: the rains penetrate the limestones, flow underground and reappear in valleys or at steps in the plateaus as considerable streams (*grosses sources*) issuing from caves. Most of the drainage of the Jura is via the Doubs to the Saône, and the Ain to the Rhône. The last-named cuts through the extreme south of the region; in the val of the Ain, near its confluence with the parent river, the largest hydro-electric power station in France has been constructed at Genissiat.

10. *The Rhône–Saône corridor*

The valleys of the Saône, and of the Rhône south of Lyon, form a distinct and continuous passage or "corridor" (*couloir*) from north to south. It is a structural depression between the faulted eastern side of the Central Massif and the outlying limestone folds of the fore-Alps. In the north it is separated from the Paris basin by the Plateau de Langres, on whose eastern side is the Côte d'Or, composed of Jurassic limestone.

Tertiary deposits of sands, clays and marls cover much of the lowest parts of the corridor, but its edges have outcrops of limestones, chalk and, near the Central Massif, crystalline rocks. Glaciers from the Alps brought down masses of debris to the valley of the Rhône; in the angles formed by the confluences of the Rhône and Saône, and of the Rhône and Isère, are low plateaus of pebbles and gravel known respectively as the Pays de Dombes and the plateau of Bas-Dauphiné. The valley of the Saône is wide and open, but that of the Rhône is made up of a number of small plains, with intervening narrow gorges or defiles where the limestones of the Alps approach nearer to the Central Massif. Fine muds and silts are deposited as alluvium in the Saône valley and in the lower Rhône, where a delta has formed.

The Saône has been canalised. Canals join it to the Loire, Marne and

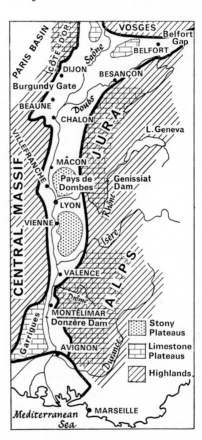

FIG. 48.—France: Rhône–Saône corridor. The Genissiat and Donzère dams are the terminal links in a chain of canalisation and hydro-electricity power stations intended to make the Rhône navigable and at the same time to improve its value for irrigation. The scheme, although of immense economic value, presents grave problems to the farming communities along the river. The construction of canals and reservoirs has disturbed the natural conditions of the intensively cultivated valley; fruit orchards have had to be moved and the network of irrigation reconstructed. The scheme, when completed, will provide 10,000 million kWh of power.

Moselle, and so to the Seine and Rhine. The Doubs is connected by canal to the Rhine via the Belfort Gap, which gives an easy passage from the north of the corridor to West Germany and Switzerland. The Rhône is navigable only in short stretches, and the Alpine régime of the river, with an enormously increased volume after spring thaws, makes control difficult. Dams, barrages and diversion channels occasioned by hydro-electric development may assist in making the river more continuously navigable. Roads and railways, however, make the Rhône corridor a major route-way, and the various easy passages west, north and east from its northern end or through the Alps have helped to make it the most important thoroughfare from the Mediterranean to northern Europe. The focal points of Dijon and Lyon have achieved much of their eminence because they are at the meeting point of routes.

11. *The Mediterranean region*

Stretching along the south of France from the eastern end of the Pyrenees to the Italian border is a region which offers many contrasts. High, rugged mountains stand next door to flat, deltaic plains; winters are wet and summers dry; winds may be warm from the sea or bitterly cold from the Alps; and areas of dense population stand cheek by jowl with others almost deserted. The Mediterranean region—the Midi—is divided into Languedoc, west of the Rhône, and Provence to the east. At the western end of Languedoc is the small basin of Roussillon. Provence comprises the Rhône delta and Lower Provence (*see* Fig. 68).

Along the coasts of Languedoc and Roussillon, longshore drift from east to west in an almost tideless sea, plus the effect of wind, has built up a fringe of sand dunes and offshore bars. Some of the latter have enclosed lagoons (*étangs*) and marshes. Behind them is a broad belt of undulating plains, with soils varying from fertile river alluvium, Tertiary and marine clays, and decayed basalt, to less fertile limestones and gravels. North of the plains is a continuation of the garrigue of the lower Rhône, on low limestone ridges which flank the southern edge of the Central Massif.

The Rhône delta contains two main distributaries, the Grand Rhône and the Petit Rhône, which diverge south-east and south-west from Arles, at the apex of the delta. The western portion of the delta, drained by the Petit Rhône, is the Camargue. The southern Camargue is an expanse of salt marsh; the north is being reclaimed. East of the Grand Rhône is the Crau, a large fan of water-worn stones swept there by the river Durance, which then abandoned its course to become a tributary of the Rhône.

The coastlands east of the Rhône delta are made up first of east–west limestone ranges as far as Toulon; then of Maures and Estérel, two low plateaus of ancient rocks; and finally of more limestone ranges, this time with a north–south trend. The western ranges rise to over 3500 ft and are separated by wide valleys and basins. A subsidence of the land at their western extremity gave rise to the Gulf of Marseille and the Étang de Berre, the latter often mistakenly regarded as part of the Rhône delta. The massifs of Maures and Estérel are fractured pieces of an old continental mass, probably of Hercynian age. They are composed of pre-Cambrian gneisses, schists and granites, and are just over 2500 ft at their highest point. They have given rise to a steep, rocky coast with few inlets. The eastern coastlands are the Côte d'Azur, a succession of small plains and, where the coast cuts across the grain of the ranges, of limestone cliffs. The largest plain is the valley of Var, behind Cannes. The Côte d'Azur, facing the south and sheltered from the mistral, is known also as the French Riviera.

Corsica, which is included with this region, is an island 3367 square miles in area, lying about 100 miles south-east of the Côte d'Azur. It is composed of the same granites and schists as Maures and Estérel, and together with Sardinia formed part of the same ancient land mass. Its eastern side has slightly folded shaly hills which are separated from the higher west by a depression. Most of Corsica lies above 1500 ft and is extensively covered by well-developed maquis. The western side of the island rises to 8890 ft.

CLIMATE

Lying as it does in mid-latitudes and on the western side of a major land mass, the climate of France may be said to be predominantly of the cool temperate western marginal type. With increasing distance from the Atlantic seaboard, however, continental influences from the east become more and more marked, so that much of eastern France has climatic characteristics which are neither truly maritime nor truly continental, but transitional between the two major types. This "transitional" climate, as it is called, is affected also by the great variations in relief in eastern France, and warrants separate consideration. In the south of France, a narrow belt lies in Mediterranean latitudes, and has a warm temperate western marginal or Mediterranean type of climate. It is possible, then, to distinguish three climatic types in France: (1) Cool temperate western marginal or Maritime, (2) Transitional and (3) Mediterranean (*see* Fig. 49).

1. *Maritime climate*

The western side of France lies open to the Atlantic Ocean, and so is situated where maritime influences are greatest. Summer temperatures are warm rather than hot, ranging from 63° F (17·2° C) in the north near the Belgian border to 69° F (20·6° C) near the Pyrenees. The prevailing winds at all seasons are the westerlies (*see* windroses in Fig. 49) which bring rain throughout the year. The annual total decreases inland from over 50 in. in the western Pyrenees and about 40 in. in Brittany to 20 in. in the east of the climatic region. Near the coast there is considerable cloud cover, but eastwards it becomes rapidly much sunnier. Over the whole region the winter half of the year has slightly more rainfall than the summer half. The wettest month is October, and there is a secondary maximum in May or June. The region with a maritime type of climate shows variations from north to south, and can be divided into three sub-types to illustrate this: (*a*) the Brittany sub-type, (*b*) the Parisian sub-type and (*c*) the Aquitaine sub-type.

(a) *The Brittany sub-type* coincides roughly with the Armorican massif. This projects westwards into the Atlantic Ocean and has a slightly higher

FIG. 49.—France: climatic regions. The length of the arms in the wind-roses indicates the approximate duration of winds. The towns shown are those for which climatic data are given in the text.

altitude than the rest of the region. This north-western corner of France has the smallest temperature range in the country, a rainfall well distributed through the year, amounting to 30 in. on the coast and 40 in. on the hills of the interior, and a minimum of frost and snow. Brest, for instance, has an average temperature of 45° F (7·2° C) in January and 63° F (17·2° C) in July, an annual range of only 18° F (10° C); its annual precipitation is 31·6 in.

(b) *The Parisian sub-type.* East of the Brittany sub-type and extending to the scarplands of the Paris basin is an area which has warmer summers,

cooler winters and less rainfall. Because the climate of Paris is typical of
the area, it is called the Parisian sub-type. Paris has average temperatures
of 36·5° F (2·5° C) in January and 65·5° F (18·6° C) in July, which is still
a small annual range; its annual rainfall is 22·6 in. In the north of the area,
temperatures nearer the sea are higher in winter and lower in summer.
Dunkirk ranges from 38° F (3·3° C) in January to 63° F (17·2° C) in
July, and its annual rainfall is 27 in.

(c) *The Aquitaine sub-type.* The southern portion of the Maritime region
is the basin of Aquitaine, and so that name is given to the climatic sub-type.
Because it is sheltered by the Central Massif, and is at a lower latitude, it
is milder than the north in winter and warmer in summer. Although
rain falls throughout the year, there is a decided winter maximum. The
greatest precipitation is in the western Pyrenees (over 50 in.), and few
places have less than 28 in. annually. Bayonne, for instance, has 46·4 in.
annually and Bordeaux 30·7 in. Bordeaux ranges from 40·6° F (4° C)
in January to 68·2° F (20° C) in July, and these figures may be taken as
typical of the area; in the south-east, however, between the Pyrenees
and the Central Massif, temperatures in July may average over 75° F
(23·9° C).

2. *Transitional climate*

The eastern side of France—that is, the scarplands in the east of the
Paris basin, the Vosges mountains, the Plain of Alsace, the Rhône-Saône
corridor as far south as Montélimar, the Central Massif, the eastern Pyrenees, the Jura mountains and the Alps—has a climate in which summer
temperatures are higher and winter temperatures lower than in the
Maritime region, and where the rainfall comes more in the summer half
of the year. The rains brought by the westerlies are fairly evenly distributed through the year, but to the summer rainfall must be added that
caused by thunderstorms, which is typical of continental summer convectional conditions. It is rainfall rather than temperature which leads to the
term "transitional" being used for the climate of this part of France, which
is neither truly maritime nor truly continental. The greatest lowland
ranges of temperature are in the Plain of Alsace. Strasbourg, for example,
has an average temperature in January of 32° F (0° C) and in July of 66·2° F
(19° C), a range of 34° F (19° C); its annual rainfall is 27·5 in., mainly in
summer. It should be noted that although average freezing point temperatures may be found in January in the Plain of Alsace, they are not
found elsewhere in the lowlands of eastern France. At Clermont-Ferrand,
for instance, which is situated 1280 ft above sea level in the north of the
Central Massif, the January temperature is 35·4° F (1·9° C), and the annual
range 30·6° F (17° C). Average July temperatures are higher in the

Rhône–Saône corridor: Lyon ranges from 35·1° F (1·7° C) in January to 68·2° F (20·1° C) in July, and has an annual rainfall of 31·3 in.

Rainfall increases near the west-facing slopes of the Pyrenees, Central Massif, Jura and Alps. Besançon, at the foot of the Jura, has an annual precipitation of 42·5 in. and Grenoble, in the High Alps, averages 37·5 in. The higher parts of the mountain ranges and Central Massif do not fall readily into any of the climatic divisions, however, for altitude and aspect cause great variations in temperature and rainfall. Puy de Dôme, at an altitude of 4823 ft in the Central Massif, has average temperatures of 28·1° F (−2·2° C) in January and 52·0° F (11·1° C) in July, and an annual precipitation of 45 in. In many parts of the mountains the annual rainfall is over 50 in., much falling as snow. In the Alps and Pyrenees there are permanent snowfields and glaciers.

3. *Mediterranean climate*

The Mediterranean coastlands of France have anticyclonic conditions in summer, and in winter are under the influence of the westerlies, which bring depressions. The results (*see also* Chapter III) are the hot, dry summers and mild, wet winters which characterise the Mediterranean type of climate. In the western half of the region the winter temperatures are lower than are usually associated with the Mediterranean coast. The January temperature of Montpellier is 41° F (5° C), and of Marseille 43·3° F (6·3° C), as compared with 46·4° F (8° C) at Nice. This is because the first two are affected in winter by the *mistral*, a strong, cold wind which blows southward along the Rhône valley from the snow-clad Alps, whereas Nice is in the lee of the mountains. Summer temperatures are uniformly high: in July they average 72·9° F (22·8° C) in Montpellier, 72·1° F (22·2° C) in Marseille and 73·8° F (23·2° C) in Nice.

The outstanding feature of the Mediterranean type of climate is the winter maximum of rainfall. Both Montpellier and Nice have annual precipitations of 30·9 in., and in both approximately one-third of the total falls in the months of October and November. Marseille has an annual rainfall of 22·6 in., nearly 40% of which falls from October to December.

SOILS

The great variety of rock structures and the many shades of difference in climate have resulted in a mosaic of soils so complicated that French geographers have listed between 400 and 600 agricultural regions in the country. These, however, may be classified into a very few major categories. It must be remembered, too, that in a country such as France, where arable farming has been continuous for upwards of 2000 years, the natural soils may have been so changed by human factors as to bear little resemblance in many places to their original make-up.

Over the greater part of France the soils are of two types, grey and brown. The grey soils were developed under oceanic influences and are found in the western half of the country. They are podsols, formed by the leaching of the heavier rains in that region. The brown soils, also called brown forest soils, lie on the Central Massif and in the regions of

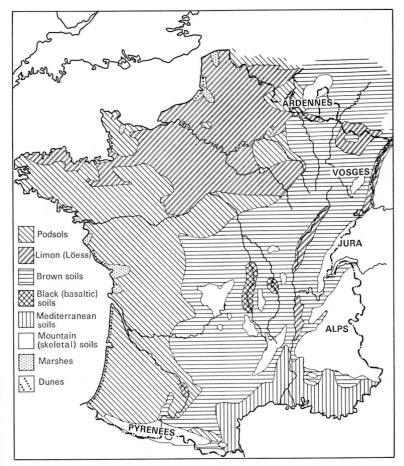

FIG. 50.—France: soils. It will be seen that the podsols (grey soils) and brown (forest) soils cover most of the area of France and that they occur where "Atlantic" climatic influences are greatest. Mediterranean soils (*terra rossa*) are red in colour, hold the winter rains and support irrigation. It is important to note that although the regional distribution of soils as shown in the map is generally accepted, the vast number of local variations in climate has enabled French soil scientists to divide the country into 400–600 agricultural regions.

H

more continental climatic conditions, that is, in the east of France. Most of the Mediterranean region has *terra rossa*, a red soil that owes its colour to the presence of iron salts which, helped by the dry summers, rise to the surface. Terra rossa contains a fair proportion of lime and magnesium salts. Its constitution enables it to hold irrigation waters supplied artificially in summer.

In the north of France (*see* Fig. 50) there are extensive deposits of *limon*, rich in humus and very fertile, for it contains the optimum mixture of mineral salts for plant growth. In origin, limon is similar to loess. It is found where a damp atmosphere checked the vast quantities of fine dust blown from the dried-up outwash of the Quaternary glaciers. The word is French for "mud" or "slime"; when rain falls on such soil the surface becomes muddy or sticky. This does not prevent its being among the most productive in France. Other soils of great fertility are the black, basaltic deposits found in parts of the Central Massif and especially in the upper valleys of the Loire and Allier on the northern flanks of the Massif.

Along the shores of the Bay of Biscay are sand dunes and marshes, infertile stretches which are slowly being reclaimed. Other regions with thin unproductive soils (known to the French as "skeletal" soils) are the uplands and mountains. The most elevated highlands are bare rock. The presence or absence of limestone in the subsoil has also an effect on the soil. In the podsol region of the west, for example, the poorest soils are where the limestone is near the surface. On the other hand, limon may be improved by the addition of lime, as in the east of the basin of Aquitaine. Soils derived from crystalline rocks are naturally infertile, but in the Central and Armorican massifs lime is used to great advantage, and in Brittany seaweed is used to increase fertility.

VEGETATION

France, like England, has little left of its natural vegetation cover. In the lowlands it consisted mainly of deciduous forests of oak, elm, beech and poplar; in the highlands, of conifers. Coarse grasses covered the limestone escarpments and plateaus, and were found also in the high valleys among the mountains. Most of the forests of the lowlands have been cleared and the grasslands improved by introducing better types of seed. Forests today cover about 18% of the country, but they are confined largely to the slopes of the Alps, Jura and Vosges. There are extensive pine forests in the Landes of Aquitaine, but they are artificial: the trees were planted to act as a wind-break against the sands blown from the dunes along the coast. Oak forests occur on the north-western slopes of the Central Massif; and in the north and north-west of France there are scattered copses and thick hedgerows of trees. Few considerable stretches of woodland are found elsewhere.

An outstanding characteristic of the rural landscape of France is its division into *bocage* and *champagne*. Bocage is the name given to the type of scenery found south of a line drawn roughly from Lake Geneva to the mouth of the Seine. Seen from the air, it is a patchwork of small fields separated from each other by hedgerows. North of the line is the champagne, a landscape of open fields, without trees or hedges, where individual fields are larger, more regular in shape and often completely unenclosed except by shallow ditches or furrows. In the Mediterranean region, enclosed fields are found in Provence, but the open-field system continues west of the Rhône, in Languedoc.

In each type of agricultural landscape the settlements are also typical. In the bocage, villages are small and have grown around loosely-grouped farmhouses. There are many farms scattered throughout the country-side, most of them sheltered by wind-breaks of trees. The villages of the champagne, on the other hand, are compact groupings in a treeless countryside; isolated farmsteads are rare. In the south of France, in the Midi, the older villages are often perched on hilltops, usually for defensive reasons, but the more recent settlements are scattered much as in the bocage. Among the mountains, both villages and fields are placed where the sun can reach them. The shady sides of valleys are left to the forest.

Chapter XV

FRANCE: HUMAN AND ECONOMIC GEOGRAPHY

HUMAN GEOGRAPHY

HISTORY AND PEOPLE

Germanic tribes (Gauls) entered France about 500 B.C. and mixed with the Neolithic peoples they found there. In the first century B.C. the Romans conquered Gaul and imposed their language on the inhabitants. With the fall of the Roman Empire, Latin was adopted by the Frankish invaders. The Franks, a barbarian tribe from the north-east, gave their name to France, which ultimately formed the western part of the giant empire of Charlemagne. After the death of Charlemagne, his empire was divided into three parts by the Treaty of Verdun in 843. The western third, bounded roughly by a line drawn from the Rhine delta to the mouth of the Rhône, was given to Charles the Bald. This was the France of medieval times, *i.e.* up to the early fourteenth century.

To the east was the kingdom of Lotharingia, a strip of country from the Netherlands to Italy, a buffer between France and the eastern third of Charlemagne's empire. This eastern region was given to Louis the German. It was known as the East Frankish kingdom, but was soon re-named Germany. Lothar's buffer kingdom included the Netherlands, eastern Belgium, the scarplands of the Paris basin including Lorraine, Alsace, Burgundy and Provence, and also the German Rhinelands, west Switzerland, and the whole of northern Italy as far south as Rome. The country was too long and narrow to form an easily controlled kingdom; under a succession of weak rulers, portions were nibbled away by the stronger kingdoms of France and Germany. In the case of France, the river Rhine and the mountains of the east—the Jura and the Alps—were regarded as natural frontiers, and the age-long antagonism of France and Germany is based on the struggle to occupy and hold Lotharingia.

France has had a stormy history. In 1066 William the Conqueror became king of England as well as Duke of Normandy, and he and his successors on the English throne continued to rule their possessions in France. French opposition to this led to war between the two countries. Near the end of the Hundred Years (1345–1456), after a series of victories at Crécy (1346), Calais (1347), Poitiers (1356) and Agincourt (1415), the English controlled the whole of northern and western France and, through an alliance with the Duke of Burgundy, a large part of the east. The tide of battle was turned by the intervention of Joan of Arc, a peasant girl from Lorraine, later canonised as Saint Joan, who appeared at Bourges with divine instructions to lead the French armies against the English. She freed Orléans and led the French towards Paris. Although she was betrayed to the English and burnt as a heretic in 1431, her spirit gave new life to the French. By 1453 the English had been driven from French soil, except for a small area around Calais which was recovered in the reign of Mary.

The following years were filled with intrigue while the House of Burgundy strove to secure the French throne. They were outmanoeuvred by the diplomacy of Louis XI, who in 1482 seized all the Burgundian possessions and added another piece of Lotheringia to his kingdom. With the Duchy of Burgundy came the whole of central and southern France. In 1480 Provence became French. On the western side, too, the boundaries were extending, for in 1491 Brittany was added. Louis was very successful in building up the French kingdom, but he made an unfortunate diplomatic mistake in allowing Charles the Bold's daughter, the heiress to Burgundy, to marry Maximilian of Austria, for through her the Low Countries became Austrian territory. Later, when Spain and Austria were joined by marriage, France was to find herself sandwiched between two enemy countries and facing new wars.

Meanwhile, in the second half of the sixteenth century, France was torn by the civil strife of the religious wars. But religious differences were forgotten in the successful struggles of the next two hundred years against the Hapsburgs in Austria, Spain and the Low Countries. The country became more united than ever before, and by 1789 France had assumed a shape little different from that of today; within her boundaries were incorporated Alsace (1648), Roussillon (1659), French Flanders and Franche Comté (1678), Lorraine (1766) and Corsica (1768).

The French Revolution and the ensuing wars brought Napoleon to the forefront. Through his early victories he spread the ideas of unity, liberty and equality throughout Europe, and he made great changes in the French legal and administrative systems, but he added nothing permanently to the territory of France. At his downfall in 1815 the boundaries of the country were almost the same as in 1789. Savoy and the area around Nice were acquired by France in 1860. Alsace and Lorraine were yielded to Germany in the years 1870–1918 and again in 1940–45. In 1945 slight adjustments were made to the Franco-Italian border.

Overseas, France developed an empire which extended through India to south-east Asia and in North America covered the basins of the rivers St Lawrence and Mississippi. Most of it soon disintegrated, and today only Madagascar, French Guiana, a few small enclaves in continental Asia, and scattered groups of islands in the south Indian Ocean, the Pacific and the West Indies remain of this once large Asian and American colonial empire. In Africa, however, France played an important role after 1830, controlling the Algerian coastlands and extending her influence southwards to the Gulf of Guinea and the equator. The modern upsurge of nationalism has made great changes here as elsewhere. In 1958 seven of France's West African territories—Senegal, Upper Volta, Ivory Coast, Dahomey, French Sudan, Mauritania and the Niger Territory—became self-governing republics, but remained within the French community. Since then Algeria has become independent. Senegal and the Sudanese Republic are now federated under the name of Mali.

France's present political and economic life shows the effects of three wars fought within her boundaries in less than a century. In 1870, and again in 1914 and 1940, she was invaded by Germany, with enormous loss of life and materials. In the war of 1914–18 it was mainly the north and north-east which suffered and the industrial regions which were destroyed, but far more serious was the loss of the 1,800,000 young men who were killed.

In the Second World War the country was occupied for four years and the conflict cost 600,000 French lives—far less than the first. On the other hand, the material losses of the years of occupation (1940–44), were greater than in the First World War. Throughout the country there was a general reluctance to assist either the provisional "Vichy" government or the occupying forces, amounting often to passive opposition. Together with the fact that hundreds of thousands of French men and women were taken to forced labour and concentration camps, it resulted in a slow, continuous and disastrous disintegration of the country's entire agricultural and industrial economy. Things were made worse by the deliberate destruction (sabotage) undertaken by the Maquis, an underground resistance movement of French patriots, and by the "scorched earth" policy of the retreating Germans towards the end of the war.

That France within the past twenty years should have recovered as well as she has speaks highly for her people's vitality and powers of recuperation. This recrudescence may be related to the balance which obtains between agriculture and industry, although this is less the case now than earlier in the century. It is undoubtedly due also to the French peasant's inherent qualities of independence, thrift, hard work and love of the land. With the help of great sums of money, technical assistance and equipment from America (Marshall Aid), the shattered transport system has been reconstructed, the mining areas modernised, agriculture improved by new methods and techniques, factories rebuilt with up-to-date machinery, and completely new industrial regions based on a vast extension of hydro-electric power brought into existence.

It remains to be seen, however, how far all this will bring the new France back to the position among the Great Powers she held at the beginning of the century. For although she is fortunate in being able to supply herself with most of her food requirements and is rich in iron ore, she is dependent for most raw materials on imports. These must be paid for in the long run by exports, not just of the luxury goods for which the country is famous, but of iron, steel and other metal products, of textiles, and of commodity manufactures in general. The present government of France is fully aware of this necessity. Largely because of it France has encouraged and helped to formulate the European Economic Community (Common Market) and has, for the time being at least, abandoned her traditional attitude of enmity towards Germany.

POPULATION

France has a population of 47,600,000 and an average density of 223 persons per square mile. This is much lower than in any of her larger industrial neighbours, the United Kingdom having 565, West Germany 592 and Italy 435. It might be concluded that France is actually under-populated and could support many more people. The position in 1800 was quite different. In that year the population was greater than that of any other European country. Her people numbered 28 million as against 10 million in the United Kingdom and 17 million in Italy. For various reasons—wars and tuberculosis probably the most outstanding—the net reproduction rate (*i.e.* the excess of births over deaths) fell throughout the nineteenth century, so that today, in spite of having the largest area, the country has a smaller total population than the United Kingdom, West Germany or Italy; and its density is exceeded by at least another dozen European countries. Recent years have seen a change, however. With a current birth rate of about 20 per thousand of the population, and a death-rate of about 13, the population is growing by well over a million a year. It will take a long time at this rate for her numbers to reach a size regarded as satisfactory for her labour requirements. In the meantime, France has had to call on foreign immigrants, mainly from Poland, Italy and Spain, to work in her industrial regions; in total, there are over $1\frac{1}{2}$ million foreign workers.

A relatively large proportion (45%) of the population is classed as rural, so that France is often said to be a country of peasants, of villages and small towns. There are only 24 towns with more than 100,000 inhabitants, and of these only Paris, Marseille, Lyon and Lille would be considered really large. In the past twenty years the position has been changing. With increased mechanisation on the farms there is a growing drift from the country to the towns. This is not entirely new, as the following contrasting examples will show, but with the accompanying development of old and new industries the movement to urban areas will be accentuated. The less hospitable agricultural regions are suffering the greater depopulation. The village of St Beauzire, in the Central Massif, which had 1518 inhabitants in 1856 has less than 850 today, whereas in the same period the rubber tyre and ancillary industries of Clermont-Ferrand, not far away, caused an increase from 38,000 to 134,263.

Although France has such a large rural population, its people are unevenly distributed. The best agricultural regions—French Flanders, the Plain of Alsace, the wine country of Bordeaux, the middle Rhône–Saône corridor, the Loire valley, the lower Seine area—all approach the national average density; but there are scanty populations in the Central Massif, the Alps, the Pyrenees, the Sologne and in the scarps of the eastern Paris basin. Some parts of these have not more than 50 persons per square mile. The Basses Alpes, the Causses, the Plateau de Langres, the Ardennes and the central Pyrenees are being slowly depopulated; the combination of harsh climate, poor soil and perpetual struggle against an unpropitious environment is driving young people to the social amenities and better-paid opportunities of the urban areas. The greatest concentrations of population are in the industrial regions around the cities of Paris, Lyon and Marseille, in the Nord coalfield, and in the Lorraine ironfield, where the average densities are more commensurate with those found in the industrial regions of neighbouring Belgium and the German Rhineland. A notable phenomenon in the distribution of population is the increased density in the High Alps. The development of hydro-electric power, electro-metallurgical and electro-chemical industries has not only halted the flow of people from the mountains but even caused a return movement.

THE ECONOMY

We shall examine the economic geography of France first by consideration of general topics and then by a closer view of regional economy, the same divisions being used as for its structure (*see* Fig. 42). In looking at agriculture, minerals, power, industries, etc., along general lines before examining them regionally, a certain amount of repetition will be unavoidable. It will occasionally be necessary also to introduce into the regional economy details of physical geography not dealt with in the previous chapter.

AGRICULTURE: (I) GENERAL CHARACTERISTICS

Farming occupies an outstanding position in the French economy. About a third of the working population gets its living from the land; many city and town dwellers own farms managed by relatives or tenants. Outside the large cities and industrial centres, there are more people in the country than in the towns. It can in truth be said that France is a country of farmers, and that love of the soil is innate in every Frenchman. To this is due in great measure the way France has been able to recover from the effects of three wars during the last 100 years, in two of which she suffered heavily from loss of life and destruction of potential. Yet her agricultural system shows weaknesses when measured by modern standards.

In the first place, the French farmer is extremely conservative. Although he works hard and carefully, he makes little use of up-to-date machinery and methods of cultivation, so that yields are not as good as they might be. Farms on the whole are too small for the owners to be able to afford much mechanisation. The vast majority are less than 25 acres, and a considerable number less than 5 acres; 70% of all farms are less than 125 acres, and are owned by over 5 million farmers, representing about 98% of the total farm-owning community. The small size of the farms is due mainly to the old laws of inheritance, by which the land was divided equally between all the children; repeated fragmentation resulted in tiny plots. New laws prohibit any subdivision which would result in farms less than 5 acres, but it will take many years to effect any substantial changes.

About 55% of the farms are owned by their occupiers and worked with the help of their families. In the Paris basin and the north and north-west of France there is much tenant farming. The largest farms are in the Paris basin and Nord, and are owned by members of the "new aristocracy," the merchants and industrialists. The smaller farms of Normandy and Brittany are in the hands of the "old aristocracy" who live in the neighbourhood. In total, 38% of all farms are worked by tenant farmers or managers. The remaining 7% of land holdings is under the *métayage*, an old-fashioned system dating back to feudal times, and very similar to the "share cropping" of the southern U.S.A., where, no doubt, it was introduced by French colonists. Under this system the land-owner supplies machinery, seeds and the use of cattle, receiving a percentage of the profits, while the tenant is responsible for the actual work. It is an unsatisfactory arrangement, gradually disappearing but still common in the basin of Aquitaine. Tenant farming and métayage both militate against the best use of the land.

The peasant-farmers are also backward in the use of artificial manures.

The whole country south of a line from Bayonne to Strasbourg, with the exception of the Midi, is in sad need of them, and even to the north of it only the areas immediately around Paris, the coastlands of Brittany and the Bay of Biscay, and the Flanders region are adequately manured. As one geographer puts it, "To the French peasant, agriculture is not a means of livelihood, but a way of life." He is very reluctant to alter it in any way. Such improvements as electricity, irrigation, and co-operative marketing have literally had to be forced on him by the Government. Farming, as carried on in France, is wasteful of its natural resources of climate and soil, and moreover is using more manpower than necessary. There is certainly a drift of rural population to the towns, especially from the Central Massif and other difficult areas, but if a more enlightened farming policy were adopted generally, far greater numbers could be spared from the farms to work in commerce and industry, to the economic advantage of the whole country.

In spite of all its shortcomings, however, French agriculture has enabled the country to be self-sufficient in all the foodstuffs produced in temperate lands, and in some years to export a surplus of wheat; and she is the most important wine-producing country in the world.

AGRICULTURE: (II) FARM PRODUCTS

Viticulture

The vine produces France's best known crop, grapes. Vines grow best where the summers are hot and, preferably, dry and where there are limestone soils. Conditions of climate limit their successful cultivation to the region south of a line roughly from Nantes to the river Meuse, where they are found everywhere at low altitudes, especially on south- or south-east-facing slopes. Nearly every farmer has a few vines growing on parts of his land which are unsuited to arable crops; for the vine prefers slopes, which aid drainage, and its long roots can penetrate the drier, permeable surface soils to the damper layers below the water-table. At the present time vineyards cover 5000 sq miles of France and produce annually over 1000 million gallons of wine. The area under vines has decreased yearly since 1939, but the wine output has varied little.

The wide distribution of the vine (*see* Fig. 51) has made wine (*vin ordinaire*) the ordinary drink of the French people; but in some parts, where soil and climate are most favourable, there are more and bigger vineyards, producing not only *vin ordinaire* but also high-class wines for the commercial market and for export. Very few of these more important areas, however, have individual vineyards larger than five acres, only 20% of the total number exceeding this size. These are mainly in Languedoc, where viticulture is practised almost to the exclusion of other agricultural crops. Languedoc produces about half the wine of France, mainly *vin ordinaire*, using co-operative methods for making and selling the wine; but it is beginning to be recognised that this monoculture is unwise. Other branches of farming, including the growing of maize and hay for cattle, and market produce for Marseille and Paris, are being introduced.

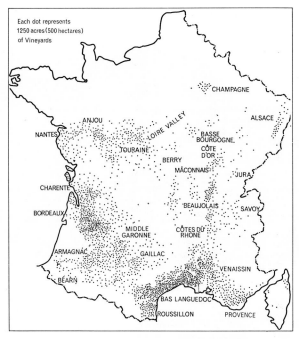

Each dot represents 1250 acres (500 hectares) of Vineyards

CHAMPAGNE
ANJOU
ALSACE
NANTES
LOIRE VALLEY
BASSE BOURGOGNE
TOURAINE
CÔTE D'OR
BERRY
MÂCONNAIS
JURA
CHARENTE
BEAUJOLAIS
SAVOY
BORDEAUX
MIDDLE GARONNE
CÔTES DU RHÔNE
ARMAGNAC
GAILLAC
VENAISSIN
BÉARN
BAS LANGUEDOC
ROUSSILLON
PROVENCE

FIG. 51.—France: viticulture. In summer a "gulf of warmth" is centred on the Mediterranean coastlands, with extensions towards Aquitaine and throughout the Rhône–Saône corridor. The mean temperatures from May to September are above 61° F (16° C). With few exceptions, the regions of viticulture lie within this "gulf" and it marks also the limits of maize cultivation.

The production of the more famous French wines depends in some degree on the care with which the vines are grown and the juice pressed and fermented, but more on the type of soil. It has been shown that vines brought from a poorer area will improve so much in the better regions as to produce wine indistinguishable from that already made there. The Bordeaux area makes a variety of wines, including Médocs, Sauternes, Graves and Barsacs; it accounts for about a quarter of France's total output. Brandy (*eau-de-vie*) is distilled from wine in the Charente valley, north of the Bordeaux area, with Cognac as the centre, and also at Armagnac, in the foothills of the Pyrenees, to the south.

The other major wine-producing areas are smaller, but important. The slopes of the Côte d'Or, overlooking the Saône valley and facing the sun, produce the well known Burgundy wines, with Beaune as the market. The lower Loire valley, in the Touraine and Anjou areas, has excellent vintages. The lower slopes of the Vosges in Alsace produce Rhine wines of high quality. Less famous wines, but still of the better types, come from

[*Courtesy of the French Embassy.*

FIG. 52.—France: Clos Vougeot, Burgundy. Flat "champagne" landscape, with no trees or hedges. Vineyards extend to the lower slopes of the highland in the background, which is the western edge of the Saône valley. The *château* now serves as a wine-producing headquarters and gives its name to the wine from the surrounding vineyards.

the Côtes du Rhône, the Jura, and the northern slopes of the Plateau de Langres.

Perhaps the most renowned wine is champagne, made in the valleys of the Aisne and Marne, with Reims and Épernay as centres. The vineyards here are located on the scarp slopes, facing the south-east. Extensive caves provide storehouses which are always at the same temperature. Champagne is a sparkling wine—that is, it fizzes when the bottle is opened; the method of making it do so was discovered in this region, and for long was kept a secret. Nowadays, by the introduction of similar fermenting techniques, some of the wines from the Loire are also sparkling. It will be noted that champagne, one of the best of the wines, comes from the extreme northern limit of successful viticulture.

North of this limit, cyder and beer are the more usual drinks, except in

Paris. Cyder apples are grown in Normandy and Brittany. The barley of the Paris basin, the Nord and Alsace, with the hops grown mainly in Alsace, forms the basis of the beer-brewing industry.

Cereals; sugar beet

Wheat is the most important cereal food crop grown in France. It is found in every part of the country (*see* Fig. 53), even in parts of Brittany, the Landes, the Central Massif, the Alps and the Pyrenees, where condi-

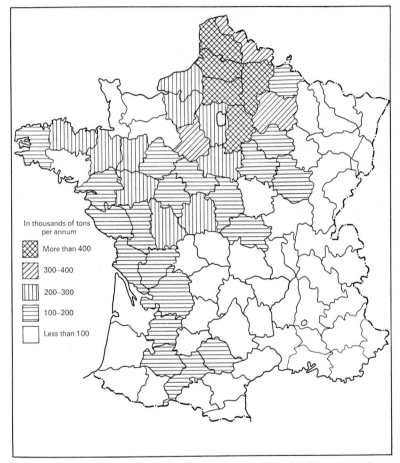

FIG. 53.—France: wheat. The production of wheat is shown by *départements*. Compare with Fig. 50, and note the large production on the *limon* soils of the Nord and the Paris basin. Since 1900 the area under wheat has been almost halved, but the total output has nearly doubled. It is now 100 million quintals yearly—roughly 10 million tons. France is divided for administrative purposes into 90 *départements* (counties), each under a *Préfet* (chief official).

tions of climate or soil are not really suitable, so yields and total amounts vary widely. The best areas are on the limon-covered plains in the north of the country, or where fertilisers are most in use. These include the plains of French Flanders and Artois to the north of the Paris basin, and their continuation southwards into Picardy, Brie and Beauce. Other major wheat producers are north Brittany, the Limagne and northern Alsace. Wheat covers nearly 10 million acres and amounts to 4¾ million tons a year.

On the rich limons of the Ile-de-France and the Nord, *sugar beet* is grown as part of the rotation, coming immediately before wheat. In these areas the conditions for growth are the best, and yields the highest, in France. Less important sugar beet areas are the Saône plains, the Limagne, and Aquitaine north of the Gironde. Annual production of sugar is 2½ million tons from 102 refineries which employ 47,000 workers in the harvest season. Outside these areas, its place in the rotation is taken by *maize*, the cultivation of which is increasing and annual production is over a million tons. It is sometimes cut before it ripens and used as green fodder or for silage, but its chief value lies in its cob (seeds), which is fed to cattle, pigs and poultry. Maize is not as yet used very extensively as human food, except in Aquitaine south of the Gironde and in Bresse (*i.e.* the middle Saône valley). These are the chief maize lands. A notable innovation has been made in the Toulouse region of Aquitaine, where American techniques and hybrid seeds have been introduced and co-operative methods used. Since 1959, yields in this region have been 32 and even 48 cwt of maize cobs per acre, as against an average for the whole of France of 21 cwt per acre.

Oats, grown as fodder for cattle and horses rather than for human consumption, have almost the same distribution as wheat in the northern half of France, but are hardly grown at all south of latitude 45 degrees N. *Barley* forms part of the rotation throughout the Paris basin, Brittany and Alsace, where it is used chiefly for brewing. *Rye*, suited to poorer soils and harsher climates, is cultivated in the high valleys of the Central Massif, Vosges and Alps, but it is gradually giving way to cultivated grasses for cattle rearing, which is increasing in these regions. In the poorest parts of Brittany *buckwheat* is a subsistence crop.

Other crops

Potatoes, like wheat, are grown everywhere in France and in most cases form part of a rotation. They are most important in Brittany, the Nord and Alsace, where they are cultivated for the markets of Paris, the industrial regions and for export. The northern half of the Central Massif is rapidly overtaking the older potato exporting areas as a commercial producer, the growing conditions there being the best in the country (*see* Fig. 54). A total growing area of 2·2 million acres produces over 7 million tons a year. The chief region for *tobacco* is the basin of Aquitaine, where the leaves can be dried in the open in late summer. Less important

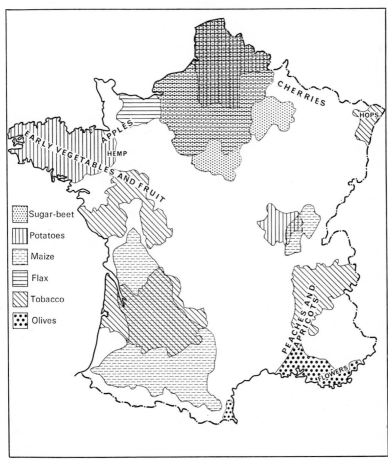

FIG. 54.—France: major field crops excluding vines and wheat, for which *see* Figs. 51, 53. Compare the distribution of maize with that of vines (Fig. 51), and of sugar beet with that of wheat (Fig. 53). For the distribution of oats, barley, rye and market garden produce, *see* text.

tobacco districts are south of the Loire in the Vendée, the Rhône valley below Lyon, the plain of Alsace and French Flanders.

There is a small and not very important extension of the *flax* region of Belgian Flanders into French Flanders, Artois and Picardy. At one time the linen industry was scattered throughout the towns of this

region, but with the advent of the cotton industry it declined, and
with it the cultivation of flax. The few linen factories which remain
depend more on imported raw materials than on flax grown locally.
Similarly, in the face of competition from more plentiful and cheaper
supplies of sisal, jute and other fibres, the cultivation of *hemp* in the south
of Normandy and Maine has almost disappeared.

The growing of vegetables for the market is widespread in the bocage
region of France, but concentrated *market-gardening* is found only around
Paris, the middle Loire valley, Lyon and southern Brittany. The last
specialises in early fruits and vegetables for the Paris market and for
export to England. *Fruit*, other than grapes, is a commercial crop mainly
in the Armorican peninsula, the Garonne basin, the Rhône corridor south
of Lyon, and the coastlands of Provence. The Armorican peninsula and
the adjacent parts of the Paris and Aquitaine basins are noted for apples.
In the northern half of the region they are grown for cyder, in the south
for table use. Dessert apples are produced also in Picardy and Alsace. The
remaining fruit regions are in the south of France, where the hotter
summers favour the cultivation of peaches, apricots and figs. *Olives* are a
product of the Midi, but exports of olive oil are only small; the domestic
demand is in fact greater than the supply, and olive oil is imported.

Animal husbandry

The area of France given over to pasture amounts to 42% of the
available surface—a surprisingly large total in a country where tillage is
regarded as the normal agricultural activity (*see* Fig. 55). The concentration is on cattle (20 million), kept for dairying in the north and north-west
of the country and for beef on the edges of the Central Massif and in the
Saône plains. Dairying is important in the foothills of the Pyrenees, and to
a lesser extent in the French Alps, where the cattle are taken to mountain
pastures in the summer. The chief dairying regions are Normandy,
south Brittany, the lower Seine basin and east Picardy, all of which supply
milk, butter and cheese to the thickly populated industrial regions of
Paris and the northern coalfields. Among the breeds kept for beef, those
of Charolais and Limousin have an international reputation, and many of
the animals are exported to improve the native stock of other countries,
including Great Britain.

Sheep rearing in France is less important and less productive than
formerly. The losses incurred during the two world wars have not
been made up and the total numbers of sheep do not average much more
than 9 millions. Most of these are in three regions: the Pyrenees, Languedoc and Provence; the Auvergne, Limousin and Périgord; the centre
of the Paris basin. In the first and second regions the sheep are kept for

wool, mutton, milk and cheese. The greatest concentrations are in the south-west of the Central Massif in summer, when flocks are brought up from the scorched lowlands of the Midi. The milk is taken to co-operative dairies in the neighbourhood of Roquefort to be made into

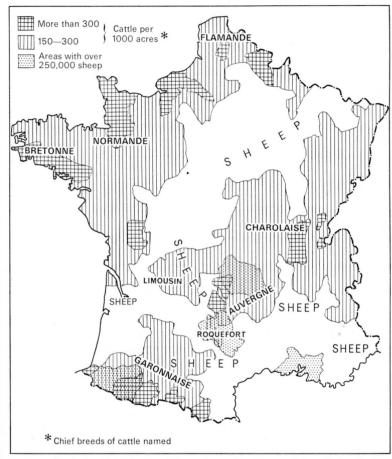

FIG. 55.—France: cattle and sheep. The cattle north and west of a line drawn through Bordeaux and Paris are reared mainly for dairy produce; those of the Central Massif and the east mainly for beef. There are nearly 20 million head of cattle and 9 million sheep in France.

cheese. Sheep rearing in the Paris basin is carried on mainly on the chalk-lands which encircle the Ile-de-France, and the output of wool and mutton is controlled by a national sheep-farmers' bureau at Rambouillet, south-west of Paris. France can supply only 8% of the raw wool consumed in its textile industry.

Horses ($1\frac{3}{4}$ million) are employed on the farms of France more than in any other country of western Europe, a sure sign of slow advance in mechanised farming. The greatest numbers are found in the Armorican region and along the north coast to Artois. South of a line from Lake Geneva to Bordeaux there are few horses, their place being taken for draught purposes by oxen. As more tractors are introduced, the numbers of horses are falling everywhere except in western Brittany, where they are reared and distributed to riding schools throughout the country. The regions noted for dairying are also the chief pig rearing areas of France (9 million pigs). Among these should be noted the sheeps' cheese district south of the Central Massif, where skimmed milk is fed to pigs. It is noteworthy, too, that the smallest numbers of pigs occur in the Midi—except in the Rhône delta, where the proximity of Marseille has encouraged a small concentration.

FISHING

France has nearly 2000 miles of coastline, facing the English Channel, the Atlantic and the Mediterranean, but its fishing industry is very unevenly distributed along it. The Mediterranean has a poor fish population, and its shores in France are lined with salt marshes. Fishing here is carried on from Marseille, Sète and Collioure, but only in small boats; the total catch, mainly sardines and tunny, is not important. The coast of the Landes is low, sandy and almost unbroken, presenting little opportunity for the development of good ports. Oysters are successfully cultivated in the shallow lagoons of Marennes, and Arcachon. Sardines are caught along the whole length of the Atlantic coast. They are canned at Arcachon, la Rochelle, Lorient, Concarneau and Douarnenez. La Rochelle is the chief port for tunny fishing, which is restricted to the summer months, when the fish swim in from the deep Atlantic. Most of the tunny is canned.

The major fishing ports are in Brittany and along the English Channel. Those nearer the North Sea—Boulogne, Dieppe, Fécamp and Dunkerque—are the herring ports. Herrings move south, arriving off the French coast in winter, when the biggest landings are made. French drifters share also in the summer herring fishing farther north in the North Sea. Boulogne is the chief fishing port of France. In spring and early summer, when herrings are scarce, mackerel are caught in the seas south of Ireland; and many of the North Sea fishermen take their drifters westwards in those seasons to share in the catch. The mackerel are landed mainly at Douarnenez, St Malo and Lorient in Brittany. They are sold either fresh or pickled in white wine.

The larger ports send trawlers and deep-sea vessels to the fishing grounds off Newfoundland, Iceland and Greenland. The chief catch is cod, which is landed principally at Dieppe, Fécamp, St Malo and Lorient. The islands of Michelon and St Pierre, south of Newfoundland, belong to France and are headquarters for the drying and salting of the cod. Many Breton fishermen find seasonal work in the factories there.

Inshore fishing for crabs and lobsters takes place from every port, large and small, on the rocky Breton coast; Lorient and St Malo also have oyster beds. Since much of the fishing is seasonal, Breton fishermen are often farmers as well, and the good returns they obtain from their land come from using seaweed as a fertiliser.

The numbers of full-time fishermen in France have fallen in recent years, partly as the result of the loss of most of the Channel fishing fleet in the Second World War, from which the industry has not yet fully recovered, and partly because the new vessels are bigger, better equipped and require less manpower. Not more than 60,000 workers are now engaged wholly in fishing; but more than three times that number are occupied in canning factories, drying sheds, port establishments and other dependent trades, or combine fishing with work on the land. The fishing industry of France plays a less important part in the country's economy than in that of any other country bordering the North Sea except Belgium.

FUEL AND POWER

Coal. France produces annually 52 million tons of coal, but she uses about 80 million tons. Lack of sufficient domestic solid fuel supplies is a great industrial handicap, and imports of coal from the U.S.A., Poland, Belgium and Germany only accentuate the shortage problem.

The coalfields of France are in three groups. The most important is the North-east or Nord coalfield, a western continuation of the Sambre-Meuse field of Belgium. It is situated along the flanks of the hills of Artois, in the departments of Nord and Pas de Calais, and produces about 29 million tons of coal a year, that is, 52% of France's total production. As in the Belgian section, the most productive seams have already been fully exploited, and mining becomes progressively more difficult and expensive. The seams are thin, faulted and distorted, so that mechanical mining has made poor headway. On the other hand, surface equipment introduced to replace the losses incurred in the two world wars is very modern and efficient. The majority of the output is steam coal, but west of Douai there are good coking coals; coke ovens and chemical works are established there. The chief mining centres are Lens, Denain and Anzin, each the centre of a separate producing basin, with Douai the main market and industrial town.

The Lorraine coalfield is a small extension into France of the Saar fields, and its output of about 15 million tons a year is of great value because of its proximity to the iron ore fields. The coal is not of as good coking quality as that of the Nord field, but new methods of preparation have made it satisfactory for use in blast furnaces: large quantities of coke are sent to the smelting works of Rombas, Micheville, Homécourt and Auboué, all of which lie between Longwy and Metz. The chief mining town of the Lorraine field is Merlebach.

The third group of coalfields lies round the Central Massif in a series of small isolated basins, the seams being preserved in hollows on the flanks of the Hercynian block, and broken and distorted by its uplift. The chief of these fields is at St Étienne (3,500,000 tons a year); and the good coking quality has led to the development there of the iron and steel industry. The same applies to the Montceau-les-Mines and Alès fields, to the north and south respectively of St Étienne. On the western side of the Central Massif there are fields at Carmaux, Decazeville and Commentry. In all, the coalfields of the Central Massif produce 26% of France's coal output.

Petroleum. This is found in France in the extreme north-east and south-west. The first to be exploited was in Alsace, at Pechelbronn, not far from Wissembourg; but more important are those at Parentis and Lacq. The Parentis field, in the Landes, after a slow start, is now a major producer. Lacq, besides having the largest output of oil, has natural gas, which is piped to Paris. St Marcet, a small town farther east in the Pyrenean foothills, has ceased to produce oil, but its output of natural gas is greater than that of Parentis and Lacq combined. The total output of petroleum in France is, however, only about 2,200,000 tons annually, as compared with imports of over 24 million tons a year.

Hydro-electricity. Inadequate supplies of coal and oil are compensated to some extent by France's water-power resources. These are naturally greatest in the Central Massif and the mountains of the south-east and south, *i.e.* where coal is least plentiful. Hydro-electric stations in the Alps are grouped in two great schemes, known as the Genissiat and Donzère-Mondragon projects. When completed, they will together form a comprehensive harnessing of the Rhône, with a chain of generating stations from Lake Geneva to the head of the river delta. As well as turning the river into a gigantic source of power, numerous diversion canals have made it more navigable; and the reservoirs held back by giant dams can provide irrigation waters to the sun-parched lands of the Midi. Smaller installations in the valleys of the Isère and its tributaries, the Arc and Drac, provide power for the mountain railways, the metal industries of Chambéry and Grenoble, and local domestic requirements, passing their surplus current to the main Rhône scheme.

One of the problems faced by engineers in the Alps is the mountain régime of the rivers. They have least water in the late summer, because of evaporation, and in winter when their sources may be frozen; but in spring, when the snows thaw, they are raging torrents. Dams must be built strong enough to withstand such varying volumes of water, and usually they are constructed where the foundations are of crystalline rock. The limestone areas of the Alps offer poor sites for hydro-electric stations, and few are found there: the jointed character of the rock, under the great pressure exerted by large volumes of water in reservoirs, might lead to disastrous landslides and floods, and at the least to wasteful losses through the permeable surface layers. This is why there is little or no development along the river Durance or in the Maritime Alps of Provence.

Hydro-electric power development in the Central Massif is mainly in the western half of the area, especially the upper Dordogne and the Lot valleys. There are other stations in Limousin and the upper Loire. The rivers of the Central Massif are not subject to such wide variations in volume as those in the Alps, but they are smaller, with less generating power. In total, however, the stations of the Massif produce about a fifth of the country's hydro-electricity.

The hydro-electric potential of the Pyrenees is large; the steeper slopes are on the French side of the range, there are numerous rivers, and the many tarns are easily adapted as reservoirs. So far, about a hundred stations have been established, but no major ones. They supply power to the railways, to local industry and to the national grid; in total they account for nearly a sixth of France's hydro-electricity. The installations are centred on Laruns and Pau in the west, Lannemezan in the centre, and Sabart in the east. Further developments are planned as more industries converge on Toulouse, Carcassonne, Tarbes and Pau.

The last of the areas producing hydro-electricity is in the Rhine valley, just below Basel, where rapids used to impede navigation. The Grand Canal d'Alsace was constructed to overcome them, and the waters impounded behind barrages to give sufficient depth in the canal are used at Kembs and Ottmarsheim for large power stations. Further stations will be built at Marckelsheim, at the northern end of the completed canal.

A hydro-electric station, making use of the rise and fall of the tides in the estuary of the river Rance, is in course of construction at Dinard, in Brittany, and should be completed in 1970.

The total hydro-electricity produced in France, though greater than in most European countries (38,000 million kWh), is only equal to the amount produced annually by thermal processes. The thermal stations are situated mainly in the North-east and Lorraine coalfields, and round Paris, Bordeaux and St Étienne.

MINERALS

Iron Ore. Over 90% of the 66½ million tons of iron ore mined annually in France comes from Lorraine. The ore, known as *minette*, is at the base of the oolitic limestones of the scarplands between the rivers Meuse and

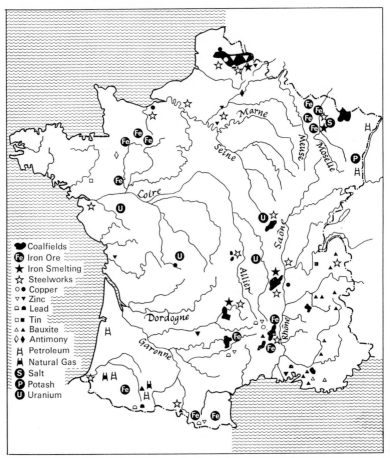

Fig. 56.—France: minerals. In the key, open symbols for metals other than iron ore and uranium denote mining regions, solid symbols the sites of smelting or processing plants.

Moselle, and is similar to the Jurassic iron ores of the oolitic escarpment in England. It contains a high percentage of phosphorus (1·7–1·9%) and could not be smelted efficiently until the invention of the Gilchrist–Thomas basic process in 1879. Its average iron content is only 33%, which is low. Besides these two drawbacks, there is the distance of the iron field from large supplies of coking coal and the uneven character of the scarp-lands, which hinders transport. Nevertheless, the enormous size of the estimated content of the field, over 2250 million tons, plus the fact that a large proportion is of calcareous ore and therefore self-fluxing in blast furnaces, have made France one of the world's leading producers of iron ore (*see* Fig. 56). The iron field is not continuous, but separated by faults into a larger northern area, with Longwy, Briey and Thionville the chief collecting centres, and a smaller producing area near Nancy in the south. The northern region is continuous with that of Luxembourg. Most of the ore is smelted locally, but large quantities are carried by canal and rail to the Saar coalfield, the Rhineland, the Northeast coalfield and the Liège district.

In north-west France there are deposits of iron ore on the northern and southern edges of the Armorican Massif. On the northern side, hematites and oolitic ores are found in a series of parallel beds south of Caen. The hematites are rich, with up to 60% iron content, but are nearly worked out; the oolitic ore, of Ordovician age, is something like the minette of Lorraine but slightly richer and less phosphoric. Some of the ore is smelted in Caen and Rouen, using imported fuel, but most goes to the United Kingdom, Belgium, the German Rhinelands and the Netherlands. The southern field is near Rouge and Segré, the ore being in low sand-stone ridges known as the Gisements d'Anjou. The output is small, amounting annually to a little over 500,000 tons, which is all sent to Caen for smelting or export.

The only other iron ore producing region of any importance is in the Ariège river valley in the eastern Pyrenees, where there are small deposits of rich hematite near Vicdessous and Rabat. These are smelted electrically at Pamiers and, with coke brought from Decazeville, at Tarascon. Another still smaller field is situated near Canigou, at the eastern end of the Pyrenees. The iron fields of the eastern Central Massif, near St Étienne and Le Creusot, are now exhausted but the iron and steel in-dustry of which they were the basis continues—an example of industrial inertia.

Bauxite. France has just one important mineral ore besides iron. It is bauxite, the principal source of aluminium. It was found first near Les Baux, not far from Tarascon on the Rhône delta (not to be confused with the Tarascon mentioned above). Les Baux—which gave bauxite its name—is now a "ghost town," the deposits being exhausted. Quarrying for the ore has moved to the river Argens area, in the Var department of Provence, round Brignoles and Le Luc. This area produces more than 90% of France's total output of over 2 million tons annually. Other producing areas are in the departments of Hérault and Ariège, on the northern flanks of the eastern Pyrenees. The bauxite is usually reduced locally to alumina, which is sent for refining to electric smelters in the Rhône corridor or the Pyrenees, or is exported from Toulon and St Raphaël.

The principal alumina works are at La Barasse, Gardanne and St Louis des Aygalades, all east of Marseille. The refineries are at l'Argentière, Riouperoux, les Clavaux, La Saussez, St Jean de Maurienne, Venthon and Chedde, in the Alpine tributary valleys of the Rhône; and at Sabart, Auzat, Lannemezan and Noguères-Mourenx along the Pyrenees. All these have hydro-electric power plants.

Uranium. France has several areas of uranium exploitation. This mineral, of such great importance in the development of atomic energy, occurs sporadically in granite formations, usually in veins only a few feet thick, but sometimes extending to great depths. It is not easy to recognise at the surface, and much research is necessary to find it. In France, deposits have been discovered in the granites in the north of the Central Massif, in the south of the Armorican Massif and in the Vosges; it is also thought to exist in the crystalline parts of the Alps and Pyrenees. It is mined at Razes in the upper Vienne valley, Lachaux in the upper Loire, Grury in the Morvan, l'Écarpière south-east of Nantes, and near the source of the Moselle. In all these areas are works for concentrating the mineral. The product is sent mainly to Marcoule, on the Rhône about halfway between the Isère and Durance. This is an atomic centre, with reactors and plutonium works.

Other metals and minerals. Lead and zinc occur in small quantities as associated ores in the south-eastern Central Massif, mainly in the Cevennes where the rivers Loire, Allier, Lot and Tarn rise close together, and in the central Pyrenees. Tin is found at Abbaretz, and antimony at la Lucette, both in the Vilaine valley in Brittany. Negligible amounts of nickel and tungsten are mined in the Central Massif.

Kaolin is found in the decayed granites of Limousin behind Limoges. Large quantities of fluorspar come from the Langeac district in the upper Allier valley. Extensive deposits of potash in the Rhine valley, a few miles north of Mulhouse, have made France second only to Germany in world production. It produces annually nearly 2 million tons of potash, which is processed chiefly for fertiliser. About 40% of the total is exported. East of Nancy, in Lorraine, rock-salt occurs in three basins, in rocks similar to those of Cheshire in England. The centres of the basins are Sarralbe, Dieuze and Dombasle; in Dombasle is one of the largest chemical works in France. Salt is obtained also by evaporation from lagoons on the Atlantic and Mediterranean coasts.

REGIONAL ECONOMY

I. *The industrial north-east*

This is taken to be that part of France north of the Hills of Artois. Agriculturally, the region may be divided into maritime and interior sectors. In the maritime sector, behind the dune-fringed coast, polders have been reclaimed from the marshes. On this fertile belt large crops of wheat, sugar beet and flax are grown. The largest towns are Calais and

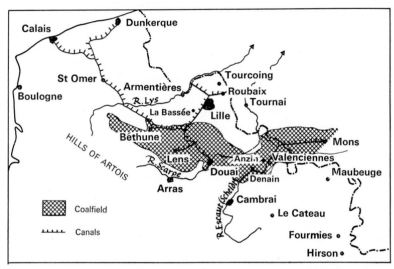

Fig. 57.—France: north-east industrial region. The Pas-de-Calais and Nord coalfield is continuous with that of Belgium. The region has almost every type of industrial activity, but the towns on the coalfield are concerned chiefly with mining, iron smelting, coking, chemicals, the generation of thermal electricity and heavy engineering; the towns outside the coalfield with textiles, light engineering and food processing.

Dunkerque (Dunkirk), situated on the coast in gaps in the line of dunes. Calais is a packet station or ferry port on the shortest sea route to England. It has a small lace and rayon industry. Dunkerque is an artificial port built expressly to deal with the products of the industrial region of interior French Flanders. There are no towns of any size among the polders, St Omer, the largest, being little more than a village (*see* Fig. 57).

Interior French Flanders is a region of intensive agriculture. Its clay soils support heavy crops of wheat, sugar beet, flax and potatoes; fodder crops, such as hay and turnips, are grown for dairy cattle; and market gardening supplies vegetables to the industrial towns. Farming in this part of France is more advanced in mechanisation and the use of manures, but there are still many small-holdings where spade labour is common. Agricultural activities in this north-eastern region, however, may be regarded merely as a background to the mining, metallurgical and textile industries which make French Flanders the most highly industrialised part of France.

Running east–west beneath the chalk of the Artois ridge is the concealed coalfield of the Nord and Pas-de-Calais. There are two productive basins, Valenciennes–Douai in the east and Lens–Béthune in the west. The mines, especially at Béthune, are very deep and the seams are broken and distorted. The deeper coals are not good for coking; they are used in railway locomotives and household stoves, or made into briquettes. About a third of the output of the field (about 29 million tons annually) goes to coke ovens centred on Douai and Denain. The gas which is a by-product is fed by grid to the whole of the industrial region from Dunkerque to Valenciennes. Other by-products have given rise to chemical works, especially in the Béthune district. Over half the coal, including coke, is used away from the coalfield. It is sent by canals and canalised rivers to Lorraine, the Lille region, Paris and central France; some is distributed via Dunkerque.

No iron ore is mined in the region, yet a major iron and steel industry has grown on the coalfield. Pig iron is produced at smelters around Valenciennes and Denain, using ore from Lorraine, Luxembourg, Sweden and Spain; but the emphasis is on the making of steel in Gilchrist–Thomas converters and Martin open hearths at Valenciennes, Denain and Douai. Some heavy engineering, including the making of girders, bridge parts and locomotives, is carried on at the eastern end of the coalfield (Valenciennes, Denain, Anzin) and at Douai, but most of the steel is sent for manufacture to other parts of France. Lille, to the north of the coalfield, has textile and agricultural engineering. The Maubeuge district, east of the field, shares in these industries.

The textile industry has existed for centuries in French Flanders. Until the nineteenth century it was concerned mainly with linen and wool textiles, but today cotton rivals wool in importance, and the linen industry has declined. Lille (199,033; with suburbs, 359,400) is the largest textile city in France. It is situated on the canalised Deûle, and has water communications with Belgium. It is the centre of cotton manufacturing, but has also wool textiles, linen and rayon mills; and as the regional capital it has engineering, food industries and chemical works.

Other cotton towns are Armentières, La Bassée, Arras, Valenciennes and Cambrai, and there are cotton mills in Roubaix although it is primarily a wool textile town. The twin towns of Roubaix (113,163) and Tourcoing (90,105) form a conurbation (267,000) almost on the Belgian border.

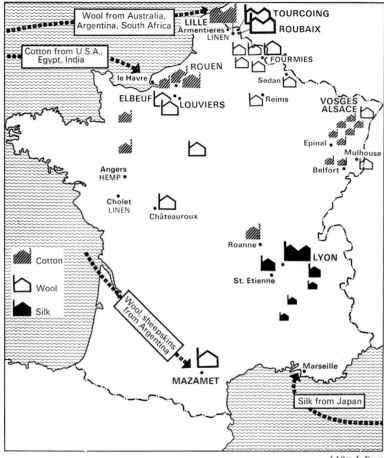

[*After J. Forez.*

FIG. 58.—France: textiles. The manufacture of man-made fibres (rayon, nylon, etc.) is largely concentrated in the older textile towns of the lower Seine, the north-east industrial region, and the district centred on Lyon.

They were both early Flemish producers of worsted cloths, and today the conurbation is the principal wool textile centre in France, noted especially for wool combing and spinning, and the production of fine worsteds. Cambrai is also a wool manufacturing town.

Linen is an old industry in Armentières, Lille, Roubaix and Valenciennes, but although fine linens are still produced and exported the industry is not as important as it used to be. The machinery, skill and organisation of the old textile industries were eminently suited to the manufacture of man-made fibres like rayon and nylon; and these are produced in all the textile towns of the region. After Paris, Lille is the most important French centre for ready-made clothing.

2. *The Paris basin*

This great basin-shaped lowland may be sub-divided into (a) the Ile de France, (b) the chalk-lands, and (c) the limestone escarpments. The Ile de France forms the innermost "saucer" (*see* Fig. 43 on p. 193) of the basin and, with Paris at its centre, is a well defined sub-region. It is completely encircled by a belt of chalk which extends to the coast in the north and covers most of Champagne in the east, Sologne and Berry in the south and Touraine, Anjou and Normandy in the west. Most of the chalk is covered by younger deposits such as limon or Tertiary sedimentaries, but in parts, as in "bad" Champagne (*Champagne pouilleuse*), it forms dry, dusty country. Along the outer edges of the chalk in the south and west are outcrops of limestone, representing portions of the outer "saucers" of the basin. For convenience, these are included with the chalk-lands. In the east of the Paris basin, however, the limestone escarpments are extensive and dominate the landscape, so they are taken as a separate sub-region. They include the Lorraine ironfield and a growing industrial region.

(a) *The Ile de France.* In the centre of the Paris basin is the Ile de France, a low plateau of Tertiary rocks, bounded on the east and south-east by steepish slopes known as the Falaise de l'Ile de France. The plateau is cut into several sections by the valleys of the Seine, Aisne, Marne and Oise; and its varied rocks, mostly covered with limon, have led to different use of the land. In the limon areas, wheat (in rotation with sugar beet and barley) is the dominant crop, as in the district of Beauce, south-west of Paris. The plain of Brie, between the Seine and Marne, has more residual clays; in addition to the crops mentioned above, it supports market gardening and the cultivation of colza and flax. Colza is a plant whose seeds provide oil for lamps; flax is here grown for linseed. In Brie, and in Valois to the north, dairying is important—especially in the river valleys—but in general wheat is the chief crop. Here and there, on the more sandy tracts in the Ile de France, are deciduous forests. The best known is the Forêt de Fontainebleau, between Beauce and Brie. It is a favourite resort of Parisians.

The focus of this fertile and productive region, and indeed of the whole basin, is Paris, the largest city in continental Europe. As with London, it is difficult to give an exact figure for its population, which is calculated variously for the city (*ville*), for "Greater Paris," and for the Parisian conurbation. The last includes all the satellite towns which fall within the city's zone of influence. The latest figures give 2,811,171 for the city,

5 millions for Greater Paris, and over 8½ millions for the whole conurbation.

Paris originated as a small settlement on an island (Ile de la Cité) in the Seine, and spread outwards on to both banks, so that today it stretches eight miles along the river. It sends its tentacles along the valleys to the north and east, especially along the Marne. Not only is it the capital and administrative centre of France, the focus of roads and railways, the headquarters of commercial enterprise and a magnet for tourists, but it is also the greatest industrial city on the continent of Europe and the third largest inland port in the country, after Strasbourg and Rouen.

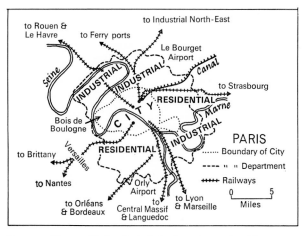

FIG. 59.—France: Paris. Paris is both a city and a *département* (administrative division) of the country. Noteworthy is the extension of industry along the Marne and inside the loops of the Seine west of the city. The authorities are trying to decentralise industry from Paris and direct new developments to provincial towns south of the Paris basin.

In the older parts of the city are the luxury trades, jewellery, perfumes, porcelain, glassware and high-class clothing. The main developments of heavy industry are in the north-eastern suburbs, in the angle between the Seine and Marne and, most of all, along the Seine to the west. Great steelworks and engineering plants turn out a full range of machinery and equipment for all types of mechanical and electrical enterprise from power stations to machine tools, helped by ease of transport along the rivers and canals. Paris is also a major centre for the automobile and aircraft industries; foodstuffs, chemicals, tobacco, paper, furniture, cement and rubber are manufactured there. The city has a large printing and publishing industry. Its university, the Sorbonne, is the oldest in the world and retains a prominent position in the educational world. The industrial side of Paris has not detracted from its beauty and attraction for tourists; its palaces and museums, churches and boulevards, shops and art treasures attract thousands of visitors yearly.

On the eastern slopes of the Falaise de l'Ile de France, the escarpment which bounds the central part of the Paris basin, are the vineyards famous for champagne, the wine which has taken its name from the province. The wine is carefully blended and its fermentation controlled in store-

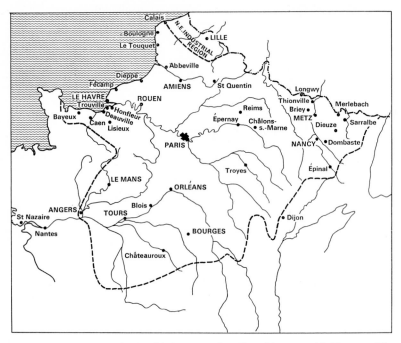

FIG. 60.—France: Paris basin, chief towns. Correlate this map with Fig. 43. The larger and more important towns are shown in capitals.

houses in the extensive caves cut in the chalk outcrops, so that skill overcomes the rather poor physical conditions under which the vine is grown in this area. Reims (138,576) and Épernay are the markets for champagne. Reims is also a wool textile, flour milling and sugar refining town.

(b) *The chalk-lands.* East of the Ile de France are the chalk hills of Champagne. This region, because of the porosity of the chalk, has little surface water, and is known as Champagne pouilleuse, "bad" Champagne. It is a sheep rearing area, and its towns are found only in the wide, clay-lined valleys which cut through the hills. The chief are Troyes (68,898) and Châlons-sur-Marne (36,800), each a market town and route centre.

Northwards, in Bray, Caux and Picardy, limon covers the chalk as far as the coast (*see* Fig. 43). Here, there are large farms specialising in wheat and sugar beet. Picardy also has extensive market gardens, and Caux has more dairy cattle than any other part of the Paris basin, producing milk and cheese for the capital. This limon-covered area is true *champagne* landscape: open fields with no hedges, scattered farmsteads and villages. The largest of the very few towns are Amiens (109,869), St Quentin and Abbeville. Amiens has a small cotton textile industry.

The coast of this region near the Seine estuary is low and sandy, but farther north the chalk hills reach the sea in steep cliffs. There are few suitable sites for ports, only Boulogne and Dieppe having much traffic. They are packet stations for Dover, Folkestone and Newhaven in England. Boulogne is the largest fishing port in France, Dieppe the fifth; they are both dependent more on the herring fishing in the North Sea than on deep-sea catches, and both have canneries and fish-meal factories. Fécamp is another fishing port, sending vessels to the Grand Banks of Newfoundland. The coast has many holiday resorts, Le Touquet and Deauville being well known.

West of the Ile de France, the meanders of the lower Seine are lined with a succession of small towns with a variety of industries where imports of fuel and raw materials and exports of finished goods are easiest. Outstanding are Rouen, 80 miles from the sea, and Le Havre, at the mouth of the Seine. Le Havre (184,133 with suburbs) is second only to Marseille among French ports. Its port, carved out of tidal marshes, can accommodate the largest liners. Its chief imports are mineral oil (easily the most important), cotton, timber, coal and vegetable oilseeds; its exports include iron and steel, cement and the manufactured goods of the Paris industrial region. Its own industries are mainly shipbuilding, ship maintenance, flour-milling, sugar refining, engineering and oilseed crushing.

Rouen (124,474; with suburbs, 246,400) grew on a spur above flood level, at the lowest bridging point of the Seine, and where sea-going ships could reach it. It is the second largest inland port of France, and an important transit or transhipment depot. It has much the same imports as Le Havre, but is a greater industrial centre. It has a large cotton industry (rivalling that of Lille) and chemical works based on imports of pyrites and phosphates. Other industries include iron smelting, shipbuilding and engineering. Some of the largest oil refineries in Europe lie along the Seine between Rouen and Le Havre. Rouen would be still more important but for the tortuous windings of the Seine, which has had to be deepened and its banks dyked to minimise flooding.

In the western part of the Paris basin, in Normandy, the limon begins to thin out, and there are patches of clay and of bare limestone. The rather wetter climate and the more varied soils lead to mixed farming, with dairying, market gardening and cyder-apple orchards, as well as wheat and sugar beet. This is the land of Calvados, a liqueur distilled from apples, and of Camembert cheese. The chief town is Le Mans, in the south of the region. Le Mans (136,083) has aircraft and automobile industries, and agricultural engineering. In the north is Caen (95,238), where local iron fields (*see* page 233) have led to iron smelting and engineering. Most of the steel produced is exported. Bayeux and Lisieux are small market towns, the former with a lace industry, the latter a place of pilgrimage. This western region shows a transition from the open-field system of farming to the bocage, with hedges, scattered trees and small irregularly shaped fields.

The south of the Paris basin is really the middle basin of the Loire. Here the underlying strata are covered by thick layers of Tertiary sands, gravels and clays, except in parts of the valley where the river has cut down through these later deposits. The valley is wide and floored with fertile black soil. Its terraces are so rich as to give some sections the name of "Garden of France." There are meadows, with dairying, and market gardens on the valley floor, wheatlands and orchards on the terraces, and vineyards on the slopes.

On bluffs along the river are modernised *châteaux*. Originally fortresses, many of them are now the headquarters of wine producers and have given their names to types of white, red and sparkling wines. The largest town is Angers (122,269), at the confluence of the Loir and Marenne, the ancient capital of Anjou (Fig. 61). It is a great wine centre and a market for hemp, which is grown in the district. Tours (96,472) is near the confluence of the Loire and Cher and at a bridging point on the main route from Paris to south-western France. Its industries, like those of Angers—wine making, flour milling, the making of agricultural machinery and fertilisers—are connected with the farming activities of the area. Orléans (88,105) is another bridge town, at the northern bend of the Loire, with important food processing and light engineering works. Blois (28,000) is at the convergence of several roads at a bridge point between Orléans and Tours.

The lower Loire belongs to the Hercynian block of Armorica, but is mentioned here because it forms the outlet to the south-west of the Paris basin. The river flows through a worn-down region of old hard rocks, known south of the river as La Vendée. The soils, except for a narrow belt along the Loire itself, are poor and thin, and mainly given over to rough pasture. In the better parts, maize is grown rather than wheat. At the head of navigation of the Loire is Nantes (246,227), with imports of mineral oil, coal, phosphates and pyrites, and exports chiefly of refined

[Courtesy of the French Embassy.

FIG. 61.—France: Angers, local publicity. Angers is situated on the river Loir, a tributary of the Loire. The placard, erected on the roadside outside the town, speaks for itself.

oil products from refineries on its outskirts and of the products of the south of the Paris basin. Nantes is a "colonial" port, something like Bristol, with tobacco and chocolate works, sugar refining and oilseed crushing; there are canning factories based on the market gardening in the Loire valley. St Nazaire (40,000) has grown at the mouth of the river as an outport for Nantes, which the larger vessels cannot reach; but it has developed into the chief shipbuilding centre of France, and has chemical works, marine engineering and canneries.

The region south of the bend of the Loire is the Sologne, an undulating plain largely covered with heavy clays. This impermeable cover resulted in many shallow lakes and marshes; until recently the region was one of the poorest in France. Much land in the north has been reclaimed for rye, barley and potatoes, while the less heavy clays support cattle, reared for both milk and beef. Sands overlie the clays in places, but they have been afforested, with a consequent timber trade and the making of barrels for the wine industry. The Sologne is still scantily peopled and there are no large towns.

I

South of the Sologne, the limestone plateau of Berry slopes up gently to the edge of the Central Massif. It is covered with a rich brown loam and has a mixed agriculture of wheat, barley, maize, fodder and dairying. Sheep are reared, and vines occur on the limestone slopes. The regional capital is Bourges (63,479), with an old metallurgical industry, aircraft factories, textiles and furniture works. Textiles are manufactured at Châteauroux (*see* Fig. 58).

(c) *The limestone escarpments.* East of the chalklands of the Paris basin is the clay vale of Champagne humide, "wet" Champagne, with dairying and scattered villages. It is bounded by the first of the Jurassic escarpments which extend to the Vosges. The limestone ridges, the Côtes de Meuse and the Côtes de Moselle, are dry, with sheep rearing. The intervening vales have clays more suited to cattle pasture than to arable farming. The whole area is, in general, poorly populated. The Argonne in the north is wetter, of sandstone and forested. Between the Côtes de Meuse and the Côtes de Moselle is a vale known as the Woëvre, where limestone washed down by numerous small streams has lightened the clay to make a fertile marl. Some wheat and fruit are grown in addition to the usual dairying and there are vineyards on the lower slopes of the Côtes de Meuse. The Côtes de Moselle are the eastern edge of a limestone plateau which extends southwards from the borders of Luxembourg and Belgium, and widens into the Plateau de Langres, the watershed between the Paris basin and the Saône. Much of the plateau is forested; in the valleys and hollows some wheat and potatoes are grown. There are vines on the eastern slopes of the Côtes, where they overlook the Moselle valley, and hops and fruit are produced on the best soils. On the whole, however, most of the region is the least populated in Lorraine.

The exception is in the north, where rich deposits of iron ore (minette) underlie the limestone (*see* Fig. 62). This is the largest iron field in Europe. The ore, although of low iron content, has led to over a hundred blast furnaces and numerous steelworks in the Moselle valley, east of the scarp, fuel being obtained from the small Sarre–Moselle coalfield, the Saar, the Ruhr and Belgium. The main output is of crude iron and steel, which are sent elsewhere to be processed. The region suffers from a shortage of labour, and there has been a considerable influx of Poles, Italians, and stateless persons to meet the demand. Integrated steelworks, with blast furnaces, forges and rolling mills, are grouped around Thionville and Nancy in the main Moselle valley, and round Longwy and Briey in side valleys. Nancy (133,532) is the largest town and a route centre. As well as being the commercial headquarters of the iron and steel industry, it has engineering, glass and wool textile industries.

The Côtes de Moselle overlook the so-called Plain of Lorraine, which extends eastwards to the Vosges. Here the soils change from Liassic clays in the north to Keuper marls in the centre and Muschelkalk limestones in the south. In the north is the small but important Sarre–Moselle coalfield, a continuation of the West German Saar field. Merlebach is the chief mining town, and it has coke ovens and engineering. Large salt deposits

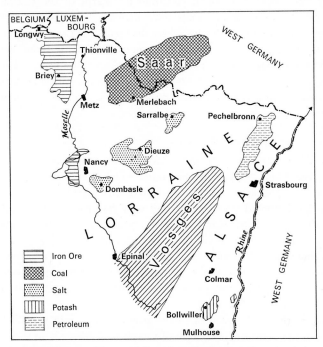

Fig. 62.—France: Alsace and Lorraine. In the text, Lorraine is included with the Paris basin, and the Vosges and plain of Alsace are regarded as a separate region. With its iron ore, coal and salt, Lorraine is rapidly developing as a major industrial region of France. The whole area shown on the map, now connected by canal or river with the Ruhr industrial region and with Benelux, figures prominently in the European Economic Community ("Common Market").

around Sarralbe, Dieuze and Dombasle have given rise to a chemical industry.

Throughout the plain there is mixed farming, the chief concern being the production of barley for brewing and rearing cattle for the milk which is supplied to the towns of the iron and coal regions. The chief centre in the north of the plain is Metz (109,678). The city is surrounded by market gardens and hop fields, and has food processing and brewing industries. It is an ancient fortress, guarding one of the main gaps on the road to Paris. Nancy serves as the market for the centre of the plain, and in the south the largest town is Épinal (28,700), on the upper Moselle. Épinal forms part of the cotton manufacturing region of Alsace, the industry having spread through the valleys of the Vosges, whose peaks tower above the town.

The numerous gaps which penetrate the scarps of the eastern Paris basin should be noted on a map. Nowhere do the ridges form difficult barriers. Even in the south-east, where the Plateau de Langres rises to over 2000 ft, roads, railways and canals connect the Paris basin with the Rhône–Saône corridor by routes with few steep gradients. The concentric curves of the escarpments make all the routes of the eastern Paris basin converge on Paris, emphasising its nodal position and suitability as a capital.

3. The Vosges mountains: the plain of Alsace

The Vosges are divided by the Saverne Gate into the Low Vosges to the north, the High Vosges to the south. The Low Vosges have little economic importance. They are covered with forests, but the difficult terrain has hindered exploitation, and very few people live there. The High Vosges are better developed. Sheep and dairy cattle are reared on the high shoulders; the middle slopes are forested, and there is a prosperous lumbering industry; in the valleys are meadows and dairy farms. As in the Jura and Alps, it is a region of transhumance. On the lower eastward-facing slopes there are vineyards which in their total production of wine rival those of the Saône valley.

Many of the small towns that have grown in the southern valleys have a share in the cotton manufacture of the plain of Alsace, and there is also an important tourist industry. The High Vosges terminate in the south at the Belfort Gate, which connects the valleys of the Rhine and Saône.

The plain of Alsace has a near-continental climate, temperatures ranging from 32° F (0° C) in January to 65° F (18° C) in July, with an annual precipitation of about 22 in., which comes mostly in summer. The warm summers and the rich soils on the loess terraces give large crops of wheat, sugar beet, barley, potatoes, hops and tobacco; there are vineyards, orchards and market gardens. Petroleum is produced on a small scale at Pechelbronn in the north and Staffelfelden in the south, the total annual output being about 50,000 tons. In a search for further supplies, potash deposits were discovered north of Mulhouse, and these are now far more important than the oil. They are made into fertilisers, or exported crude down the Rhine.

The outstanding industry in Alsace is the manufacture of cottons (*see* Fig. 58). It began as a wool textile industry, helped by plentiful soft water and local wool supplies in the southern Vosges. Some woollens are still made, but there was a switch to cottons after the Industrial Revolution. The centre of the industry is Mulhouse (110,735), on the Rhône–Rhine Canal, and there are also engineering and chemical works (based on the potash) and railway repair shops. It is an important rail junction. Colmar (54,264) is another cotton town, with large dyeworks. Both Mulhouse and Colmar are in the basin of the river Ill, a tributary of the Rhine.

The largest city of Alsace is Strasbourg (233,549), on a terrace above flood level near the confluence of the Ill with the Rhine and opposite the exit from the Saverne Gate. It is a crossroads position, at the intersection of routes north–south along the Rhine valley, and east–west from the Paris basin to the industrial regions of West Germany. It is the terminus of the Rhine–Rhône and Marne–Rhine canals; and the Rhine, already navigable for small boats, has been improved so as to allow large barges to reach Strasbourg and enter the port-basins constructed there. Strasbourg has developed into the greatest inland port in France, about half the cargoes passing along the canals. Its bulk imports are mainly coal, petroleum and cereals, and its exports potash and fertilisers. The city has shipbuilding, engineering and chemical works, electrical and rayon manufacturing, and processes the products of the plain in breweries, tanneries, canneries and tobacco works. *Pâté de foie gras*, made from goose livers, is one of its specialities. It is interesting to note that the printing industry, for which Strasbourg is important, started centuries ago in 1436, when Gutenberg, the first printer, lived there.

A large proportion of the people of Alsace, and some near the borders of northern Lorraine, speak German. The language was forced on them during the period 1871–1919 when the territory was annexed to Germany; but they have always considered themselves truly French in nationality. They demonstrate, however, more German characteristics of temperament and industry than most Frenchmen, and maintain a sturdy independence.

4. *The Armorican massif*

This peninsula projecting into the Atlantic has the most equable climate in France. Mild winters, warm summers and a rainfall which is evenly distributed throughout the year but is not excessive have helped the region to become a major producer of vegetables, fruits and flowers, especially early varieties. These are sent to the Paris markets or exported, a large proportion to England. The soils of the crystalline massif are naturally thin and poor but have been enriched by a judicious addition of fertilisers, the chief of these being seaweed gathered along the shores. At the eastern end iron ore is mined in two areas (*see* Fig. 56). The interior uplands

of Armorica are largely bleak moorland, but their outer slopes and
all the lower lands and river valleys are given over to arable farming or
permanent pasture. The richest districts, those most noted for market
gardens, are in a belt along the south of the peninsula, where it is sheltered
from east winds.

The Armorican peninsula has a true *bocage* landscape—small fields with
thick hedges or boundary walls of stone; but although *bocage* means

FIG. 63.—France: Armorican massif. In the text, the lower
Loire valley leading to Nantes, and the Vendée, are treated
with the Paris basin, of which they form a south-western
outlet.

"wooded scenery" there are very few patches of woodland in Brittany.
The trees, including such varieties as oak and ash, are in the hedges.
Apple orchards are to be seen everywhere, and cyder is the popular
beverage.

Wheat is the main crop in the north of the peninsula. Elsewhere there
are crops of oats, barley, rye and buckwheat. Cereal cultivation, however,
is giving way to potatoes and fodder, the latter for dairy cattle; for the
chief occupation of Armorica after market gardening is the production of
milk and butter. With 3 million head of cattle, the region is one of
France's main dairying areas. Pigs (1,500,000) and horses (250,000) are

important too. Animal husbandry is helped by the climate, which enables cattle and horses to remain out of doors all the year round in pastures which are always green. Sheep rearing is an occupation of the moorlands, but the numbers of sheep are small—less than 200,000—and their wool is coarse.

The southern portion of Armorica includes the lower course of the Loire and the region of the Vendée. These have been described in the account of the Paris basin.

The coastlands of the Armorican massif are more thickly populated than the interior, for in addition to farming activities the inhabitants are engaged in fishing and catering for tourists. The picturesque scenery of the rocky coasts and the many secluded inlets and villages along the rias attract thousands of visitors, and most of the settlements on the coast of Brittany combine the functions of fishing ports and holiday resorts.

A large proportion of all the fishermen of France live on the Breton coast. A considerable number of them are farmers who supplement their income by seasonal work at sea. Fishing from the northern coastal ports is principally for herring and mackerel (*see* "Fishing," p. 228) and from those in the south for sardine and tunny, which are canned. Lorient (47,000), which as its name suggests was originally a port for products from the Far East, is the chief fishing port, followed by Concarneau and Douarnenez. On the west and south of Armorica, inshore fishing for lobsters, oysters and other shellfish has local importance. Some of the ports on the northern coasts send vessels to the cod fishing grounds off Newfoundland, Iceland and Greenland. The chief northern ports are St Malo and Dinard, which are also premier holiday resorts. A hydro-electric station is being built at Dinard.

On a deep, sheltered harbour in the west of the Armorican massif is Brest (142,901), the largest port in the region and a naval base. Its chief imports are coal, mineral oil and wine; it has shipbuilding, marine engineering and chemical industries. Brest's value as a commercial and passenger port is reduced by its comparative isolation from the rest of France, its restricted hinterland and distance from the capital. Its function is tending to become more and more that of a naval station and dockyard. Cherbourg, at the northern end of the Cotentin peninsula, has a harbour which will accommodate the largest liners and is a port of call for vessels *en route* from the Americas to England, the Netherlands or West Germany.

The largest town in the interior of Brittany—in fact the only settlement of any size—is Rennes (157,692), situated in the centre of a fertile basin cut in soft shales and sandstones by the river Vilaine. Rennes is an industrial town, with tanneries, boot and shoe factories, chemical works, light engineering, food processing and butter factories. The Vilaine has been

canalised; barges connect the town by water with Nantes in the south and
Dinard in the north.

5. *The basin of Aquitaine*

This is primarily an agricultural region, but because of the variety of
soils in the basin there are big differences in productivity from district to

FIG. 64.—France: Basin of Aquitaine and Pyrenees. For the minerals of this area,
see Fig. 56. The limestone district of Quercy is known as the Causses, as distinct
from the Grandes Causses of the Central Massif (Fig. 65).

district. The farming system of métayage (share-cropping), although
declining, is still widespread and on the whole the area occupied by each
farm is small.

The northern part of the Aquitaine basin is called Charente, after the
river which drains it. It is an undulating plain of chalk, covered by layers
of fertile marl. The chief occupation is dairying, and the main field crops
are wheat, potatoes and fodder in the north, maize in the south. The vine-

yards of the Charente are famous for brandy, which is distilled around Cognac (25,000). The chief town is Angoulême (51,223), which has flour milling, paper manufacture and agricultural engineering. On the coast is La Rochelle (68,445), once the headquarters of the Huguenots. It is a centre for sardine and tunny fishing, and its industries—shipbuilding, canning, fertilisers—are related to this. Some of its commercial functions have been taken over by La Pallice, its outport.

Between the Charente plain and the Central Massif is a zone occupied by hilly chalk-lands in the north, and by limestone plateaus and scarps in the south. The area is crossed by many rivers, the biggest ones being the Dordogne and Lot, and comprises the regions of Périgord and Quercy. Much of Périgord is covered with oak forests, in which pigs are reared, feeding on the acorns. The pigs are also employed to root for truffles, a table delicacy which grows underground and for which Périgord is noted. The chief towns are markets in the wide valleys, the largest being Périgueux (40,700) and Bergerac (24,000), both of which manufacture boots and shoes. The region has been helped in recent years by hydro-electric development on the upper Dordogne.

The limestone plateaus of Quercy, known as the Causses, are not to be confused with the Grandes Causses of the Central Massif. They have similar karst characteristics, with sink-holes, underground caves, subterranean rivers and a general absence of surface drainage. The rivers emerge from the limestone in deep, cliff-lined valleys, and it is in these valleys that most of the scanty population lives. Agriculture is limited to patches of terra rossa in hollows on the plateaus, or to stretches of alluvium in the valleys; it is usually of a subsistence nature. Sheep rearing is important in Quercy, and there is some dairying in the valley of the Lot, around Cahors (15,000). Rocamadour, a village clinging to the face of cliffs in the Alzou valley, makes cheese and attracts tourists by reason of its picturesque situation. The caves, too, draw visitors to explore their deep shafts and subterranean windings.

The eastern end of the basin of Aquitaine, where the Tarn and Garonne leave the Central Massif and the Pyrenees respectively, is a mass of gravel plateaus which are unproductive, but the valleys of the Garonne and of the tributaries converging on it soon become wide, terraced and covered with alluvium. The region is fertile and has a rich and varied agriculture, with fields of maize, tobacco and market garden products. Two towns dominate it, Toulouse (330,570) and Montauban (41,500). Toulouse commands the western approach to the Naurouze Gap, which leads to the Gate of Carcassonne and the Mediterranean coastlands. It is the regional capital, a rail and canal junction. It has large food processing industries based on local produce, and makes farm implements, chemicals, electrical apparatus and clothing. Natural gas occurs at St Marcet, south-west of Toulouse, and is piped to the city and to Bordeaux for domestic and industrial purposes.

The region drained by the lower courses of the Garonne, Dordogne and their tributaries is Gascony: a rich, undulating plain floored by Tertiaries, with alluvium near the rivers. The chief agricultural products are maize, wheat, tobacco, fruit, early vegetables and vines. The basin of Aquitaine is the principal maize region in France, and Gascony produces the bulk of the crop. The area under wheat is decreasing as more land is given to maize, which is used both for human consumption and as animal and poultry fodder. The market town for the east of this prosperous region is Agen (35,000), but the great metropolis is the city and port of Bordeaux (254,122; conurbation, 415,700), in the west.

Bordeaux is the centre of the wine trade of Aquitaine. The sides of the Garonne valley for miles above the city, and the banks of the lower Dordogne, are lined with vineyards which produce large quantities of high-class wines. The most important districts are Médoc, north of Bordeaux, producing red wines (claret); Graves, east of the port, with red and white wines; and Sauterne, still farther east, with sweet white wines.

The rivers Garonne and Dordogne flow into the Gironde, an estuary fifty miles long, which leads north-west to the Bay of Biscay. The Gironde is clogged by river silts and marine muds, so constant dredging is needed to maintain a navigable passage to Bordeaux, which is situated at the mouth of the Garonne. Bordeaux is the chief port of south-west France, importing mineral oil, coal and colonial products. In its industries —sugar refining, oilseed crushing, chocolate and tobacco manufacture, aircraft construction—it resembles Bristol; and like the English town it requires an outport for larger vessels. This is Pauillac, halfway along the Gironde. Bordeaux also has electrical engineering and chemical works; and a timber and paper industry has developed because of the proximity of the forests of the Landes. Coal and oil fuel supplies in Bordeaux are supplemented by hydro-electricity from the Pyrenees and natural gas from St Marcet. Pauillac has oil refineries.

South of Gascony the river Adour flows directly to the Bay of Biscay. The Adour basin is somewhat similar to the Toulouse region, except that there is more waste land where the river leaves the Pyrenees and in the agricultural districts wheat is more important than maize. Peach and apricot orchards are found everywhere, even on the unpromising gravel fans. The larger towns of the basin, such as Tarbes (50,719). Pau (61,468) and Oloron-Ste Marie (11,000), are situated along the southern edge of the basin. In all of them hydro-electricity brought from the Pyrenees is helping the development of electro-chemical and electro-metallurgical industries. Tarbes has also a leather industry, Pau manufactures textiles and Oloron-Ste Marie makes berets. Bayonne (33,000), a small port three miles from the mouth of the Adour, has purely local importance commercially. It has developed more as a tourist centre, having good communications with the coastal holiday resorts of Biarritz (23,000) and St Jean-de-Luz. These are also sardine-fishing ports, and Biarritz has canneries.

The coast-lands of Gascony south of the Gironde have wide stretches of dry sands and frequent marshy lagoons in the region known as the Landes. Pine forests, planted in the nineteenth century to act as a wind-break and stop the drift of sand to the more productive part of Gascony, cover more than half the surface. There is little cultivation of crops except where the inner margins of the Landes have been reclaimed. The forests yield timber, resin and turpentine; in clearings and on the coastal dunes where special grasses have been planted to fix the sand, sheep are reared. The coast of the Landes is straight and unbroken except for an opening leading to Arcachon, which has large oyster beds and shares in the sardine fishing. Mineral oil was discovered in 1954 at Parentis, south of Arcachon. The field now yields over a million tons of oil a year.

In the south of the Aquitaine basin, flanking the central Pyrenees and rising to 2000 ft up their slopes, are undulating plateaus composed of thick deposits of gravels washed down by the torrents of the Ice Age. The plateaus are gashed by the valleys of many rivers, and most of the population lives in these lowlands. The district is known as Lannemezan. It is one of the most thinly peopled parts of France. The chief occupations are the rearing of sheep and beef-cattle, with arable farming of the subsistence type. Viticulture is possible on the valley slopes, and Armagnac has become noted for brandy.

6. The Pyrenees

The chief occupation in this poorly populated region is the rearing of sheep and dairy cattle, of which there are roughly equal numbers. Cattle are more common in the western and central Pyrenees, where it is wetter; the largest flocks of sheep are in the eastern Pyrenees. Transhumance is practised, but in the case of cattle it has declined in recent years. The animals are kept in the low valleys during summer so that their milk is more readily available for the co-operative dairies and the tourist resorts which are springing up at the foot of the mountains. Shepherding communities live isolated lives in many of the interior valleys, and tend to be self-sufficient and independent. Thus isolation has enabled Andorra to exist as a separate political unit to the present day, but in the past decade tourists have begun to break down its seclusion.

In the central and western Pyrenees, and to a lesser extent in the eastern Pyrenees, the advent of hydro-electricity is likely to work a miniature industrial revolution. A heavy rainfall, together with a large number of corrie lakes or mountain tarns which can be used as reservoirs, has encouraged the construction of more than a hundred hydro-electric power stations. None is very big, but in total they generate one-sixth of France's hydro-electricity. Most of the current is collected and distributed from transformer stations at Laruns and Pau in the west, in the Lannemezan in the centre, and at Sabart in the east. As we have seen, this has encouraged the development of electro-chemical and electro-metallurgical industries in the towns of the adjacent basin of Aquitaine. Within the Pyrenean zone, there is electro-smelting of iron at Pamiers, the ore being brought from a small field at Canigou, and chemicals are manufactured south of Lourdes, in the valley of the Gave de Pau. The Tarbes–Lourdes–Bagnères-de-Bigorre triangle is a growing industrial region, producing electrical apparatus. In general, however, industrial activity in the Pyrenees proper is sporadic and scattered. The development of hydro-electric power has so far been of greater benefit to the towns of the southern Aquitaine basin, which serve as markets and centres for the people of the Pyrenean zone. An exception is Lourdes, on the Gave de Pau, which has become a major pilgrimage centre with millions of visitors yearly.

The western Pyrenees, which have more rounded peaks and more forests than the eastern ranges, support a somewhat denser population. They were the home of the Basques, an ancient people who inhabited the south-east coastlands of the Bay of Biscay. Their descendants today number about 600,000 in all, of whom one-sixth live in France and the remainder in northern Spain. The Basques have their own language, which seems to have no affinity with any other European tongue, and they preserve their own customs and pastimes.

7. *The Central Massif*

The climate of the Central Massif is affected by its height and its position in Europe. The western side has an oceanic climate modified by increasing altitude; the east shares in the beginnings of a continental climate; and the south comes under very much modified Mediterranean influences. These differences in climate, and the resistant character of most of its rocks, have resulted in the Massif in a variety of soils; but all of them, except those developed from basaltic lavas and those in the northern valleys, which are alluvial, are thin and poor. On the basis of structural and soil differences (*see* Fig. 45 on p. 200), the Central Massif may be divided into: (*a*) the eastern margins from Morvan in the north to the southern end of the Cevennes, (*b*) the Grandes Causses and south-western Massif, (*c*) Limousin in the west and north-west, and (*d*) the centre of the Massif, with which are included the upper valleys of the Loire and Allier.

(a) *The eastern margins.* The granitic plateau of the Morvan affords poor pasture for cattle on its upper slopes. The area is largely forested with oaks, beech and chestnut; timber is sent to Paris via the canalised Yonne. South of the Morvan is the faulted depression of Autunois, where coal

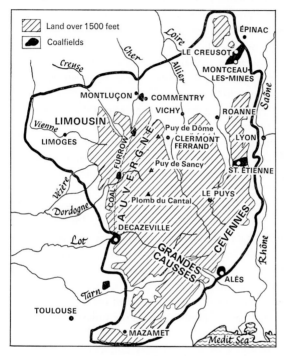

Fig. 65.—France: Central Massif; relief, drainage and towns. Correlate this map with Figs. 45, 55 and 56. Note the peripheral positions of the chief settlements and of the coalfields.

measures have been preserved in two basins, around Autun and Mont-ceau-les-Mines. The Autun coals are of poor quality and are used in a thermal electric station at Épinac. Far more important is the southern field (2,500,000 tons a year), which supplies iron and steel works, railway engineering and armament manufacture at Montceau-les-Mines (25,000) and Le Creusot (25,000).

The eastern margins of the Massif are a faulted scarp overlooking the valleys of the Saône and lower Rhône. Southwards through Charolais, Beaujolais and Lyonnais, the edge of the plateau increases in elevation to well over 2000 feet; to the south of Lyonnais is a break, in the St Étienne district, and then the scarps rise in Vivarais to 3000–5000 ft; in the Cevennes, where they change to a north-east–south-west direction, the plateau edge has an average height of 4000–4500 ft, with rounded mountains rising above it for another 1000 ft. The highest point is Lozère (5584 ft). The whole region is the most elevated part of the Massif, with the exception of parts of the volcanic district of the centre.

Charolais is famous for its white beef-cattle, some of which are sent for fattening to the sugar beet districts of the Paris basin. Many are exported to improve the stock in other countries, including England. The eastward-facing scarps are much dissected by short valleys throughout the length of the Massif, and on their slopes vines are grown, especially in Beaujolais and Mâconnais. The St Étienne depression, which cuts diagonally across the eastern rim of the Massif, has a small but important coalfield. St Étienne (205,633) is the centre of a thriving industrial region, with iron and steel works, cutlery, armaments, motors, cycles, aircraft and textile (silk ribbons and rayon) manufacturing. The St Étienne depression provides the easiest route from the Rhône valley to the Central Massif.

The plateau in Vivarais and the Cevennes supports very few people, and the outer slopes are forested. Much of the forest of beech, pines and Douglas firs is State-owned, and carefully conserved and exploited. The south-eastern edge of the Cevennes is severely faulted, and some of the faulted basins contain fertile marls. Here, there are distinct signs of Mediterranean influences in the agriculture. In the terraced valleys there are mulberry and olive groves, vineyards and orchards of peaches and apricots; wheat and maize are cultivated on the valley floors. A small coalfield has led to engineering and chemical works at Alès.

(b) *The Grandes Causses*. The crystalline rocks which underlie the southern Central Massif were faulted into a great trough in which were deposited thick beds of limestone. The region was uplifted, and the limestones were tilted, faulted and cut deeply by rivers flowing from the Massif to the basin of Aquitaine: the river Lot in the north, the Tarn and its tributaries in the centre and south. The result is a number of limestone blocks, some rising to over 2000 ft and one, Méjan, to 4193 ft. This is a typical karst region. Much of the drainage is underground and large areas have no surface water at all. The plateaus are criss-crossed by deep crevices, and there are solution hollows like the *polja* and *dolina* of Yugoslavia. Dry valleys are numerous, and their floors may contain terra rossa, a residual soil from the dissolved limestones. Sink-holes lead to a vast network of underground passages and caves.

The Grandes Causses have a covering of short grass on which sheep are reared. This is one of the principal sheep rearing regions of France. The herds (600,000 sheep altogether) are augmented in summer by transhumance from the Mediterranean coastlands. The sheep are reared for milk as well as for wool; ewes' milk is made into cheese in co-operative dairies at Roquefort, on the western edge of the Grandes Causses (see Fig. 55). Over most of the region the population is scanty and dependent on subsistence agriculture.

West of the limestone region, crystalline rocks reappear in the bleak uplands of the Ségalas plateau, Monts de Lacaune and Montagne Noire. The first two are composed of granites, gneisses and slates, the Montagne Noire of pre-Cambrian rocks. This is the most southerly extension of the Central Massif. It rises in the Monts de Lacaune to 4145 ft and in the Montagne Noire to 3970 ft. The region has just as few inhabitants as the Grandes Causses; they depend on sheep rearing and on poor crops of rye, buckwheat and potatoes. The only settlement of any size is Mazamet, on its southern margins. Mazamet specialises in "dead" wools, i.e. the fleece which is stripped from sheep which have been slaughtered; it also has small-scale wool textile and clothing manufactures.

Most of the rivers which flow through this south-western corner of the Central Massif—the Dordogne, Cère, Truyère and, to a lesser extent, the Lot and Tarn—have been harnessed in their upper courses for hydro-electric power (see Fig. 45 on p. 200). The Central Massif as a whole produces about a fifth of France's total output, helped by a rainfall of over 50 in., steep gradients and the crystalline character of the surface, which facilitates an almost complete run-off and provides a solid foundation for dams and barrages.

(c) *Limousin.* This is the name given loosely to the west and north-west of the Central Massif. It includes the plateaus of Millevache and la Marche, as well as the rolling slightly elevated plains of Limousin proper, around Limoges, and of Bourbonnais. The higher areas are of granite, while the lower districts nearer the margins of the Massif are covered with thin soils washed down by rivers. The region is predominantly pastoral, Limousin cattle being famous for their beef and as draught animals. Bourbonnais is more arable, with a bocage landscape, and with wheat and fodder crops. Dairying is more important here than beef-producing.

The only large towns are Limoges in Limousin and Montluçon in the Bourbonnais. Limoges (120,596) is a regional centre at a bridge-point on the river Vienne. It has ancient metal crafts (gold and silver) and an important porcelain industry based on local supplies of kaolin. One branch of the porcelain industry turns out insulators for generating stations and transmission lines. The town's coach-building industry gave us the word "limousine." Montluçon (58,855) has blast furnaces and steelworks, using coal from nearby coalfields. It produces motor accessories and tyres (Dunlop). The coalfields lie in what has been called the "coal furrow," a narrow belt of down-faulting from Commentry in the north to Decazeville in the south, on the eastern margins of Limousin. The coal, in several basins—Commentry, Ahun, St Eloi, Champagnac and Decazeville—has led to small engineering and textile works, which are mainly

[*Courtesy of the French Embassy.*

Fig. 66.—France: Saint-Flour, Central Massif. The town is situated on a shoulder of the Cantal. The whole of the view shown in the photograph was part of a gigantic volcanic crater. The volcanic rocks (tuff) in the foreground, bare or with a few scattered shrubs, contrast with the fertile basaltic soils and rich farmlands in the middle distance. Cultivation is successful at surprisingly high altitudes. Saint-Flour is nearly 3000 ft above sea level.

of local importance. The total output from the mines is small, and is decreasing. Fortunately, hydro-electric power can take its place. Stations on the upper Vienne also supply Limoges with some of its power.

(d) *The centre of the Massif.* Most of the centre and north of the Central Massif is of volcanic origin, and in many places the rocks have broken down to form rich, black, basaltic soils. In Auvergne, as the region is called, most of the area is given to pasture but there is a surprising amount of arable farming, even as high as 4000 ft. Rye, oats and potatoes are grown in the high basins; cattle—stall-fed in winter—and sheep are reared. Milk and cheese are sent to the Rhône valley and to Paris from thriving markets such as Le Puys and St Flour (*see* Fig. 66). The volcanic region is also a tourist district.

The rivers Loire and Allier cut through the volcanic rocks of the plateau, then flow through two rift valleys which are separated from each other by the crystalline Monts de Forez. The Loire has entrenched itself in the plains of Forez and Roanne, both of which are mixed farming districts, with wheat, sugar beet, fodder crops and vegetables the chief crops, and dairying for milk and butter. The market is Roanne (53,203), a focus of routes from the Central Massif, the Paris basin and, by a pass across the Monts du Lyonnais, from Lyon. Roanne and nearby small towns have a cotton industry.

The valley of the Allier is called the Limagne. It is really a series of small basins separated by granitic sills, and in them are Tertiary sands, clays and loams, mixed with basaltic soils and river alluvium. Limagne has the same farming activities as the plain of Roanne, but has richer soils and higher yields. Vines, although not important, are grown in both rift valleys. The small towns scattered through the Limagne are markets, with local industries. Vichy is a spa: its alkaline waters are bottled and sold all over France, and some is exported. Thiers is famous for cutlery. One market town, Clermont-Ferrand (134,263), has far outgrown the rest, to become the second largest city of the Central Massif. The reason is human rather than geographical: Michelin, who invented the pneumatic tyre at the same time as Dunlop, built his factories there. Today there are textile and engineering works too.

To sum up, although some parts of the Central Massif are relatively productive in agriculture and industry, the region on the whole is one of poor soils and scanty mineral wealth. It has tended rather to be a reservoir of labour for the rest of France, and its people have emigrated on a large scale. In the worst equipped parts this migration continues, but improved methods of cultivation and an increase of industry based on hydro-electric power have slowed it down and even reversed the process in parts which are better endowed, such as the Limagne, the St Étienne district and the basin of Le Puys.

8. *The French Alps*

The limestone regions of the northern Alps are forested, with some lumbering, but the chief occupation here and in the High Alps is transhumant cattle rearing, for milk. The animals are taken up to the mountain pastures ("alps") as soon as they are clear of snow, and the valley villages are vacated. When the snows melt on still higher pastures, there is another move upwards with some of the cattle. The people live in chalets and send the milk to factories in Grenoble, etc., by cable cars, milk tankers,

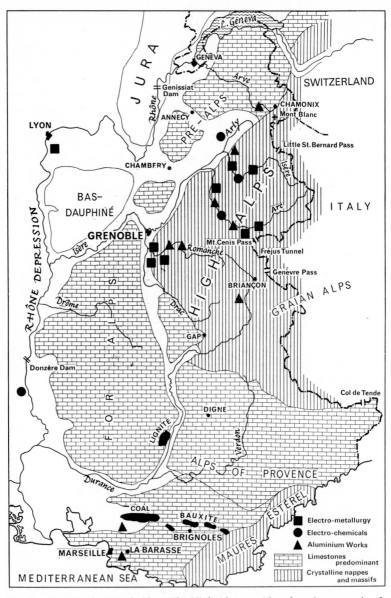

Fig. 67.—France: the French Alps. The High Alps provide a first-class example of a new type of industrial region, developed at high altitudes entirely by hydro-electric power. Along the valleys of the Romanche, Arc and upper Isère, a chain of hydro-electric power stations provides current for the industrial establishments shown and has revolutionised living conditions for the mountain farming communities.

lorries and milk pipelines. There is a large output of cheese (Gruyère). In the meantime, hay is produced in the valleys for winter fodder. The valleys of the Rhône, south of Lake Geneva and of the lower Isère (Grési-vaudan), are rich pasture lands, with arable farms and vineyards. Here are situated Grenoble (162,764), Annecy (33,100) and Chambéry (32,100).

Grenoble, the "Gateway to the Alps," is a route centre, with ancient glove (from lambskins) and silk industries. There are now electro-chemical and -metallurgical works, and the making of turbines and other equipment for power-stations. In all the towns of the northern Alps old crafts such as glove-making, watch-making, wood-carving and silk manufacture are found. Metal crafts based originally on local deposits of gold, silver and copper, long exhausted, continue side by side with new metallurgical and chemical industries based on water power. Even at Chamonix, the largest of many tourist resorts in the higher valleys of the High Alps, there are electro-chemical works.

In total, the High Alps generate nearly 60% of the country's hydro-electric power; most of it comes from the valley of the Rhône below Lake Geneva and from the valleys of the Isère, Arly, Arc and Drac. There are over ten integrated schemes, involving more than 150 stations. Besides feeding current into the national grid, they are transforming other-wise unproductive mountain country into a prosperous industrial region (*see* Fig. 67).

The southern Alps, dry limestones made drier by the summer droughts, are less productive and less populated than the mountains of the north. In fact, large areas are completely deserted and in others, where life became too hard, most of the inhabitants have moved away, leaving only scattered, isolated farmsteads. Sheep are far more plentiful than cattle; in summer they are taken up to the high pastures from the valleys of the Durance and its tributaries, where most of the people live, cultivating small patches of wheat, maize, tobacco, vines and olives. The appearance of olives marks the beginning of a Mediterranean régime. The chief towns are little more than large villages; the chief are Gap (17,300) and Digne (10,400). Briançon is a holiday resort near the head of the Durance valley. The Durance has been dammed to provide water for irrigation rather than for power.

9. The Jura mountains

Rainfall is heavy in the Jura, as much as 70 in. annually in the higher parts. About one-third of the surface is forested, mainly with conifers. Grasses in the valleys and on the lower slopes of the High or Folded Jura support dairying, which is the chief farming occupation. Much of the arable farming is of a subsistence type, with an emphasis on fodder crops, and there are some vineyards and fruit orchards. The chief product is cheese, especially of the Gruyère variety. The Low or Plateau Jura have more sheep than cattle, but the farms on the whole are more prosperous than in the High Jura (*see* Fig. 47).

Besançon (63,500), on the Doubs near its exit from the plateau to the Saône valley, is the largest town of the Jura region, with cheese factories, and distilleries producing absinthe and cherry-brandy. It is the centre of the French watch-making industry, which was introduced from Switzerland and is found also in many of the villages in the vicinity. In Besançon there is cotton and rayon manufacturing—an extension of the textile industry of Alsace.

10. *The Rhône–Saône corridor*

The Rhône–Saône corridor may be said to terminate in the north at Belfort (51,280), a fortress town commanding the gap of the same name. Its strategic position between the approaches to Paris and the Rhineland has made it important for centuries. Today, owing to the convergence of routes on the gap, it is a busy commercial town, with manufactures of electrical machinery, locomotives and turbines (*see* Fig. 48).

The plains of the upper Saône are alluvial, and include extensive wheat lands, but further south there are clays which were deposited on the floor of a lake which formerly filled this part of the valley. Here the chief occupation is cattle rearing for dairy produce and beef; maize begins to take the place of wheat, and fodder crops are grown. On both sides of the Saône valley there are vineyards producing the famous Burgundy wines. Those from the "Côtes" on the western side are the best known. From Dijon southwards for a distance of 35 miles, the scarps of the Côte d'Or, Mâconnais, Beaujolais and Lyonnais are covered with vineyards—an outstanding example of monoculture. The centres of the wine industry are Dijon (141,104), Beaune (12,000), Chalon (34,000), Mâcon (22,400) and Villefranche (20,000). Dijon is the "wine capital" of Burgundy. It also has cycle and aluminium works, but it is primarily important as a route junction between the Rhône–Saône corridor and the Paris basin.

The valley of the Saône above the confluence with the Rhône is occupied by the Pays de Dombes, a low plateau of boulders, pebbles, gravels and boulder clay. It is a poorly peopled region, liable to flooding; for when the faster-flowing waters of the Rhône are augmented in spring by thawing snows, the much slower Saône is ponded back and overflows its banks. This poor region is gradually being reclaimed by digging drainage channels along its edges, and cattle rearing is increasing in the northern portion. Elsewhere, agriculture is largely restricted to grass, potatoes and poor crops of wheat. In the best reclaimed areas, orchards and market gardens help to supply the needs of Lyon.

At the confluence of the Rhône and Saône is Lyon (535,784), the third city of France. Its central position in the corridor, with easy access to the St Étienne coalfield, has made it a commercial and industrial regional capital, a road and railway focus, and an important inland port. In this last capacity, most of its water traffic moves northwards along the Saône; the Rhône as yet has not been fully canalised. The industries of Lyon, already well developed because of the proximity of the St Étienne coalfield, have expanded in recent years through the generation of hydroelectric power in the Rhône valley and the High Alps. Its chief manufacture is of silk. Silk-worms, reared on mulberries introduced in the sixteenth century, are cultivated as a cottage industry outside the city and in the valley to the south. But the output of filament or silk yarn is less than 5% of the factories' requirements, and large quantities are imported, mainly from Japan. Silk manufacture is carried on by thousands of small firms in Lyon and its neighbourhood as a modernised and electrified domestic industry, but there is a growing concentration in large factories in the city, with consequent savings of power and labour. Lyon also has extensive engineering, tinplate and chemical works; and the silk industry has attracted a large part of France's weaving of man-made fibres, such as rayon and nylon.

Below Lyon the Rhône flows alternately through small, hilly plains and narrow gorges. The plains open out where the river is joined by its tributaries, the largest lowlands being in the lower valleys of the Isère, Drôme, Jabron, Aygues and Durance. The surface soils, piled in river-terraces, are stony and more suitable for tree-crops than for arable farming; wheat, melons and potatoes are grown in occasional patches of clays or alluvium, however, and there are market gardens near Lyon and Valence, in the latter case using irrigation. Both banks of the Rhône are lined with orchards of peaches, apricots, cherries and pears; mulberry trees are cultivated in groves or line the roads from Lyon to Montélimar. The stony plateau of Bas-Dauphiné, near the Rhône–Isère confluence, shows little development, and is used mainly for rough pasture and military training.

Below Montélimar, where the valley begins to open to the plain of Avignon, olives make their appearance, and wheat and vines are important. The main cultivation is of early vegetables and table grapes, which are sent to Lyon, Paris and Marseille. Excellent wine (Château neuf du Pape) is produced near Avignon. On the west the plain rises to the limestone foothills at the base of the Central Massif. These have scanty grasses and lime-loving shrubs; such landscape is known as *garrigue* (garigue). Where there are siliceous outcrops the vegetation consists of dwarf shrubs, often tangled and matted, called *maquis*.

The many small towns and villages along the Rhône have been over-shadowed by Lyon. Most have silk manufacture and food processing, helped by plentiful hydro-electric power. The Donzère-Mondragon scheme, not far from Montélimar, has one of France's largest generating stations, and is integrated with the Genissiat scheme in the north of the Rhône valley. The chief market towns are Vienne (30,000), Valence (55,023) and Avignon (75,181). Montélimar is well known for its nougat. Avignon is the centre of a vegetable-canning industry.

11. *The Mediterranean region*

West of the delta of the Rhône, a dune-lined coast is backed by the small plain of Roussillon near the Spanish border and by the larger plains of Languedoc. There is little agricultural activity in the coastal belt, and the only town of any account is Sète (Cette) (38,000). It is a port at the terminus of the Canal du Midi, which runs via the Gate of Carcassonne to Toulouse, but until recently its importance was declining, mainly because the harbour was silting up. Its main trade is in wine and petroleum, and the latter has given the port new life. Oil refineries have been built at Frontignac, a suburb on the edge of an étang, and the harbour has been dredged and modernised. There is fishing for tunny, sardines and anchovies, but it is of minor importance.

The plains of Languedoc were one of the granaries of imperial Rome, but the cultivation of wheat is now confined largely to the west, towards Carcassonne. Here there is mixed farming, with wheat, maize, fruit, cattle and pigs. Carcassonne (37,000) was sited on a hill commanding the passage between the Pyrenees and the Central Massif. The old town, surrounded by impressive walls, has been supplanted by a new one at the foot of the hill, and important food processing and textile industries have developed there. The old town remains as a tourist attraction.

Most of the rest of Languedoc is given over to viticulture. Vines are to be seen everywhere, in one of the best examples of monoculture in Europe. Languedoc is the world's greatest producer of wine, accounting for nearly half the total output of France. The wine is almost entirely *vin ordinaire*, which is distributed throughout the country via the Rhône–Saône corridor, the Gate of Carcassonne, or by sea from Marseille.

Monoculture, *i.e.* dependence on a single crop, as in Languedoc, has its dangers. Winds like the mistral may do great seasonal damage; but far more serious are the virus diseases which may destroy the vines and poison the soil. In the years before 1880, for instance, a type of aphides, *phylloxera*, destroyed four-fifths of all the vineyards. The disease was ultimately conquered by the use of newly-discovered sprays and by the introduction of resistant stock from the vineyards of California. The revived industry adopted co-operative methods of cultivation, wine-making and marketing. New threats to Languedoc's monoculture come from the great increases in the amount of land devoted to viticulture in

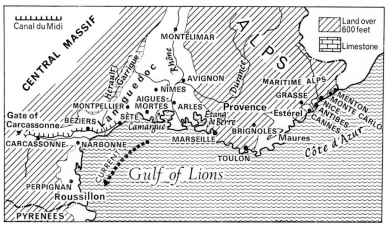

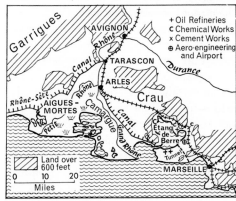

FIG. 68.—France : Mediterranean region. Although the Garrigue is the only area marked on the above map as limestone, most of the Alpine region shown is composed of similar rock. The map at the left shows the Rhône delta and Marseille in more detail.

Algeria, and from the French government's campaign against excessive wine-drinking which is alleged to be rampant in France.

The chief centres of wine production in co-operative factories are Montpellier (123,367), Nîmes (105,199), Béziers (78,544) and Narbonne (38,000), around all of which monoculture is giving way to mixed farming. Nîmes is a route centre, and has railway repair works and wool textile manufacture.

North of the plain is a continuation of the garrigue country of the lower Rhône. The limestone ridges flanking the Central Massif support a xerophytic scrub in which aromatic shrubs such as thyme and lavender are mixed with short grasses. Sheep rearing is important in these foot-hills and transhumance is normal, the sheep being moved to the higher Central Massif in summer. In some of the valleys are Government-sponsored plantations of pine trees.

The western part of the Rhône delta is the Camargue, drained by the Petit Rhône and bounded in the east by the Grand Rhône, the main distributaries of the river. The southern Camargue is an expanse of salt marsh, useless except for the production of salt in evaporating pans at Aigues-Mortes and chemicals at Les Salins-de-Giraud, both tiny settle-ments near the seaward ends of the two Rhônes. An interesting feature of the southern Camargue is the herd of horses which roam wild, feeding on scanty grasses near the coast. In the north the Camargue is being re-claimed, and there is mixed farming, with wheat, vines, vegetables and cattle. About 100,000 tons of rice are also produced annually in this part of the delta. East of the Grand Rhône is the Crau, a large fan of water-worn stones swept there by the Durance, which then abandoned its course to become a tributary of the Rhône. The Crau, dry on the surface, scorched in summer and swept by the mistral in winter, is a desolate area. Sheep are taken there in winter, to feed on the scanty garrigue and coarse grasses which root between the stones.

East of the Rhône delta the highland areas of the limestone Basses Alpes and the crystalline Maures and Estérel have little economic value except for sheep rearing, but their valleys are important. In the valleys of the upper Argens and its tributaries deposits of bauxite are quarried (see Fig. 67). The bauxite is reduced to alumina (aluminium oxide) near Marseille, using lignite from a nearby field as fuel, and the alumina is sent for final smelting to electro-metallurgical stations in the High Alps and along the Pyrenees. In the valleys between the Maures and Estérel massifs there are forests of cork-oak, which provide corks for the wine industry. In the valleys of the Côte d'Azur flowers are cultivated for the cut-flower trade and the manufacture of perfumes; early vegetables and peaches are grown too. The centre of the perfume industry is Grasse, north-east of Cannes.

The French coast immediately east of the Rhône delta is very broken and has several good harbours. The currents are from east to west, keeping the harbours relatively free from the silts brought down by the Rhône. It was a foregone conclusion that a major port should grow on one of these openings at the southern end of the Rhône–Saône corridor, and the development of Marseille (Fig. 68) can be attributed primarily to its position. Excellent roads and railways have been constructed from the city through the corridor, and it has become the centre of an industrial region which extends to the shores of the Étang de Berre. It imports oil-seeds, sugar, timber, wheat, rice and tropical produce, processing them and exporting the finished products. Its water communications inland are relatively poor. Barge canals connect the port to the Étang de Berre and the lower Rhône, but no further. Plans have been made, however, to improve the navigation of the Rhône and enable large barges to traverse the river to Lyon.

Marseille (783,738) is the second city of France, with one of the most cosmopolitan populations in the world. Its industries include vegetable-oil refining, the making of soap, margarine and chemicals, flour milling, sugar refining, marine engineering and shipbuilding in the city area; and the new developments around the Étang de Berre are within its industrial boundaries. Marseille lies in a good position on the tanker route from the oilfields of the Middle East, and the Étang de Berre, connected by canals to the port, offers convenient sites for oil refineries. Already there are three large ones on its shores, with associated chemical industries, including the manufacture of explosives. Marseille's hinterland covers the whole of France, parts of Switzerland and Belgium, and even—for passengers and mails *en route* to the Far East—extends to the British Isles; thus it is one of the chief liner and passenger ports of Europe.

Toulon (172,586), in a good harbour backed by fortified limestone hills, is France's Mediterranean naval base, with naval and civil dock-yards. It exports bauxite from the quarries of Brignoles, to the north. The chief towns of the Côte d'Azur are holiday and tourist resorts. They are in four groups centred on Cannes, Nice, Monte Carlo and Menton. With its sun-drenched beaches, casinos, luxury trades and nearby mountain scenery, the region, known also as the Riviera, has become the "playground of Europe."

Corsica. The island of Corsica is the most under-developed part of metropolitan France. Most of the surface lies more than 1500 ft above sea level and is extensively covered by thick maquis, among which only sheep and goats can find subsistence. The main lowlands, along the east coast, are malarial; the small population of this side of the island lives in dirty, neglected villages in the valleys which run from the coastal plains into the plateau. The most habitable parts of Corsica are the strips of lowland at the heads of rias on the west coast. Farming is primitive, and subsistence crops of wheat, maize, potatoes and vegetables are supplemented by edible chestnuts gathered from the forests in the valleys. Ajaccio, the largest town, is situated on a ria and, like Bastia, a tiny port in the north-east, has tunny and sardine fisheries. In recent years, efforts have been made to develop a tourist industry in the north of the island, as an extension of the tourism on the French and Italian Rivieras.

ECONOMIC SUMMARY

France is often quoted as a country with a well-balanced economy, and this is certainly true by comparison with some of the more industrialised countries of Europe, such as the United Kingdom, West Germany, Belgium and the Netherlands. At the same time, although both her industrial and agricultural economies have yielded excellent results and have great potentialities, neither kept pace with the general advance in standards made by most major countries during the present century. A growing imbalance was discernible between agriculture and industry, mainly owing to a shortage of domestic coal and oil supplies, and in some degree to a deficiency of labour. France was fully aware of it, and by the introduction of agrarian reforms and the rationalisation of heavy industry has done much to restore the equilibrium.

Agriculture would appear to have the better immediate prospects. Already in good years the country can supply its own needs in cereals, sugar, dairy products, vegetables and meat. It is of course the world's greatest producer of wine. It has the climate and the soils for further development of most of these products; all it needs to ensure a surplus for export is the co-operation of its farmers. This is only slowly being given by the agricultural communities in the south of the country; but by insistence on the laws governing land tenure, by the development of co-operation and the introduction of new techniques, new seeds and more fertilisers, above all by the increase in mechanised methods and scientific knowledge, considerable advance has been made in the north. In the south—especially in some parts of the basin of Aquitaine, the lower Rhône valley and Languedoc—the resistance of the peasant population is being broken down by the obvious success of "American methods" and by the introduction of improved systems of irrigation which have followed the harnessing of streams for hydro-electricity.

In industry, as in agriculture, France was slow to adopt modern methods. There remains a wide distribution of craft industries, such as the making of high-class silk goods, jewellery, watches, carved wood, and the fashions for which Paris is famous. Most of these are luxury trades and as such highly susceptible to competition in other countries from mass-produced imitations or substitutes. Moreover, they involve uneconomic use of hand labour.

For its size, France has few major industrial regions. The largest are the Nord coalfield, the Lorraine coal and iron fields, the Seine basin from Paris to the sea, and the Lyon–St Étienne region. Smaller and more localised regions occur around Marseille, Bordeaux and Nantes. A new industrial region, based on hydro-electric power, is developing in the

High Alps around Grenoble. In all these, metallurgical industries are foremost, those concerned with iron and steel in the coalfield areas and the western ports, with aluminium in Marseille and the Alps. Shortage of coke and of labour militate against much further development of heavy engineering in the north, but the electro-chemical and electro-metallurgical industries in the mountains are showing significant advances.

The north-east industrial region has the most comprehensive range of iron and steel goods, almost every town specialising in some branch of heavy or light engineering and producing goods which vary from bridge parts, turbines, diesel engines and boilers, to sewing machines, iron-mongery and pins. The Lorraine region concentrates more on the production of pig iron and steel than on engineering. Its products are sent to other centres in Franch or are exported. The lower Seine has a great variety of metallurgical industries, especially around Paris. Here is the centre of the motor industry, with firms such as Citröen, Simca, Renault and Ford: and here, too, armaments are made. The Lyon–St Étienne region specialises in light engineering, lorries, cutlery and machine tools; not far away, Le Creusot makes armaments and railway locomotives.

The agricultural machinery industry is widespread. It is making great strides not only in the regions mentioned above, but in Bordeaux, Marseille, Strasbourg, Toulouse, Orléans, Limoges and other major agricultural regions. Electrical engineering too, is on the increase, especially near the Alps, Pyrenees and Central Massif, where it is providing employment in districts which previously had little to offer. The aircraft industry is another which is scattered, the chief centres being Paris, Bourges, Toulouse and Tarbes—the last two, in the relatively remote south, being concerned mainly with military aeroplanes. Ship-building has had to remedy the shipping losses of two world wars, but has benefited by the reconstruction on modern lines of shipyards destroyed by bombing. St Nazaire is the chief shipbuilding port, and there are important yards at Boulogne, Le Havre, Dunkerque, Rouen, Brest, Bordeaux, Marseille and Toulon.

Textile manufacturing in France is more widely distributed than any other industry, especially in the case of wool textiles. The greatest concentration of the latter is in the north-east, around Lille, Roubaix and Tourcoing; other centres occur in the Ardennes at Fourmies and Sedan, on the lower Seine at Elbeuf and Louviers, and on the edges of the Central Massif at Mazamet and Châteauroux. It may be said that every town of any size which is situated near a sheep rearing district will have a share in the wool textile industry, which employs about one-fifth of France's textile workers (*see* Fig. 58).

The cotton industry is found chiefly in four areas. The most important, both for spinning and weaving, is in the east around Belfort and Épinal, and throughout southern Alsace; it accounts for about 45% of total production. Next in order is the north-east industrial region, with extensions into Picardy and the Aisne valley, making about 35% of the total. The remaining 20% is shared mainly between the region which lies between Laval and Cholet in Anjou, and the Roanne basin in the upper Loire. The latter region has little spinning, receiving the yarn from the Vosges and Alsace factories.

The silk industry, concentrated in the Rhône valley from Lyon south-wards, is not as important as it used to be and sericulture in the mulberry groves has declined. Nevertheless, the manufacture of silk tissues and ribbons still employs nearly as many people as the cotton industry. This is because much silk is made in small family factories or in rooms in private houses in villages east of Lyon. In recent years large silk factories have been built in Lyon, with a consequent saving in labour and manufacturing costs, and more efficient marketing. Gradually, much of the domestic manufacture is disappearing, and factories for the making of rayon and nylon are employing the displaced silk workers. Man-made fibres are manufactured also in the towns of the Aisne valley.

The linen industry of France is nowadays largely confined to the districts of Armentières in the north-east, and Cholet in Anjou. Angers is the only remaining important centre for the manufacture of hemp.

The devastation of the industrial regions in the north of France during the war led the Government to a policy of decentralisation, as far as possible. Since 1954 there have been deliberate efforts to transfer manufacturing industries to towns in the centre and south of the country. Sometimes it was because of the decline of an extractive industry, such as coal mining; more frequently it was to assist the economy of a struggling market town, especially if it was near a supply of hydro-electricity. This policy of decentralisation, accompanied as it is by the building of up-to-date factories and the introduction of the most modern techniques, is doing much to bring the industrial economy of France once more into line with that of the rest of the Western world. There seems little doubt that the balance of the country's whole economy, agricultural, industrial, social and political, is being restored to what it was at the beginning of the century.

STUDY QUESTIONS

1. "The structure of France has little unity." Discuss this statement. (O. & C.)

2. Describe, and suggest reasons for, the variety of the climate in France, with special reference to the influence of the sea. (O. & C.)

3. It is frequently stated that France is practically self-supporting in food supplies. To what extent is this true? (O. & C.)

4. What, in your opinion, have been the most important factors that have influenced the position of France's eastern frontier? (O. & C.)

5. Analyse the factors that have influenced the locations of the main textile industries of France. (J.M.B.)

6. Discuss the assertion that the economy of France is based upon a balance of agriculture and manufacturing rather than upon industrial exports. (J.M.B.)

7. Comment on the statement that the coal and iron resources of France are inadequate and badly distributed. (J.M.B.)

8. Discuss the importance of viticulture in France. (J.M.B.)

9. Give an account of the chief developed mineral resources of France, and illustrate their importance to the economic life of the country. (J.M.B.)

10. Write a short essay on "Hydro-electricity in France."

11. To what extent have the relief and drainage features of France influenced the development of the pattern of communications? (O. & C.)

12. Draw a sketch-map to illustrate the division of France into natural regions. State briefly the main physical features of each region. Select one of these regions, other than the Paris basin, and discuss its importance in the economic life of the country. (O. & C.)

13. Write a geographical account of the Paris basin and comment on the importance of this region to France. (O. & C.)

14. Describe, with the aid of a sketch-map, the scenery and characteristic occupations of the regions passed through in the course of a journey from Paris to Marseille *or* from Paris to Strasbourg. (O. & C.)

15. Give a geographical account of *either* the Central Massif *or* the French Alps. (O. & C.)

16. Write a reasoned account of the geography of Alsace-Lorraine.

17. Indicate a regional division for the basin of the river Rhône, and give a comprehensive account of any *one* of the regions recognised. (J.M.B.)

18. Select three cities in France that differ widely from each other in their main functions. Describe and account for these differences. (J.M.B.)

19. Describe the major regional contrasts found within the basin of the river Loire. (J.M.B.)

20. Select any *two* important agricultural areas in France which differ markedly in rural economy from each other and describe such differences. (J.M.B.)

21. Write a comparative account of Brittany and Mediterranean France from the points of view of (a) relief, (b) climate, (c) economic activities.

22. Describe the site and importance of *three* of the following: Marseille, Bordeaux, Strasbourg, Lyon. Illustrate your answer by means of sketch-maps.

23. Write an essay on "Paris—the Metropolis of France."

24. Analyse the location of mineral-oil refining in north-western Europe. (O. & C.)

25. Write a short essay on *one* of the following: (a) the Landes, (b) the Polders, (c) the Campine, (d) Sweden (south of Stockholm.) (O. & C.)

26. Show by a sketch-map the position of the coal basin of North France, Belgium, the Netherlands and Aachen, and describe briefly the industries that have grown up on it. (O. & C.)

27. Comment on the role of hydro-electric power in the countries of western Europe. Show how climate, relief and drainage affect the generation of hydro-electricity. (O. & C.)

28. Account for *three* of the following: (a) the distribution of population in

Belgium, (b) the interest of Norway in her mercantile marine, (c) the export of foodstuffs from Denmark to Great Britain, (d) the export of Swedish iron ore through Narvik. (O. & C.)

29. Comment geographically on the following: (a) "The Netherlands are protected by their polders and marshes." (b) "France has striven for centuries to attain her natural frontiers." (O. & C.)

30. Describe the distribution of viticulture in the countries of western Europe and suggest the factors that limit the cultivation of the vine. (O. & C.)

31. Give an account of the factors which determined the site and growth of *three* of the following: Stockholm, Rotterdam, Marseille, Liège, Bergen.

32. Plan a tour by road, of not more than 1500 miles, beginning at the Hook of Holland and ending at Boulogne, for a person who wishes to see the variety of physical environment in western Europe. Give reasons for the route you choose and illustrate it with a sketch-map. (O. & C.)

Chapter XVI

CENTRAL EUROPE

THE BOUNDARIES OF CENTRAL EUROPE

Central Europe is sometimes taken to include all the countries between France and Russia, bounded on the north by the Baltic and Finland, and on the south by the countries abutting on the Mediterranean Sea. This large expanse, however, is capable of sub-division into a northern region comprising Germany, Switzerland, Czechoslovakia, Austria and Poland, and a south-eastern section containing Hungary, Yugoslavia, Rumania and Bulgaria. There are good reasons for such a division into a *central* Europe which contains the first series of countries, and a *south-central* Europe for the rest.

In the first place, the area covered by central Europe, as here conceived, has been dominated in history largely by Germanic peoples and culture. Although at present Poland and Czechoslovakia are Slav in government and in outlook, the influences of past German sovereignty over parts of them still remain. Boundaries in this northern region have fluctuated frequently with pressures from east and west, but there has always been a kind of historical unity based on the German language, and this encouraged Hitler's Germany to claim as part of its "empire" all those areas in which even a minority spoke its tongue.

Geographically, too, the region has a certain amount of unity. It is transitional between the maritime west and the continental east in climate and economic development, and it shows differences from south-central Europe in both. Structurally, the whole north of the region is part of the Great European Plain, which widens gradually eastward towards Russia and has an extensive cover of glacial deposits. South of the Plain is a belt of hills and plateaus, a continuation of the Hercynian blocks of France and Belgium, running through Germany, Czechoslovakia and Poland. South of this again is a belt of varying width, known in part as the Alpine foreland, and containing sections of the basins of the Rhine and Danube. This separates the Hercynian blocks from the fourth belt, that of the limestone and crystalline folds of the Alps. Only a very small area of the Alps is situated in Germany, but much of Switzerland, Austria, and eastern Czechoslovakia is Alpine, and southern Poland is bounded by the Beskids and the Carpathians, which are part of the Tertiary

273

orogeny. In places, *e.g.* between Czechoslovakia and Austria, the Hercynian blocks and the Alpine folds approach each other, reducing the Foreland to a narrow strip along which the Danube flows in a gorge; and in Czechoslovakia, an easy passage between Hercynian Bohemia and Alpine Slovakia—the Moravian Gate—provides a route north–south across Europe.

South-central Europe, on the other hand, is made up of countries which are orientated to the south-east and are given geographical unity as part of the Danube basin. Their climate is continental, but their lower latitudes give them warmer summers than central Europe; and their nearness to the Mediterranean (in the case of Yugoslavia and Bulgaria) may result in occasional winter maxima of rainfall, which would not happen in the more northerly region. Historically, the countries of Hungary, Rumania, Yugoslavia and Bulgaria have more eastern than western affinities, although at the present time Yugoslavia seems to be trying to face both ways at once. Its Government is Communist, but not of the Russian type, and it is willing to "co-exist" with the Western powers. In general, however, south-central Europe appears to have its future more closely allied with eastern Europe—that is, with the U.S.S.R. —than is the case with central Europe. For this reason alone it merits separate treatment.

STRUCTURE AND RELIEF

The structure and relief of central Europe—that is, of Germany, Poland, Switzerland, Austria and Czechoslovakia—have features common to more than one of these countries. Accordingly, they are treated here without reference to political boundaries, except where it may be necessary for clarity. Five major divisions can be recognised: (1) the Germano-Polish Plain, (2) the central highlands, of Hercynian origin, (3) the Alpine foreland, (4) the Alps, (5) the Pannonian lowlands.

1. *The Germano-Polish plain*

This is part of the Great European Plain, which stretches without a break from the North Sea to the Ural mountains. The plain has a foundation of Permian and Triassic limestones and sandstones in the north, and of Tertiary sedimentaries in the south, but only in a very few places do they appear on the surface. Throughout the plain there is a cover of superficial and unconsolidated glacial deposits to a depth varying from 40 to nearly 600 ft, the result of the advances and retreats of the ice sheets of the Quaternary Ice Age. In the south of the plain, especially in East Germany, there are deposits of brown coal or lignite in the Tertiary strata. The Germano-Polish plain may be sub-divided into (*a*) the coastal plain and Baltic Heights, (*b*) a region of outwash plains, and (*c*) a belt of loess and loams (*see* Fig. 69).

(*a*) *The coastal plain and Baltic Heights.* The Quaternary ice sheets advanced from a centre in Scandinavia southwards towards the central highlands in three or possibly four phases. The first advances travelled farthest and either did not leave terminal moraines or spread them so lightly as not to form significant hills, for although borings have yielded clays of these earlier glaciations there are no signs of them to be found on

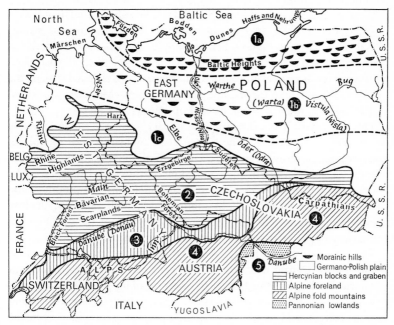

FIG. 69.—Central Europe: major structural divisions. The numbers correspond with the regional divisions used in the text.

the surface of the plain. Later advances, especially the last, left lines of morainic hills across the plain, roughly concentric to the southern shores of the Baltic Sea.

The highest and most continuous line of morainic hills lies nearest the coast, and is known as the Baltic Heights or the Baltic Lakes Plateau. The size and extent of these hills indicate that the end of the ice sheet must have remained there for a very long period. The area is a low plateau of broken rocks, knit together by glacial clays, rising at its highest point to 1088 ft, near the Gulf of Danzig. Its surface is extremely undulating, and in the clay-lined hollows are thousands of small lakes. They are in two

K

main groups, the Pomeranian lakes in the west of the plateau, and the Masurian lakes in the east. Some of them are drying up, to form bogs and marshes.

Between the northern edge of the Baltic Heights and the coast, a narrow plain slopes gently northwards. Near the foot of the moraine it is covered with boulder clay and, towards the coast, with loams derived from the ground-moraine. The coastline of this region of glaciation varies in form from west to east, the rivers Elbe and Oder offering good lines of demarcation.

West of the Elbe the North Sea coast is low-lying and lined with mudflats and sandhills. A few miles offshore lie the East Frisian islands, which were once a continuous belt of sand dunes. The tidal flats between the coast and the islands are the *Watten* (*wadden* in the Netherlands); parts of them have been reclaimed to form *Marschen*, which is German for "marshes" but is here the name given to polders. Marschen are found also around the mouths of the rivers Ems, Weser and Elbe.

The Baltic coast, from the Danish boundary to the river Oder, is made up of *Förden* and *Bodden*. The förden coast, which extends to Lübeck Bay, has long, narrow, deep inlets, which are thought to be the drowned mouths of sub-glacial streams, and akin to those of Denmark. The bodden coast, from Lübeck Bay up to and including the mouth of the Oder, shows the effect of slight submergence, with irregular, shallow openings and offshore islands. Some of the mouths of the openings are being closed by spits which are caused by longshore drifting.

The west–east drift is more noticeable east of the Oder, where as far as the Gulf of Danzig it has resulted in a straight, dune-lined coast. An eastward-flowing current, helped by the prevailing westerlies, has built spits across irregularities in the coast, straightening it and entrapping lagoons behind sand dunes. Where the openings were wider, as in the cases of the Gulf of Danzig and the Kurisches Haff, the spits have not as yet formed a complete enclosure. These spits are called "nehrungs" (Ger. *Nehrungen*), and the partially formed lagoons behind them are "haffs" (Ger. *Haff*, "bay" or "gulf").

(b) *The outwash plains.* South of the Baltic Heights, in a broad belt running from west to east, is a series of plains composed of sands and gravels washed from the front of the melting ice sheets. Here and there, parallel to the Baltic Heights but lower and less continuous, are lines of morainic hills which mark the slow retreat of the glaciers from their furthest advance. Between all the lines of moraines there are depressions, called *Urstromtäler* in Germany and *pradoliny* in Poland. Each line of moraines represents a pause in the movement of the ice sheet, during which the load of boulders and clays was piled up, forming a barrier against the flow northwards of melt-water or of rivers from the south. The general slope of the Germano-Polish plain is from south to north, and rivers from the Erzgebirge, Sudetes, Carpathians and other southern highlands were forced to turn east or west when they came to the morainic barrier. The river waters were augmented by melt-water from the glaciers, and together they carved out for themselves deep, east–west channels. These channels are the urstromtäler or pradoliny.

Sometimes a vigorous stream flowing from the northern slope of a moraine would cut back its source and capture a river which was flowing in a more southern depression. This explains the sudden change of course of some of the Germano-Polish rivers, such as the Elbe, Oder and Vistula, on all of which elbows of capture are easily recognisable in an atlas. As a result of capture, some parts of the urstromtäler and pradoliny no longer contain rivers, but these stretches provide excellent routes for canal construction, since they have easy gradients. The Mittelland Canal, for instance, joins the river Ems to Berlin via the urstromtal immediately south of the Baltic Heights; the Oder–Vistula Canal is constructed in the pradoliny which is its continuation in Poland.

West of the river Elbe the surface, it is thought, was not covered by the ice sheets of the latest glacial phase. In this region, moraines are fragmentary and of older glaciations, and there are no urstromtäler. The surface is of outwash sand, flat and infertile, and is intersected by marshy river valleys. As in the Netherlands, it is called *geest*. Within the geest, there is a higher area, equally sandy and infertile—the Lüneburger Heide (Ger. *Heid*, "heath"), which rises to 1663 ft in the Wilseder Berg, east of Bremen.

(c) *The belt of loams and loess.* South of the morainic zone the sandy soils of low fertility give way gradually to loams and loess, and this belt extends to the foot of the central highlands in the south. The loams are found mainly south of the geest and heide in the west, in Lower Saxony and the northern part of the Rhine lowlands. The loess covers extensive areas in the south of East Germany and Poland, and there are patches in the lowlands of the Rhine. Loess was formed in inter-Glacial or post-Glacial times, which were dry, so that the wind could pick up and carry fine particles of rock from the debris left by the ice sheets. This dust was carried southwards until it was forced to settle by the damper conditions nearer the mountains, and was deposited on the plains flanking the highlands. At first it was powdery and yellow, as in the Hwang-ho basin in China, but it gradually developed in Europe into fertile brown forest soils (loams) or black earth (chernozem).

The south of the Germano-Polish plain is rich in minerals. They include coal and lignite in the Rhine valley, Ruhr, Saxony and Upper

Silesian fields, iron ore in Hanover and Silesia, petroleum south of Brunswick and in Poland, potash salts east and west of the Harz mountains, and common salt south of these and in south Poland.

2. *The central highlands*

The Germano-Polish plain is bounded on the south by a region of great diversity. A belt of highlands, stretching from the Schwarzwald (Black Forest) in the west to the Lysogóry in eastern Poland, dates from the Hercynian mountain-building period. The Hercynian folds were eroded to a peneplain, and in Tertiary times the forces which caused the Alpine orogenesis faulted and dislocated the Hercynian strata, lifting some parts as great horsts or massifs and depressing others to form plains, basins and rift valleys (*see* also Chapters I and XIV). Sometimes the uplifted blocks were forced northwards, to appear in the present topography as isolated massifs such as the Harz mountains; occasionally there were volcanic eruptions and intrusions, as may be seen in the extinct craters of the Eifel and the basaltic Vogelsberg. The amount of uplift of the Hercynian rocks was greater in the south of the region, so that the general slope of the central highlands is to the north. The northern Black Forest is lower than its southern section, and the same applies to the Bohemian plateau. Sedimentary strata, such as sandstones and limestones, which lay on the flanks of the Hercynian ridges, were uplifted and eroded in a series of scarps, best seen in southern West Germany and, to a lesser extent, in southern Poland. The central highlands are today a maze of granite plateaus, ranges of hills with rounded tops, steep limestone scarps and plateaus, lower sandstone ridges, eroded volcanic craters, and intervening lowland plains, enclosed basins, and rift valleys.

Starting in the west, the chief Hercynian fragments in central Europe are as follows. The river Rhine, after its abrupt bend near Basel, flows northwards through a rift valley or *Graben*, bounded on its eastern side by the Black Forest, an elongated horst. The western side of the valley is enclosed by the Vosges (in France) and the Hardt (in Germany). North of the Black Forest is the Odenwald, a plateau with an east–west trend; to the north-west are the Middle Rhine Highlands, through which the Rhine flows in a gorge. These highlands include the massifs of the Hunsrück, Taunus, Eifel and Westerwald. East of the Taunus, the Vogelsberg rises like an island in the depression of Hesse, which terminates eastwards in the Rhön and Thuringerwald (Thuringian Forest). On the northern side of the latter another depression, that of Thuringia, has the isolated horst of the Harz on its northern edge.

The western portion of Czechoslovakia is a diamond-shaped block, the Bohemian massif, a horst made up of several minor horsts and basins. Here the folding of the Alps and Carpathians caused such faulting, tilting and warping as to give the massif a definite basin shape, with high surrounding rims. On the south-west are the Böhmer Wald (Bohemian Forest) and Bayerischer Wald (Bavarian Forest); on the north-west are the Erzgebirge (Ore mountains); the Sudetes, which include the Riesengebirge (Giant mountains) and the Adler Gebirge (Eagle mountains), form the north-eastern rim; and the very much lower Moravian Heights enclose the south-eastern side.

Between the Black Forest and the Bohemian Forest is a series of scarps, plateaus and basins drained largely by the rivers Main and Neckar and partly by the left-bank tributaries of the upper Danube (Donau). Triassic rocks (Bunter sandstone, Muschelkalk, Keuper marls) were here overlain by Jurassic limestones and Tertiary sands, loams and clays. These were uplifted and tilted by the Alpine orogenesis, and the resultant denudation produced a number of west- or north-west-facing scarps. The most prominent of these are the limestone scarps of the Swabian and Franconian Jura, which rise to over 1100 ft, and whose dip slopes are plateaus. The name "Jura" for these heights is now being replaced by the German *Alb* (Alp)—Schwäbische Alb, Frankischer Alb.

In Poland, a limestone scarp runs parallel to the Sudetes, extending roughly from Częstochowa to Kraków, and beyond it is a wide, limestone plateau, similar to those in West Germany. North-east of the plateau is the Lysogóry, an isolated crystalline horst which rises to over 2000 ft. East of the river Vistula, a low plateau of chalk extending into the Ukraine appears to be a continuation of the Polish limestone plateau. It is covered with a mantle of loess, and might be included with the loess belt already mentioned.

3. *The Alpine foreland*

Between the central highlands and the Alpine folded mountains is a belt known as the Alpine foreland, varying in width from about 50 miles in south-west Germany to less than 6 miles in Austria, and finally disappearing in south Poland. It is composed of *molasse*, great masses of material eroded from the newly rising Alps in Tertiary times; and these were covered during and after the Ice Age by glacial deposits.

The Swiss plateau or Mittelland is at the western end of the foreland. It slopes from a height of 4500 ft near the Alps to 1300 ft at the foot of the Jura, 30 miles away. This is the most elevated section of the foreland, but its most extensive development is in the south of West Germany, where it spreads from the Bavarian Alps to the Franconian Alb, reaching 50 miles wide in places and varying in height from 3000 ft near the mountains to 915 ft at Passau, at the confluence of the rivers Danube and

Inn. At the eastern end of the German foreland the glacial deposits thin
out and molasse appears on the surface. In the north, towards the Danube,
there is a cover of outwash sands and clays; and this area, together with
alluvial stretches in the river valleys, has productive soils. On the whole,
however, the molasse and the sands, gravels and boulders left by the
glaciers are infertile. The Swiss plateau might be regarded as exceptional,
for although it is higher, careful cultivation has made it productive and it
yields large crops of grass fodder for the dairying industry.

In Austria, where the Alps are near the Bohemian massif, the foreland
narrows to less than 6 miles wide. In this section it is a hilly mass of
molasse, mainly of Tertiary rocks, bounded on the north by the river
Danube, which flows in a trench along the foot of the Bohemian massif.
The foreland widens again in the plains of Moravia, between the Carpathians and the Moravian Heights. Here the molasse is covered by Tertiary
marls and clays, which are fertile, and by occasional patches of alluvium
deposited by the river Morava and its tributaries. Molasse appears again
at the northern end of the plains, where the Carpathian folds approach
the Sudetes to form the Moravian Gate, which leads to the Polish lowlands. The surface of the "gate" is high enough to act as a divide between
waters flowing to the Black and the Baltic seas. Beyond the Moravian
Gate there is very little appreciable foreland between the Carpathians and
the limestone scarplands of southern Poland.

4. *The Alps*

In central Europe, the folds of the Alps cover most of the area of
Switzerland, Austria and the tiny state of Liechtenstein, and extend into
the south of West Germany. Outside central Europe, the Alps are
continued in France, northern Italy and Yugoslavia. Our attention is
directed here to the central European section, but for better understanding
of the system as a whole it will be necessary to refer here and there to the
French and Italian ranges. The Carpathians are also a part of the Alpine
orogeny, but they are considered separately in the chapters on Poland
and Rumania.

The Alps extend in a great arc from the Gulf of Genoa to the plain of
Hungary. The system is over 500 miles long and varies in width from
less than 60 to about 150 miles. The highest peaks are in the west, the
most notable being Mont Blanc (15,781 ft), Monte Rosa (15,217 ft),
Weisshorn (14,799 ft), Matterhorn (14,779 ft), Finsteraarhorn (14,026 ft)
and Jungfrau (13,669 ft), but in the east there are many over 10,000 ft,
especially in the Upper Engadine, in Switzerland, where Piz Bernina
reaches 13,287 ft.

Some account of the birth of the Alpine system was given in Chapter I.

The mountain folds were lifted high out of the sea, reaching their maximum during the Oligocene and Miocene epochs. The uplift was not continuous; its phases took possibly two million years. The Pyrenees, for instance, are older than the Alps proper, and they in turn were folded before the ranges in the Balkan peninsula. Although the Alpine orogenesis is dated as at least a million years ago, complete stability has not been reached yet. Volcanic activity and earthquakes, especially in the eastern part of the system, denote a continuance of earth movement.

The rocks from which the Alps were folded consisted of shales and limestones resting on a crystalline foundation of ancient origin. When they were folded, the consequent pressures and stresses metamorphosed

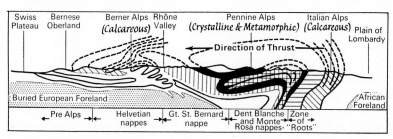

FIG. 70.—Nappes. A simplified structural section from north to south across the Alps, to show the formation of nappes. Use this diagram in conjunction with Fig. 80.

much of the shales into slate, the limestones into marble, and the older rocks became gneisses and schists. Most of the pressure seems to have come from the south, so that the folds were crushed against the worndown Hercynian mountains in the south of ancient Europe. The eroded stumps of these ranges were lifted, broken and displaced, to form the rejuvenated central highlands described earlier. Faced by the resistance of the older and more stable formations, the Alpine folds in the west collapsed and broke, and were driven northwards as fractured recumbent folds in huge overthrusts known as *nappes* (Fig. 70).

Because of this dislocation, reconstruction of the movement of the Alpine folds is difficult, but at least four major nappes have been distinguished, each consisting of sedimentary rocks, principally limestones, with a crystalline and metamorphosed core. In the west the simple and regular folds of limestone, such as are found today in the Jura mountains, were covered in the French Alps by the Helvetian nappe, which caught up in its northward movement some of the marginal Hercynian blocks, to form the Alpine massifs of Savoy in France. This was followed by the Pennine nappe, which gave rise to the high Pennine Alps, and then came the Grisonid and Tirolid nappes, which affected eastern Switzerland and western Austria. A fifth nappe, the Dinarid, overrode the Tirolid nappe and seems to have collapsed in a different direction, for its recumbent folds and thrusts are in southward-facing positions.

The western nappes, the Helvetian and Pennine, were piled higher than those in the east: a line drawn from Lake Constance to Lake Como may be used to divide the whole Alpine system into two parts, western and eastern Alps, based on this difference in altitude. The western Alps, lifted higher and subject in consequence to more active erosion, had most of their younger surface sedimentaries carried away, exposing the granites and gneisses of the crystalline foundation in the jagged peaks of the Pennine and Lepontine Alps. Less active denudation east of the line has left a more complete cover of younger rocks, especially limestones, although in the Upper Engadine area, where the Grisonid nappe is eroded, outcrops of older rocks are exposed. The Dinarid nappe had little or no effect on the region under discussion. It forms part of the Dinaric Alps in Yugoslavia, and it is thought that it also lies deep below the alluvial deposits of the Plain of Lombardy.

During the period of uplift and immediately afterwards, rapid erosion reduced the Alpine folds to peneplains and rounded peaks. But towards the close of the Tertiary period a new earth movement, this time vertical rather than lateral, raised the whole mountain system, rejuvenating the river drainage and giving new vigour to erosive agents. The uplift was greater in the west, and it is considered that the greater height of the western Alps is due more to this later epeirogenic movement than to the earlier folding and piling of nappes.

The present relief of the Alps bears considerable relation to their structure, but it has been profoundly affected by glaciation, which began during the Quaternary Ice Age and still continues. At the present time snow and ice accumulate in the higher valleys (above 7500 ft in the north and 10,500 ft in the centre of the system) and approximately 1400 square miles are covered by glaciers, two-thirds of them in the western Alps. During the Ice Age a thick sheet of ice covered the whole area, with the exception of a few small stretches such as Provence in France, and Styria (Steiermark) and Carinthia (Kärnten) in Austria. Many of the higher mountains must have projected above the ice sheet as nunataks and were torn and shattered by the action of frost into jagged, needle-like peaks (known as *aiguilles* in France and *Hörne* or *Spitzen* in Switzerland).

In post-Glacial times, as the ice sheet decreased in size and more normal glaciers took its place, great hollows, or *cirques*, were scooped in the high valleys. Where there were several cirques in close proximity, continued erosion enabled them to intersect and produce pyramidal peaks, such as the Matterhorn. River valleys, already deepened by the late Tertiary rejuvenation, were further and more vigorously incised by valley glaciers, to give them the familiar flat-bottomed U shape, and tributary hanging valleys, with steep slopes and numerous waterfalls, lay along their sides. Two great longitudinal trenches which cut through the Alps from end to end owe their width and prominence to glacial action in valleys which existed before Glacial times. The greater of these furrows is occupied by the upper courses of the rivers Rhône, Vorderrhein and Inn; the other trench may be traced on the map from the northern end of Lake Como along the valleys of the Upper and Lower Engadine. It may be noted that these trenches divide the Alps into three structural belts. Between the two valleys there is a central crystalline zone, and north and south of them are belts composed mainly of limestones.

All the characteristics of valley glaciation, in addition to those mentioned above, are to be found in the Alps. Moraines of all types, roches moutonnées, erratics, screes and perched blocks are common. Most of the numerous lakes owe their origin to glacial action of some kind. The marginal lakes in Switzerland and northern Italy are evidence of the morainic barriers built along the outer edges of the limestone belts. On the northern side are Lakes Geneva, Neuchâtel, Thun, Brienz, Lucerne and Constance; on the south, Lakes Maggiore, Lugano, Como, Isea and Garda. Chiemsee, in Germany, and Wörthesee, in Austria, have similar origins.

Below the level of the fractured peaks and the eroded cirques, some of the higher mountain slopes lay during the Ice Age under stationary portions of the ice sheet. The areas here disclosed by the melting of the "dead ice" are flattish or rounded shoulders which were later clothed with soft grasses and Alpine plants. These are the well-known Alpine pastures called "alps," which have given their name to the whole mountain system.

The Alps, lying as they do athwart the western portion of peninsular Europe, would appear to present a formidable barrier to communications between the north and south of the continent. This is not the case, for although the terrain is difficult and in some parts impassable, it contains many practicable routes. The valleys of the Rhône–Rhine, Inn, Enns, Mürz and Drau offer comparatively easy east–west passages for both roads and railways, for they are wide and flat-floored, have gentle gradients, and the cols at their heads are not high. Routes from north to south are more difficult, as they have to cross high ranges, and the tortuous approaches to the passes which traverse the mountains are sometimes broken by deep gorges, which have had to be bridged.

For centuries the most important north–south passes for road traffic have been the St Gotthard and Brenner, through the western and eastern Alps respectively. There are major roads across the Great St Bernard, Furka, Splügen and Maloja passes. Railways follow most of these routes, using tunnels to overcome the difficult higher reaches. The railway through the Brenner Pass (4495 ft) faced the fewest problems and needed only short tunnels, but the railway routes through the Mont Cenis, Simplon, Lötschberg, St Gotthard, Tauern, Karawanken and Semmering passes necessitated some of the longest tunnels in the world. Most of the routes through the higher passes are blocked by snow in winter, often for long periods. In spite of all the difficulties of topography and climate, however, the engineering genius of the mountain peoples—especially the Swiss—has produced, besides the better-known international routes, a network of minor roads and railways, cliff-lifts and funiculars which covers the whole mountain system and has given impetus to the character-istic dairying and ever-growing tourist industries.

5. *The Pannonian lowlands*

Included with central Europe is a small portion of the Pannonian basin, a major region of south central Europe which is examined in greater detail in Chapters XXIII and XXIV. Here the lowlands are the plain of Vienna and the Burgenland in Austria, and the Danubian plains in Czechoslovakia. The plains of Vienna and the Danube are flat agricultural lowlands in countries predominantly mountainous; the Burgenland is more hilly, with patches of deciduous forest covering the upper slopes, but with farming everywhere else.

CLIMATE

The general climatic characteristics of central Europe may be gathered from the account of the climate of Europe given in Chapter III. The Germano-Polish plain shows a west–east transition from maritime to continental conditions, and the central highlands are not high enough to offer any marked contrast to conditions on the plain. Maritime conditions are more obvious in west and north-west Germany, continental conditions in eastern Poland and parts of Czechoslovakia and Austria.

Temperatures in the plain are fairly uniform both in winter and in summer, lower latitudes being counterbalanced in the south by a gradual increase in altitude. January temperatures range from 32° F (0° C) in Hamburg to 26° F (−3° C) in Warsaw; Berlin in the same month averages 31° F (−0·5° C), Leipzig 30° F (−1° C) and Vienna, on the southern edge of the central highlands, 29° F (−2° C), while Munich, at the foot of the German Alpine foreland, has 27° F (−2·5° C). July temperatures vary little from 64° F (18° C), which is about the same as

London. Hamburg averages 63° F (17° C), Berlin and Leipzig 65° F (18° C), Warsaw 66° F (18·5° C) and Vienna 67° F (19° C). Sheltered areas, such as the Rhine rift valley, have slightly warmer summers, approaching 70° F (21° C) in places.

In the northern plain, the central highlands and the foreland, annual precipitation decreases towards the east, from 27·5 in. at Hamburg to 20 in. at Posnan; Berlin has 22 in., Leipzig 25 in. and Warsaw 23 in. Munich, at an altitude of 1739 ft, has 34 in.; and in general it may be noted that precipitation increases with altitude in the central highlands and the foreland, some places registering over 50 in. annually. Most of the rain falls in spring and summer; the winters have snow rather than rain, and falls in the central highlands are heavy. The rivers are frozen for periods ranging from three weeks on the Rhine to five or six weeks on the more eastern streams.

Climate in the Alpine region is transitional in several ways. The mountain system lies between the continental climate of the north and the Mediterranean type of the south, so its northern and southern halves present some contrasts, especially in the periodicity of the maximum precipitation—in summer in the north, in winter in the south. There is also a transition from maritime conditions in the west to the continental type of climate in the east.

Temperatures are affected by aspect, southward-facing slopes being warmer than those which face north, which have longer periods of shade. The sunny slopes (adrêts or Sonnenseite) are chosen for settlement and agriculture. The colder shady slopes (ubacs or Schattenseite) are usually forested and uninhabited, except when cattle are taken to the alps in late summer, when the snows have melted. In the deep valleys, especially those where Mediterranean climatic tendencies are greatest, the summers are dry and scorchingly hot, so that irrigation may be necessary. The winters often bring inversions of temperature, when cold heavy air drains into the valleys from the mountains above and the lower levels are actually far colder than the higher slopes.

Annual precipitation in the Alps is greater than in the regions to the north and south, being caused partly by the westerlies (orographic rain) and partly by the depressions (cyclonic rain) they carry. The heaviest precipitation, which is invariably of snow in winter, is in the High Alps in France and the St Gotthard massif in Switzerland—up to 90 in. annually; while the outer eastern ranges have about 60 in. The Venetian Alps, overlooking the Gulf of Venice, have over 100 in. annually, brought by depressions passing in winter along the Mediterranean. The total precipitation, even on the highest parts of the Alps, is generally less than on lower mountains which are situated nearer to the Atlantic coasts, as in

Scotland and Norway. The valleys, especially those which lie transversely in the lee of high mountains, are much drier, often with less than 30 in. annually. As already mentioned, they may require irrigation, *e.g.* in the Valais in Switzerland and the Inn valley in Austria. The former, in the upper Rhône basin, is the driest part of Switzerland, with 24 in. of precipitation annually.

Differences of temperature between the Alpine region and adjacent areas, or even between mountain slopes and the valley below, may cause local winds in the Alps. We have seen how cold air from the French Alps is drawn down the Rhône corridor by depressions moving eastward in the Mediterranean, to become the violent mistral; a similar cold wind, known as the *bora*, blows southwards at the head of the Adriatic Sea. In transverse valleys opening out to the north of the Alps, a warm dry wind, the *Föhn*, may blow in late winter and spring. The *Föhn* occurs when a depression passes close to the Alps along the northern plain. Air is drawn northwards from the Alpine valleys and replaced by warmer air from over the Mediterranean. As it descends from the higher mountains, it becomes, by compression, adiabatically still warmer—and drier—and melts the snow. Temperatures may rise by as much as 40° F (22° C) in 24 hours. The rapid melting of snow by the *Föhn* may cause disastrous floods and avalanches, but it is still welcomed in spring because it clears the mountain pastures and enables cattle to be taken up the slopes.

STUDY QUESTIONS

1. Illustrate the ways in which ice sheets have affected the drainage of the areas they formerly covered. (O. & C.)
2. Describe the structure and physical history of the Germano-Polish plain, showing how they have influenced the present landscape. (O. & C.)
3. Give an account of inland waterways in Europe between the rivers Rhine and Vistula. (J.M.B.)
4. Discuss the surface character and the drainage system of the lowlands which lie between the rivers Weser and Vistula. (J.M.B.)
5. Give a reasoned account of the transitional character of the central European climate. (J.M.B.)
6. Contrast the landscapes you would expect to find in the central highlands and Alps of central Europe. Give reasons for the differences you note.

Chapter XVII

GERMANY: HUMAN GEOGRAPHY

EVENTS LEADING TO PARTITION

GERMANY, as it existed in 1937 (*see* Fig. 72), has been divided into the German Federal Republic (West Germany), the German Democratic Republic (East Germany), and the Eastern Territories, which were taken by Poland and the Soviet Union. This division was to have been temporary, until a final peace treaty was signed; but the present *de facto* boundaries are regarded by the Communist *bloc* as permanent, certainly as far as the Eastern Territories are concerned, and the prospect of a definite peace treaty seems remote. Berlin, the pre-war capital of Germany, lies in East Germany and is divided into West Berlin, which is a part of West Germany though physically separated from it, and East Berlin, which is the administrative capital of East Germany: an anomalous position fiercely resented by both east and west. West Germans look forward to the day when the country is once again united—at least, those sections they call West Germany and Middle Germany; for they reserve the name "East Germany" for the Eastern Territories which lie within the present boundaries of Poland and the Soviet Union.

EARLY HISTORY

The division of Germany shows very significantly how trends in human geography can be traced over periods extending sometimes into hundreds of years; for the boundary line between East and West Germany is neither accidental nor arbitrary. It is based on events which took place over a thousand years ago.

The Germano-Polish plain contains no physical barriers to the east–west movements of people, and from earliest times it has seen frequent fluctuations of boundaries and a turbulent history: the central uplands to the south have never presented serious obstacles to migration or invasion. Even in the Alps, Switzerland is the only country which has shown any real degree of permanence, for the numerous passes allowed penetration elsewhere either northwards or southwards.

With the decline of the Roman Empire, barbarian tribes in the northern plain moved to the west and south. The Franks advanced from the lower Rhine valley into France; the Alemanni, from the lower Oder basin, invaded south-western Germany (Swabia), parts of Switzerland, and Austria; the Saxons moved into Belgium and northern France, at the western end of the plain, and some crossed over to England (*see* Fig. 10). Bohemians spread from their plateau home to the scarps of south Germany, where they became known as Bavarians, and Burgundians occupied the plain of the river Saône. During the third and fourth centuries these peoples gradually established the patchwork of small states in central Europe which lasted until the nineteenth century. Behind the migrating tribes came Slavs from the east, occupying the basins of the Oder and upper Elbe in the north, and the lower Danube plains in the south, to form the nuclei of the present states of Czechoslovakia, Poland, Rumania and Bulgaria.

After 771, Charlemagne, the greatest of the Frankish leaders, defeated all his Germanic rivals and extended his conquests to include the northern plain as far east as the Elbe and Saale rivers, most of the central uplands, the whole of the Alpine region, and two-thirds of continental and peninsular Italy. After his death, Charlemagne's empire was partitioned in 843 into a western portion, predominantly Latin and later to become France; an eastern portion, mainly Germanic; and a central strip between them, linguistically mixed. This last was called Lotharingia, after Lotharingius, its first ruler, who gave his name also to Lorraine. By further partitions, in 870 and 887, most of Lotharingia was given to the eastern kingdom; but (*see* Chapter XV) the struggle for this buffer region has continued between the French and the Germans to the present century.

The eastern limits of Charlemagne's empire lay in the northern plain along the Elbe–Saale line, and it was this frontier of over 1000 years ago which was used to demarcate West Germany from East Germany. In the days of the first "Germany," however, it was not regarded as a hard and fast boundary, for in a zone stretching from the Bay of Lübeck to the northern edges of the Bohemian plateau lived a mixed population of Germans and of Slavs who were migrating westwards. The Elbe–Saale should be regarded more as a cultural boundary, separating the more civilised Germans of the west from the semi-barbaric "mixed" peoples. In the west the combination of Roman culture and Germanic (Teutonic) vigour had resulted in the development of towns, industries and an advanced agriculture using iron ploughshares. In the clay lands, much of the forest had been cleared and its place taken by arable farming. There was none of this in the purely Slav lands to the east. From the tenth century onwards, by invasion or colonisation, much of the former Slav territory became German. Towns grew and farmland increased, but many of the contrasts remained.

[*Courtesy of the Federal German Embassy.*

FIG. 71.—West Germany: Neuschwanstein castle. Situated in Bavaria, it was built by King Ludwig II, 3000 ft above sea level.

Noteworthy were the contrasts in settlement patterns, some of them visible today. The medieval towns, so common in the west, still have narrow, winding streets and an irregular lay-out, as if they have grown piecemeal without any planning; the typical rural settlement is the large, nucleated village set in an open-field system. The whole pattern indicates development by trial and error. In the east, on the other hand, there was definite planned growth supervised by *locatores* or overseers, who were made responsible by the German rulers in the west for the lay-out of towns and villages, and the organisation of the farming community. The older towns in the east all have a central market square surrounded by a grid-iron arrangement of streets enclosed by an oval wall. The villages vary in type. There are "street villages" and "round villages," with their farmlands arranged in regular open fields; in "forest villages" and "marsh villages," each farmer's lands are in one piece, as against the complicated and fragmented field system of the west.

The largest farm was always that of the *locator*, and this preferential treatment led in the course of centuries to a system of great estates and absentee landlords unknown in the west. The locatores became the

Junkers (squires or young noblemen), a military aristocracy who exerted feudal overlordship (especially in Prussia) as late as 1918, when many of the large estates were confiscated, divided into small farms and given to the tenants.

In farming, the contrast between east and west is all the more marked today because of the imposition in East Germany of the Communist system of collective and State farms. By April 1960 not a single privately owned farmstead remained in East Germany. The former field boundaries are being obliterated and the village patterns altered in response to the new conditions of State ownership and collectivisation. Farther east, beyond the Oder–Neisse line, in the lands taken by Poland and the Soviet Union, there was a still greater upheaval. Almost every German who lived there was killed or expelled and the sequestrated lands given to Polish or Russian immigrants. The war-devastated cities and towns show in their reconstruction marked signs of Russian planning and architecture.

THE "MARCH" LANDS

In the eleventh century the Germans drove the Slavs of the northern plain eastwards beyond the river Oder and set up a string of defensive settlements, called "Marches" (Ger. *Mark*, pl. *Marken*) stretching from the Baltic coast to the Gulf of Venice. The only Slav communities to remain west of the Oder were in Bohemia and Moravia, and they acknowledged German overlordship. The Marches proved very successful, not only as barriers against Slav penetration but as centres for further German expansion. Their establishment was to have important consequences.

Firstly, the East Mark (Ostmark) became the nucleus round which developed Austria (Österreich, "Eastern kingdom") and the Austro-Hungarian Empire; the Northern Mark (Brandenburg) grew into the kingdom of Prussia, the dominant state in pre-1945 Germany. Secondly, as centres from which German peoples could expand eastwards, the Marches led to the idea of *Lebensraum* ("room in which to live," hence, lands to colonise), which encouraged Germans to move into lands—mainly Slav—which were thinly populated. Colonists entered Silesia, Bohemia, Hungary and East Prussia. During the fourteenth and fifteenth centuries, German farmers, craftsmen, miners and merchants spread to the eastern Baltic shores and along the Danubian plains as far as Transylvania and the Rumanian Dobrogea. These pockets or islands of German speech and influence formed troublesome minorities in the countries in which they were located, and were a factor in the two ill-fated attempts by Germany in this century to subjugate their adopted homelands. Since the Middle Ages, Germany has regarded nationality and language as synonymous terms, and her formula, *ein Volk, ein Reich* (one people, one state), has repeatedly been the excuse for wars to include these pockets of German speech within her boundaries.

MODERN GERMANY

In 1701 the Margrave (ruler of a March) of Brandenburg assumed the title of King of Prussia. By the end of the Seven Years War in 1763, Prussia was the dominant German state in the northern plain, although Austria—whose king was also the Holy Roman Emperor—was politically more influential in Europe as a whole. The Napoleonic wars, however, saw the end of the Holy Roman Empire and after 1815 Austria seemed to lose interest in central Europe, turning instead to the south-east, where she began to build up a new empire along the Danube.

The German states of the north and west, imbued with the doctrines of the French Revolution, began to dream of a new empire which would include every area where German was spoken, even as a minority language. In 1849 the imperial crown was offered to the king of Prussia, but he refused it, saying the time was inopportune. In 1867, however, Prussia became leader of a North German Confederation and controlled the Germano-Polish plain from the Netherlands to the Russian frontier. Four years later, in 1871, after Germany had defeated France in a lightning attack, the Prussian king was crowned Emperor of Germany at Versailles, and was acclaimed by every German state except Austria, which remained aloof.

Until 1870, "Germany" existed merely as a generic name for nearly forty small states, of which only Prussia and Austria had any importance. The new, unified Germany found herself far behind the other countries of the west in economic and political development but, by superhuman efforts in the coalfield areas of Westphalia, Saxony and Silesia during the next forty years, German industrial output caught up with and in some cases surpassed that of many older countries. In politics her methods, if questionable, were equally effective; and she gained colonies in Africa and among the Pacific islands.

Her social economy remained more backward, and a wide gap opened between the military aristocracy of Junkers and the industrial barons on the one hand, and the workers and farming communities on the other. Her treatment of racial minorities within her boundaries, too, smacked in its harshness of medieval times. Poles in the east, Danes in North Schleswig, and the peoples of Alsace and Lorraine were ready to turn on their oppressors at the first opportunity.

The First World War. Germany's rapid growth to the status of a great power led her to ambitions of territorial expansion and plunged Europe into the First World War (1914–18). Germany and her ally, Austria, were completely defeated. Both monarchies were terminated, Alsace and Lorraine were returned to France, and North Schleswig to Denmark. The "new" countries of Czechoslovakia and Poland came into being, taking from Germany rich industrial districts and agricultural land. East Prussia was separated from Germany proper by a "corridor" of territory given to Poland as an outlet to the sea, and Danzig was made a "free city." The Austro-Hungarian Empire was dismembered, and Austria's area reduced almost to that of the East Mark (Österreich) of the fifteenth century.

The Second World War. The harshness, as the Germans considered it, of the terms of the Treaty of Versailles which terminated the First World War, was a factor in the growth of the National Socialist (Nazi) Party. Adolf Hitler soon became its Führer (leader). In 1933 he succeeded in taking over the Government and rapidly led Germany back to power. Bit by bit he abrogated most of the terms of the Treaty. In 1938 he annexed Austria. In the same year he took over the Sudetenland, the German-speaking part of Czechoslovakia, and six months later the rest of the country was occupied. The dangers of the old ideas of *Lebensraum* and *ein Volk, ein Reich* were at last realised by the Western powers; and when Hitler ordered the invasion of Poland in September 1939 he precipitated the Second World War. At first the tide ran in his favour, and at one point Germany controlled Europe from the Arctic to Crete, and from the Volga to the Atlantic, with the exceptions of the Iberian peninsula, Switzerland, Sweden and the British Isles. Defeat was inevitable, however. It came in 1945, leaving Germany crushed, her rulers dead or in captivity, her cities in ruins, her entire economy shattered and government non-existent.

THE DIVISION OF GERMANY

The end of hostilities saw Germany occupied by Soviet troops in the east and by British, American and French troops in the west. The Potsdam conference of 1945 gave Poland German territory east of the Oder and Neisse rivers, including the port of Stettin, to compensate for the Polish lands occupied by the Soviet Union. East Prussia was shared by Poland and the Soviet Union. As we have seen, this was to be a temporary arrangement meant to last only until a definite peace treaty was signed. The stated objectives of the occupying powers were to purge Germany of its Nazi philosophy, rebuild its economy, and reconstitute the country within its pre-1937 boundaries, so enabling it to take its place again in the concert of nations.

It was soon obvious that the clash of ideologies and economic policies between the Soviet Union and the Western powers made the achievement of these objectives highly improbable. So the Western powers formulated their zones of occupation, and in 1949 brought into existence the Federal German Republic, with a limited constitution and a provisional capital at Bonn. In 1954 the Federal Republic became an independent sovereign state, known generally as West Germany. In 1949 the Soviet-occupied zone was proclaimed by the Soviet military

FIG. 72.—Germany: political divisions since 1945. The inset map shows the present division of Berlin. *Note:* the German Federal Republic calls the German Democratic Republic "Central Germany" and the area under Polish administration "Eastern Germany," as it was prior to 1945. The names of provinces are shown.

administration a state in its own right and entitled the German Democratic Republic, or East Germany. It differs in its constitution from West Germany in that its rulers are selected and controlled by the Soviet Union. In spite of its title, it has no free elections, nor its people any freedom of contact with the Western world, from which they are cut off by the "Iron Curtain."

The boundary line between East and West Germany lies for the most part along the Elbe and Saale rivers, the ancient frontier of Charlemagne's empire. In the north it leaves the Elbe near Lauenburg and continues to the Bay of Lübeck; in the south Thuringia, whose economy is orientated eastwards, is included in East Germany, although it was originally part of Lotharingia.

Berlin lies inside the Democratic Republic. It is divided into West Berlin, previously occupied by the Western powers but now a part of West Germany, and East Berlin, claimed as part of the Democratic Republic and acting as its capital. Since August 1961 a Communist-manned barrier of concrete and barbed wire—the notorious Berlin Wall—blocks all passage between East and West Berlin, except on permits issued by East Germany.

PROBLEMS OF A DIVIDED GERMANY

GERMAN REFUGEES

An aftermath of the Second World War was one of the greatest migrations of peoples in history. "Colonies" of Germans outside the boundaries of the *Reich*, especially in eastern and south-eastern Europe where they had existed for centuries, were expelled. Along with Germans driven from Poland and Czechoslovakia, they made their way to West Germany. They were followed by refugees from East Germany and East Berlin in such great numbers that the Communists took steps to obstruct further flight by erecting walls and "death strips." To the end of 1960, 9,700,000 surviving expellees arrived in West Germany from outside German boundaries, and 3,500,000 came from East Germany and East Berlin. In the same period, 1945–60, numbers going eastward to the Communist zone amounted to 212,000.

AGRICULTURE

Some of the contrasts between the agricultural economies of West Germany and East Germany have already been mentioned and their historical basis explained. Here we shall consider in more detail the effects on German agriculture of the division of the country into two states, isolated from each other by contrasting political systems.

Pre-war Germany was not really an agricultural country. Although it was often maintained that the industrial districts now in West Germany could be fed by the farmlands of the east, it was always necessary to import large quantities of cereals and other foodstuffs. Today, West Germany relies more than ever on imports of food, and the surplus of the east goes mainly to the Soviet Union. The farmlands of East Germany used to produce 55% of the wheat, 57% of the potatoes and 67% of the sugar beet of Germany; 48% of the agricultural land, and 55% of the arable farming were in the east.

In spite of her loss of foodstuffs from the east of the country and a tremendously increased population, West Germany produces today 73% of the cereals, 86% of the meat, and 45% of the food fats (butter, vegetable oils, etc.), she requires. This has been accomplished by careful crop rotation and the scientific use of fertilisers, using the potash deposits near the Harz mountains and the by-products of iron smelting. Most of Germany's potash deposits, however, lie in East Germany.

Farm holdings in West Germany are small, 28% in 1961 covering less than 5 acres. Most of them are broken into many pieces, separated from each other and of irregular shapes: a relic of the old open-field system. This makes it difficult to use machinery of any size. In Bavaria and other southern regions, where fragmentation is worst, even a tractor is an uncommon sight. Farming in such areas is inefficient in the modern sense, and the West German Government has declared a long-term policy of consolidating the small, scattered holdings so as to make them more capable of up to date economic management.

In contrast, farming in East Germany, where the land holdings were much larger, is highly mechanised and the modernising process has been intensified by collectivisation. But strangely enough the yield per acre has fallen in East Germany and today is lower for every crop than it was in 1937. This is partly because more fodder crops are grown at the expense of cereals, partly because attempts have been made to bring under cultivation lands too sour for agriculture, and partly because the collective system is resented by the farming community, which has lost the incentive of ownership. Yields in West Germany, especially of sugar beet, are higher not so much because of better knowledge but rather by reason of harder work on peasant-owned land. It should be remembered, however, that in general the adverse climate and the soils of the northern part of East Germany are inimical to successful peasant-farming, unless it is supported by large Government subsidies.

The most important cereal crop in Germany is wheat, which is grown wherever the soil is suitable but predominates in the loess lands at the foot of the central uplands. Next to wheat comes rye, which is hardier and will thrive in the poor soils of the northern plain. Rye tends to be used less, and wheat more, as a bread grain; but because it is replacing oats as fodder for cattle and pigs the acreage under rye in the sandy heathlands has increased. Oats are still important as a fodder crop, however, though output in West Germany has declined from 2,800,000 tons in 1937 to 2,100,000 tons in 1960. Barley is grown widely as fodder and as the basis of the extensive brewing industry.

Potatoes are next to cereals in importance. In addition to being used as human and animal food, they are the raw material for the manufacture of alcohol and alcoholic spirits. They are grown mainly in the north-east of West Germany, the north of East Germany, and as a rotation crop in the wheatlands of the south of both countries. Sugar beet, too, rotates admirably with wheat, and so its distribution is chiefly in the southern loess lands. Other vegetable crops include tobacco, hops, hemp, flax and rape seed. Soya beans, which have a variety of uses, are grown by many farmers in the loess lands.

Market gardening is very important in Germany, the large concentrations of people in the industrial areas—especially in the Rhinelands, Saxony and Berlin—demanding constant supplies of fresh vegetables. Orchard fruits come chiefly from the sunnier south and south-west. Vines are grown along the slopes bordering the Rhine rift valley and the river Moselle, and there are widespread vineyards in the scarplands of Franconia and Swabia, though here their number is dwindling.

The rearing of cattle, pigs and poultry is more extensive than when Germany was united. East Germany used to receive much of its dairy produce from the west. Now land which at one time grew rye has been given over to fodder crops, and cattle and pigs are prominent in the plains north of Berlin. The most important dairying regions are in the north-west of West Germany, where the maritime climate helps the growth of rich grasses. These are followed by the Alpine foreland and the Alps, both of which supply milk to the Rhine industrial areas and make cheese. The numerous cities of Germany have encouraged a wide distribution of milch cattle, as well as of mixed farming, over the whole of the northern plain and in the foothills of the central uplands. The clays and lakes of the Baltic Heights are noted for geese and ducks. The increasing development of mixed farming throughout Germany has led to a sharp rise in egg production.

POPULATION

WEST GERMANY

The population of the German *Reich* in 1939 was 69 million, of whom nearly 43 million (62%) lived inside the present boundaries of the Federal Republic and West Berlin. The density of population in these areas was 443 per square mile, as compared with an average of 378 for the whole country. From 1939 to the end of 1960, the population of West Germany increased by over 13 million, so that at present it amounts to over 56 million, of whom 2·2 million are in West Berlin; the average density is 592 persons per square mile. A large part of the increase is the result of the influx of expellees from the German Eastern Territories and abroad, amounting with children born since 1939 to nearly 10 million, and of "new settlers" who, to the number of $3\frac{1}{2}$ million, crossed from East Germany and East Berlin to the Federal Republic.

The pre-war area of West Germany produced about 59% of the

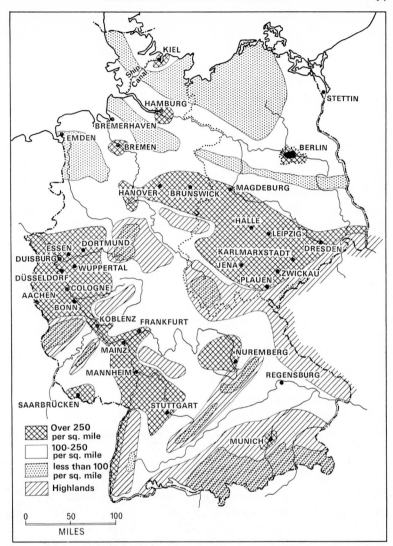

FIG. 73.—Germany: distribution of population. The dotted line is the boundary between the Federal and Democratic Republics.

Reich's industrial output, but its agricultural total was less. The Federal Republic's capacity to feed itself was further reduced by the great increase in population immediately after the war. It fell from 80% self-sufficiency in 1939 to 66% in 1950; today it is back at 80%. The density of population (excluding West Berlin) has risen from 423 to 548 per square mile, which has made it vital for West Germany to increase its home-grown supplies of foodstuffs and to develop its natural resources—which, apart from coal, are not great—and its industries. Its industrial rebirth since the war has shown West Germany's powers of recuperation, and deserved the description of "economic miracle" (*Wirtschaftswunder*).

The distribution of population in West Germany is somewhat unequal, but even the least-peopled *Länder*, Schleswig-Holstein, Lower Saxony and Bavaria, have densities of 350 per square mile. These *Länder* have areas of scanty population in the *Märschen* and *Heide* of the north-west, the Rhön and Vogelsberg, and the Alpine foreland, but such poorly peopled districts are few in West Germany.

The Länder of West Berlin, Hamburg and Bremen have naturally the greatest concentrations, as they are cities which have been given provincial status. West Berlin, with an area of 186 square miles and a population of 2,202,200 in 1961, has the enormous density of 11,843. Hamburg and Bremen have been independent cities since the days of the Hanseatic League, and retained their status when the Federal Republic was formulated in 1955. The Hamburg *Land*, with an area of 289 square miles and a population of 1,837,000, has a density of 6356; Bremen, 156 square miles and 704,300 inhabitants, of 4515 persons per square mile. The greatest concentrations of people in West Germany, other than in these cities, are in the industrial regions. The greatest is the Rhine–Ruhr zone of the *Land* of North Rhine–Westphalia. Of the 52 cities of West Germany with more than 100,000 inhabitants, 23 are in this *Land*, which has a population of 15,852,000 and a density of 1209 per square mile. The other industrial regions are the Rhine–Main (with Frankfurt and Mainz), the Rhine–Neckar (with Mannheim, Ludwigshafen and Heidelberg), the Saarland, and the districts round Nuremberg, Stuttgart and Munich.

EAST GERMANY

The population of East Germany, including East Berlin, was 17·0 million in 1964, with a density of 408 per square mile. The population for the same area was 16·7 million in 1939, with a density of 401, so it would appear that during the past twenty years, even allowing for loss of life during the war, there has been almost a standstill in the growth of population when compared with the rise in West Germany from the 1939 figure of 43 million to 56 million in 1964. This slow rise is accounted for in part by the lower industrial potential of East Germany, and the fact that for some reason population seems to increase more rapidly in industrialised countries; but a further factor in East Germany was the drift to the west of nearly 3½ million Germans, including their children born after 1939.

These refugees, known in West Germany as "new settlers," fled from the way of life being imposed in the Soviet Zone and have been absorbed mainly into the agricultural communities of the northern plain of West Germany. Their loss has been of great consequence to East Germany, for they included large numbers of highly skilled technologists and progressive scientific agriculturalists. They have been a source of strength to the régime they fled to and have helped to widen the gap which has opened between East and West Germany.

STUDY QUESTIONS

1. Examine the geographical problems that have arisen as a result of the division of Germany into East German and West German states. (O. & C.)

2. How far is it true to say that the division of Germany into two states is a natural consequence of its history?

Chapter XVIII

GERMANY: REGIONAL GEOGRAPHY

WEST GERMANY

MUCH of the physical, climatic, historical and human geography of the region now occupied by West Germany and East Germany has been dealt with in previous chapters. In this chapter, attention is concentrated on the economic aspects. Each country is divided into the physical regions outlined in Chapter XVI, but the usual plan adopted in this book of separating descriptions of physical features and structure from those of the economy is not followed. Where necessary, more detail of the physical geography of each division is given, but the student is advised to read this chapter in conjunction with that on central Europe (Chapter XVI). The economic geography of each physical division should equally be supplemented by Chapter XVII. This combination of physical and economic geography is used to avoid needless repetition of information already given earlier, and also because West Germany and East Germany are here still regarded geographically as portions of an undivided Germany, so that Chapters XVI, XVII and XVIII, are complementary.

The Federal Republic of Germany, with which is included West Berlin (186 square miles), shows most clearly the division into (1) the northern plain, the German part of the Germano-Polish plain, (2) the central highlands, (3) the Alpine foreland, and (4) the Alps (*see* Fig. 74).

1. *The Germano-Polish plain*

This may be divided into several sub-regions: (*a*) the reclaimed *Marschen* near the North Sea coast, (*b*) the geest and peat bogs south and east of these and bounded by the Elbe, (*c*) the förden lands of the Baltic coast, mainly of boulder-clay, (*d*) south of the förden the Börde zone of loess, and (*e*) the "bays" of lowland which project from the northern plain into the central highlands, in Münster, Westphalia and along the Rhine as far as Bonn. The important Ruhr industrial region lies on the southern edges of the Rhineland "bay," and extends into adjacent parts of the central highlands. These lower portions of the central highlands— Sauerland, Bergischerland and Siegerland—play an important role in the economy of the Ruhr industrial region, and so are here included in the treatment of the northern plain.

(a) *The Marschen.* The marshy lands of the North Sea coasts of West Germany have been reclaimed in much the same way as in Holland, and reclamation continues, 30,000 acres of marine silts having been added as polders during the present century. The earliest polders are given over

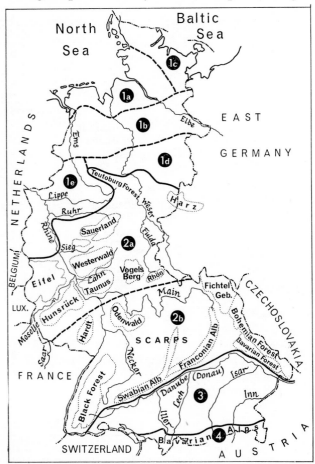

Fig. 74.—West Germany: physical divisions. The numbers correspond with the regional divisions used in the text. (*See also* Fig. 69.)

chiefly to dairy farming and the fattening of cattle for beef; the more recently reclaimed lands produce large crops of wheat and potatoes. Those nearer the lower course of the Elbe specialise in market-gardening and fruit for the cities of Hamburg and Bremen.

This short stretch of coast shares in the North Sea fishing industry. West Germany's fishing fleet is third largest in Europe (after the United

Kingdom and Norway). It is now one of the best-equipped in the world, as wartime losses have been replaced by modern vessels. Here, too, are the ports of Hamburg, Bremen, Emden and Wilhelmshaven, all of which suffered terribly from bombing but have been largely rebuilt.

Fig. 75.—West Germany: northern plain and adjacent highlands. The area within the dotted rectangle—the Ruhr industrial Region—is shown on a larger scale in Fig. 76.

Hamburg (1,840,543) is easily Germany's largest port, situated at the lowest bridging point of the Elbe. It has the great advantage that ships can arrive and leave at any state of the tide, no enclosed docks being necessary. Hamburg's natural hinterland, the Elbe basin, runs far into East Germany and Czechoslovakia, but at least half of it has been cut off by the Iron Curtain. It is less favourably situated than Bremen to act as the chief outlet of West Germany, yet it remains the chief port because of its greater capacity to deal with bulky raw materials. It leads in ship-building and marine engineering, and has oil refineries, oil-seed crushing works, flour mills, non-ferrous smelting, and the manufacture of tobacco, soap and margarine.

Bremen (569,862), on the Weser, has a hinterland entirely in West Germany. Its industries are similar to those of Hamburg but on a much smaller scale. It is also the chief importer of coffee, cotton, jute and wool, and has a small textile industry.

Emden, at the mouth of the Ems, was designed to attract some of the traffic which passed to Germany through Rotterdam. It is linked to the Ruhr region by the Dortmund–Ems Canal, opened in 1899, and has become its seaport. Mineral ores constitute 85% of its incoming cargoes and coal over 90% of its exports. Emden is also West Germany's chief herring-fishing port. It has a population of 85,000.

Wilhelmshaven (100,858), in the little Jade Bay, was specially built to serve as Germany's chief naval base. Since the navy was almost its sole source of livelihood, the fleet's surrender after the Second World War crippled the port. It is slowly recovering as an oil refining and chemical centre, with oil pipelines to Bonn and the Ruhr cities. It is once more a naval base, housing the new Federal fleet. Bremerhaven (142,289) is the outport of Bremen and shares in its industries.

(b) *The Geest*. There is an abrupt change inland from the fertile *Marschen* to the far less fertile geest, the area covered by the older moraines and by outwash sands from the glaciers. The geest was originally covered with oak forests. These were cleared from the better soils for agriculture and from the less productive parts for timber for building and fuel. Sheep rearing became important in the clearings. The poorer lands, grazed by sheep, gradually developed into heather-covered heathland (*Heide*), the largest being Lüneburg Heath, part of which is preserved in its original state as a national park.

Most of the geest has now been improved by deep ploughing and the application of mineral fertilisers, and sheep rearing is only a minor occupation. Rye, oats, potatoes and root crops are the main products. Pine plantations have replaced the oak trees. In the worst-drained clays are peat bogs, the largest being along the lower Weser and near the Dutch frontier. The peat is dug for fuel and as bedding for pigs. Small but important oilfields occur on the southern edges of the Lüneburg Heath and in the bogs west of the Ems, producing 95% of West Germany's 5 million ton total of domestic mineral oil, and a third of her require-ments. The only towns of any size in the geest are Oldenburg (125,471) and Lüneburg, both of them markets and regional centres.

(c) *The Förden*. East of the Elbe we pass via the neck of the Jutland peninsula to the coastlands of the south-west Baltic. This is the region of the *Förden*, long, narrow inlets carved out by sub-glacial streams in the boulder-clay which covers most of the area. It is an attractive agricultural region of mixed farming, with beech woods on morainic hills and numerous lakes in the hollows. The major towns—Flensburg, Kiel and Lübeck—are all ports, though in the case of Flensburg (94,000), West Germany's most northern town, this function is of minor importance. There is a shipbuilding industry, but the town's main trade is as a market.

Kiel (272,507) is situated at the eastern end of the Kiel Canal, which was constructed in 1887–95 and widened and deepened 1907–14 to provide a quicker and safer passage from the North to the Baltic Seas than by going round Jutland. In tonnage handled (30 million a year), the Kiel Canal is one of the most important in the world. The main cargoes are timber and iron ore westwards, coal and mineral oil eastwards. Once the German Baltic naval base, Kiel is now a shipbuilding, fishing and transit port.

Lübeck (235,438) is West Germany's chief Baltic port, though less important now than when it was a headquarters of the Hanseatic League. It has blast furnaces, despite its distance from any coalfield or iron ore supplies.

(d) *The Börde.* South of the Lüneburg Heath is the *Börde*, a zone of loess soils in Lower Saxony. Not only is it a very fertile region, with wheat, sugar beet and dairying, but it has valuable supplies of rock salt, potash, iron ore, brown coal and a little bituminous coal. These resources have led to the development of industry; the Mittelland Canal, which links the Rhine with the Elbe, has played an important part in its growth.

Hanover (Hannover) (574,047) is the largest town, a route centre at the head of navigation of a Weser tributary, with food processing, engineering, fertiliser works, vehicle and rubber industries—it has the largest tyre plant on the Continent. Brunswick (Braunschweig) (245,027) is a modern industrial city that retains many of its medieval buildings. It has vegetable canning, sugar refining, flour milling, engineering, optical works and book publishing. In the last twenty years two new towns have developed: Salzgitter and Wolfsburg. Salzgitter (111,681) has grown on the ironfield, the low-grade ore being utilised by new smelting techniques. It has six blast furnaces producing over a million tons of steel a year. Wolfsburg (57,000), founded in 1938, is the home of the Volkswagen plant. The site was chosen because of proximity to the Salzgitter steel works, the Mittelland Canal, and the railways which cross the börde. There are branch Volkswagen motor works in Hanover and Brunswick.

(e) *The lowland "bays."*

(i) *The Westphalian–Rhineland "bay."* The "bay" of lowland which runs southwards between the Rhine highlands as far as Bonn is one of the most favoured agricultural areas in Germany. It has fertile loams in the north, loess in the south, and is sheltered by the highlands. Wheat and sugar beet are cultivated intensively. Market-gardening predominates in the southern part, and dairying north of the Ruhr–Rhine confluence. The lands near the Rhine are dyked to prevent flooding and are very like polders. Rural settlement in the north consists mainly of isolated farm-steads; in the south, nucleated villages are more common.

Stretching west from Cologne to the Belgian border are enormous deposits of brown coal. There are three main uses for it. It is made into briquettes for domestic fuel; fed raw into furnaces for the generation of electricity; and can be used in the chemical industry to produce tar and lubricating or fuel oils. Generating stations use about a third of the total output—over 80 million tons a year—to produce nearly a third of West Germany's electricity requirements. In the northern part of the bay are salt and potash, used in the chemical industry. Along the southern edges, on the flanks of the Rhine highlands, lies the Ruhr coalfield, with an extension west of the Rhine near Duisburg.

Leaving the coalfield for separate consideration (*see* below), the largest cities of the Rhine lowland bay are Cologne and Düsseldorf, on the traffic artery of the river. Cologne (Köln) (818,450) dates back to Roman times, its name being derived from *Colonia Agrippina*. It grew up at a bridge point on the Rhine where routes along the river were crossed by east–west roads at the foot of the highlands; and it could be reached by sea-going vessels from Rotterdam. It is the greatest railway junction in West Germany. This fact, plus its proximity to the Ruhr, made it a commercial, banking and insurance centre as well as a major river port. It has been noted for centuries for its manufacture of eau-de-Cologne, but its food industries, engineering and automobile (Ford) plants are now more important.

Dusseldorf (705,122), nearer to the Ruhr, is the administrative capital of the industrial Rhinelands, with iron and steel works and chemical manufacture. Bonn (143,883), formerly a quiet residential and tourist town, has become the provisional capital of the Federal Republic, with large Government offices. It is still non-industrial. Krefeld (214,447), west of the Rhine but connected to it by canal, is the German silk and velvet centre, the industry being introduced in the seventeenth century by Huguenot refugees from Lyon. It has also cotton and rayon manu-factures and chemicals. Near by is München-Gladbach (152,736), with cotton and textile machinery industries. On the Rhine near the confluence of the Wupper is Leverkusen (90,000), with large chemical works (Bayer) and the manufacture of dyes and photographic materials (Agfa).

The Ruhr industrial region. South-east of the Rhine lowland bay, coal seams outcrop along the valley of the Ruhr and dip away to the north. The beds exposed by the erosive action of the river Ruhr gave rise to the industries in its valley; but the development of the region into one of the most highly industrialised in the world is based more on the "concealed" coalfield which extends northwards beneath the river Lippe. It contains extremely thick beds of good coking coal, admirable for smelting. In the extreme north of the field, at depths of over 3000 ft, are deposits of rich bituminous coal with a high gas content, valuable in the chemical industry. Most of the mining is now concentrated in the concealed coalfield, the Ruhr pits being concerned mainly with the production of anthracite for fuel.

It will be noted that, as in South Wales, different types of coal are mined in different parts of the field. The Ruhr seams, however, are much thicker. Another point of difference concerns the appearance of the newer mining towns. Many of them were already market towns in a rich agricultural region, and intensive cultivation continues around the pit-head installations. The miners are housed in well laid out estates in the towns. Throughout the coalfield there is a notable absence of derelict land and slag heaps, owing to the late start on the concealed portion and the lessons learnt from earlier mining along the Ruhr. Most of the old slag heaps have been afforested. The canals, too, so neglected in many coalfields, are of recent construction and form a busy network of waterways competing successfully with the railways and roads.

The iron and steel industry which is outstanding in the Ruhr region commenced with the use of black band ores found in association with the coal. They soon became exhausted or inadequate, and ore was brought first from the Siegerland and the valley of the Lahn in the south, then from Lorraine, Luxembourg, Sweden and Spain. Most of it travels to the iron-works by barges, which take return cargoes of coal.

The Ruhr coalfield, with its extension towards Aachen, has a larger output and possibly a greater reserve than any other in Europe. In 1960, 125 million tons of coal were mined from 130 pits. In the same year the Federal Republic produced 34·1 million tons of raw steel, as compared with 24·7 million tons in the United Kingdom and 17·3 million tons in France. Mining and steel-making have given rise to a great industrial zone which extends along the river from Duisburg to Dortmund, a distance of 45 miles, and is reaching farther and farther north as new mines are opened. The main concentration along the Ruhr contains about thirty cities in such close proximity as to form a conurbation (*see*

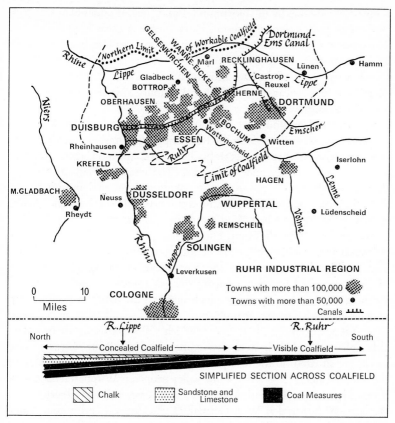

Fig. 76.—West Germany: Ruhr industrial region. Most of the coal mining is in the north, around Gladbeck, Marl and Recklinghausen, in the Lippe valley.

Fig. 76). Some of these cities are of medieval origin; others have grown from nothing since the development of the coalfield. Recklinghausen (130,551), for instance, the latest town to become a mining centre, preserves much of its medieval appearance; whereas Herne (112,971) is completely modernised and Oberhausen (258,529) is entirely new.

Essen (729,657) is the metropolis of the Ruhr. Its iron and steel works, engineering, chemical and railway plants, and—before the two world wars—its huge output of armaments, were integrated in the giant combine controlled by the Krupp family, which to a large extent was responsible for the development of the region. After the war the Western allies tried unsuccessfully to split the combine into smaller units, and the Krupp cartel is growing once again.

Dortmund (645,425) is at the eastern end of the industrial belt, which

L

is opened to Emden by the Dortmund–Ems Canal. Besides blast furnaces, steelworks and engineering shops, Dortmund is a great brewing centre. The western outlet of the region is the inland port of Duisburg (504,412), at the confluence of the Rhine and Ruhr, and the terminus of the Herne Canal, a tributary of the Dortmund–Ems Canal. Its shipping turnover, 30 million tons a year, is greater than Hamburg's; it also has steelworks and marine engineering.

The largest iron and steel plant of the Ruhr was built by Krupp at Rheinhausen, a small town on the Rhine opposite Duisburg. Other large cities are Gelsenkirchen (383,533), Bochum (361,546) and Hagen (196,924), all with iron smelting and steelworks. The chemical industry extends throughout the region too, based on coking and gas coal and producing dyes, benzole, petrol, plastics and fertilisers. Thermal-electric power stations generate over half West Germany's electricity.

Overshadowed by the Ruhr, but forming part of this great mid-Rhine industrial area, are the valleys in the highlands immediately to the south. The high-grade iron ores of the Siegerland and Bergischeland were originally smelted by charcoal from the oak forests on the hills, helped by the numerous swift streams which supplied the hammer-ponds. This activity gave rise to the manufacture of cutlery and tools in Solingen (170,917) and Remscheid (127,585), which still specialise in them today, although much of their steel now comes from the Ruhr works. These towns are situated on the low plateaus on opposite sides of the valley of the river Wupper. Upstream, in the valley proper, is Wuppertal (422,400), formed by the amalgamation in 1930 of the twin cities of Elberfeld and Barmen. Wuppertal is West Germany's chief cotton and rayon manufacturing centre, as well as having carpet, chemical and textile engineering works. Built along the river in the valley bottom, it is a "ribbon" town 10 miles long, and is noted for the overhead railway which hangs above the river from end to end of the city. In the foothills of the Eifel, west of the Rhine, is a small outlier of the Ruhr coalfield. A wool textile industry, based on local coal, has grown in the area and Aachen (171,437) is now the Federal Republic's chief centre of this industry.

Away from the industries of the valleys, the Sauerland, Siegerland and Bergischeland are poorly peopled. They serve as catchment areas for the large water supply required by the cities and industries of the Ruhr and middle Rhine. There are more reservoirs among these hills than in any other part of West Germany; to them must be added those which trap the headwaters of the Ruhr in the Sauerland. The famous Möhne dam is here. These highland areas serve also as holiday playgrounds for the crowded population of the cities to the north. The Sauerland, which is still largely forested, supplies pit-props to the coalfield.

(ii) *The Münster "bay."* North-east of the Ruhr region is the Münster "bay," separated from the börde of Hanover by the low Hercynian ridge of the Teutoburg Forest. The Münster lowland is mainly agricultural, the distribution of its soils and villages being similar to that in the Rhineland bay. Its crops are much the same, too; but on the loess in the south, barley is grown extensively to supply the breweries of Dortmund, and in the west tobacco is important. Münster (184,291) is the only large town in the bay, a market for the wheat, sugar beet and cattle. It is helped by its position on the Dortmund–Ems Canal. The tops of the Teutoburg Forest (about 1000 ft high) are forested with oak and beech. On the northern side of gaps through the ridge are Bielefeld (174,374), with linen manufacturing, and Osnabrück (139,444), a market town and railway junction.

2. *The central highlands*

The central highlands or Hercynian lands of West Germany may be divided into (*a*) a northern portion consisting of the Middle Rhine Highlands, the Vogelsberg and the Harz mountains, (*b*) a southern region which includes the Rhine rift valley, the Black Forest, the Bohemian Forest and the intervening scarps and vales (*see* Fig. 74).

(a) *The Middle Rhine Highlands.* These are geologically a single horst of Palaeozoic slates and shales, with quartzites sticking up as ridges above the plateau surface in the Taunus and Hunsrück. It was uplifted in Tertiary times and tilted, so that in the south it reaches nearly 3000 ft in height, and falls northward to about 1000 ft. The Rhine, whose erosive power kept pace with the uplift, cut a deep gorge through the rising block; its tributaries, the Moselle and the Lahn, carved their valleys in a south-west to north-east down-warping which crossed the middle of the horst. The result was the formation of four highland units separated by the rivers: Hunsrück and Taunus to the south, Eifel and Westerwald to the north. Viewed from above, they are an undulating plateau, with occasional ridges or peaks where quartzites and volcanic rocks have resisted denudation; but from the rivers and adjoining plains, they have the appearance of rugged mountains. In the Eifel are about fifty volcanic cones of ash and stones, erupted towards the end of the Quaternary Ice Age. There are numerous hot springs and crater lakes, the latter formed in hollows left by explosions of volcanic gases.

The Middle Rhine Highlands are a region of great natural beauty, and attract yearly many thousands of tourists. They are poor in minerals, but their basalt and volcanic ash are quarried for building and road-metal; clays east of Koblenz are used for pottery. Basalt blocks from the Siebengebirge (Seven mountains), on the western edges of the

Westerland, are sent to the Netherlands for the construction of dykes. Farming in the highlands is poor. Even in the valleys the amount of land available for cultivation is limited by the precipitous slopes. It has been increased by terracing and planting vineyards, chiefly on the sunny sides of the Rhine and Moselle valleys.

Navigation through the Rhine gorge is difficult because of the speed of the river and its numerous rocks. One of the most famous of these latter is the Lorelei, which caused frequent shipwrecks until a clear passage was blasted in 1834. The rivers Moselle and Lahn have winding courses in deep, incised meanders. The Lahn has little value for shipping, but the Moselle has been canalised to provide an outlet to the Rhine for the iron ore of Lorraine.

The largest town of the area is Koblenz (87,000), at the confluence of the Rhine and Moselle, and the only bridge point in the 80 mile long gorge. Being in a "crossroads" position to the Lahn valley, Koblenz is the regional centre and market, especially for the wine trade. Vineyards cover the slopes of the Moselle valley; Trier (Trèves) (85,000), on the river near its entrance into West Germany, is another wine centre. This ancient city, with its impressive Roman remains, has been revitalised by the canalisation of the Moselle: extensive new port facilities have been provided to deal with the transit trade in iron ore from Lorraine.

In a wider part of the Lahn gorge is the small town of Wetzlar, the home of the famous Leitz optical firm. The Lahn is navigable up to this point for barges, which carry limestone from adjacent quarries to the Ruhr blast furnaces. East of the town the valley swings to the north and changes in character from a gorge to a narrow rift valley, a continuation of the Rhine rift valley. We leave the Rhine highlands and enter a region of Triassic limestones and sandstones, and numerous outcrops of basalt. In the valleys are loess deposits, with intensive cultivation of wheat and sugar beet, and many large villages. The higher parts, on the other hand, are infertile and largely forested: the scanty population is among the poorest in the Federal Republic. The chief occupation is cattle rearing, but the farmers must supplement their income by working in the quarries, especially in the Rhön mountain district. The Vogelsberg, a worn-down and dissected mass of basalt (the largest in Europe), is another poor region.

Only in the lowland to the north, the vale known as the "corridor" of Hesse, are there many towns. Of these, only Kassel has more than 100,000 inhabitants. Kassel (208,955) is at the junction of routes through the Hessian corridor from the middle Rhine, and from Thuringia to the lower Rhine. It is a market town with agricultural engineering and chemical works. Smaller towns include Göttingen (79,000) and Giessen, both with universities; Hamlin, a flour milling centre, but better known for its Pied Piper, is a minor port on the Weser, whose headwaters, the river Fulda, come from the Rhön mountains. The Eder, a tributary of the Fulda, has been dammed to form the Eder Lake, the second largest reservoir in West Germany. Its purpose is to regulate the flow of the Weser, which is navigable below Minden but decreases rapidly in volume during dry weather.

In the east of the region, West Germany contains a small portion of the Harz mountains, an isolated and much peneplained Hercynian horst. At one time silver and other ores were mined and there was a thriving craft industry. Today the mines are exhausted and derelict. The scanty population is occupied with poor farming of hardy crops such as hay and potatoes, with dairying and work in the forests that cover much of the mountain slopes. A reminder of the prosperous days of the past is the College of Mining at Clausthal-Zellerfeld. The region has also developed a tourist industry.

(b) *The southern region*. South of the Middle Rhine Highlands and the hills of Hesse, West Germany presents a patchwork of scarps and vales, where fertile basins alternate with forested uplands. The highest parts, the Black Forest and Oden Forest in the west, and the Bohemian Forest in the east, are well-rounded ridges of granite and gneiss, with large areas of forest. The Hardt mountains, separated on the west by the Rhine rift valley, are a northern continuation of the Vosges and of similar structure. The eastern slopes of the Black Forest and Odenwald have a cover of Bunter sandstone (Lower Triassic), with infertile soils, and are largely forested. This is followed by rolling lowlands of Keuper marls, muschel-kalk (shelly limestone) and ancient alluvium, very fertile and intensively cultivated. East of these is the low, discontinuous sandstone (Upper Triassic) scarp, separated by less extensive vales in Swabia and Franconia from the much more impressive limestone (Jurassic) scarps of the Swabian and Franconian Alben. The vales are floored by marls (Liassic) in the south and are fertile, but the northern portion has infertile outcrops of Bunter sandstone. (*See* Fig. 77.)

The Franconian Alb dips slowly eastwards, forming a plateau with frequent bare, white limestone platforms. Then, across a narrow valley of marls and alluvium, rise the slopes of the Bohemian Forest and, in the south, the Bavarian Forest. The whole region, even the vales, rarely falls below 1000 ft in elevation, and the scarps rise in the Franconian Alb to over 3000 ft. This disadvantage of height is compensated in the vales by their southerly latitude and the shelter afforded by the neighbouring hills. These factors, together with fertile soils and an abundant water supply, have made the lowlands extremely productive and they have led to the development of many small market towns and a few large cities.

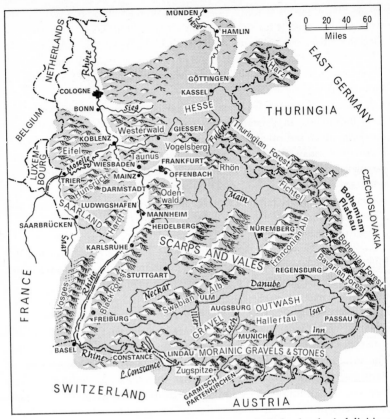

FIG. 77.—West Germany: highland region. The map includes the physical divisions marked (2), (3) and (4) on Fig. 74.

The frequent occurrence of *Wald* (Ger. "forest") in the names of mountains is indicative of the woodlands which at one time covered the highlands. Today, the Black Forest, Bohemian Forest and Odenwald are forested over less than half their area, the better slopes and valleys having been cleared for farming. Arable land is scarce, and most cultivation is for cattle fodder. Dairying is the chief occupation, and cattle are taken in summer to mountain pastures, much as in the Alps. Most farmers own a piece of the forest and augment their income by lumbering, or in saw-mills. Wood carving and the making of furniture are carried on in domestic workshops; the production of cuckoo clocks, especially in the Black Forest, has led to a watchmaking industry in scattered factories. In the Bohemian Forest is a domestic glass industry, based on quartz sand and wood ash, and using timber as fuel. Both the Black Forest and the

4. *The German Alps*

Only a small portion of the Alpine system—the Bavarian Alps—lies in Germany, whose southern boundary runs in part along the most northerly of the limestone ridges. Here is West Germany's highest peak, the

[*Copyright Bundesbildstelle, Bonn.*

FIG. 78.—West Germany: the Walchensee and Köchelsee. These two lakes, the Köchelsee (in the background) and the Walchensee, are in the German Alps, north-west of Garmisch-Partenkirchen. The hydro-electric power station shown makes use of the difference in level (600 ft) between the two lakes; the catchment area has been enlarged by tapping the river Isar and by diverting the river Rissbach, which used to flow to the Inn. The power station is the most important in West Germany and can supply current to the whole of Bavaria.

Zugspitze (9711 ft), and some of its well-known mountain resorts, such as Garmisch-Partenkirchen, noted for winter sports, and Oberammergau, with its renowned Passion play every ten years. Farming is at subsistence level in the many valleys which give passage through the Alps; the main occupations are dairying and forestry. Rye, oats, hay and potatoes are grown as high as 3000 ft above sea level, often wholly by hand labour where the steep slopes preclude the use of machinery. Cattle are taken in summer to the high pastures. Where the slopes are too steep for cattle, hay for their winter feed is grown and cut by harvesters secured by ropes for safety. The upper Lech valley, the Allgäu, is noted for its butter and cheese.

Timber plays a most important part in the economy of the region, thousands of rafts being floated annually down the Isar and Lech. Tree felling is very selective, since the clearing of large spaces might increase the danger of avalanches and landslides. Besides its use for building and paper making, the wood is used locally for carving and for musical instruments, as in Mittenwald, where violins are made. Most of West Germany's hydro-electric power is generated in the Alps, the largest single station being the Walchensee-Köchelsee plant (see Fig. 78). This makes use of two natural lakes north-west of Garmisch-Partenkirchen, one lying 600 ft above the other. To increase the catchment area, the Isar has been tapped and a tributary of the Inn completely diverted. The power generated is not much used in the Alpine region, but is transmitted to Munich and other towns, even as far as the Ruhr industrial belt.

EAST GERMANY

The region which in 1945 became the Soviet zone of occupation was declared in 1949 to be the German Democratic Republic. It is known to the Western world as East Germany, although West Germans prefer to call it Middle Germany, reserving the title "East" to the territories now administered by Poland and the Soviet Union.

East Germany comprises the pre-war provinces and *Länder* of Mecklenburg, West Pomerania, Brandenburg, Anhalt, Thuringia and Saxony, including East Berlin (156 square miles). With the advent of the Republic, the *Länder* were abolished as governmental divisions and in their places were set up 14 *Bezirke* (districts) based on their principal towns. To these were added East Berlin as a separate *Bezirk*. The old *Länder* names—Saxony, Thuringia, etc.—continue to be used, however, for geographical and most non-political purposes. East Germany is bounded on the west by a line from the Bay of Lübeck to the river Elbe, then winding south to include Thuringia, terminating at the western "corner" of Czechoslovakia. Its eastern boundary, except for the district of Stettin in the north, is the Oder–Neisse line.

Most of East Germany lies in (1) the middle portion of the Germano-Polish plain (see Fig. 79); only a small piece in the extreme south belongs to (2) the central highlands. The plain may be divided into (a) the Baltic coastal zone of ground-moraine, which has formed fertile undulating lowlands, and a belt of lowland south of this, but composed

Fig. 79.—East Germany: physical divisions. The numbers correspond with the regional divisions used in the text. (*See also* Fig. 69.)

of boulder clay, (*b*) a zone of morainic hills, known as the Baltic Heights or Baltic lake plateau, with gravelly or sandy soils over large areas, and smaller stretches of badly-drained boulder-clays with lakes; (*c*) the region of the urstromtäler, east–west valleys carved out in the outwash sands south of the Baltic Heights by north-flowing rivers blocked by the ice sheets and forced to turn along the front of the continental ice mass. The valleys, connected to each other by diagonal depressions, were originally filled with lakes and swamps, but they have been largely reclaimed and are now fertile strips in the sandy plains. (*d*) South of a line drawn east–west through Magdeburg the plains are covered with thin boulder-clays overlain with alluvium on which, in the southern portion, are deep deposits of loess. It is a region of rich brown forest soils and chernozem.

1. *The Germano-Polish plain*

(a) *The Baltic coastal zone.* The Baltic coast of East Germany is a drowned coast, with irregular, shallow inlets and low-lying offshore islands—a type known as a *Bodden* coast (Ger. *Bodden*, "bay"). The numerous inlets have given rise to many ports. Rostock was important in the days of the Hanseatic League, but the growth of Lübeck, Stettin, Hamburg and Bremen, plus the fact that the hinterland of this coast is entirely agricultural and had little need for outlets, prevented port development except for minor coastal traffic. Rostock, the largest, handled only half a million tons of shipping before the war. With the division of Germany in 1945, however, which placed Lübeck in West Germany and gave Stettin to Poland, the need for outlets for the industrial regions in the south made East Germany increase the harbour facilities of Rostock and develop Wismar and Stralsund, which had decayed.

Rostock (161,754) has been chosen as the shipbuilding centre of East Germany, which is in great need of a merchant fleet. It is the headquarters of the fishing and fish processing industries; and an autobahn connecting it to Berlin has deflected some of the exports of that city from Stettin and Hamburg. As in all East Germany, there is a shortage of labour; in 1959 many hundreds of Dutch shipyard workers were imported into Rostock. Stralsund (64,000), after a long period of stagnation because of its shallow waters behind Rügen Island, also takes some of Berlin's trade. Wismar, still with fewer than 50,000 inhabitants, deals with the trade of the west.

The belts of ground moraine and boulder-clays which form the coastal plain up to 50 miles wide are very fertile, with crops of wheat, rye and potatoes, and some dairying. The economy is completely agricultural, with few towns. Schwerin (92,000), a market, is the largest, with engineering, chemical and food processing works.

(b) *The Baltic Heights.* The Baltic Heights, morainic hills to the south of the plains, have soils varying from boulder-clay to sands and gravels, and are about 30% forested. In the hollows are many lakes, Lake Müritz the largest. All this northern region contained very large estates up to 1918. From then to 1945 the large farms were split into smaller holdings held by tenant farmers. Since then, there has been systematic expropriation and collectivisation, so that today there are no independent farmers. The collective system applies to the whole of East Germany; the "agricultural productive co-operatives," as they are called, were so resented that in the years 1952–59 126,000 farm owners and workers fled to West Germany.

(c) *The region of urstromtäler*. South of the Baltic Heights is a belt of outwash sands and urstromtäler. The sands are naturally quite infertile, and about a third of the area is still covered with pine forest. The centre of the region, known as the Middle March, is crossed by two urstromtäler, valleys which used to be swampy and impassable but are now drained and reclaimed. The land between the valleys has patches of loam, and some agriculture. The Oderbruch (Ger. *Bruch*, "marsh"), the part of the Oder valley where the river follows an urstromtal, has been reclaimed and produces large crops of wheat, rye, sugar beet and tobacco. The proximity of a large population in Berlin has led to an extensive market-garden industry in this belt, which has been made productive by the heavy use of artificial fertilisers from the potash beds near the Harz mountains.

The whole region is dominated by Berlin, with all roads, railways and canals converging on the city, so that other towns found it difficult to achieve any size or importance. In the vicinity of Berlin is Potsdam (114,521), which grew as a garrison and royal residence, then as a dormitory town for Berlin. Today it is the railway engineering and film studio centre of East Germany. In the west is Brandenburg (85,000), with steel works using imported scrap iron and coke, and the largest tractor works in East Germany. It has many medieval buildings, as has Frankfurt-am-Oder (56,000), a small river port and the agricultural and forestry centre of the east. Eisenhuttenstadt, formerly Stalinstadt (18,000), on the Oder where a canal joins the river from East Berlin, is a brand-new town. Building started in 1951 around blast furnaces and steelworks built to fill the gap in steel supplies left by the separation of the Ruhr and Upper Silesian smelting areas from the economy of East Germany. Eisenhuttenstadt depends entirely on imported fuel and raw materials.

Berlin (3,270,000) (West Berlin, 2,198,000, East Berlin, 1,072,000 in 1962) grew originally where routes converged to cross an urstromtal, in the middle of a fertile stretch of boulder clay. It was not a position which promised to become important, but as Berlin became the capital first of Brandenburg (1470), then of Prussia (1800) and finally of Germany (1871), it developed slowly and then more rapidly into one of the major cities of the world. Road, railway and canal communications were made to converge on it; it became the most important industrial city and the second largest inland port of pre-war Germany. Situated in a region devoid of mineral resources or fuel, its industries tended to be those which depended rather on skill, such as electrical apparatus, optical instruments, machine tools and luxury goods; but there were also large chemical and engineering works, textile factories, and the usual range of foodstuffs, furniture, etc., associated with the large market of a major capital.

After the intensive bombing of the war, and its division into East and West, Berlin entered a new era. When it was first occupied by British, French, American and Soviet troops, it was not envisaged that there would be any permanent change in the unity of the city. But in 1948, Soviet measures forced Berlin's civic authorities to restrict themselves to the sectors occupied by the Western powers, and so West Berlin came into existence. Since 13th August 1961 it has been cut off from the eastern sector by a wall built by the Soviet-dominated East Germans. East and West Berlin became virtually two cities, with separate water, gas and electricity supplies, separate reconstructed civic centres and separate currencies. The result is that West Berlin, although part of West Germany, forms a political and economic island shut off from the regions which supply its food, fuel and most of its raw materials, so that its economy must absorb greatly increased transport costs.

In spite of this isolation, West Berlin's industrial output is greater than before the war; but its political position is hazardous and uncertain. East Berlin, on the other hand, would seem to be better placed as having free access to the supplies and markets of East Germany and the countries of the Soviet *bloc*. In point of fact, however, reconstruction and new development have been much slower, since East Germany as a whole is a poorer country than West Germany, and there has been much popular resistance to Sovietisation. The political separation of Berlin into two parts is a geographical anomaly, unsound historically and economically. It remains as a source of disruption and contention in post-war Europe.

(d) *The alluvial and loess plains of south-east Germany*. These regions are the richest parts of the country. From the Harz mountains and the Thuringian Forest in the west to Lausitz (Lusatia) in the east is an expanse of wheat lands, sugar beet, barley and stall-fed cattle. Its chernozem and brown forest soils are extremely fertile. No trace remains in these lowlands of the forests which once covered them, nor are there any hedgerows or fences to break the continuity of cultivation. In this productive belt are a great number of large villages and many ancient towns. The general density of the rural population is among the highest in western Europe.

The largest cities are route centres, for two ancient trade arteries ran north and south of the Harz mountains, one following the valley of the

Elbe, the other the foot of the central highlands; these were crossed by roads coming from the south through the mountains, especially from Bavaria and Bohemia. At the crossing points grew towns like Magdeburg, Halle, Leipzig, Dresden and Erfurt. To this wealth of agriculture and trade centres must be added the abundance in the Middle Ages of minerals in the mountains of East Germany, and the (much more important) exploitation since 1850 of the vast deposits of brown coal which cover most of the lowlands themselves. Almost everywhere, too, are the common salt and potash beds left by the Permian Sea. In the south, in the shadow of the Ore mountains, is the Saxony coalfield.

The largest city of the south is Leipzig (585,258), in a nodal position on the river Saale. Its ancient importance as a trade centre, with twice-yearly fairs, was enhanced in the last century by the discovery round it of thick deposits of brown coal (lignite). Lignite occurs in beds of from 50 to 350 ft, at depths varying from 40 to 200 ft, and is mined in open pits, some of which are like giant quarries. It has only about half the calorific value of hard coal, and breaks into powder when transported. Its first use was as fuel in beet-sugar refineries, which are widespread in the Leipzig lowlands but, with the invention of briquettes, transport became more economic and large quantities were sent to Berlin for burning in stoves. Later, enormous power stations were built to consume brown coal locally, supplying Berlin and the entire southern region with electric current. The latest development is to use lignite as fuel in chemical works which also process it as raw material to produce tar, oil, nitrogenous fertilisers, plastics, dyestuffs, explosives and hard coke. The latter can be mixed with ordinary coke for use in blast furnaces.

A second lignite field occurs in Lausitz, west of the Neisse, with the small town of Senftenberg its centre. The two fields yield over 200 million tons of lignite annually, making East Germany the world's most important producer. Leipzig, the focus of the producing area, has chemical and engineering works, the manufacture of textiles and musical instruments, and a printing industry which until 1945 was the largest in Germany. It is the most important railway centre in the south.

East and south of the Harz mountains are vast beds of salt and potash. The deposits of common salt and the brine springs have been important for centuries, and gave rise to towns like Halle (276,191); but common salt did not become the basis of any great industries until the value of potash was realised about a century ago. Common salt is used today in the manufacture of caustic soda, and this in turn is a raw material for the chemical, soap and glass works of Halle and Bitterfeld, a small but important town north of Leipzig. Potash, which overlies the salt east of the Harz mountains from Stassfurt to Halle and is also found in smaller deposits to the south, was at one time regarded as a "rubbish salt" and thrown away. It is now converted into fertiliser, or used in the manufacture of glass, soap and a whole range of chemical products, in Halle and the neighbouring towns of Eisleben, Stassfurt, Calbe and Leuna, none of which has as yet 50,000 inhabitants. Leuna is being developed as East Germany's leading chemical centre.

North of the salt-field, in a continuation of the fertile *Börde* of Hanover, is Magdeburg (262,437), an ancient market town for the wheat, rye and sugar beet of the region, and a port at the junction of the Mittelland Canal with the Elbe. Its chief industry is heavy engineering. South of the Harz is Thuringia, an area of rich loams and loess, with the usual crops of wheat, sugar beet, barley and hops, and in addition flowers and fruit. Its centre is Erfurt (186,369), the oldest city in East Germany. It has clothing and footwear factories, and radio and television works. Jena (81,000) has an optical industry (Zeiss) and Gotha has been noted for nearly two hundred years for its publication of maps and atlases.

At the eastern end of the plain is Dresden (491,699), a beautiful city at a crossing point of the Elbe. Built originally as a fortress commanding the route along the Elbe into Bohemia, it developed in modern times as a centre of specialised industries such as the manufacture of cigarettes, optical instruments and aircraft, and the making of precision tools. It is best known for its porcelain—Dresden china—although this is actually made at Meissen, a few miles downstream. Görlitz (92,000) and Cottbus (65,000) are centres of the wool textile industry which has grown in Lausitz; other wool textile towns are Gera (101,414) and Plauen (80,000) in the upper Saale valley. This industry is based on raw wool from merino sheep introduced into Saxony from Spain in the eighteenth century, and reared in the foothills of the Erzgebirge.

In the south near Zwickau and near the eastern border round Görlitz are two small coalfields, producing in total less than three million tons of hard coal a year. East Germany is deficient in coal, except the lignite already mentioned, so this supply, though limited, is of great economic importance. The coal seams are becoming exhausted, however. East Germany already imports 4 million tons of coal and 2 million tons of coke a year from the Soviet Union, Poland and Czechoslovakia, and will become increasingly dependent for supplies on these outside sources. Situated on the northern margins of the larger of the two coalfields are Karl-Marx-Stadt (286,100), known as Chemnitz until 1953, and Zwickau (128,723). In these towns the cotton textile industry occupies first position, but they also manufacture wool, jute, linen and rayon. They are important producers of motor cars and motor cycles, which are made also at Eisenach, in Thuringia.

2. The central highlands in East Germany

East Germany is bordered on the west and south by a rim of Hercynian uplands which, though not large in area, had a wealth of minerals. Silver, copper, lead, zinc and iron have been mined in the Harz and Ore mountains (Erzgebirge) since the early Middle Ages; Freiberg, in the Erzgebirge, claims to have the oldest mining college in the world. The extraction of these minerals led to the development of craft industries in the numerous villages of the valleys among the mountains. With the decline in output due to the exhaustion of the ore deposits, their inhabitants had to look for other means of livelihood. They turned to different, though still highly skilled, forms of craft which required a minimum of raw materials, such as lace making in the Erzgebirge, toy making in the Thuringian Forest and violin making in the Vogtland.

The only mining of importance in the Erzgebirge today is for small amounts of silver and uranium at Aue, near Oberwissenthal. The greatest activity is near Gera, already mentioned as a textile town, where a major deposit of uranium is being exploited. Mining died completely in the Harz, but a new start was made to mine copper at Mansfeld, in the eastern foothills. This district produces enough copper for East Germany's requirements. In and round the Harz are beds of low-grade iron ore, yielding roughly 2 million tons a year. It is smelted at Calbe, using coke from the Zwickau coalfield.

The mountains, especially along the southern border, are still largely forested, with subsistence agriculture round the many craft-industry villages in the valleys. They are picturesque regions and attract large numbers of tourists, mainly to the Harz and the Thuringian Forest. Another attractive area is the valley of the Elbe, where the river passes through a gorge in the mountain rim. This stretch, from Meissen to the Czechoslovak border, is known as the "Saxon Switzerland," a favourite resort of rock-climbers on its sandstone cliffs. Its northern portion is a small rift valley, with alluvial soils and arable farming, producing early fruits and vegetables, peaches, apricots and vines.

STUDY QUESTIONS

1. Divide the Federal Republic of Germany into its principal geographical regions and write a detailed account of *one* of them. (O. & C.)

2. Show how the agricultural land use of Germany west of the Elbe reflects the physical geography of the area. (O. & C.)

3. Account for the importance of the Rhine as a route and as a waterway.

4. Write a geographical essay on the distribution and development of industries in West Germany. (O. & C.)

5. Draw a sketch-map of the German North Sea coast and account for the development of the ports you show. (O. & C.)

6. "The prosperity of West Germany is a matter of great concern to the ports of the Netherlands." Explain why this is so. (O. & C.)

7. Draw a sketch-map to show a division into physical regions of the country through which the Rhine flows between Basel and the Dutch frontier and describe, with the help of diagrams, the physical characteristics of each of the regions shown on your map. (O. & C.)

8. Select *three* cities in West Germany that differ widely from each other in their main function. Describe and account for these differences. (J.M.B.)

9. Give an account of the coal and lignite resources of West Germany and illustrate their importance in the economic life of the country. (J.M.B.)

10. Examine the influence of water transport on the industrial development of the Ruhr. (J.M.B.)

11. Write an essay on "The Agriculture of West Germany."

12. With special reference to its industries and the sources of the raw materials used, write an account of the Ruhr (Westphalian) coalfield. (O. & C.)

13. Analyse the factors that have influenced the locations of the main textile industries of East and West Germany. (J.M.B.)

14. Describe the main regional contrasts found within the basin of the river Elbe, inside the boundaries of Germany.

15. "The present political division of Germany separates two areas hitherto economically interdependent." Discuss this statement. (J.M.B.)

16. Draw a sketch-map to show the distribution of the iron and steel industries in Germany (East and West), and suggest reasons for their localisation. (O. & C.)

Chapter XIX

SWITZERLAND

SWITZERLAND, though small in size—Albania, Belgium, the Netherlands and Luxembourg alone have a smaller area in continental Europe—presents several geographical anomalies. About seven-tenths of its surface is mountainous, much of it bare rock or covered with snow and ice, yet the country as a whole is prosperous. With the exception of a few tiny deposits of coal and lignite, there are no mineral ores worth mentioning, yet 49% of Switzerland's population works in industry and trade, a percentage exceeded only by such highly industrialised countries as Great Britain and Belgium. It is land-locked and far from sources of mineral fuel or raw materials, yet it takes a very prominent position in international commerce. Its people speak several languages, yet, unlike the rest of Europe where language has become the criterion of nationalism and independence, Switzerland has shown no desire to split on this basis. Similarly, there is complete tolerance as far as religion is concerned; 52·6% of the population is Protestant, 45·6% Catholic, but religious differences seem to have been a factor in helping the Swiss people to respect the rights of others.

The country has been strongly influenced in its culture and political development by its physical surroundings. The way of life in the isolated and easily-defended valleys was such as to breed a love of liberty and independence in the individual, but with a regard for, and a necessity to co-operate with, others who lived in the same valleys. This led gradually to a democracy in which all men were truly equal, in which all had their rights, and all had to perform the duties which are the natural corollary to rights.

PHYSICAL ASPECTS

STRUCTURAL DIVISIONS

Switzerland may be divided into three parallel belts, which lie roughly in a south-west to north-east direction. They are: (1) the Jura mountains, most of the area of which is in France, (2) the Swiss plateau, which is known also as the Mittelland or the Alpine foreland, and (3) the Swiss Alps. The Jura occupy only one-tenth of the surface of Switzerland, the

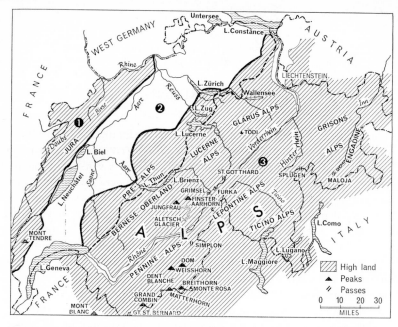

Fig. 80.—Switzerland: physical divisions. (1) Jura mountains; (2) Swiss plateau or
Mittelland; (3) Alpine region, sub-divided into pre-Alps and Alps. (*See also*
Fig. 69.)

Swiss plateau nearly one-third, and the Alps the remainder—almost
three-fifths of the total area (*see* Fig. 80).

1. *The Jura mountains*

For the general structure of the Jura mountains *see* Chapter XIV and Fig.
47. In Switzerland they run in several well-marked parallel limestone
ranges north-eastwards from the Rhone to the Rhine, decreasing in height
to the north, where (with the aid of tunnels) they are crossed by several
railways. In the southern half of the Jura, several peaks are more than
5000 ft in elevation, the highest in Switzerland being Mont Tendre, west
of Lausanne, which reaches over 5450 ft. In this portion it is possible, however, to cross the Jura in two places without tunnelling, from Neuchâtel
to Pontarlier, and from Lausanne to Vallorbe. The main rivers of the
Swiss Jura, the Doubs and the Birse, flow in longitudinal valleys, which
are connected by transverse valleys or *cluses*. The Doubs forms the
boundary of Switzerland for part of its course; the Birse flows to the
Rhine near Basel.

2. *The Swiss plateau*

Stretching in a south-west–north-east direction and forming a "corridor" between the Alps and the Jura is the Swiss plateau, 180 miles long and up to 30 miles wide. It extends from Lake Geneva (Léman) in the south to Lake Constance (Bodensee) in the north. This Alpine fore-land, composed of Tertiaries, was first dissected by rivers and then covered with the moraines and debris brought down by the glaciers of the Ice Age and later. The result is a hilly surface, with low morainic ridges, drumlins, undulating ground moraine and wide river valleys cut anew by a disturbed drainage system. The plateau slopes from about 4500 ft near the Alps to 1300 ft westwards at the base of the Jura. It is drained almost entirely by the river Aare and its tributaries, which flow to join the Rhine. Its surface contains many lakes, of which Geneva, Neuchâtel, Biel and Constance are the largest. The lakes on its eastern margin, with the possible exception of Lake Zürich, belong to the Alpine zone, and are dealt with below. They all drain to the Aare.

3. *The Swiss Alps*

The Alps in Switzerland are grouped round the St Gotthard massif, which forms a hydrographic centre, *i.e.* a centre from which many rivers flow radially. The Vorderrhein and Hinterrhein flow to the east as the headwaters of the Rhine; the Rhône rises in glaciers near the Furka Pass and flows to the west; the Aare begins on the northern side and drains lakes Brienz and Thun before crossing the Swiss plateau; and the Ticino on the south becomes a tributary of the Po. The eastern portion of the Swiss Alps is drained by the Inn, which flows to the Danube.

Between the Swiss plateau and the Alps proper is a narrow belt, some-times called the pre-Alps, and composed of flysch, molasse and other young rocks, which have been covered by glacial deposits. Among the pre-Alps, which in places rise to over 5000 ft, are the moraine-dammed lakes, Brienz, Thun, Lucerne (Vierwaldstättersee), Zug and Zürich. Brienz and Thun were originally one lake but have been split by deltaic material brought by mid-lake feeders, in much the same way as Derwent-water and Bassenthwaite were divided in the Lake District of England.

The Swiss Alps are divided into two parts by the great longitudinal trough in which flow the Rhône and Rhine. North of the trough are the Bernese Alps or Bernese Oberland, built mainly of limestone but with crystalline masses near St Gotthard. The north-facing side is pierced by many valleys, which are continuous with those of the pre-Alps and give access to several passes, among which the Lötschberg (4000 ft) and Grimsel (7102 ft) are perhaps the best known. The Bernese Alps rise to

14,026 ft in Finsteraarhorn and to 13,667 ft in the Jungfrau. They contain
the largest extent of glaciers in the Alps, the Aletsch Glacier being the
biggest single ice sheet. The Oberland is a favourite resort of tourists,
who can approach its heights easily from Interlaken, Kandersteg, Wengen
and Grindelwald. The slopes overlooking the Rhône valley are much
steeper and less accessible than those on the northern side. On the east
the Bernese Alps finish abruptly at the valley of the upper Aare, and from
here to the upper Reuss are the Vierwaldstätter or Lucerne Alps, which
are lower and more easily crossed. Beyond the Reuss are the Glarus or
Tödi Alps, a more continuous and difficult range which stretches to the
Rhine valley. The Tödi reach 11,887 ft at their highest point, and are not
crossed by road or railway. West of the Rhine and north of the Wallen-
see, the range decreases in elevation to just under 8000 ft, in the Alps of
Appenzell.

   South of the Rhône–Rhine trench the Swiss Alps are mainly of crystalline rocks, including granites, gneisses and schists, with occasional bands
of shales and slates. From the French border in the west to the Simplon
they are known as the Pennine Alps or Valais Alps. Here the Swiss Alps,
including the Oberland to the north, are at their widest and highest. The
northern slopes are the steeper, but many valleys cut them, giving access
to the high mountains which form the boundary between Switzerland
and Italy. The highest peak is Monte Rosa (15,203 ft); Dom (Mischabel)
(14,941 ft) and the Matterhorn (14,780 ft) are among many others which
tower to more than 13,000 ft.

   At the eastern end of the Pennine Alps the Simplon tunnel ($12\frac{1}{4}$ miles)
carries railway lines from Berne and Paris into Italy. East of the Simplon
the narrower range of the Lepontine Alps, although lower, is still a
formidable barrier. The centre forms part of the main St Gotthard
massif, which connects it with the Oberland. Here is the only good route
across the range: the St Gotthard Pass (6928 ft) has been the main north–
south passage through the western Alps since the Middle Ages, providing
a route from Italy to Zürich and northern Europe. The railway, which
follows the road as far as possible, traverses the range by a tunnel $9\frac{1}{3}$ miles
long. South of the Lepontine Alps is a portion of the less crystalline Ticino
Alps. Eastwards the Adula Alps, pierced by the San Bernardino (6768 ft)
and Splügen (6944 ft) passes, are followed by the Grisons (Graubunden)
Alps, lying on each side of the Engadine, the name given to the upper
Inn valley. Near the source of the Inn is the easy Maloja Pass (5910 ft).

CLIMATE AND VEGETATION

   The climate in the Jura mountains is severe in winter. Rivers freeze
and snow lies on the ground for several weeks, blocking the passes. On

the other hand the summers, especially in the interior valleys and on the south-east facing outer slopes, are hot enough for vines to be cultivated successfully. Much of the area of the limestone ranges is bare of vegetation and shows karst characteristics, but in general the Jura are clothed with coniferous forests to their summits.

On the Swiss plateau the climate varies with altitude, but not to such a degree as one might expect in a region which ranges from 4500 ft down to 1300 ft above sea level. In winter, for instance, mean temperatures in January are evened out by the prevalence below 2500 ft of cold, damp mists. The January mean temperatures of Berne, 28° C (−2° C), and Lucerne, just off the plateau, 30° F (−1·1° C), may be taken as typical of the Swiss plateau in winter. Summers in most parts have at least one month with over 60° F (11° C). Annual precipitation is between 30 and 45 in., according to altitude and aspect; in winter it falls as snow. The Alpine foreland was originally a region of coniferous forest in the higher parts and mixed forest in the lower. The mixed forest has been largely cleared for cultivation, but the climate on the whole is more suitable for grass and fodder crops than for cereals.

The climate of the Alps may be described as a "mountain" climate, offering great differences in seasonal or even diurnal ranges of temperature, and in the amount and seasonal occurrence of precipitation in locations which are very near to each other: in other words, the climate depends on altitude and aspect (see also Chapter XVI).

Theoretically, temperature decreases 1° F for every 300 ft increase in altitude (1° C for every 540 ft), but in practice it is found there are great variations from this average according to whether measurements are taken on north-facing or south-facing slopes, or at lower and higher stretches of the same slope. In the latter case, variations may be caused by differences in the moisture content of the atmosphere at different levels.

Temperature readings are also affected by "inversion." Cold air at high altitudes, being denser than warmer air, drains down the mountain slopes to form stagnant masses in the valleys, so that temperature there is lower than on the mountain peaks. Temperature inversion is commonest in winter. In that season the coldest part of the Swiss Alps is the deep valleys in the east, where January mean temperatures of 22° F (−5·6° C) are common. To avoid the cold winter air of the valley bottoms, Swiss Alpine villages are built some distance up the slopes, on the sunnier side. In winter, too, the valleys may be covered by low clouds, whereas the higher slopes are clear and sunny; in summer the reverse is the case, the peaks being encompassed by clouds and the valleys clear. The cold, crisp, dry air of the mid-altitudes in winter, healthy and invigorating, has encouraged the building of sanatoria and winter sports resorts. Davos, in eastern Switzerland, at an elevation of 5121 ft, is noted for both. The valleys in the north of the Swiss Alps experience the föhn in winter and early spring, a warm, dry wind which causes remarkable rises in temperature in the course of only a few hours. It is most frequent in the upper valleys of the Rhine, Reuss and Aare, and raises the January mean temperatures of these favoured areas to about 32° F (0° C), which is several degrees warmer than the average of the southern valleys of the Alps.

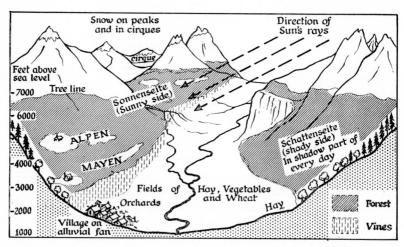

FIG. 81.—Switzerland: section across a Swiss Alpine valley. Note (*a*) the U shape of the glaciated valley, (*b*) the village and vineyards on the sunny side of the valley, (*c*) the village protected from avalanches by the forest behind it, (*d*) the châlets of the *mayen*, which are used in the early summer, and of the *alpen*, the higher mountain pastures which are free of snow in the later summer.

Summer temperatures in the valleys average, in July, from 62° F (16·7° C) to 70° F (21·1° C), depending on their depth and shelter. At about 5000 ft the mean July temperatures are around 52° F (11·1° C). Hotels and health establishments are rarely built much above this height.

Precipitation in the Alps is heavy but not abnormal. Their distance from the Atlantic and the fact that anticyclonic conditions are frequent in winter make the Swiss Alps less wet than lower mountains nearer the ocean. The greatest precipitation is in the St Gotthard massif, which has over 100 in. annually. The Santis group, in the Alps of Appenzell, has 96 in., and the Grisons Alps, in the east, over 60 in. The valleys have a good deal less precipitation, ranging from 50 in. in the Rhine valley where it begins to open out towards Lake Constance, to less than 24 in. in the upper valley of the Rhône, which is the driest part of Switzerland.

Throughout Switzerland there is more rainfall in the summer than in the winter half of the year. The seasonal differences are not so great in the south, where Mediterranean influences begin to be felt. Except in very low valleys, which may have occasional rain, precipitation in winter takes the form of snow, which may reach total depths of 25 ft or more. The line of permanent snow is 9000 ft in the west of the Alps, 10,500 ft in the drier east.

Natural vegetation naturally varies with altitude. The valley floors and the slopes up to about 4500 ft have mixed deciduous and coniferous trees; the valleys and the slopes facing the sun have been cleared for cultivation. From 4500 ft to nearly 6000 ft is a zone of coniferous forests, broken by natural clearings of grassland. These are the alps, or mountain pastures, and they are continued above the tree-line. The alps merge into a zone of Alpine flora or bare rock, above which are the eternal snows.

HUMAN GEOGRAPHY

HISTORY AND PEOPLE

Switzerland at one time formed part of the Holy Roman Empire. In 1291, the *cantons* or provinces of Uri, Schweiz (Schwyz) and Unterwalden, which jointly controlled the northern approaches to the St Gotthard Pass, the most important route through the western Alps, rebelled against the Hapsburg emperor and declared their independence. They signed an "Everlasting League," which was joined by the German-speaking cantons of the north, and later by French- and Italian-speaking cantons in the west and south. All efforts to invade and subjugate the cantons were unsuccessful, and in 1648 the independence of Switzerland was formally acknowledged. Since then, with the exception of a few years when it was part of Napoleon's French empire, it has remained free and neutral. In consequence of its neutrality, which was guaranteed by the Treaty of Vienna in 1815, Switzerland has become the home of many international organisations, such as the Red Cross, the League of Nations (1919–46), the World Health Organisation and the International Labour Organisation.

Switzerland, established in 1291, claims to be the oldest republic in the world. It contains nineteen cantons and six half-cantons, each of which sends representatives to the Federal Council, which sits at Berne. Berne, however, is only the nominal capital of the country; Zürich, Basel and Geneva are all larger and have greater economic importance. Moreover, every canton is sovereign within the Confederation and has its own capital city, and each denies the right of Berne as the seat of government to claim for itself the title of federal capital, which seems typical of Swiss ideas of democracy.

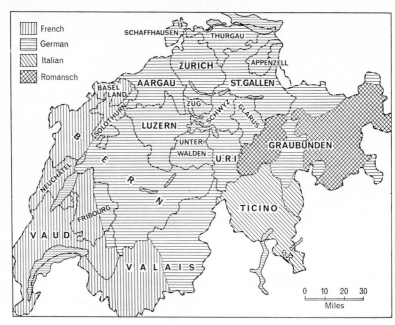

FIG. 82.—Switzerland: cantons and languages. There are 22 cantons or states in the Swiss Confederation, each self-governing in much the same way as the states of the U.S.A., and each sending two members to the Council of States, the second chamber of the Federal Government. Three cantons are divided into half-cantons: Unterwalden into Obwalden and Nidwalden, Appenzell into Catholic Innerrhoden and Protestant Ausserrhoden, and Basel into Basel City and Basel Country. The name of the small canton of Geneva is omitted from the map.

POPULATION

The population of Switzerland is 5,565,000, with an average density of 349 persons per square mile. This average is somewhat misleading, since only 76·4% of the surface is productive, and large areas have no population at all. The average density in the productive area is 456 persons per square mile; but because one-third of this area can be used only for pasture, and another third is covered with forest, this figure too is deceptive.

Three-quarters of the total population live in the Mittelland, and more than half in cities and towns of over 10,000 inhabitants. Omitting temporary residents, 74·4% of the people of Switzerland are German-speaking, 20·2% French, 4·1% Italian, and 1·1% Romansch, which is a derivative of Latin and is regarded as the original Swiss language. Generally speaking, the different language groups live in areas adjacent to Germany, France and Italy. In the middle of the country the linguistic boundary occasionally runs through a canton or city. In Fribourg, for instance, the majority are French-speaking, the minority German, whereas in Bienne two-thirds speak German and one-third French.

THE ECONOMY

ECONOMIC POLICY

Switzerland is a small country, mountainous, overpopulated, and with very limited natural resources. Yet its economic prosperity, political stability and perpetual neutrality, have made it one of the most important states in Europe and the Western world. This is partly because it lies astride historic trade routes from the north to the south of Europe, but mainly because the Swiss people have learnt to overcome their difficult environment and to use both it and their meagre resources to the greatest advantage.

About a quarter of the country's surface is high, bare and unproductive. Of the rest, only one-eighth is suitable for arable farming. The amount of food which can be grown falls far short of the country's requirements, and large quantities have to be imported. To pay for them Switzerland depends on its highly organised pastoral industries, its specialised manufactures, its tourism, its through freight traffic and its investment of capital in foreign countries.

Agriculture employs less than a sixth of the working population. Small farms predominate, and even the most prosperous farmers rarely have more than 75 acres. Not more than one farm in eighty has more than 14 acres, and over 20,000 have less than 1 acre. These last are chiefly in the Alpine valleys, where in many cases the peasant must struggle for a livelihood. The farms in the centre and north of the Swiss plateau show the most mixed characteristics, with dairying, wheat, oats, rye, potatoes, fruit and fodder crops. Cattle here are usually stall fed, except for a few weeks after the harvest. Farms nearer the Alps make use of mountain pastures as soon as the snows begin to melt, the cattle being taken to higher alps as the summer advances and brought down in autumn to sheds. These farmers are transhumant, living in summer in chalets, making cheese or sending the raw milk to co-operative dairies in the valleys or on the plateau. In the south of the Alpine foreland a large acreage is devoted to sugar beet and tobacco, because of the better soils, warmer summers and lighter rainfall. The dairy factories produce tinned cream, condensed and dried milk, butter, cheese and casein, most of which is exported.

Switzerland is almost completely lacking in minerals, for the output of a few anthracite mines in the Valais, and of iron ore worked in Gonzen and the Fricktal, is negligible. The only mineral exploited regularly is common salt, in the Rhine valley above Basel, and near Bex in the Rhône valley. On the other hand, Switzerland has a wealth of water power, which is of more lasting economic value than even its prosperous tourist industry.

Scattered along the main valleys in the mountains are thousands of hydro-electric power stations, mostly small and serving only local requirements, except where they are near the large towns of the Swiss plateau. In total they produce annually over 6·2 million kW, and there are so many that the whole country is covered by a close electric grid. It is estimated that by 1975 Switzerland will be producing 35,000 million kWh a year, and that in consequence industry on a large scale will penetrate the Alpine valleys. This development has already begun, as the numerous (though scattered) factories in the Rhône–Rhine trench and on the shores of lakes Geneva and Constance demonstrate. One result of the industrial development of the Alpine region will be to stem the flow of emigrants from the mountains to the Swiss plateau, which is over-populated, or abroad. This drift of people from highland to lowland is a serious problem, as it is in most countries of peninsular Europe which have mountain regions.

In all its manufacturing industries Switzerland depends on its import of foreign raw materials and partly-manufactured goods, and a very high proportion of its finished products is exported. Situated in the heart of Europe, its imports and exports face long land journeys and high freight charges, so that its products must be of high quality and attractive to potential customers abroad. In this respect Switzerland has had marked success, and has been helped by the inventive genius of its people and the abundance of hydro-electric power. The watch, clock and embroidery industries are typical examples. They require a minimum of raw materials and a maximum of skill; the value of the finished products is high, and they have a world-wide reputation. These are ancient industries, descended from domestic crafts and now modernised; to them may be added the making of precision tools and instruments, telescopes, microscopes, cameras, electrical equipment of every type, surgical and dental instruments, and heavy goods, such as turbines, diesels and electric locomotives.

It is a natural consequence of Swiss dependence on large imports from and exports to foreign countries that it should be vitally concerned that free trade should exist throughout the world. The country made no effort in 1957 to join the European "Common Market," formed in that year, even though total Swiss trade with its members—France, West Germany, Italy and Benelux—is greater than with all the rest of the world.

Switzerland preferred to join EFTA, in association with the United Kingdom, Norway, Sweden, Denmark, Portugal and Austria, because it did not involve setting up tariff barriers against the rest of the world. This shows clearly the country's fixed intention to maintain its policy of political neutrality and economic autonomy.

THE TOURIST INDUSTRY

In the past century the numbers of tourists visiting Switzerland have become a significant factor in the country's economic life. What began as a mere trickle of mountaineering enthusiasts has grown to a flood of

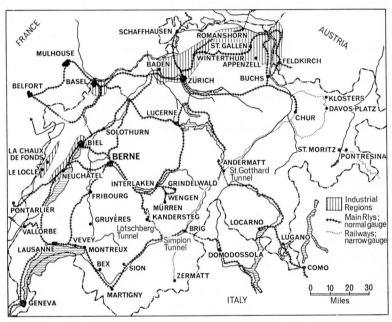

Fig. 83.—Switzerland: chief towns and railways; industrial regions. Correlate this map with Fig. 80 and work out the influence of the physical features on the railway network, especially in the Alpine region.

millions of visitors annually. The first influx of climbers was resented by the mountain Swiss, but when it was realised that tourists were a new source of income to this poorly endowed land, primitive inns and shelters began to be replaced by hotels. With surprising speed the Swiss became experts in hotel management; the mountaineering visitors were soon outnumbered by tourists attracted by the majestic beauty of the Alpine peaks rather than by a desire to climb them, or drawn by winter sports, which have become increasingly popular since 1920.

The industry was helped by the widespread development of hydro-electric power and of a transport system which made even the most remote districts easily accessible. The conversion of all Swiss railways to electrical operation was completed in 1961; and by means of electrically driven chairlifts, ski-lifts and aerial cableways, tourists can reach without effort some of the high peaks and enjoy the magnificent scenery to be found everywhere in the mountains.

Most tourists do not penetrate deep into the Alps, but make their "headquarters" in the towns of the Swiss plateau or in centres in the outer ranges of mountains. On the plateau the chief tourist centres are Lausanne, Geneva, Berne and Zürich. The shores of all the lakes at the foot of the Alps are lined with resorts, the largest of which are Lucerne (Luzern) and Interlaken. On the southern margin of the mountains are Locarno on Lake Maggiore, and Lugano; situated where Mediterranean influences bring more sunshine both in summer and winter, they attract many visitors from Italy and Yugoslavia. The chief Alpine resorts are Kandersteg, Mürren, Wengen and Grindelwald in the Bernese Oberland, Zermatt for the Matterhorn and Monte Rosa, St Moritz and Pontresina in the Engadine and Davos-Platz in the Grisons. These are noted mainly for winter sports (*see* Fig. 83).

REGIONAL ECONOMY

1. *The Jura*

The chief occupations in the Jura mountain region are lumbering and dairying. The best dairy farms are in the north, where the Jura are lower and the valleys wider. In this northern part, where several valleys converge on that of the Rhine, and where that river turns northwards into its rift valley, is situated Basel (Basle, Bâle) (229,000), the western gateway to Switzerland. Basel is a major route centre and important river port, coal, coke and iron ore being brought by barges from Strasbourg and the Ruhr. A chemical industry based on local deposits of salt developed in the town and its position between the textile regions of Alsace and northern Switzerland encouraged specialisation in the manufacture of aniline dyes. Today, about one-sixth of the country's exports are chemical products, chiefly dyes and pharmaceutical drugs. Their manufacture has helped to make Basel the third city of Switzerland (*see* Fig. 84).

The original home of the Swiss watchmaking industry was located in the Jura and, although the headquarters of the large firms are now in Geneva, the making of components and fine mechanisms is still scattered through the villages and towns in the south of the mountains. La Chaux

FIG. 84.—Switzerland: Basel, an aerial view. At the southern end of the Rhine rift valley and on an elbow bend of the river, Basel (Basle, Bâle) is a railway centre and river port. It is the centre of the Swiss dyestuffs and pharmaceutical industries.

de Fonds (35,000) and Le Locle are renowned for their manufacture of clocks and watches.

2. The Swiss plateau

The most extensive farming occupation on the plateau is dairying. This concentration on dairy products began towards the end of the nineteenth century, when imports of cheap grain from countries with more favourable growing conditions forced the Swiss to convert their croplands to pasture. By far the greatest number of cattle in Switzerland is on the plateau and not, as is popularly thought, in the Alpine region. Shortages of foodstuffs created by the two world wars caused a temporary increase in the acreage of cultivated land, but it is slowly declining again. It was 642,500 acres in 1961, as compared with nearly 900,000 acres in the early 1950s. Fruit-growing, however, especially of peaches, apricots and other stone-fruits, has increased. Vines flourish on the shores of lakes Geneva, Neuchâtel, Biel and Zürich.

Most of the country's industrial activity is found on the plateau. The metal-working and machinery industry is the most important branch;

M

all forms of electrical engineering and the making of agricultural and textile machinery, diesel engines and precision instruments is concentrated in a belt from St Gallen in the east to Basel in the west. The centre of the industry is Zürich (443,000), the largest city in Switzerland. It is also the centre of the textile industry. The wool textile industry which grew up there originally has been outstripped by the spinning and weaving of fine cottons and man-made fibres. St Gallen (St Gall) (76,000), Winterthur (80,000) and Appenzell are other cotton manufacturing towns, and they have silk and embroidery industries as well. Basel has small-scale silk ribbon manufacture.

In the centre of the plateau are Berne (166,000) and Fribourg (30,000), both residential rather than industrial towns, although the chemical industry of the Basel area has spread to Berne, the federal capital. In the south of the Swiss plateau the shores of Lake Geneva are dotted with industrial towns and tourist resorts. The industries are usually connected with watchmaking, jewellery and foodstuffs, such as condensed milk, infant foods and chocolate. The firm of Nestlé has its headquarters at Vevey, and the Ovaltine and Tobler factories are in the region. The largest city, Geneva (176,000), besides its watchmaking and tourist trades, is internationally known as the European headquarters of branches of the United Nations, such as the International Labour Organisation and the World Health Organisation, and of the International Red Cross, the Universal Postal Union, the International Telecommunications Union, and other world organisations. They are located in Switzerland because of its traditional neutrality. Lausanne (126,000) has tourist, foodstuffs and cutlery industries and is a railway centre.

Biel (Bienne) (59,000), on Lake Biel, and Solothurn, farther north-east, share in the watchmaking industry, which has spread also to Schaffhausen (30,000). The latter town is situated on the only piece of Swiss territory north of the river Rhine, where rapids have enabled the generation of hydro-electricity.

3. *The Alps*

In general, the Alpine region of Switzerland is poor and unproductive. Over half its surface is forested, and much of the remainder is bare rock or covered with snow or ice, leaving only a small proportion available for farmland or pasture. Forest industries play a very minor part in the country's economy, timber in the Alps being used mainly as building material or fuel. The best farmlands are in the Rhône and Rhine valleys, and produce crops of hay, potatoes, rye, oats, wheat and even maize: the upper valleys of the Reuss and Inn are also among the more favoured cultivable areas.

The Rhône valley in Switzerland has long, straight stretches and a wide floor from Lake Geneva to Brig, a market town. Other markets of local importance in the valley are Sion, Martigny and Bex. Vines are grown in the sunny climate of this part of the valley. Above Brig the valley narrows and becomes steeper, and leads at its head to the Furka Pass (7972 ft), which opens on the other side to the Vorderrhein valley. Beyond the pass, at the intersection of the Rhône–Rhine and St Gotthard routes, is the tourist resort of Andermatt, at a height of about 4700 ft.

[Courtesy of the Swiss National Tourist Office.

Fig. 85.—Switzerland: Val de Bagnes, with the Mauvoisin power station. The main barrage and reservoir are seen in the far distance, up the valley. In the foreground is the village of Fionnay, with the power station and compensation reservoir. The stream in the valley flows from the Pennine Alps to join the Rhône. Note some of the characteristic features of this glaciated valley.

The Rhine valley does not begin to widen until it turns north at Chur, but from there to Lake Constance it is wide and well cultivated.

Most Alpine villages are little more than hamlets (*see* Fig. 85). As already noted, aspect is very important, and insolation strongly influences the location of settlements. The German-speaking Swiss divide the slopes into the *Sonnenseite* and the *Schattenseite*, the sunny and the shady sides; they build their villages so as to obtain the maximum insolation, and at the same time to be protected by forests from avalanches, which are common in spring. Alpine farms are primarily pastoral, and agriculture is concerned in the first place with the production of hay and other winter provender for their cattle.

In the summer the cattle are taken to the mountain pastures, where the herdsmen live in strongly built chalets of timber, anchored by huge boulders against winter storms. Cheese is made there and carried to the villages, where hay and fodder are being grown. In the Alps the carriage of raw milk is increasing, as hydro-electrically-driven factories are penetrating farther into the valleys, but at present it has little importance. Isolated farmsteads and tiny hamlets may be found high up the slopes, for potatoes, for instance, are grown as far up as 4000 ft and, on the south-facing shoulders of the Valais Alps, rye is cultivated at an altitude of 6500 ft. Most of the Alpine farmers live a hard, austere life, little concerned with or affected by the tourism popularly associated with the Alps, except near the recognised resorts. Even the greater prosperity and larger size of the farms in the wider main valleys are only relative, for rarely has the individual farmer more than 10 acres. They are all in better circumstances now, however, than fifty years ago. The excellent motor coach road system built for tourists and the advent of hydro-electricity have benefited all the mountain dwellers and, as the forerunners of industrial development, may profoundly affect the culture of the mountain people.

STUDY QUESTIONS

1. Illustrate the influence of the position and relief of Switzerland upon the life and trade of its inhabitants. (O. & C.)

2. Explain, with the aid of a sketch-map, the location of industry in Switzerland. (O. & C.)

3. Describe the natural regions of Switzerland. (O. & C.)

4. Describe and explain the distribution of population in Switzerland. (O. & C.)

5. Write a geographical study of trans-Alpine routes.

6. Give a reasoned comparison of the characteristic features of the external trade of Sweden and Switzerland. (J.M.B.)

7. Describe how you would plan a programme for a party of schoolchildren who are to spend a short holiday in Switzerland so that they would best learn its geography. (O. & C.)

8. Show what part the Alps play in the national economy of Switzerland.

Chapter XX

CZECHOSLOVAKIA

CZECHOSLOVAKIA is said to "sit in the saddle of Europe," because its position in the middle of the continent gives it control of a major north–south trade route—the Moravian depression and gap—which cuts Czechoslovakia in two. On each side of this depression is an east–west mountainous barrier which stretches from the Soviet border to the western end of Bohemia. Czechoslovakia came into existence as a sovereign state in 1919, after the First World War. The very different physical regions of Bohemia, Moravia, Slovakia and Ruthenia were joined to form the new country, mainly but not wholly on a basis of ethnic characteristics and cognate languages; but differences of peoples, cultures and economic development have not made the amalgamation entirely successful, as we shall see later.

PHYSICAL ASPECTS

STRUCTURAL DIVISIONS

Czechoslovakia may be divided into (1) the Hercynian block of Bohemia in the west, (2) the lowlands of Moravia in the centre, and (3) the folded ranges of the Carpathian mountains and the Danubian plains of Slovakia in the east (*see* Fig. 86).

FIG. 86.—Czechoslovakia: physical divisions. The numbers refer to sections in the text. (1) Bohemia; (2) Moravia; (3) Slovakia.

1. *Bohemia*

Bohemia is a rectangular or diamond-shaped horst with north–south, east–west diagonals. It is one of the larger remnants of the Carbo-Permian or Hercynian orogenesis. Its folds, which were peneplained, submerged in a shallow sea and covered by sands and silts in Cretaceous times, were again uplifted, fractured and tilted in the Tertiary "Alpine storm." The main uplift was in the south-west, where the crests of the Bohemian Forest (Ger. Böhmerwald; Czech. Šumava) rise to over 5000 ft. The eastern edge of the massif is lower and wider, the Czech-Moravian Heights not rising in altitude to more than 2750 ft. Bohemia is bounded on the north-west by the Ore mountains (Ger. Erzgebirge; Czech. Krusné Hory), and on the north-east by the Giant mountains (Ger. Riesengebirge; Czech. Krkonoše) and Sudetes. All these northern ranges contain subsidiary horsts, formed by faulting and dislocation. The movements were accompanied by volcanic outpourings of Tertiary basalts, especially at the foot of the Ore mountains, where there are many mineral springs. The highest peak of Bohemia is Snow mountain (Czech. *Snezka*) (5256 ft), in the Giant mountains. The latter get their name from the legendary giant, Krakonoš, who supposedly ruled over them.

Inside the mountainous edges, Bohemia is a basin which slopes down from over 2500 ft in the south to less than 700 ft in the north. The southern half of the basin is sometimes called the Bohemian plateau, and the northern half the Bohemian plain; but in both halves the surface contains depressions and hills, so that the general effect is one of marked undulation. The plateau is composed of older rocks, mainly granites and schists, with occasional slightly higher ridges of quartzites, such as the Brdy Forest, south of the river Berounka (Ger. Beraun). In the south of the plateau are two faulted depressions, Budějovice (Ger. Budweiss) and Třeboň (Ger. Wittingau), filled in by Tertiary sands and marls; farther north, the Plzeň (Ger. Pilsen) and Kladno basins have been carved out by the river Berounka.

The plain part of the basin is covered by Tertiaries and recent alluvium, with occasional sprinklings of loess. A large portion is taken up by the flat valley of the river Labe (Elbe), 20 miles wide and upwards of 60 miles long. A series of faulted depressions occurs along the foot of the Ore mountains, the most important being the basins of Karlovy Vary (Ger. Karlsbad) and Teplice (Ger. Teplitz), which are separated from each other by the volcanic mass of Doupov (3000 ft). Both basins contain important beds of lignite; and Teplice, with a cover of loess, is a rich farming area. There are similar, but smaller, basins at the foot of the Giant mountains.

The Bohemian basin is drained by the Labe (Elbe) and its tributaries, the Vltava, Berounka and Ohre. The Elbe leaves Czechoslovakia by a defile through the Ore mountains below the town of Ústí (Aussig). The Elbe is fully navigable, the Vltava partly so, providing a valuable link with East Germany and with the port of Hamburg in West Germany.

2. *The Moravian lowlands*

The Moravian lowlands largely comprise the basin of the river Morava, which flows south to join the Danube. It is difficult to mark the western limit of the plain, for the Czech-Moravian Heights slope gently eastwards, but the Carpathians rise steeply on the eastern side, forming a definite boundary there. The lowlands narrow towards the north, where the Jeseník, one of the ranges of the Sudetes, is separated from the Beskids, part of the Carpathians, by a gap only a few miles wide. This is the "Moravian Gate" which links the Danube lands to the Germano-Polish plain, making the Moravian lowlands one of the most important passages in Europe, both commercially and strategically. North of the Gate a small portion of Upper Silesia belongs to Czechoslovakia. The Moravian lowlands are broken by outliers of the Carpathians, to give a

[*Courtesy of the Czechoslovakian Embassy.*

Fig. 87.—Czechoslovakia: a village in the Giant Mountains. This peaceful rural scene is typical of the Giant Mountains in north-east Bohemia. The mountains are a favourite summer and winter resort for the people of Prague.

very irregular relief on the eastern side. On the whole, they are covered by Tertiary sands and marls, in which the rivers have cut deep valleys. The soils are fertile, except in the lower valley of the Morava, which is marshy.

3. Slovakia: the Carpathians and the Danube plain

East of the confluence of the Morava with the Danube, the Little Carpathians (Malé Karpaty) stretch to the north-east, growing higher and wider. Here the White Carpathians (Bílé Karpaty) link them to the main east–west ranges. The northernmost folds of the White Carpathians are the Beskids, only a small portion of which is in Czechoslovakia. They are parallel dissected ranges which rarely rise to more than 4500 ft, and are easily penetrable. South are the High Tatra, a range varying from 6000 to 8000 ft and the highest in the Carpathians. They are composed of crystalline rocks and are similar to the central zone of the Alps, which they resemble also in the land forms left by glaciation. Here is Gerlach Peak (8711 ft), the highest mountain in Czechoslovakia. Separated from the High Tatra by the Vah valley are the Low Tatra; and again to the south are the Slovakian Ore mountains, the source of antimony, magnesite and iron ore. The Vah, the longest river of Slovakia, has a mountain course broken by many rapids before it flows across the Hungarian plain to the Danube.

South of the Carpathian ranges, Czechoslovakia includes a portion of the Hungarian plain, with the Danube as the boundary. This flat or gently undulating lowland is composed of marls nearer the mountains and of alluvial gravels and silts towards the Danube. It is a rich agricultural region, occupied until 1945 by Magyar or Hungarian peasants rather than by Slovaks, and is regarded by Hungary as rightfully a part of its territory. It was occupied by Hungary in the Second World War but was restored to Czechoslovakia in 1945, when many of the Magyars were expelled across the Danube or taken to the depopulated Sudetenland.

CLIMATE AND VEGETATION

Czechoslovakia has a continental climate, but because it stretches west–east through a distance of nearly 500 miles, the western end of the country is only moderately continental, whereas in the east it is definitely so. Prague, for instance, ranges from a mean of 30° F (−1·1° C) in January to 66° F (18·9° C) in July; in Slovakia, January mean temperatures are around 22° F (−8·9° C) and in July 67° F (19·4° C). Summer temperatures do not vary much throughout the country; it is the winter which shows the greater continentality. In the mountains of southern Bohemia and Slovakia, temperatures are lower at all times. The average annual precipitation in the country is 28·23 in. In the Bohemian Forest it reaches nearly 50 in., and slightly less in some parts of Slovakia, but Prague registers only 19 in. In winter, Czechoslovakia lies under the influence of the continental anticyclone, so that rain-bearing westerlies cross it only infrequently. Precipitation falls as snow in that season, but the total amounts to only a few inches of rainfall. In Prague there is more than twice as much precipitation in the summer (69%) as in the winter half (31%) of the year.

Over a third of Czechoslovakia is covered with forests—chiefly fir, spruce, pine and larch at higher altitudes, and the usual European deciduous varieties in the lowlands. The most extensive forests are on the slopes of the Bohemian Forest, the Giant mountains, the Beskids, Tatra and Slovakian Ore mountains. All the forests have herds of wild boar, and in Slovakia bears and wolves may still be encountered. Most of the deciduous forests have been cleared for agriculture. In the north of Bohemia, in the valley of the river Labe, there is an approach to steppe vegetation, in consequence of the low rainfall. Grasslands are also found in the plains of southern Slovakia.

HUMAN GEOGRAPHY

HISTORICAL OUTLINE

Although Czechoslovakia as a country is less than fifty years old, its roots lie deep in history. The area had been inhabited by emigrant Slavs from the east long before the seventh century, during which the Samo Empire (a temporary union of western Slav tribes) came into being, to be followed in the ninth century by the Great Moravian Empire. When this broke up a century later, Bohemia, with Moravia, became a separate kingdom. Precious metals began to be mined, craftmanship and trades developed, and towns grew up, Prague the biggest of them. At the beginning of the fourteenth century, the Luxembourg family ascended the Czech throne. Prague, as the seat of Charles IV, who was also elected Holy Roman Emperor, became one of the chief cities of the medieval world. The Czech kingdom was powerful and prosperous, but its people, now ruled by Germans, had lost their independence.

They became more and more restive at the demands of their feudal overlords and turned for leadership to John Hus, a social and religious reformer. His execution in 1415 led to a great popular uprising, and for 20 years the Hussite movement united the oppressed Czechs. It spread to Slovakia in the east, at that time ruled by Hungarian princes, but in both provinces the movement proved ineffective. In the sixteenth century the

Hapsburgs became rulers of Bohemia, and in 1620 they destroyed all resistance by a victory over the Czech nationalists near Prague. Czech leaders were executed and their lands confiscated. The country was "Germanised" and added to the Austrian crown. Slovakia, too, when Hungary fell to Austria in the eighteenth century, became part of the Austro-Hungarian Empire.

Throughout the seventeenth and eighteenth centuries there were many peasant uprisings, but all ended in defeat, cruel reprisals, and the apparent death of nationalism in both Bohemia and Slovakia. Hope still smouldered, however, and after 1848, the "year of revolutions" in Europe, nationalist resistance movements among the Czechs and Slovaks became strong and continued to the First World War. From 1917, there were strikes and popular demonstrations against Austro-Hungarian rule. When the Empire ceased to exist in 1918 an independent Czechoslovak republic was proclaimed, and confirmed by the Allies in the following year. The Slavs' five centuries of struggle against German rule had ended in success.

The new republic, formed of a highly industrialised and prosperous Bohemia and Moravia, and a much more backward but still ambitious Slovakia, promised to become a well-balanced country. But a powerful minority of 3 million Germans who lived in the Sudetenland, in Bohemia, claimed self-determination and in 1938 became the excuse for Germany's claim to that territory. To avoid open war, the Czechoslovak government ceded the Sudetenland to Germany. Still not satisfied, Germany sent her troops in March 1939 to occupy Bohemia and Moravia, which became a German "protectorate." She declared Slovakia "independent," though "protected." Czechoslovakia's freedom had lasted only twenty years.

The end of the Second World War in 1945 saw the defeat of Germany, the occupation of Czechoslovakia by Soviet forces, and the enforced migration of the Sudeten Germans to Germany. The expulsion of most of the Hungarians who lived in the southern plains of Slovakia, and the annexation of Ruthenia by the Soviet Union, left Czechoslovakia a more completely Slav state than it had ever been before. Ruthenia, at the eastern end of the Carpathians, was more akin in people and language to the Ukraine than to Slovakia.

The Communist party in Czechoslovakia, which between the wars had not been very powerful, was now actively supported by the U.S.S.R. and took control of the Government. By 1948 all industry and much of the land had become State property. Czechoslovakia became part of the Communist *bloc*, and in 1960 changed its name to the Czechoslovak Socialist Republic.

POPULATION

The population of Czechoslovakia at the last estimate (1964) was 13,868,000, of whom 9,630,000 live in Bohemia and Moravia and 4,238,000 in Slovakia. Czechs in the west and Slovaks in the east make up 95% of the inhabitants. The remainder are of Hungarian, German, Polish and Ukrainian origin. The Hungarians, or Magyars, form the largest "minority," about half a million of them on the Danubian plains of Slovakia. The average density of population in the country is 281 persons a square mile, with the greatest concentrations in the Bohemian and Moravian plains. Many parts of the mountains in the south of Bohemia and in Slovakia are poorly peopled.

The Czechs and the Slovaks form an uneasy combination. It is true that Bohemia, rich in minerals and industry, Moravia with a mixed economy and a large coalfield, and Slovakia, with forests, minerals, power resources and agricultural lands, seem to be complementary, and that Czechoslovakia is better balanced economically than any of its neighbours. Yet in its two peoples, different in culture and advancement, the country faces problems which are difficult to solve permanently. The more numerous Czechs, in the richer and better developed west, tend to force their culture and way of life on the Slovaks, an independent mountain people whose mental outlook is more eastern and whose traditions and actions are coloured by a thousand years of Hungarian overlordship. There is in Slovakia a distinct separatist movement, decidedly anti-Czech. The consequent political and social tensions are held in check only by the domination of the Soviet Union, which exercises control of the Government. From an economic point of view, Soviet influence has been of great advantage to Czechoslovakia in its post-war reorganisation and rehabilitation; but the ultimate stability and prosperity of the country will depend on its ability to integrate more successfully its eastern and western halves.

THE ECONOMY

AGRICULTURE

The chief farming regions are the Labe plain and Ohre valley in Bohemia, most of the Moravian lowlands, and the plains in the south of Slovakia (*see* Fig. 88), but cultivation of the hardier cereals, oats and rye, and of potatoes is common everywhere, even at high altitudes. Cereals (wheat, barley, oats and rye) account for half the arable land; maize and rice are grown on a small scale in southern Slovakia. A special variety of barley, for malting, is produced in the Labe plain and the Pilsen basin;

hops are cultivated round Žatec in the Ohre valley, Roudnice in the Labe plain, and Uštěk in northern Bohemia. Sugar beet is grown in all the lowlands in rotation with wheat; potatoes are the chief crops in the Moravian Heights. There are vineyards and tobacco fields in southern Moravia and in south-west and south-east Slovakia, and market-garden-ing is common round all the large towns. Flax and hemp are products of southern Bohemia and northern Slovakia. No part of Czechoslovakia is outstanding for dairy produce, cattle and pigs being found on all farms

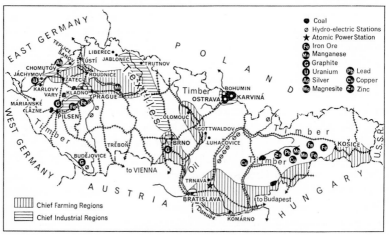

FIG. 88.—Czechoslovakia: economic. Correlate this map with Fig. 86. Note the growing industrial regions around Brno and Bratislava.

in the lowlands. Sheep rearing, mainly in the mountains of northern Bohemia and Slovakia, has declined in recent years.

Standards of agriculture vary considerably. In lowland Bohemia and Moravia, farms are larger, more mechanised and more efficient; but as one moves further eastwards in Slovakia, farming becomes more primi-tive, with a very restricted range of crops. There the land holdings are small, and on the mountain slopes mechanisation is difficult or impossible. In consequence, the rural population of Slovakia is poor, and tends to drift to the richer plains or to the towns in Bohemia. This movement is a good thing for Bohemia, where there is a labour shortage; but for Slovakia it means loss of population and another reason for discontent.

In 1960, 26% of all workers were engaged in forestry or agriculture as compared with 38% in 1950, which indicates a transfer from agri-culture to industry. This is largely the result of increased mechanisation and a reorganisation of land use. The basis of agriculture in Czecho-slovakia, after the First World War, was small peasant-owned farms carved from the large estates taken from Austrian or Hungarian land-owners. These small, individual holdings were uneconomic in manpower and could afford neither machinery nor fertilisers; their yields were low, especially in Slovakia.

To improve matters, the Communist Government, after the Second World War, introduced a land reform in several stages. The State took over 11 million acres of farm land and forests, and distributed most of it among farm workers and small farmers, who were then encouraged to form agricultural co-operatives. These are associations of farmers from one or more villages, who pool their fields, farm buildings, livestock and machinery, and by joint use of labour and means of production can achieve results denied to the individual. Their surplus products are sold at fixed prices to the State, which may provide loans for new machinery, fertilisers and research. Nominally, the farmer owns his land, with rights of inheritance, and may sell it; but so long as he is a member of a co-operative, he is answerable to the State officials who tell him what crops to grow, what livestock to keep and scrutinise the results—which, on the whole, are far better than pre-war.

Forests exceeding 5 million acres were taken over completely by the State, and the larger estates which had not been distributed among small farmers became State farms. Farm land takes up 58% of the area of Czechoslovakia, and of this about a fifth is occupied by State farms whose main function is to try out new methods of cultivation and produce improved seeds and livestock.

About an eighth of the farm land is still in the hands of individual farmers, mainly in the valleys and on the slopes of the Bohemian Forest and the mountains of Slovakia. Their farms, ranging in size from 5 to 12 acres, are usually too small or too hilly for much mechanisation and too scattered for co-operation. So they continue in the old, backward tradition, except that they are expected to contribute more to the national output than formerly, and are visited by experts, who provide classified seeds and fertilisers.

There is no doubt that the co-operative system, which covers roughly two-thirds of the farming community, has had beneficial results. In all the main crops, with the exceptions of rye and potatoes, the total annual output has increased considerably. In the cases of rye and potatoes the areas devoted to their growth have been reduced, and new crops introduced in their places.

Czechoslovakia's extensive forests have led to an important lumbering industry, especially in Slovakia, but timber and timber products do not rank high in the country's exports. Home demands use most of the sawn timber, and the woodworking industry's output for foreign consumption is concerned mainly with furniture, paper, pencils, matches, toys and musical instruments.

MINERALS AND POWER

Mining in Czechoslovakia is an ancient tradition, deposits of mineral ores in the Erzgebirge having been exploited as early as the twelfth century. All deposits of economically important minerals are owned by the State, and so are the industries using them.

Coal, the chief mineral wealth, occurs in Upper Silesia around Ostrava-Karviná, and in three small basins in Bohemia—Pilsen, Trutnov and Kladno. The Upper Silesian coalfield is the most important. It is a continuation of the Polish Silesian field, and contains bituminous coal and anthracite. Its annual production, over 26 million tons, is about four-fifths of the country's total. There are also lignite or brown coal deposits in a narrow field at the foot of the Erzgebirge, with centres in Chomutov, Šanov and Teplice. Lignite occurs in the upper Nitra valley in Slovakia. Graphite, mined north of Pilsen in Bohemia and near Brno in Moravia, is the basis of Czechoslovakia's famous pencil industry.

Rich, though not very extensive, deposits of iron ore are mined in the Slovakian Ore mountains, and between Prague and Pilsen. Further deposits have been found in northern Moravia. The total annual output, 3 million tons, is insufficient for the needs of Czechoslovakia's iron and steel industry, so iron ore and pig-iron are imported from East Germany and the U.S.S.R. Manganese occurs in east Bohemia and eastern Slovakia; lead, zinc and copper in central Bohemia and central Slovakia. Substantial amounts of silver (198,000 lb annually) and small quantities of gold are mined in the Erzgebirge and Slovakian Ore mountains. Uranium, extracted from pitchblende, is produced at Jáchymov̂. Kaolin in west Bohemia is the raw material of a porcelain industry, and suitable sands in north-east Bohemia have led to an important glass manufacture.

Czechoslovakia has more than a thousand mineral springs, mainly in north-west Bohemia and western Slovakia. Around them have grown spas such as Karlovy Vary, Mariánské Lâzně (Marienbad) and Luha-čovice.

As might be expected in a country as mountainous as Czechoslovakia, there is an abundance of water power. One of the major watersheds of central Europe may be traced, with the headwaters of the rivers Elbe and Oder on the northern side, and of the Morava, Vah and other tributaries of the Danube on the south. Yet the development of hydro-electricity is of very recent date, mainly since 1945. Rapid progress has been made, and already there is a generating capacity of 600,000 kW. The largest projects are on the rivers Vltava in Bohemia and Vah in Slovakia. The principal works in Bohemia are at the dams of Slapy, Lipno and Orlik. Long term plans provide for the construction of more than seventy others. On the 245 miles of the Vah, a system of sixteen power stations has been completed, and on the Orava, one of its tributaries, the biggest dam in Slovakia has been built. Notwithstanding this development of hydro-electric power, 89% of the nation's electricity is still generated by thermal plants. Together with the hydro-electric power stations, they produce 25 million kWh annually. An atomic power plant is at present under construction near Trnava in Slovakia.

REGIONAL ECONOMY

1. *Bohemia*

Prior to 1939, the young state of Czechoslovakia was concerned chiefly with light industries such as the manufacture of cotton textiles, light metal goods, pottery and glassware, most of them in Bohemia. Since 1945 the whole of Czechoslovak industry has been reorganised and nationalised on Soviet lines, concentrating on heavy iron and steel goods and textiles, and its industrial capacity has increased enormously. The change was possible because the principal raw material of the country is coking coal; this, helped by large imports of ores and pig-iron, led to smelting and heavy engineering.

Bohemia has the oldest and most highly developed economy in Czecho-slovakia, especially in the northern lower half of the plateau. The plains of the rivers Labe and Ohre are the richest agricultural part of the country, with good crops of wheat and other cereals, and sugar beet. Vegetables and market produce are grown around all the large towns, and most farmers keep dairy cattle. No part of Czechoslovakia is outstanding for dairy products: cattle and pigs are found on all farms in the lowlands. A special variety of barley for malting is grown in the Labe plain and the Pilsen basin, and hops are cultivated around Žatec in the Ohre valley, Roudnice in the Labe valley, and Úštěk in northern Bohemia. These are the basis of a well-distributed brewing industry, and light beer is the national beverage. Pilsen is the centre, and exports large quantities of lager beer. Potatoes are grown everywhere, even at high altitudes, and used for the manufacture of alcohol and spirits as well as for food. Sheep rearing, at one time very important in the Erzgebirge and Sudetes, has declined in recent years.

The Prague–Pilsen–Kladno triangle contains the greatest concentration of industry in Bohemia. In it are the three basin coalfields of Pilsen, Trutnov and Kladno. It specialises in engineering products of all kinds, including agricultural machinery, electrical apparatus, textile machinery, locomotives, bridges, cranes, motor cars, bicycles and even ships' engines. Prague (Praha) (1,003,000), the capital of Czechoslovakia, is the chief industrial city, with 11% of the country's manufactures. It is centrally situated in Bohemia, with easy communications to all parts of the plateau. Besides engineering and its functions as a capital, Prague has important food processing industries, notably the curing of ham, brewing, chocolate, printing, film and gramophone industries. Pilsen (Plzeň) (138,000), already mentioned as a brewing centre, has the country's largest engineering works, the V. I. Lenin (formerly Škoda) plant, producing turbines, machine tools, armaments and locomotives.

At the foot of the Erzgebirge, based on the lignite field there, is located half the chemical industry of Czechoslovakia. The chief chemical works are at Teplice-Šanov (52,000) and Chomutov (30,000). Teplice-Šanov is noted for glass and crystal manufacturing, Chomutov for iron and steel

[*Courtesy of the Czechoslovakian Embassy.*

Fig. 89.—Czechoslovakia: the Rosenberg pond. Scattered throughout southern Bohemia are numerous artificial lakes for fish-breeding and fish supply, well-known in central Europe as early as the Middle Ages. The largest is the Rosenberg Pond, 1208 acres, where men are shown fishing for carp, a popular Czech Christmas dish.

works. Karlovy Vary is important for porcelain, and Jablonec for costume jewellery. In the north-east, Czechoslovakia's textile region stretches along the foot of the Sudetes in Bohemia and crosses towards Brno in Moravia. The textile industry has been reorganised, thousands of small factories being merged into large, up-to-date works; it is now second only to the engineering industry in the number of people employed. The Bohemian centres are Liberec, noted for cottons, and Trutnov, noted for linen. Ústí (64,000), on the Labe where it begins its flow through the mountain rim of northern Bohemia, is a gateway town and the largest industrial city in the north. It has textile, machinery, bead and coloured glass manufacturing. It is also the centre of a tourist industry which has grown in the "Saxon Switzerland" as the picturesque mountain region of the Elbe exit from Czechoslovakia is called. Tourists and seekers after health also visit the spas of Karlovy Vary and Mariánské Lâzně in western Bohemia, and the hostels and holiday camps in the mountains.

Southern Bohemia is higher and less hospitable than the north. Much of the region is forested, and agriculture is found mainly in the river valleys, where oats and rye take the place of wheat, and flax and hemp are grown. Lumbering is an important occupation, especially in the Bohemian Forest, and the development of hydro-electric power provides work for many. The current is carried to the towns to the north. The largest town in the south is Budějovice (64,000), on the river Vltava, guarding the route through the Bohemian Forest to Linz in Austria. Around Budějovice are stands of cedar trees which, along with the graphite of the Pilsen basin, have led to the manufacture of pencils at the L. & C. Hardtmuth works. In southern Bohemia there are numerous artificial lakes, specially constructed to supply fish for food (*see* Fig. 89).

2. *Moravia*

Most of the Moravian lowlands are agricultural, producing the same crops as Bohemia. Potatoes are the chief crop in the Moravian Heights in the west, and there are vineyards and tobacco fields in the south.

In the north of the region, outside the Moravian Gate, is the Czechoslovakian portion of the Upper Silesian coalfield, for convenience included here with Moravia. Its principal city is Ostrava (235,000), which has large steel and chemical works. By far the greatest proportion of the country's blast furnaces is sited on this coalfield, and most of its pig-iron (5 million tons annually) and crude steel (7 million tons) are produced in a conurbation of over 500,000 people which includes Ostrava, Karviná and Bohumin.

The chief industrial region of Moravia proper is centred on Brno (314,000), the second city of Czechoslovakia. Situated towards the south of the lowlands in a valley which leads through the Moravian Heights to the Labe plain, and in the middle of the best sugar beet district in the country, it became an important route and market centre. It is Czechoslovakia's textile metropolis, at the southern end of a textile belt which stretches into Bohemia. It manufactures cotton and rayon but specialises in woollens. Other industries include food processing and sugar refining; engineering is rapidly overtaking textiles in importance. Olomouc (70,000), to the north, has industries similar to those of Brno but on a smaller scale. Gottwaldov has the largest boot and shoe factory in Europe. The Moravian lowlands have a large number of small but progressive towns, for they form a major commercial route from the Danubian countries and southern Europe to the Great European Plain in the north.

3. Slovakia

Prior to the Second World War, economic development in Slovakia lagged far behind that in Bohemia and Moravia. The region was regarded as a source of timber, mineral ores, cattle, and cheap labour for the western part of the country. In 1937 only 2·9% of the working population of Slovakia was engaged in industry, as compared with 10·9% in the Czech lands. In the years 1920–36 over 200,000 people emigrated from Slovakia, largely because of the deliberate closing down of factories and increasing unemployment. Since 1945, however, the position has changed. In that year Slovakia was given provisional self-government within the Czechoslovak Republic, and it became the declared policy of the country to give priority to Slovakia's economic and cultural advance so as to achieve a better balance with conditions in Bohemia and to pacify the independent and isolationist Slovaks.

Not a great deal could be done to improve the small, hilly farms among the mountains, except to send experts to advise on the better use of fertilisers and selected seeds; but in the south, on the plains taken from Hungary, co-operatives and State farms were introduced and peopled by Slovak peasants, who replaced the expelled Magyars. In industry, however, there was marked progress, with great development of hydro-electricity and the planning of two industrial regions, one in the east of Slovakia, the other along the river Danube with Bratislava as its centre.

Communications are a problem in Slovakia. Railways are the chief means of transport in Czechoslovakia, but the railway system was developed when the country formed part of the Austro-Hungarian

Empire. Consequently it was orientated on Vienna in the west and Budapest in the east: north–south connections were more important than west–east ones. When Czechoslovakia became an independent country it was necessary to make big changes in the railway network, which was reasonably adequate in Bohemia and Moravia but poor in Slovakia, where the mountain ranges presented difficulties. The Bohemian and Moravian railways, centred respectively on Prague and Brno, have been formed into a dense and extensive system, but in Slovakia there is only one main line from Bohemia to the eastern boundary, passing through the mountains via the valley of the Vah. There is as yet no good, continuous west–east railway along the plains of the south. This deficiency in rail communications is one reason for Slovakia's slow economic advance, but an ambitious programme of road construction is now doing much to help its infant industrial economy.

A string of hydro-electric power stations has been constructed along the rivers Vah and Orava. The small towns in the shadow of the High Tatra are changing their domestic craft industries to the manufacture of furniture, paper and light engineering products, in electrically-powered factories. Lumbering and allied occupations and trades are being more fully developed. More iron mines are being opened up. Košice (80,000), in the eastern and at one time most backward part of Slovakia, already had small sawmills, paper and wool textile industries. Now it has large iron and steel works in operation; when they are extended as planned, Košice will be the greatest producer of sheet steel in the country.

The capital of Slovakia is Bratislava (242,000), on the left bank of the Danube, which here passes through a few miles of Czechoslovak territory. Bratislava has long been an important river port, with sugar refineries, flour mills, oil refineries and chemical works. Now a pronounced effort is being made to extend the industrial region that grew around the port, so as to include the bank of the Danube as far as Komárno, a smaller port with a shipbuilding industry. New chemical works are being built, and a pipeline from Brody in the western Ukraine will bring Soviet oil to Bratislava and increase the refinery and chemical output of the region. Bratislava and Komárno, besides dealing with the imports and exports of Czechoslovakia downstream to Rumania, Bulgaria and the Soviet Union, serve also as transit ports for goods passing to and from southern Poland.

Most of the new developments in Slovakia, as indeed in the rest of the country, are inspired and financed by the U.S.S.R. The Soviet Union is Czechoslovakia's best customer, taking 40% of all her heavy engineering products and sending in return large quantities of foodstuffs, coal and mineral ores.

1. Describe the relief, structure and mineral resources of the Bohemian Massif. (J.M.B.)

2. Compare the mining and manufacturing industries of Bohemia with those of Silesia. (J.M.B.)

3. Discuss, with reference to specific areas, the characteristic features of agriculture in Czechoslovakia.

4. Divide Czechoslovakia into natural regions and discuss the important physical characteristics of each region. (J.M.B.)

5. Give a reasoned account of the distribution of population in Czechoslovakia. (J.M.B.)

Chapter XXI

AUSTRIA

AUSTRIA, like Switzerland, is essentially an Alpine country, but because it is drained almost entirely by the Danube and its tributaries it may also be regarded as one of the Danubian countries. It extends 360 miles from east to west and varies in width from 160 to not more than 25 miles. In shape it forms a roughly rectangular block from the Hungarian border to Salzburg, then continues westwards towards Switzerland in a narrow and irregular "tail."

PHYSICAL ASPECTS

STRUCTURAL DIVISIONS

Austria may be divided into: (1) the Alpine region, which occupies most of the country, (2) the Danube valley, including the southern tip of

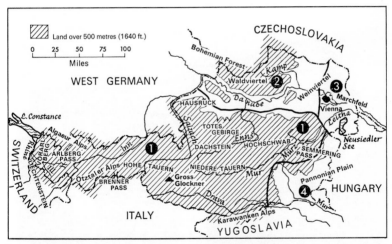

FIG. 90.—Austria: physical features and divisions. The numbers correspond with the regional divisions used in the text. The small country of Liechtenstein is at the western tip of Austria.

the Bohemian massif, (3) the Vienna basin, and (4) the Burgenland (*see* Fig. 90). The country is cut from end to end by large river valleys. The Ill, Alfenz and Bregenzer Ache in Vorarlberg are tributaries of the Rhine, and the Inn, Salzach, Mur-Mürz and Drava flow to the Danube.

359

1. *The Alpine region*

The Alps in Austria are a continuation of the eastern Alps of Switzerland, but the ranges lie more east–west, the mountain mass is wider and the height gradually decreases eastwards. The region may be sub-divided longitudinally into a belt of flysch stretching from Salzburg almost to Vienna, succeeded by a northern zone of limestone mountains bounded on the south by the valleys of the Inn, Salzach and Enns; a central series of crystalline massifs; and a second zone of limestone heights south of the river Drava.

The belt of flysch sedimentaries is narrow and hilly, especially in the Vienna Forest (Wienerwald). The northern limestone zone rarely rises to more than 6000 ft. On its northern side it is well watered, but farther south the high plateaus of Totes Gebirge, Dachstein and Hochschwab have karst characteristics, with little surface drainage. South of the

[*Courtesy of the Austrian Embassy.*

Fig. 91.—Austria: the European bridge. Opened in 1964, it is built over the Brenner Pass, which connects Austria and Italy. It forms part of the Alpen Autobahn, which traverses some of the most beautiful scenery in Europe. The roadway has a maximum height of 618 ft above the base of the piers, the highest bridge in Europe.

Hochschwab, around Eisenerz, is a mass of slates and shales which contain the chief body of iron ore in Austria.

The crystalline Alps stretch from Vorarlberg to the beginnings of the Hungarian plain. In the west, in Vorarlberg and Tyrol, the mountains are lower and pierced by wide valleys. East of Tyrol they gain in height and width, the High Tauern (Hohe Tauern) reaching 12,461 ft in Grossglockner. The High Tauern are continued by the Low Tauern (Niedere Tauern), and together they form a difficult barrier between north and south. Their inaccessibility has discouraged any extension of the tourist industry of Tyrol and Vorarlberg, where it is so successful. At the western end of the High Tauern is the Brenner Pass (4494 ft), the lowest crossing point of the crystalline mountains (see Fig. 91). The Tauern, with their snow-clad and pyramidal peaks, cirques and valley glaciers, show in the west and centre of the range all the marks of frost and ice erosion, but in the east these glaciated features disappear and the mountain tops are more rounded.

Eastwards the Alps descend to ranges of foothills which border the Hungarian or Pannonian plain. This end of the crystalline mountains is cut by the valleys of the Mur and Mürz, and to the south of the zone the river Drava widens its valley in the basin of Klagenfurt. Along the southern edge of this basin lie the Karawanken Alps, a steep-sided, snow-capped limestone range nearly 7000 ft in height. It forms the boundary between Austria and Yugoslavia, and is crossed by the Loibl Pass (4480 ft).

2. The Danube valley and south Bohemian massif

The river Danube, from its entry into western Austria to the small town of Krebs, flows in a narrow, deep valley very like the Rhine gorge in appearance but quite different in origin: it is a "corridor" between the Alpine mountains and the Hercynian massif of Bohemia, and so resembles the valley of the Rhône below Lyon. On the south of the river and north of the belt of flysch is a continuation of the Alpine foreland of West Germany, but whereas in Germany it is wide, in Austria it is merely a narrow strip of Tertiary sands and conglomerates, only 6 miles across in places. In general the foreland is hilly, especially near the German border, where it reaches a height of 2500 ft in the Hausrück.

North of the Danube is a region floored by ancient crystalline rocks, similar to those of the Bohemian massif. In the west, from the boundary roughly to Krems, they form hills up to 2300 ft high. This portion is known as the Waldviertel (forest quarter). East of Krems the ancient rocks sink below Tertiary sands and clays, which in places have a cover of loess. This area is a low, undulating plateau hardly distinguishable from the Moravian plains to the east or the Vienna basin to the south-east.

Its fertile soils have earned for it the name Weinviertel (vine-growing quarter).

The river Danube has eaten its way irregularly into the soft rocks of the foreland, so as to produce a series of relatively wide basins separated by gorge-like stretches. These narrows cause the Danube to flow swiftly, reducing its value for navigation. In spring, when melting ice floes form jams, the lowest parts of the basins near the river are often flooded. East of Krems the Danube valley widens gradually and merges into the Vienna basin.

3. *The Vienna basin*

This represents an area of sinking between the eastern ranges of the Alps and the Carpathians. The Vienna basin proper is bounded on the east by the Leithagebirge south of the Danube, and the Little Carpathians (Malé Karpaty) north of the river, but the basin is usually taken to include the lowland which extends to the Hungarian border east of these hill ranges. This eastern portion is physically part of the Little Alföld of Hungary, and includes most of the Neusiedler See.

The Vienna basin is a plain lying astride the Danube, in length nearly 60 miles from north-east to south-west, and about 20 miles wide. It is floored by Tertiary sands and clays, similar to those of the Weinviertel but with a more extensive cover of loess, especially in the eastern portion of the basin. Near the Danube are deposits of alluvium.

4. *Burgenland*

South of the Vienna basin is a region of low hills separated by wide river valleys, forming the western margins of the Hungarian plain, and covered with sedimentaries of the same age and origin. For a short time after 1918 the region was a part of Hungary, but because it contained a vast majority of German-speaking inhabitants a strip of territory about 20 miles wide was then included within Austria's boundaries.

CLIMATE AND VEGETATION

The general characteristics of the climate of the Alpine region of Austria are similar to those found in eastern Switzerland; but in the lowlands of the east of the country, conditions approximate to those of Hungary, though with a greater annual rainfall. Mean temperatures in January are everywhere below freezing point, and in July between 65° F (18·3° C) and 70° F (21·1° C). Innsbruck, nearly 2000 ft above sea level, ranges from 26° F (−3·3° C) in January to 64° F (17·8° C) in July. Vienna, 1300 ft lower but more exposed to continental influences, has a January mean of 29° F (−1·7° C), and of 67° F (19·4° C) in July. Klagen-

furt, in a valley shut off from maritime influences, ranges from 21° F
(−5·6° C) in January to 66° F (18·9° C) in July, and Graz from 26° F
(−3·3° C) to 65° F (18·3° C).

Annual precipitation, as might be expected in a country as mountainous
as Austria, varies considerably from place to place but, except in the
Vienna basin, is rarely less than 30 in. The wettest part of the country is
the High Tauern, where an annual fall of 70 in. is common, and the driest
the Vienna district, with a total of about 25 in. In the valleys of the Alps
the precipitation averages from 30 to 40 in.; Innsbruck, for instance, has
32·8 in. and Klagenfurt 38·7 in. Maximum precipitation is in the summer
half of the year, Innsbruck having 65% and Vienna 60% of their totals
from April to September inclusive.

Two-fifths of Austria is forested, mainly in the Alps and the Waldviertel. 80% of the trees are coniferous. Deciduous trees are found on
the lower slopes of the mountains, mixed with the conifers, and they
occur in extensive clumps in the Burgenland. In the Vienna basin and
the Weinviertel, the natural vegetation was deciduous trees with steppe
grasses here and there, but they have been cleared for agriculture.

HUMAN GEOGRAPHY

HISTORICAL OUTLINE

The history of Austria may be said to date from 803, when Charlemagne created the Ostmark as an eastern defence area against attack from
the plains of the lower Danube. Within a couple of centuries the country
became one of the strongest of the States which made up the Holy Roman
Empire, and its rulers were invariably chosen as Emperors. The Hapsburg
dynasty held the throne of Austria (Österreich—the East March) from
1282 to 1918, when the country was proclaimed a republic. The Holy
Roman Empire had an uneasy history. It was never very stable, and it
began to topple in the eighteenth century when Prussia, originally another
of the Marches, broke away to form the nucleus of modern Germany.

Austria, however, was building another empire. It began to expand
towards Bohemia and Polish Galicia, then to northern Italy and later, by
defeating the Turks, to the whole of the Hungarian basin and parts of the
present Yugoslavia. The Austro-Hungarian Empire remained in existence
until the end of the First World War (1918), when it completely disintegrated in defeat. Hungary became an independent state; part of
Lower Austria went to make up Czechoslovakia; half the Tyrol was given
to Italy; portions of Styria and Carinthia were allocated to Yugoslavia.
Later, because a large majority of its inhabitants were German-speaking,
the Burgenland was recovered from Hungary. The wheel of history had

made a full turn, and Austria was left with little more than the area it had as Charlemagne's Ostmark.

The country was so reduced in size and so impoverished that its survival seemed impossible. Most of the country is mountainous and so lacking in resources that its people, used to receiving their grain from Hungary, their wine and fruit from South Tyrol, their industrial requirements from Bohemia and their overseas products via the lost port of Trieste, were left virtually destitute. To make matters worse, out of a total population of about 7 million, 2 million were concentrated in Vienna, the capital, and had to be fed by the rest of the country. The consequence was a period of inflation, famine and widespread poverty, and of frantic search for ways to improve their lot. Austria was now almost entirely German in language and had definite leanings towards German culture. But incorporation with Germany, which would have solved her problems, was expressly forbidden by the Peace Treaty, and an attempted customs union with Germany was declared to be against the Geneva Protocol.

Austria was left to fight its own economic battle, but adjustments to the new circumstances were hindered by the intense regional loyalties of its people. The country is made up of the provinces of Vorarlberg, the Tyrol, Salzburg, Carinthia, Styria, Upper and Lower Austria, Burgenland and the district of Vienna; each province has its own government and capital, its own traditions and way of life. The Austrian is more attached to his province than to the country as a whole, and he shows little concern for—is often not even aware of—national problems. The demands made by Vienna and densely peopled Lower Austria on regions of scanty population and meagre resources resulted in tensions between town and country, creating yet another problem to solve.

Austria's economic recovery was slow and painful, but by 1938 there were signs of a return to stability. In that year, however, Germany, fired by territorial ambition, invaded Austria and declared its annexation (*Anschluss*). During the Second World War, eastern Austria was invaded again, this time by Soviet armies; so that when the country was liberated in 1945 by Allied forces, its condition was worse than in 1918. Many of its towns were in ruins, the countryside was devastated, and more than half its newly established industrial equipment was destroyed or pillaged either by Germany or the Soviet Union.

Austria, like Germany, was divided into four zones of occupation by the Allies, who split Vienna too into four sectors. Occupation ceased in 1955, after the Allies had done a great deal to give Austria a new start by providing capital, materials and labour for reconstruction. But ten years of occupation by foreign troops had weakened the political structure of the country, and the Iron Curtain, by shutting off the eastern frontiers, still hinders normal trade relations along the Danube or through Trieste. Progress towards complete recovery is slow, and it is difficult to foresee Austria's future as an independent state. Although new industries are being developed and the economy is gradually being stabilised, it is a poor country, too much dependent on the friendship and generosity of the countries of the west. By its position in Europe, Austria should be orientated towards the east and south-east, from which unfortunately it is shut off by ideological barriers.

POPULATION

The population of Austria totalled 7,074,000 in 1961, nearly half of whom live in Lower Austria, including Vienna. The average population density is 219 persons a square mile but the distribution is very uneven, some parts of the Alpine region being almost uninhabited whereas in Lower Austria the density amounts to over 600 persons a square mile. This province is the industrial heart of Austria. Although it is also one of the best developed agricultural regions in the country, it cannot feed its large population and has to obtain a great deal of its foodstuffs and domestic raw materials from the rest of Austria.

THE ECONOMY

AGRICULTURE AND FORESTRY

The economy of Austria is based chiefly on its forests, pastures and arable land rather than on its mineral wealth or industrial development. The country is twice as large as Switzerland and has more natural resources, yet Switzerland has a far more stable economy and better prospects than Austria. This relative underdevelopment may be attributed to Austria's unfortunate political history of the past fifty years, but it is undoubtedly due also to the outmoded traditionalism of the provinces which make up the country.

Lumbering is important throughout the Alpine region and in the Waldviertel. The timber, as in Switzerland, is used in the mountains for the construction of farm buildings and as fuel. The surplus from all lumber camps goes mainly to the furniture and paper factories in and around Vienna; a little wood-pulp is exported. The future development of the forest industries is dependent on an increase of hydro-electric power.

Austria is basically agricultural, and its main occupation is cattle rearing on the slopes of the Alps, which are cultivated for grass and hay to their furthest limits. Transhumance is practised. Cows' and sheep's milk provides cheese, but the remoteness of most mountain pastures and the poor communications prevent the dairying industry from reaching the same proportions or success as in Switzerland.

Farming in the narrower mountain valleys is concerned chiefly with the production of fodder crops, but in the wider parts of the main valleys, the Weinviertel, the Vienna basin and the Burgenland, wheat, barley, rye and maize are grown in rotation with sugar beet and potatoes. Vineyards are found throughout the provinces of Vorarlberg, south Styria, Burgenland and especially in the Weinviertel of Lower Austria. The country, however, is faced with the problem of feeding a capital which contains too great a proportion of its inhabitants, and finds the task beyond its powers, so that large quantities of foodstuffs have to be imported.

MINERALS AND POWER

Austria has considerable deposits of iron ore around Eisenerz in Styria, and there are smaller amounts worked at various sites in Upper Austria. Iron ore and salt, which is mined in the valley of the Salzach, are Austria's chief minerals. It is one of the world's chief sources of graphite, over 80,000 tons being produced annually. There are also scattered deposits of lead, zinc, antimony, tin and manganese. Most of these ores, together with gypsum and talc, are exported because of lack of fuel to smelt or process them. Increased power from water, oil and lignite has led to some growth in their use at home.

There are negligible coal resources in small fields situated between Vienna and Wiener Neustadt, but just to the west of these towns is a lignite field which produces about 6 million tons annually. In 1930 oil was discovered north-east of Vienna, and today derricks surround the villages of Zistersdorf, Gänserndorf and Dürnkrut. The oilfield is claimed, probably optimistically, to be one of the largest in Europe. Its output—at present about $2\frac{1}{2}$ million tons annually—is of the greatest importance to Austria, in view of its shortage of solid fuel. Much of the oil is surplus to the country's requirements and is exported, largely in exchange for coal.

Hydro-electric possibilities are as great as in Switzerland, but the expense checks full development. The largest power stations are at Kaprun in the High Tauern (see Fig. 93), near rapids in the Danube above Krems, and along the Kamp, a Danubian tributary which flows from the Bohemian Forest. There are small power stations on the river Mur, and among the mountains of Vorarlberg, Salzburg and the Tyrol are many others. In these provinces much of the railway system is now electrified, and current is exported, chiefly to West Germany.

REGIONAL ECONOMY

1. *The Alpine region*

The Alps are Austria's principal source of timber, dairy produce and hydro-electric power, developed or potential, but the numbers of people employed in these industries are much smaller than of those living in the towns of the valleys of the Inn, Salzach, Enns and Mur. These are centres of manufacturing or tourist industries; but it should be noted that manufacturing is as yet poorly developed in Austria, and that tourism lags behind the highly organised Swiss industry.

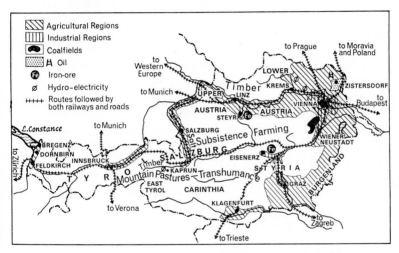

FIG. 92.—Austria: economic. Correlate this map with Fig. 90 and note the small proportion of the country with well-developed agriculture and industry.

The greatest industrial activity in the Alpine region is in Vorarlberg and around Graz. Vorarlberg, the westernmost province of Austria, is orientated towards Switzerland and has greater affinity to that country than towards the rest of Austria, from which it is shut off by mountains. There are better communications to Switzerland than to the east, where the only exits are by the Arlberg Pass (5910 ft) and by tunnel. Because of its closer connections with Switzerland, Vorarlberg asked in 1919 to become part of the Swiss Confederation, but its request was refused. In its small towns of Dornbirn (28,000), Bregenz (21,400) and Feldkirch (17,300), there are embroidery and cotton textile manufactures similar to those in the Swiss industrial region of St Gallen, of which Vorarlberg is an extension (*see* Fig. 92).

Graz (237,000), the second city of Austria, is situated on the river Mur, where its valley begins to widen. Originally it was a fortress town, guarding the southern approaches to Vienna. Today it is the centre of a small industrial region, using the iron ore brought from Eisenerz (12,400; a mining town) for its metallurgical and engineering industries. It also has flourmills, chemical works, pulp and paper mills, and is a market town, with vineyards, market gardens and rich pastures in the surrounding lowlands. Klagenfurt (69,200), in a basin formed by the river Drava (Drau), is the chief town of Austrian Carinthia. It is a railway centre and has engineering works but its main function is as a market for the wine, fruit, wheat and timber produced in that part of the river basin.

Tourism is of increasing importance to Austria. The country has attractions for visitors similar to Switzerland's, both for holidays in summer and for winter sports. As the birthplace of Haydn, Mozart, Schubert, Bruckner, Mahler, Schönberg, Wolf and the Strausses, it draws large numbers of enthusiasts to the musical festivals held in Salzburg. The chief Alpine tourist area is in the provinces of Tyrol (Tirol) and Salzburg; the centres are Innsbruck and Salzburg, the only towns apart from Vienna, Graz and Linz with more than 100,000 inhabitants. Salzburg (108,100) got its name from the neighbouring salt mines but is better known for its tourist facilities and musical festival. Innsbruck (100,700), the capital of the Tyrol, is "the bridge over the Inn." It also commands the Brenner and Arlberg passes, leading respectively to the south and east, and this position made it an important trading town. Its situation in the most picturesque part of Austria has determined its function as the hub of the tourist industry.

2. The Danube valley

Included here with the deep trench in which the river Danube flows are the Alpine foreland to the south and the edge of the Bohemian massif to the north. The foreland is like the Swiss plateau, with hills of conglomerate or molasse rising from gravel plains and cut by numerous valleys which slope to the Danube. Much of the lower surface is covered with loess. The hills are forest-clad, but overall only about a tenth of the area is forested; the remainder is arable land, producing wheat, orchard fruits and fodder crops, the latter for dairy cattle. Similar crops are grown in the basins cut by the Danube into the foreland. In these wider parts of the river trench the Danube frequently overflows its banks in spring, and the areas subject to flooding are kept as water meadows. The gorges which separate the basins, especially the Wachau, i.e. the stretch from Linz to Krems, are renowned for their scenic beauty and for the castles which overlook them. The most famous of these Schlösser is Dürnstein, where Richard the Lionheart was held prisoner.

On the northern side of the Danube, from the German border to Krems, the granite, gneiss and schists of the Bohemian massif rise first by cliffs and then by steep, rounded slopes to the edge of the Bohemian plateau, 1000 ft above the river, which is here about 2500 ft above sea level. The slopes are covered with firs and pines, except where clearings have been made on flatter shoulders. In these the farmers grow rye, oats and fodder, and rear a few cattle; they supplement their income by

[*Courtesy of the Austrian Embassy.*

Fig. 93.—Austria: hydro-electricity in the Kaprun valley. On the left is the Mooserboden reservoir and dam, and on the right the Limbergs reservoir and dam, which are at the head of the Kaprun valley. The reservoirs are enlarged corrie lakes and form part of the Glockner–Kaprun hydro-electricity development scheme. Note the arêtes and hanging valleys on the mountains.

lumbering. Hydro-electric power stations have been constructed on the river Kamp, in the east of the region. This forested area is the Waldviertel. East of Krems, a fault has let down the crystalline rocks to form the plain of Tullnerfeld, otherwise known as the Weinviertel. Soils derived from Tertiary sedimentaries and loess are very fertile and support rich cultivation, including the vines from which the region takes its name.

Linz (196,000) is the largest city in the Danube valley and the third in Austria. Situated in the widest of the basins along the river, it has become an important port. It is a bridge point, and routes along the Danube valley and between the Bohemian plateau and the Alps meet at the town. It has textile, chemical and machinery industries. During their occupation of Austria in the Second World War the Germans built blast furnaces and steel works in Linz, bringing iron ore and pig-iron from regions more vulnerable to Allied air attack. Today the smelting industry depends on domestic supplies of ore from Eisenerz and Upper Austria, and is less important than during the war; some of the steelworks have been moved to the outskirts of Vienna. On the foreland, south of Linz, is Steyr (38,300). At one time it was the centre of the armament industry of the Austro-Hungarian Empire; it still has a small share in the iron and steel and engineering industries.

The Danube valley in Austria is one of Europe's main thoroughfares, traversed by roads and railways on both sides of the river. Those north of the river hug the base of the Bohemian slopes, and in places a passage has had to be hewn in the cliff face. South of the river, both road and railway have had to make detours in the foreland to avoid the gorges.

3. The Vienna basin

The Vienna basin is agriculturally the most important part of Austria; the portion north of the Danube, the Marchfeld, is intensively cultivated for wheat, sugar beet, potatoes, market produce and fodder. The economy of the region is dominated by Vienna (1,627,500), the capital of the country, with nearly seven times the number of inhabitants of Graz, the next largest city. Vienna (Wien) began as a fortified settlement on the Wien, a little tributary of the Danube, from which it took its name. Only in recent years has the city spread to the banks of the Danube. In this area the river is liable to floods and its waters are turbid, *not* blue. Its course is braided, and one of its branches, the Donau Kanal (Danube Canal), flows through the modern part of Vienna between reinforced banks. Vienna is one of the most beautiful cities in Europe, with a great circle of boulevards and parks surrounding the older inner city, replacing the walls and ramparts of the eighteenth century.

As one of the outposts of the Holy Roman Empire, the city had been important since the Middle Ages but it was not until the eighteenth century, when the Hapsburgs drove the Turks out of Hungary and began to extend their rule eastwards, that it became the permanent capital of what was to become the Austro-Hungarian Empire—which had eight times the area and seven times the population of the present Austria. Vienna grew rapidly in size, gathering people from all parts of the Empire, and by 1910 it had a population of over 2 million. It was not only the administrative and commercial centre, but had become the focus of an industrial region, one of the most important in south-east Europe.

The breakdown of the Empire in the world war of 1914–18 left the city in a parlous state, stripped of its international importance, the overgrown capital of a minor country. Its magnificent palaces and Government buildings were too big for the work done in them, the industries could not find markets for their products in the new, smaller Austria, and the population outside the capital could not grow sufficient food for the people of the city. Shortages of foodstuffs, raw materials and capital led to inflation and famine, but the subsequent period of adjustment to the new circumstances had hardly begun when the Second World War broke out in 1939. After fierce fighting, during which many of its great buildings and industrial plants were destroyed, the city was occupied by Allied troops, who remained in possession for ten years. Its population had fallen by 1951 to 1,738,000.

Today, the problem of a too-large Vienna remains acute, though the experience of the years between the two world wars has helped the city to recover more rapidly than was expected. The population has further decreased to 1,627,500 (1961) and the numbers in the rest of the country increased, a welcome readjustment. Its industries—engineering, machinery, textiles, electrical equipment of all kinds, paper, furniture—have been mainly concerned since the war in the reconstruction and development of Austria itself, but its luxury trades—fashions, musical instruments, including pianos, porcelain and glassware, etc.—together with its importance as a cultural and musical centre, have helped Vienna to function better today than at any time since 1918. But there is still a long way to go.

One of Vienna's greatest assets as capital of a large empire was its position at "the crossroads of Europe." It is situated where Alpine ranges and Hercynian blocks approach each other, and where both abut on the Pannonian plain; it commands the passage west along the Danube narrows and looks east to the lowlands of Hungary; it lies on an easy north–south route from the plains of northern Europe to the Adriatic Sea; so that whoever holds Vienna holds the link between eastern and western Europe. It is an obvious position for a great city, and such it became as the capital of the Empire, the centre of control for territory which encompassed it for hundreds of miles in every direction. Today, its situation is still as important, but its function as capital of Austria is weakened by the fact that it lies too near the eastern frontier, too adjacent to the line of demarcation between the opposing ideologies of eastern and western Europe.

Wiener Neustadt, in the south-west of the Vienna basin, lies within Vienna's sphere of influence and is connected to it by canal. It is the

N

chief town of the coal and lignite fields, and has engineering works and thermal-electric power stations.

4. *The Burgenland*

Although this region south of the Vienna basin is often called lowland, it is only relatively so, for it is made up of the low ranges and wide valleys of the Alpine foothills. Its rolling surface has fertile soils, sometimes of loess, and its economy is entirely rural, with no large towns. Wheat, barley, maize, sugar beet and fruit are the main crops, and there are vine-yards on the low slopes. Industry in the modern sense is only just be-ginning to penetrate the region, but there are small, old-established manu-factures of textiles, furniture and footwear scattered through the Burgen-land, and breweries and sugar refineries send their products to Vienna.

LIECHTENSTEIN

Liechtenstein (64 square miles) is the smallest independent state in Europe, except for the Vatican state, San Marino and Monaco. It lies between Austria and Switzerland, extending for a distance of about 12 miles between south-west Vorarlberg and the river Rhine and controlling the valleys of western Switzerland and of the upper Rhine. Within its boundaries is an easy crossing point of that river.

In the south-east the surface is mountainous, rising to over 8000 ft in the Rothe Wand, on whose summit the frontiers of Austria, Liechtenstein and Switzerland meet. The rest of the country forms part of the Rhine river plain, and has the same economy as the neighbouring Vorarlberg, with mixed farming and vineyards. The chief industry in the small towns is cotton manufacturing, an overspill from St Gallen in Switzer-land. There is a growing tourist trade, which has been encouraged by Switzerland, which also controls the transport system and most of Liechtenstein's commercial activities. The capital, Schaan-Vadus, is connected by road and rail bridges to Buchs, in Switzerland.

The lands which comprise Liechtenstein were bought by the Liechten-steins, a prominent Austrian family, early in the eighteenth century and in 1719 were raised to the status of principality by the Holy Roman Emperor. It formed part successively of the Holy Roman Empire (till 1806) and of the German Confederation (1815–66), and has been sovereign in 1806–15 and since 1866, except for a short period during Germany's occupation of Austria during the Second World War.

The total population of Liechtenstein is 17,000 and its chief town, Vadus, little more than a village. The people are German-speaking, although many of the place-names, including that of Schaan-Vadus, are Romansch, which was the original language.

STUDY QUESTIONS

1. Divide Austria into natural regions and discuss the importance of *one* of your divisions in the economic life of the country.

2. "Vienna stands at the crossroads of Europe." Explain this statement, with special reference to the city's post-war problems.

3. Write a comparative study of the Alps in the geography of Austria and Switzerland.

Chapter XXII

POLAND

POLAND is a country which demonstrates the instability of boundaries that are not clearly delineated by physical features. Poland is a buffer country, sandwiched between Germany and Russia. Consequently it has

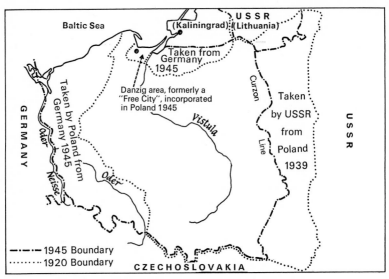

FIG. 94.—Poland: boundaries. Showing the westward march of Poland since its reconstitution as a sovereign state in 1919.

been invaded and occupied on many occasions. Its present boundaries were fixed by the allied powers after the Second World War as a temporary and provisional arrangement; but it is tacitly agreed today that they are permanent. The eastern frontier is the Curzon Line, suggested by Lord Curzon as the limit of the area inhabited mainly by Poles; on the eastern side, the southern half of East Prussia is also administered by Poland. The western frontier is the Oder–Neisse line, except in the north, where East Pomerania, which includes Stettin (Szczecin), was given to Poland. The new western boundary means that the whole of Silesia, with the exception of a small portion of the Upper Silesian coalfield in Czechoslovakia, is now Polish. In the north the Baltic coast is the boundary, and in the south the frontier traverses a mountainous course through the Sudetes and the Carpathians.

PHYSICAL ASPECTS

STRUCTURAL DIVISIONS

In its structure Poland bears a distinct resemblance to West Germany, in that a northern glaciated lowland is followed southwards by fragments of the worn-down Hercynian system and Alpine ranges. The Alpine foreland, however, so prominent in the south of West Germany, is

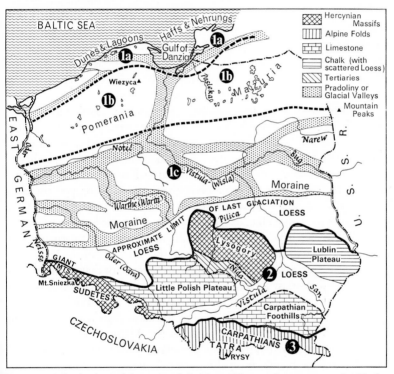

FIG. 95.—Poland: physical features and divisions. The numbers correspond with the regional divisions used in the text.

reduced to a minimum in Poland. The country may be divided into: (1) the Germano-Polish plain, with three distinct regions, (2) the Sudetes and southern plateaus, and (3) the western Carpathians (*see* Fig. 95).

1. *The Germano-Polish plain*

(a) *The coastal plain.* From the mouth of the Oder (Odra) to the Gulf of Danzig, Poland has a straight, unbroken shoreline. Strong sea currents, aided by the prevailing westerlies, have caused longshore drifting of sand from west to east and have built spits across indentations in the coast, straightening it and entrapping lagoons behind a barrier of sand dunes. Eastwards from the Gulf of Danzig, the larger openings in the coast are not completely enclosed, but long spits (nehrungs) shut in lagoons (haffs) which are open to the sea. Wind and waves are gradually adding to the dunes, the sands of which are spreading inland.

(b) *The Baltic Heights and lake zone.* Behind the belt of sand are low, narrow plains of ground moraine, and these rise southwards to drumlins and morainic ridges, in places over 900 ft high. Occasionally there are higher clay-covered masses of boulders left by the Ice Age glaciers; the most elevated is Wiezyca (1075 ft). The morainic ridges are known as the Baltic Heights or the Baltic lake zone. The latter name comes from the large number of lakes, nearly 9000, trapped in clay-lined hollows. The lakes are in two distinct aggregations, the Pomeranian lakes west of the Vistula and the Mazurian lakes east of the river.

(c) *The outwash plains and pradoliny.* South of the Baltic Heights is a zone of glacial outwash which has formed extensive plains. Nearer the Heights, the soils are coarse gravels and sands but farther south, by a process of sorting, they are composed of finer sediments, with patches of loess. The monotony of the plains is broken by low hills, where moraines of an earlier glacial phase have been greatly eroded—or possibly they represent the slow retreat of a tongue of penetration by glaciers of the same age as the Baltic Heights. The plain is cut by wide east–west valleys (*pradoliny*) which have determined the drainage pattern of the rivers. The most distinctive of the pradoliny may be traced from east to west, commencing with the valley of the Bug, continuing with that of the Vistula (Wisla) from Warsaw to Bydgoszcz, and then via the Noteć and Warthe (Warta) valleys, to join an East German urstromtal west of the river Oder.

The chief rivers of the plain are the Vistula and its tributaries in the centre and east, and the Oder in the west. Many of the rivers bend abruptly where they pass from one pradoliny to the next. The Oder and its tributary, the Neisse, form the western boundary of Poland.

2. *The Sudetes and southern plateaus*

To the south of the outwash plains, Poland has a foundation of rocks of Hercynian age, that is, of Carboniferous and Permian strata, which are overlain in much of the region by Triassic sandstones and Jurassic limestones.

Along the south-western margin of this zone, Hercynian rocks are thrown in a much-faulted series of small horsts to form the Sudetes, broken ranges of which the highest are the Giant mountains (Ger.

Riesengebirge; Pol. Karkonosze), in which Mount Sniezka rises to 5210 ft. Between the Silurian, Carboniferous and Permian rocks of the horsts are basins of Triassic and Tertiary sandstones, marls and clays. The small Waldenburg (Wałbrzych) coalfield is preserved in one of the basins; farther south, east of the upper Oder, which drains this western region, is the extensive Upper Silesian coalfield. Most of the region away from the Sudetes is undulating lowland, and has a surface cover of loess.

North and east of the valley of the upper Oder, a number of low, Jurassic limestone scarps form the edges of the Little Polish Plateau, a rolling, loess-covered platform, underlain by strata of Hercynian age. The soils which have developed on the limestone outcrops are known in Poland as *rendzina*; they are fertile, but less so than loess. The Little Polish Plateau extends eastwards to the upper Vistula, and is split from north to south by the river Nida valley, a synclinal depression filled in its upper reaches by a variety of fertile Tertiary and infertile glacial soils, and in the south by loess and rendzina. In the north-east of the Little Polish Plateau, Palaeozoic sandstones and quartzites come to the surface in the Lysogóry, a hill mass 2000 ft high, which rises like an island of ancient rocks above the Triassic strata surrounding it.

East of the Little Polish Plateau, and separated from it by the Vistula valley, is the East Polish Plateau or Lublin tableland, a chalk platform averaging 750 ft in height, which continues into the Ukraine. Between the limestone and chalk plateaus and the Carpathians is a triangular depression drained by the upper Vistula and San. This lowland is the nearest approach in Poland to an Alpine foreland; but the infertile gravels, so conspicuous in the south of West Germany, are here far less in amount and are covered with loess, which is found also in patches on the chalk plateau.

3. *The western Carpathians*

Separated from the eastern end of the Sudetes by a gap which forms the northern exit from the Moravian Gate are the young folded ranges of the western Carpathian mountains. The northernmost folds consist of rounded hills and mountains, the Beskids, and are composed largely of Mesozoic sandstones. The Beskids are divided into the Silesian Beskids, the High Beskids, the Low Beskids, and the Bieszczady. They average less than 3500 ft in height.

The central zone of the western Carpathians, the Tatra, is of more resistant crystalline and metamorphic rocks than the Beskids, and is higher and more rugged. Only the northern slopes of the Tatra are in Poland, most of the range—including its highest peak, Mount Gerlach (8711 ft)—being in Czechoslovakia. The highest mountain in Poland is

FIG. 96.—Poland: Zakopane. A general view of Zakopane, a holiday resort in
the Polish Tatra mountains. Note the scattered character of the small town,
the fir forests on the near slopes, the farming—rye, sheep, cattle—in the
clearings and the snow-clad range in the background.

Rysy (8200 ft), a few miles to the north-west of Gerlach. The Tatra were
affected by the glaciers of the Ice Age and have all the characteristics of
mountain glaciation, with pyramidal peaks, arêtes, cirques, hanging
valleys and ribbon lakes, very reminiscent of the western Alps but on a
smaller scale.

CLIMATE AND VEGETATION

The northern position of Poland and its distance from the Atlantic
Ocean are factors in making its climate the most continental in peninsular
Europe. The absence of high land over most of the country has resulted
in a great degree of uniformity of temperature and rainfall distribution
over most of its surface. Average temperatures in January range from
25° F (−4° C) to 30° F (−1° C), and in July from 63° F (17° C) to 67° F
(19·4° C), the lowest temperatures in winter and the highest in summer
being found towards the south-east. Szczecin (Stettin), for example, has
mean temperatures in January and July of 30·7° F (−1° C) and 65° F
(18·3° C), Poznan (Posen) 29·3° F (−1·5° C) and 65·5° F (18·6° C), and

Warsaw (Warszawa) 26° F (−3·3° C) and 66° F (18·9° C). The lowest temperatures are in the Tatra mountains, but even there, except on the snow-clad peaks, they are not more than 5° F (2·6° C) less than on the plains.

Annual precipitation away from the mountains in the south is between 20 and 24 in., with a pronounced maximum in summer, and falling as snow in winter. Stettin has 21·5 in., Wrocław (Breslau) 22·9 in., Poznan 20 in. and Warsaw 23 in.; Kraków, near the Carpathians, receives 25·2 in. The wettest region is in the Tatra, where there is an average annual precipitation of 60 in.

The natural vegetation of the mountainous south and of most of the north of Poland is coniferous forest. Today, 24·8% of the country is still forested, with 75% pine, 10% spruce and 3% fir. Of the remaining 12% deciduous trees, oak and ash are the most important. The largest forests are in the western Carpathians. Other extensive tree-clad areas are the Lysogóry, the Lublin tableland, the middle Oder basin, the Noteć basin in the north-west of the Polish part of the Germano-Polish plain, around Białystok in the east of the plain, and throughout the Baltic Heights.

Southwards in the Germano-Polish plain the forests were mixed conifers and deciduous trees, thinning out to give place in the valleys and basins between the southern plateaus to grasses of a steppe variety. Most of these grasslands were in loess-covered areas, and, together with land cleared of forest in the outwash plains and on the plateaus, have been ploughed for agriculture. Arable land now constitutes 51·2% of Poland's surface, and natural grasses only 5·7%.

Swamps occur in some of the pradoliny and around the lakes of the Baltic Heights; the sand-dune belt near the coast, and the higher parts of the western Carpathians have little or no vegetation. So-called waste land makes up nearly a tenth of the area of Poland.

HUMAN GEOGRAPHY

HISTORICAL OUTLINE

Poland is an outstanding example of a country whose physical boundaries are so weak that stronger states can easily overrun them. The plain of Poland presents few problems to movements of migrating or invading peoples from either the Russian or the German side, and on several occasions in history the country has ceased to exist as a separate state.

Poland emerged as an independent country early in the Middle Ages. Its territory lay mainly to the west of the river Vistula, and extended towards the lower Oder. In the eastward Germanic migrations of the fifteenth century the Poles were driven from much of their western lands, but in turn moved into western Russia. During the sixteenth and early seventeenth centuries, Poland reached its zenith of power. It merged with Lithuania, and together they pushed their frontiers south-eastwards beyond the river Dnieper, making Warsaw their joint capital.

In the wars of the seventeenth century, the allied Polish and Lithuanian armies were defeated by the Russians, and Poland was pushed back to the west of the Pripet marshes. In the following century, Poland and Lithuania disappeared as separate states, their lands being partitioned between Germany, Austria and Russia. Poland was independent again for a short time during the Napoleonic wars, but with the downfall of France was partitioned once more. The country was reconstituted as a sovereign state in 1918; Lithuania, which was then in Russian hands, was also made independent.

The boundaries of Poland determined by the Allies proved unsatis-factory to Poles, Germans, Lithuanians and Russians alike. Ultimately they became one of the causes of the Second World War. On the west, the frontier enclosed territory which had been developed by the Germans, although many Poles lived there. In the north, German-owned East Prussia was separated from the "Fatherland" by a strip of country, the Polish "corridor," which ran to the Baltic and gave Poland a passage to the sea. Danzig, the port at the mouth of the Vistula, was denied to the Poles and made a Free City, administered by the League of Nations and available to both Poles and Germans. German merchants had been largely re-sponsible for the growth of Danzig, and continued to function there. The Poles refused to use the port and built Gdynia, nearer the sea, as their Baltic outlet. In 1920, Poland was successful in a campaign against Russia, which was weakened at the time by revolution. Poland occupied considerable Russian territory in the Pripet marshes area and claimed in addition the district of Vilna, in Lithuania.

All these lands were lost in the first campaign of the Second World War. In 1939 the Germans marched into the much-disputed Polish corridor, overran western Poland and captured Warsaw. Within a few months Russia invaded Poland from the east and Vilna was restored to Lithuania. Once again Poland ceased to exist as a separate country. On the cessation of hostilities in 1945, it was re-established, but with boundaries changed once more. The Russians retained most of the land they occupied in east Poland and the Curzon Line became the frontier (*see* Fig. 94). To compensate for the lost territory, Poland was given all the German lands east of the Oder–Neisse line, together with the district around the port of Stettin, which was renamed Szczecin. The southern half of East Prussia became Polish, and Danzig (Gdansk) a Polish port.

In fifty years Poland's boundaries had shifted three times, presenting enormous problems of organisation and economic reconstruction. In its latest position the country has better prospects than before, for the lands taken from Germany are richer than those lost to the Soviet Union. Moreover most of the people of German stock were expelled and replaced by Poles evacuated from the Soviet-expropriated lands in the east; so that Poland today has a more homogeneous population than for centuries past. It must be remembered, however, that in this shift of population the country has lost much of the technical skill and industrial competence by which the Germans had built up the economy of their eastern lands. Only slowly is Poland adjusting itself to its new circumstances and to the change of orientation from Berlin and Vienna to Moscow, for the country is now dominated by the U.S.S.R.

POPULATION

Poland has a total population of 30,483,000, with an average density of 252 persons a square mile. Over much of the Germano-Polish plain the density approaches the national average, but distribution is scanty in the Baltic Heights and the coastal plain. The district of Koszalin, for instance, which covers this region west of the Vistula, has only 93 people per square mile. The highest density is in the district of Katowice, on the Upper Silesian coalfield, where it is 844 persons per square mile. A "district" in Poland is an administrative division of the country; the Katowice "district" covers the whole of the Upper Silesian industrial region. There are other concentrations of population around Warsaw, Łódź, Poznan, Gdansk, and Szczecin, and all of them are increasing with the growth of industry in Poland.

This industrial development is altering the ratio of urban to rural population. In 1949, the earliest date for which figures within the present boundaries of the country are available, 36·2% of Poland's people lived in towns, whereas today the urban percentage has risen to 49, a striking increase. To quote Witold Lipski, a Polish economist, "an agricultural-industrial country is rapidly becoming an industrial-agricultural country."

THE ECONOMY

AGRICULTURE

Until 1938 Poland was almost completely agricultural, with three-quarters of its workers on the land and only one-tenth in industry. With the acquisition in 1945 of the German portion of the Upper Silesian coalfield and its industries, and with the introduction of land reforms and

State ownership of industry and natural resources, there was a change in the country's economic structure. Industry now plays a more important part. Nevertheless, Poland is still primarily an agricultural nation, but the standard of farming is relatively low. The most efficient farms are in the region previously held by Germany, that is, west of a line

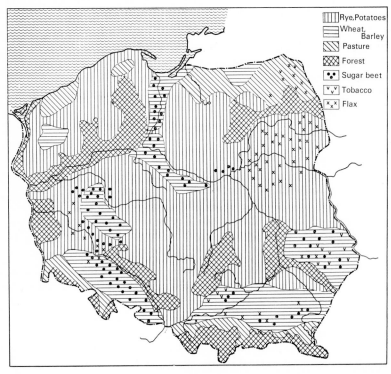

FIG. 97.—Poland: agriculture. The predominance of rye is noteworthy, although the area under wheat is increasing. Note the association of sugar beet with wheat, and the concentration of flax cultivation in the north-east. Poland has over 9 million cattle, 14 million pigs and 3½ million sheep; the country exports sugar, meat, eggs, butter, poultry and potatoes.

drawn roughly from Gdansk to Opole; the standard of farming decreases eastwards and south-eastwards towards the Soviet border.

As already noted, 51·2% of Poland is arable. More than three-fifths of this area is taken up by rye, oats, wheat, barley and maize, in that order of importance. Rye is grown everywhere except in the lower Vistula plains and at the foot of the southern mountains. It occupies one-third of the area devoted to cereals: the annual crop is nearly 9 million tons. Wheat is the food grain next in importance, totalling nearly 3 million tons a year. Over 3 million tons of oats are produced for fodder. Barley, mainly for the brewing industry, amounts to $1\frac{1}{2}$ million tons annually. Maize occupies only small areas in the San–Vistula lowlands.

Second in terms of area occupied are potatoes, sugar beet, flax, hemp, oilseeds, tobacco and hops. Potatoes are a main crop in Poland, with an average annual production of 45 million tons on nearly one-fifth of the arable area. Poland is third in the world for potato cultivation. Potatoes are used for human food, animal fodder and industrial purposes; only a small proportion is exported. Sugar beet (7·6 million tons yearly) is important in the Western Territories, especially Silesia, and in the south it is grown in rotation with wheat on the loess lands. Flax is produced extensively in the north-east quarter of Poland, and tobacco in the San–Vistula depression and on the Lublin tableland. Hemp, hops and rape seed (for oil) are crops of the warmer and more fertile south.

Stock raising is of increasing importance in Poland's economy. The country has over 9 million cattle, more than half for dairy purposes, and nearly 14 million pigs, mainly in the river valleys and the pradoliny. Sheep, reared principally in the Baltic Heights and the southern mountains, amount to $3\frac{1}{2}$ millions. There are nearly twice as many sheep as in pre-1938 Poland. Poultry are found everywhere, and Poland is one of Europe's chief exporters of eggs.

Polish agricultural holdings are divided into State farms, co-operatives and peasant farms. The Poles are firmly opposed to "collectives," such as are found in East Germany and other Sovietised lands. In this respect, the experience of the old German province of East Prussia is noteworthy. The south of the province was given to Poland, which expelled the Germans and peopled its farms with Poles displaced from White Russia and the Ukraine. Many of the farms were amalgamated into collectives, but resistance was so great that in 1956 they had to be broken up again and restored to peasant owners.

State farms occupy 11·5% and co-operatives 1·2% of all agricultural land. State farms are found mainly in the Western Territories, where they occupy a quarter of the area. Co-operatives are best developed in regions with the highest level of farming, that is, in the provinces of Poznan and Bydgoszcz. State farms are the largest in the country, but even so they rarely exceed 250 acres. Their function is to try new methods, new mechanical aids, new fertilisers, and to develop improved seeds and livestock. In all these they are having great success, their agricultural output increasing at twice the rate of that of peasant holdings.

The co-operatives are organised like those in western European countries, with one important exception. The units which make up the co-operatives are in private ownership, as elsewhere, but the methods and control of co-operation are organised and directed by Government officials and not by the farmers themselves. The State farms and co-operatives are known in Polish economic parlance as the "socialised" sector of its agriculture.

The rest of the farms, roughly 87% of the arable land, are owned by individual peasant farmers, and at present 63% of them are less than 12·5 acres. In total they account for the largest proportion of the nation's agricultural output, but the small size of each farm, and the fragmented character of some of them, have made the adoption of mechanised methods and the use of costly fertilisers and seeds uneconomic, in spite of Government loans and scientific advice. The Government is combating this backwardness by encouraging the formation of agrarian circles in villages. They are given tractors, reaper-mowers, sheaf-binders, power threshing machines, potato diggers and the like, which the farmers may borrow at very low cost. It is hoped that this will eventually lead to co-operation. More and more villages are being connected to the electric grid; repair shops are being built; irrigation and drainage schemes are being developed; and fertilisers and pesticides are made available. This last will require the building of new chemical factories and the extension of those already in existence. A big nitrogenous fertiliser plant is planned at Puławy which will operate on natural gas brought from the Soviet Union by a pipeline now under construction, and the chemical factories at Tarnow, Kędzierzyn and Tarnobrzeg are being extended.

It should be noted, however, that neither the soil nor the climate of Poland is especially suitable to any phenomenal increase in agricultural yields. Podsols form 67% of the soils, and black earth (chernozem) a mere 1·7%; some areas of poor or medium quality soils need improvement, calling for large investment outlays on drainage, irrigation and natural or mineral fertilisers. Summer temperatures are no higher on the average than those of Britain, but the vegetative period is shorter than in western Europe, and this hampers or even prevents the cultivation of certain crops. Poor soils and an unfavourable climate explain the predominance of rye in the farming economy, the relatively small area given to wheat, the infinitesimal amount of maize and the almost complete absence of vineyards.

MINERALS AND POWER

Most of Poland's mineral deposits are in the south, in Upper Silesia, the Sudetes, the Little Poland Plateau and the sub-Carpathian lowlands. The chief mineral is coal, found in two basins: a small one in the Wałbrzych district of Lower Silesia and a much larger one in Upper Silesia. Coal has also been discovered in the Bug river valley around

Lublin but is not yet exploited. There are rich seams of brown coal or lignite in west Poland, yielding over 10 million tons annually. The chief mines, which are open-cast, are around Turoszow and Konin. The lignite is used mainly on the spot in thermal-electric power stations, which supply current to a large part of central Poland. Mineral oil is

FIG. 98.—Poland: minerals. With the exception of the coal deposits shown inside the dotted rectangle, the coalfields of Poland produce lignite or brown coal. The dotted rectangle encloses the industrial region of Upper Silesia, which is shown on a larger scale in Fig. 99.

extracted in the sub-Carpathian region around Krosno and Jasło, but Poland's petroleum deposits are small. The annual output at present is only 200,000 gallons, about one-sixth of the country's requirements. The deficiency is supplied by the Soviet Union.

First place among other mineral resources is taken by iron ore, but Poland has only low-grade ores (35% iron content) and not enough of them. They occur near Częstochowa and Wieluń, in the area around

Kielce and Radom, and in the Sudetes. Lead and zinc are mined near Bytom, Tarnowskie Góry, Olkusz and Bolesławiec, in sufficient quantities to provide for domestic uses and allow about 98,000 tons to be exported. Copper is found in Lower Silesia and the Łysogóry. Further newly discovered deposits in the former area promise to make its exploitation more important than that of zinc, over 1½ million tons of ore being extracted in 1963. Other mineral ores occurring in small quantities in the south include nickel, manganese and magnesium.

The chief non-metallic minerals are sulphur and salt, both of which have given rise to chemical industries. Very rich sulphur deposits were found near Solec and Tarnobrzeg as recently as 1961. Extraction commenced in 1962 and amounted to 132,000 tons. It is estimated that by 1965 the output of raw sulphur will be 2,400,000 tons, yielding 400,000 tons of pure sulphur. This would make Poland one of the world's foremost producers. Large deposits of rock salt occur at Wieliczka and Bochnia, which are east of Kraków, and at Ciechocinek and Inowrocław, south-east of Bydgoszcz. In all these areas, and at other places in the sub-Carpathian region, there are brine springs.

Poland depends for its power more on thermal-electric than on hydro-electric stations, yet there are over 100 hydro-electric power plants in the country. The great majority are along the Sudetes and the western Carpathians; others are in the upper valleys of the rivers flowing from the Little Polish Plateau.

REGIONAL ECONOMY

1. *The Germano-Polish plain*

(a) *The coastal plain and* (b) *the Baltic Heights.* The Baltic morainic zone is one of poor farming, except in the valley of the Vistula (which cuts through it), where wheat is grown with some success. The sandy belt near the coast is planted with binding grasses, such as marram, to prevent the movement of the sand dunes. Among the dunes the chief occupation is sheep rearing; rye, potatoes and vegetables are subsistence crops. Elsewhere on the coastal plain, heavy clay soils support similar crops, with cattle rearing near the Vistula. East of the Vistula, flax cultivation is important, and oats and fodder crops are fed to cattle, which are reared mainly for beef. The Baltic Heights have extensive forests of pine and, to a lesser degree, spruce and fir. Lumbering supplies timber to the towns of the Germano-Polish plain to the south; some is floated down the Vistula to Gdansk. Geese are an important product of the lakes regions.

Except around the mouths of the rivers Oder and Vistula, the region is the most sparsely peopled in Poland. The straight, unbroken coast has a few fishing villages. The largest is Kołobrzeg (Kolberg), connected by rail to the rich farming region of Bydgoszcz (Bromberg) and Poznan, and dealing with a minor share of their imports and exports. At the mouth of the Oder is Stettin (Szczecin) (269,000). For centuries it was a German port, the Baltic outlet for Berlin, but in 1945 it was given to Poland to serve its Western Territories (the name given by the Poles to the area taken from Germany). The boundary line between the two countries is the river Oder as far as Stettin, but just above that city it veers to the west so as to include both sides of the river mouth in Poland. While in German hands the port had a large shipbuilding industry, iron smelting and steelworks, timber, chemical and food industries. All these have continued, but on a much smaller scale. Stettin should have a rich future, for it is one of the main ports for the productive farmlands of Lower Silesia and the Upper Silesian industrial region.

In the Gulf of Danzig, west of the mouth of the Vistula, is the conurbation of Gdynia–Sopot–Gdansk. Gdansk (286,500) is Poland's chief port, well situated to serve the whole of the Vistula basin, that is, most of the country. Its industries are much the same as Stettin's, but it has larger shipyards and electrical engineering works and is the chief timber port, with pulp and paper mills. The port of Gdynia, a few miles nearer the open sea, was established by the Poles in 1921 to avoid the use of Gdansk, which was then a Free City under its old name of Danzig, and whose merchants and manufacturers were chiefly German. Gydnia was approaching Gdansk in importance and volume of shipping, if not in size, when Poland was given possession of the older port in 1945. To avoid duplication of function, many of Gdynia's industrial activities were then transferred to Gdansk and it became a kind of outport. Together with the residential and holiday town of Sopot, it now forms part of the growing conurbation of Gdansk.

(c) *The outwash plains.* The region of undulating outwash plains is predominantly agricultural, with at least four-fifths of its area growing rye and potatoes as the chief crops. In the Western Territories and in the provinces west of the Vistula are the majority of Poland's State farms and co-operatives. These areas have the best soils, although in general—with the exception of a few patches of loess in the west and of alluvium in the valleys of the Oder and Vistula—the podsols of the plains are not very productive, and need large quantities of fertilisers. Over most of the outwash plains the farms are small and owned by peasants. In the valley of the Warta, with Poznan as the market, and along the Vistula from Warsaw to Bydgoszcz, wheat is the outstanding crop, with sugar beet grown in rotation. Wheat, barley, sugar beet and flax are cultivated also in the south-west of the plains and, in the east, the province of Białystok is the chief flax region.

Most of the larger towns of Poland are in the plains; but the country has relatively few. In the whole of Poland, including the industrial region in the south, there are not more than nine towns with over 200,000 inhabitants, and only another thirteen with more than 100,000. Those in the plains grew originally as markets at the crossing points of rivers, then developed into regional centres, with flour mills, breweries, textile manufacture, and engineering. Most are in the western half of the plains, where, in the valleys of the Noteć, Warta and Oder, there are large deposits of brown coal, the raw material of the thermal-electric stations scattered throughout the region.

Easily the largest city in Poland is Warsaw (Warszawa) (1,136,000) the capital. It is situated above flood level on the left bank of the Vistula, where an absence of marshes facilitated bridging. It is centrally placed in Poland, and the road and railway systems are focused on it. Before 1938, Warsaw had a population of 1,300,000; in the following year it was partially destroyed by the invading Germans. The destruction was completed in 1945, when they in turn were driven out by the advancing Soviet forces, and the population fell to 479,000. With peace the city is recovering its former eminence as an administrative and commercial centre, and has all the industries associated with a modern capital. In addition, there are flour mills, sugar refineries, breweries, distilleries, vegetable canneries and important engineering, chemical and motor car industries.

Łódź (708,400), the second city of Poland, is its textile centre, manufacturing cotton, wool and rayon. With Warsaw, it leads in electrical engineering. Cottons are by far the most important textile product of Poland, and large quantities are exported. Łódź is the only city of the plains not on a river. Białystok, in the east of the Germano-Polish plain, is the centre of the linen manufacture. Poznan (Posen) (407,800), on the river Warta, was developed by the Germans before the First World War and became Poland's largest user of timber in its paper, cellulose and furniture factories. It is also the centre of the brewing and distilling industry, as well as having pottery and glass works. Wrocław (Breslau) (429,200) was the largest city lost by Germany to Poland, having 630,000 inhabitants in 1939. When the Germans were expelled, its population fell in 1946 to 171,000. As the hub of Silesia, and with the links that are being made with the industrial region to the south, it has grown again rapidly—to 341,000 in 1950, 396,000 in 1957 and 429,000 in 1963. Wrocław is a regional centre of trade and industry, and a market for timber and furs. With coal and steel from the Wałbrzych coalfield in the Sudetes, it has developed engineering and chemical industries.

Bydgoszcz (231,500) and Toruń (104,800) are situated at the northern edge of the plain. They are timber ports which collect the logs sent down by river and canal from the forests of the Baltic Heights. It should be noted that although Poland has within its boundaries two large navigable river systems—the Vistula and most of the Oder—and although they are interconnected along the pradoliny, river traffic is relatively small. Much of it consists of timber rafts, some of which are floated to the northern timber towns from as far inland as Kraków.

2. The Sudetes and southern plateaus

The mountains of the Sudetes have lumbering and dairying industries. They also provide tourist facilities and hydro-electric power. Otherwise they enter little into the economy of southern Poland. The plateaus which flank them and extend eastwards across Poland, however, are the industrial heart of the country, and include the richest farmlands too.

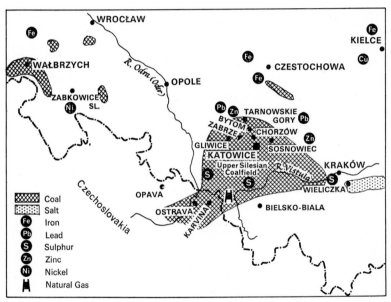

FIG. 99.—Poland: The industrial south. Note the mineral deposits shown on this map and omitted from Fig. 98.

Loess covers more than half the area, but has developed into black earth only in the east. Nevertheless it is everywhere fertile enough for southern Poland to be the most important wheat, sugar beet and tobacco region in the country. The higher parts of the Little Polish Plateau and Lublin tableland are forested, and the lumbering industry sends timber rafts to the north, via the Vistula and its tributaries, which drain most of the plateaus. Sheep are reared on the limestone areas and in the Sudetes; Bielsko-Biala, Bielawa, Prudnik and Kraków (all in or near the Upper Silesian coalfield) have wool and cotton textile industries.

Southern Poland possesses most of the deposits of useful minerals in the country (*see* Fig. 99), the chief being coal, iron, copper, zinc, salt, petroleum and natural gas. The coal is contained in a small field around Wałbrzych and in a much more extensive one in Upper Silesia. With an annual output of about 120 million tons of coal, the Upper Silesian coalfield (Fig. 100) is one of the largest in Europe. The main producing area is situated some miles north of the eastern end of the Beskids; part of the coalfield extends across the frontier into Czechoslovakia. Nearby resources of zinc, lead and iron ore contributed to the development of an important industrial district in the nineteenth century, when the coalfield lay in territory ruled by Austria. The coalfield area was later divided between Austria and Germany, then after 1918 between Germany, Poland and Czechoslovakia. Since 1945, Silesia and the coalfield, except for a small piece left to Czechoslovakia, have been given to Poland.

These political shifts of ownership were detrimental to the full development of the field, but since the latest unification great strides forward have been made. The advance has undoubtedly been helped by the fact that towards the end of the Second World War the Soviet troops took over the area so quickly that little material destruction occurred, and mining and heavy industry could be resumed with negligible loss of efficiency. Furthermore, many of the German inhabitants were not expelled, since they could prove residence through their ancestry for many centuries. These "autochthones," as they were called, had been largely responsible for pre-war development. Now, with the greater resources made available by most of the coalfield's being brought under one government, they were able to plan its industrial growth more profitably.

The iron and steel industry developed on the same wide scale as on the Ruhr, but is hampered somewhat by the shortage in the seams of anthracite and good coking coal. The chemical industry, especially the manufacture of fertilisers, has grown enormously. An increasing number of thermal electric power stations supply current not only to the coalfield area but to a large part of the south of East Germany.

Katowice (269,000) is the chief city of the coalfield, and with the neighbouring Bytom (Beuthen) (179,000), Gliwice (Gleiwitz) (134,900), Zabrze (Hindenburg) (188,800) and Chorzów (146,700) forms a giant iron smelting, steel making and heavy engineering combine.

Away from the coalfield, but forming part of its industrial region, are

Fig. 100.—Poland: Rybnik coalfield. This forms part of the Upper Silesian coal-producing area and lies near the Polish border south of Katowice. The Upper Silesian basin has an estimated content of 70,000 million tons of hard coal.

Kraków (Cracow) (479,000) to the east, and Częstochowa (163,800). Kraków, on the upper Vistula and the largest city of southern Poland, was once the capital. It lies in a strategic position, controlling the passage between the Carpathians and the Lysogóry, and only in recent years has it changed from an administrative and military city to a great industrial centre. It has engineering, chemical, textile, footwear and food industries; immediately to the north, in the new town of Nowa Huta, are blast furnaces and large steelworks. Częstochowa, too, has steelworks, and wool and cotton textile industries.

The industrial region between Kraków and Częstochowa, which includes the Upper Silesian coalfield, is the most highly developed part of Poland, with the best system of roads and railways and the densest population.

Iron ore deposits in the east of the Little Polish Plateau have given rise to a small industrial grouping around Ostrowiec, which has iron smelting and steelworks. Lublin (180,700), on the chalk plateau farther east, is in a loess-covered, fertile, wheat and sugar beet producing region, and has flour mills and sugar refineries. In the extreme south-east of the region the oil and natural gas deposits around Jaslo, Krosno and Sanok are gradually becoming exhausted. Most of the small output goes to the Soviet Union.

3. The western Carpathians

The Carpathian region is Poland's largest source of timber. Sawmills, some driven by hydro-electricity but many still using crude water power, are found in all the valleys. The Carpathians have the scenic beauty of the Alps and are visited annually by thousands of tourists. Holiday and health resorts are found on all accessible slopes, the chief being Zakopane, noted for winter sports (*see* Fig. 96).

STUDY QUESTIONS

1. Indicate a regional division for the basin of the river Oder, and give a comprehensive account of any *one* of the regions recognised. (J.M.B.)

2. Locate the chief industrial areas of Poland and Sweden. Compare their relative power resources and manufactures. (J.M.B.)

3. Discuss, with reference to specific areas, the characteristic features of agriculture in Poland. (J.M.B.)

4. Divide Poland into its principal geographical regions and write a detailed account of *one* of them.

5. Compare the Baltic coastal lands of Sweden and Finland with those of Denmark, Germany and Poland.

6. Discuss the factors which have influenced the development of *three* of the following: Danzig (Gdansk), Kraków, Wrocław (Breslau), Stettin (Szczecin).

7. Explain what is meant by a "buffer state." With special reference to Poland, indicate the geographical and historical disadvantages of a buffer position.

REVISION QUESTIONS

1. As one travels eastwards from the coast of the Netherlands to Poland, agriculture becomes increasingly more backward. Write a short essay expanding this statement and showing how far it is true.

2. Examine the main characteristics and the human significance of *three* contrasted types of coastline along the North and Baltic seas.

3. Compare the positions, chief manufacturing industries and commercial activities of Copenhagen, Stettin and Bordeaux.

4. Why do some canals in Europe remain important means of transport at the present time? (O. & C.)

5. Discuss the significance of the North and Baltic Seas in the geography of northern Europe.

6. Describe the site and importance of *three* of the following: Bergen, Duisburg, Gothenburg, Hanover, Munich. Sketch-maps are essential.

7. What are the factors which have influenced the development of Rotterdam, Zürich and Berlin?

8. Locate the main coalfields of peninsular Europe and indicate the characteristics of one of them as a coal-producing area. (J.M.B.)

Chapter XXIII

SOUTH CENTRAL EUROPE

PHYSICAL ASPECTS

STRUCTURAL AND PHYSICAL DEVELOPMENT

The countries of south central Europe are here taken as being Hungary, Rumania, Bulgaria and Yugoslavia. They are sometimes called the Danubian countries; for although the Danube flows also in West Germany and Austria, and skirts part of Czechoslovakia, in none of them is it the dominant stream. From its entry into Hungary, the Danube is bordered by wide plains on both sides. As its basin opens to the east, giving an easy entrance to peoples moving from the still wider plains of Russia and beyond, it has been a magnet attracting wave after wave of migration and invasion during the past two thousand years. The middle and lower Danube basin, enclosed between mountain systems to the north and south, is a definite geographical entity from a physical point of view, but the numbers of different races which have penetrated into it and its mountain surround have resulted in a human geography with little unity of any kind. In the area covered by the Carpathians and their associated highlands, the Danubian plains, and the jumble of the Balkan mountains, the Dinaric Alps and the ancient massifs trapped between them, is a patchwork of peoples, languages, religions and cultures unmatched in the world by any region of comparable size (*see* Fig. 101).

Broadly speaking, south central Europe may be said to date structurally from the end of the Cretaceous period. The whole region was submerged beneath the Cretaceous Sea; from its waves emerged the folds of the Alpides in the great arc of the Carpathians, Transylvanian Alps and Balkan mountains. These were followed in the early Tertiary period by the Dinarides, folded ranges east of the Adriatic Sea with a trend from north-west to south-east. Between the two systems, and sometimes caught up in the nappe formations which were a part of the mountain-building movements, were great blocks of earlier mountains, already mentioned as the Hercynian ranges. These ancient rocks, worn down and peneplained until few traces of their folding remains, were fractured and dislocated in the new orogenesis. Some parts were uplifted as massifs like the Rhodope and Bihor plateaus, others subsided to leave great

393

depressions, as in the Pannonian (Hungarian) and Rumano-Bulgarian basins; still others form areas of harder rocks among the limestones of the Dinarides or the sandstones of the Carpathians.

The uplift of the Rhodope and Bihor was accompanied by faulting, so that both contain minor horsts and fault-bounded basins. In all the hollows enclosed by the folding and uplift were the waters of the ancient sea, in many lakes, large and small. The greatest of them was the Pannonian Sea, in what is now called the Hungarian basin. The Aegean Sea

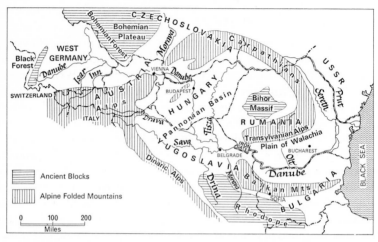

FIG. 101.—The Danube basin. The Danube is truly an international river, flowing through or skirting eight countries. The states in its middle and lower courses are regarded in this book as South Central Europe. They are Hungary, Rumania, Yugoslavia and Bulgaria.

extended far to the north, branches penetrating via the valleys of the Vardar, Morava and Struma to the foot of the Balkan mountains.

Prolonged erosion during Tertiary times reduced all the ranges to plateaus or peneplains. Then, towards the end of the era, an epeirogenic movement lifted the whole region once more. Where the uplift was sufficient and the climatic conditions favourable, as in the High Tatra and the Prokletije (northern Albania), glaciation in the Quaternary Ice Age produced the characteristic pointed peaks, cirques, arêtes, and U-shaped valleys associated with the western Alps; but in general the mountains retained their rounded summits and peneplained appearance. This is most apparent in the softer sandstone areas of the eastern Carpathians. The Transylvanian Alps are more crystalline, and have developed a more rugged outline. The resistance to erosion of the hard limestone of which the Dinarides are often composed has led to the formation of steeper slopes and difficult terrain—sometimes almost impenetrable, as in the mountains of Calabria and Dalmatia. Nowhere, however, are the ranges as high as the western Alps, the High Tatra reaching less than 9000 ft, the eastern Carpathians averaging 5000 ft, and the Transylvanian Alps, Balkan Mountains and Dinarides rarely more than 7000 ft.

Following the epeirogenic uplift, the fresh-water Pannonian Sea began to drain away through a newly-formed gap (the Iron Gate) between the Transylvanian Alps and the Balkans. Early in the succeeding Quaternary era, the northern waters of the Aegean Sea receded to their present position. The retreat of the water was not continuous, as the numerous ancient shorelines and wide terraces show. They are especially prominent in the valleys of the Vardar and Struma, and along the Danube in the Hungarian plain. Lakes Balaton and Neusiedler are remnants of the Pannonian Sea, which on its disappearance left a great basin floored with Tertiary rocks in which the rivers cut deep channels. The Tertiaries were gradually covered by sedimentaries washed down from the surrounding mountains, and by stretches of loess. Much of the latter has since been eroded.

The faulting and dislocation of the Hercynian blocks were accompanied in places by volcanic outpouring of basaltic lavas, which have decomposed into fertile soils; and the old massifs contain many igneous intrusions rich in mineral ores. Such is the case, for instance, in the Bihor plateau and between the Rhodope and the Balkan mountains. Volcanic activity in the Alpine folds was, however, rare. Most of the volcanic rocks found in them come from the broken-up Hercynian massifs involved in their folding.

Earth movements in this part of Europe still continue, though there are no active volcanoes. Earthquakes are common in the Dinarides and may have disastrous results, as in 1962 when Skopje was destroyed with great loss of life. The Pannonian basin is a true plain of subsidence, the downward movement continuing well into the Quaternary era; possibly it still goes on. The Walachian plain and the lowlands surrounding the Bihor plateau are stable, as the relative absence of post-Tertiary deposits on the surface indicates.

CLIMATE

The climate of south central Europe is merely a southern modification of the continental conditions found in central Europe. The basin of the middle and lower Danube, which comprises the greatest part of this division of Europe, is nowhere open to maritime influences, either from the Atlantic or the Mediterranean. Although winds blowing from both the seas may have a slight seasonal impact on climatic conditions in south central Europe, the climate may be said in general to have hot summers, cold winters and a low annual precipitation with a summer maximum. There are exceptions, and they will be noted later.

Making allowance for differences caused by altitude, as in the Carpathian system, the mountains of Yugoslavia and the Rhodope, temperatures in summer are fairly uniform and high, ranging from 70° F (21·1° C) in the west of the Hungarian plain to 75° F (23·9° C) in the east of Rumania. The highest temperatures are found on the Danubian plateau in Bulgaria, where an average July temperature of 80° F (26·7° C) may be registered. Winter temperatures, too, vary little throughout the Danubian plains, averaging about 25° F (−3·9° C) in December. In the valleys of the Carpathians, and especially in the Transylvanian basin, the winters are more severe, with heavy snow. The lowest temperatures are found once again on the plateau in the north of Bulgaria, where −10° F (−23° C) is not uncommon in January.

Annual precipitation in the lowlands and sheltered valleys is low, rarely exceeding 25 in., and most of it comes in summer. In the Hungarian and Rumanian plains it averages from 27 in. in the west to 23 in. in the east. Belgrade has only 18·5 in., and parts of the Morava and Maritsa valleys 17 in. The least rainfall, 15 in., is found on the Danubian plateau, in Bulgaria. This region has probably the most continental climate in peninsular Europe.

The Adriatic coastlands and the lower Vardar valley in Yugoslavia have a Mediterranean climate, with hot, dry summers and warm, wet winters. These conditions sometimes penetrate into the adjacent regions. Temperatures range from about a mean of 78–80° F (25·5–26·5° C) in July to 40–42° F (4·5–5·5° C) in January. The annual precipitation in low-lying areas is around 25 in., but the outer slopes of the Dinaric Alps have remarkably high totals. An annual precipitation of 183 in. has been measured in the mountains of Montenegro, and averages of 120 in. are common. The valleys of this region are wet, with average falls of 50 in. The Julian Alps, on the north-west of Yugoslavia, register 50–60 in. a year.

THE RIVER DANUBE: NAVIGATIONAL PROBLEMS

The Danube has the longest course and its basin the greatest area of any river in peninsular Europe, but its economic value is in no way commensurate, being far less than that of the much smaller Rhine. This is partly due to natural hindrances to navigation, partly to political difficulties.

The basin of the Danube may be divided into three distinct sections (*see* Fig. 101). From its source in the Black Forest to the narrows above Vienna, the Upper Danube flows in a narrow valley between the Alps and the Hercynian highlands, receiving most of its waters from the Alpine side. In this part of the course its value for navigation is negligible, although small barges and tourist steamers ply between Regensburg and Vienna. A canal, the Ludwig Canal, connects Regensburg via Nuremberg to Bamber, at the limit of navigation on the Main, and so joins the Danube to the Rhine; but it can accommodate only the smallest barges. It was hoped to construct a large canal capable of taking barges of up to 1500 tons, to provide water communication between the North and Black Seas, but the Iron Curtain was drawn across the basin below Vienna, so the scheme had to be dropped for the time being. The greatest value of the Upper Danube lies in the hydro-electricity stations along the tributaries Isar, Lech and Iller, which flow from the German Alps. These provide power to the whole of Bavaria. The Upper Danube has an Alpine régime, with most water in spring and early summer, when there is a tendency to flood (for the régime of the Danube, *see* Chapter II).

The middle Danube extends from the Vienna narrows to the Iron Gate, an elongated gorge between the Transylvanian Alps to the north and the Balkan mountains to the south. In its middle course the river traverses the Pannonian basin, a wide plain so flat that the Danube has developed great meanders and numerous "braidings" (where the river splits and joins again). The middle Danube varies greatly in volume. It contains most water in spring; but in its long, slow journey across the plain it loses much by evaporation, so that by the end of the summer it is in many places too shallow for large shipping unless deep channels are dug in its bed. In the south of the Pannonian basin the Danube is joined by the Drava and Sava, coming from the Slovenian and Austrian Alps. These, with tributaries from the foot of the "karst" Dinaric Alps, may bring water in winter from a region which is under Mediterranean influences, increasing the volume of the Danube before it arrives at the Iron Gate but not to any great extent. The middle Danube presents many difficulties in river control. For long stretches, where it braids, there may be serious flooding in spring. At low water in autumn navigation is likely to be impeded by sandbanks and mudflats. Moreover, in winter, the river freezes for up to two months from Budapest to its delta, stopping all water-borne traffic.

In its lower course the Danube, from the Iron Gate to the delta, flows through another plain, receiving enough water from the Alpine ranges to the north and south to maintain a regular flow, even in late summer—for most of the rains in this part of its course fall in the summer months. The lower Danube for much of the way forms the boundary between Rumania and Bulgaria. It is bordered on its left bank by a belt of swampy land up to nine miles wide which makes it difficult to find sites for towns; and in this section there is only one bridge, at Cernavodă. What appears on a map to be a through route at Giurgiu is really a car ferry to Ruse (Ruschuk). The delta is a maze of lagoons, reed-covered marshes and swamps, threaded by many distributaries. There are three navigable channels through the delta but only the middle one, the Sulina, is used extensively, and then only by dint of constant dredging. The others are employed by sturgeon fishers or reed collectors, the reeds being the basis of a cardboard industry.

Flowing through or forming the boundary of eight countries and giving water communication between western and eastern Europe, the Danube should be a major international waterway. Since the middle of the nineteenth century efforts have been made to render it available to, and fit for, shipping of all countries. Unfortunately, the riparian states prior to 1945 were too poor and backward to do much for themselves in improving navigation or introducing river control. Since then they have been too concerned with building up their own internal economies to afford the money necessary for international projects. Moreover, some of the countries have alternative means of exit for their trade. Czechoslovakia, though it has the important port of Bratislava on the Danube, has its main outlet via the river Elbe. Yugoslavia is developing good ports on the Adriatic Sea. Bulgaria regards the Maritsa, rather than the Danube, as its chief river, and also has ports on the Black Sea.

Much work has been done to improve navigation in Hungary and Yugoslavia by cutting channels to by-pass meanders, and to use some of the waters for irrigation. In the last century a deep passage was blasted through the rock-strewn Iron Gate. But little has been done so far to impound the waters in the upper courses of the Danube's tributaries so that spring floods in the plains could be minimised and hydro-electric power generated by dams and reservoirs. Such control would also ensure a more uniform level in the navigable stretch of the main river and make the raising of its banks easier and cheaper. In addition, it would provide more water for irrigation and facilitate the establishment of industries on the banks of the river, where few exist at present.

In 1854 a European Commission of the Danube was formed by Austria, France, Great Britain, Prussia, Russia, Sardinia, Turkey and—later—Rumania, to clear the mouths of the Danube and give access to Galati and Brăila. Beyond Brăila it had no jurisdiction, although it encouraged improvements in the Hungarian section of the river. The Commission was re-formed in 1921 by Great Britain, France, Italy and Rumania, but again it concerned itself only with free entry into and navigation on the river.

In 1948, a completely new commission included only the countries along the Danube—Great Britain, France and Italy being excluded. The U.S.S.R., which had regained possession of Bessarabia, north of the delta, became the dominant power on this commission. Although the Danube is still international in name, it has in effect become a Soviet-controlled river, which the Western powers may use only on Communist terms. The commissions have never gone beyond their function of keeping the Danube open to navigation; questions of water control and irrigation away from the main stream lay outside their orbit.

It has been suggested that the present commission might be reconstituted in such a way as to enable it to develop the Danube basin as a whole, taking in all such projects as improvements in navigation, strengthening banks, constructing reservoirs and hydro-electric power stations, and developing irrigation systems, much on the lines of the Tennessee Valley Authority. All this would in turn lead to the growth of the towns along its banks and to new industries, which are sorely needed. The difficulty of achieving such a truly international objective, however, is that even if the riparian states were willing they are too poor to finance the gigantic schemes necessary. It is doubtful, moreover, although they are all Communist countries, whether their historic jealousies would allow them to spend money which might benefit one to the apparent disadvantage of the others. International development, including participation by the countries of the free world, is the answer to the economic problems of the Danube; for the separation of East from West by the Iron Curtain has not only reduced the amount of traffic on the river, but also stopped the flow of financial help which at one time poured from the countries of western Europe.

HUMAN GEOGRAPHY

HISTORICAL DEVELOPMENT

South central Europe is in the direct line of approach for incursions of people from Asia. The route along the Danube plains is open, and the mountains—at least in the outer zones facing east—not very difficult to penetrate. As early as the seventh century, Slavs and Magyars had moved into the area, the Slavs being divided into northern and southern sections by the Magyars, who advanced into the Pannonian basin. The northern Slavs entered the Germano-Polish plain and the mountains on its southern borders. Ultimately they reached and occupied Slovakia and Bohemia. The southern Slavs (the Yugo-Slavs) settled in the more difficult mountain lands of the Balkans, Macedonia and the Dinarides. In the course of time they were split into separated communities, more or less isolated from each other in their remote valley fastnesses and comparatively free from danger of attack. They were basically all the same people, speaking different dialects of the same language, but in their isolated environments they developed ways of life so distinct from each other as to make them separate groups with a high sense of local patriotism, which in the course of centuries was to develop into a fierce nationalism.

The subsequent historical development of each of the countries in south central Europe is considered further in the relevant sections of the chapters concerned.

POST-WAR PROBLEMS

The countries of south central Europe are young and only slowly emerging from a backwardness forced on them through many centuries. Their boundaries, except in Yugoslavia, are mainly ethnic. In Hungary, Rumania and Bulgaria these are reasonably satisfactory, but not wholly so. The Hungarians claim the lands lost to Czechoslovakia, Yugoslavia and Rumania as being originally inhabited by Magyar-speaking people; Bulgaria wants a large part of Macedonia; and Rumania's ambitions to increase its territory are resented by both Hungary and Bulgaria.

The linguistic and cultural problems of Yugoslavia are more acute. Three official languages are recognised, Serbo-Croat over most of the country, Slovene in the north-west, and Macedonian in the south-east; there are many minorities speaking Bulgar, Magyar, German, Italian, Greek and even Turkish. Yugoslavia is a federal republic, that is, it is made up of several small republics. The strongest is Serbia, but jealousies and feuds persist, preventing the development of a true national tradition and militating against a sound and permanent economy. Croatia, for instance, one of the more progressive republics, has strong separatist inclinations. The Macedonians, partly in Yugoslavia, partly in Greece, resent the inferior status they hold in each country. At the same time, it must be recognised that Yugoslavia enjoys a greater degree of internal unity at the present time than she has ever had since 1919.

In all the countries of south central Europe, gigantic efforts were made after 1918 to redress the backwardness of centuries and catch up with western Europe. Existing industries were expanded and new ones introduced; communications were improved, especially along the Danube, which was internationalised; cities were rebuilt on western lines; and agrarian reforms developed. The war of 1939–45 destroyed much of these efforts, but the planned economic rehabilitation imposed or fostered by the Soviet Union and carried out on Communist lines has in less than twenty years worked wonders of recovery. None of these countries, however, is very rich in natural resources; it is doubtful if, even with the help of the Soviet Union, the standard of living of much of their populations can be raised to a level regarded as normal in the West. At the same time, conditions of life are princely compared with fifty years ago, though it is not yet clear whether Soviet domination means beneficent development or whether south central Europe, like Poland and Czechoslovakia, is being exploited politically and economically as a western bastion of the Soviet empire. Sovietisation has certainly been of advantage to the material well-being of all the backward countries; but the resurgence of national spirit, born of newly-won independence and a land-hunger only partially appeased, will present problems in the future. Already in several of the countries popular uprisings against the so-called dictatorship of the U.S.S.R. have had to be put down by force.

STUDY QUESTIONS

1. Justify a division of the middle and lower basin of the river Danube into physical regions and comment on any differences in land use found in the regions you note.

2. Give an account of the hindrances to navigation found on the river Danube and of the efforts made to overcome them.

3. "South central Europe shows a patchwork pattern of peoples, languages and religions." Comment on this statement.

Chapter XXIV

HUNGARY

HUNGARY, or the Hungarian People's Republic, lies in a great lowland in the middle Danube basin. The highlands that surround the basin allow easy access from every direction, and this fact has played no small part in Hungary's history. Historical events, in turn, have had a share in shaping the features of the Hungarian landscape, as will be seen later in the chapter.

PHYSICAL ASPECTS

In the Carboniferous era the area now occupied by Hungary formed part of the great mountain system (Hercynian or Variscan) which ran from western France to the shores of the Black Sea. To the south was the ancient Tethys Sea. By the end of the Permian era the range had been strongly eroded, and fractured by tectonic forces. Subsidence took place and the fragmented range was covered by the sea, leaving only small portions sticking up as granitic islands. The crystalline Velence hills and the eastern end of the Mecsek mountains are the present-day remains of the Hercynian ranges; but drillings in other places have struck the ancient rocks at depths of only 5000 ft below the surface of the plain. In the Mesozoic period the greater part of Hungary was covered by the sea and, in the ensuing millions of years, thick deposits of sedimentaries were laid down in it. These were uplifted and folded slightly in the Middle Jurassic era to form the central highland belt of Transdanubia, the name given to the region west of the river Danube. The mountains, of which the Bakony Forest and Bükk hills are the chief parts, are composed of Triassic limestone and dolomite. They rarely rise to more than 2000 ft, and some areas show karst characteristics. At their feet, Carboniferous strata, including coal measures, were formed, but today the only coal deposits of importance are near Pécs.

In the Tertiary period the Alpine storm raised the Carpathians to the north and the Alps to the south, while the central portion of the country sank deeper. In the shallow bays and coves at the foot of the mountains, soft coals (lignite) were formed and are worked today at Tatabánya, Salgótarján and in the Sajó valley. As the central part subsided and the marginal mountains rose, faults occurred and there were volcanic extrusions of basalt, forming the hill masses of the Börzszöny, Mátra and Zemplén. The highest point in Hungary, Kékes peak (3313 ft), is in the Mátra hills.

The uplift of the surrounding mountains had cut off the waters covering the lower levels from the outer sea, forming a lake. Rivers poured down the slopes and began to fill the basin with their detritus. So was formed the Great Hungarian Plain, a lowland almost as flat as a table. The Quaternary period brought only minor changes in the physical features. The waters were drained off, leaving a few fragmental lakes in the west, of which Balaton and Fertö (Neusiedler See) are the largest. During the glacial period, winds carried vast quantities of dust into the country. It settled and became yellow loess. Little or none was deposited in the Kisalföld (Little Plain) of north-west Hungary, but in south-east Transdanubia loess reaches a depth of over 160 ft. Most of the Great Plain has no loess today, the rivers having carried it away.

The present surface features of the Great Plain have been shaped by its network of rivers, which have etched the surface into a series of wide, shallow valleys. As they reach the plain from the mountains the velocity of the rivers is checked, and they have built a broad row of alluvial fans. The sand of these detrital cones was blown into dunes or spread by the wind. In this way were formed the sandy tracts of the Nyír in the north-east and on the plain between the rivers Danube and Tisza. The Great Plain continues to subside very slowly, while the areas to the north-west of the central highland belt are rising.

The Danube is Hungary's chief river, traversing the country for 255 miles. The first part of its Hungarian course is from west to east and then, at Visegrád, it takes a sharp turn to the south. The river splits and joins up again several times, enclosing long, narrow islands; at Visegrád it flows through a picturesque, wooded valley crowned by the ruins of medieval castles. Below Budapest the Danube braids again and meanders before it crosses the southern boundary. In this part of its course it receives the tributaries Sio, which drains Lake Balaton, and the Drava, whose confluence is actually in Yugoslavia. The whole of the Hungarian section of the Danube is navigable. The meanders have been cut through to improve navigation; and by regulating its flow the danger of floods caused by piling ice floes in spring has been averted. As part of the flood control, a canal was constructed to carry waters through the western part of the Great Plain, where they can be used for irrigation.

Rising in the Ukraine and flowing from north to south roughly parallel to the Danube is the Tisza, which drains the eastern part of the Great Plain. Its course is extremely tortuous and lined with ox-bow lakes. Most of its meanders have been cut and the river confined within embankments;

o

the marshes which used to cover its flood-plain have been reclaimed. In the north, near the confluence of the Bodrog, is the hydro-electric power station of Tiszalök, producing 50 million kWh per annum. From its dam flows the Eastern Main Canal, carrying irrigation waters to the east of the Great Plain.

STRUCTURAL DIVISIONS

Hungary may be divided into four natural regions (*see* Fig. 102). They are (1) the Alföld or Great Plain, (2) the north central highland belt, (3) Transdanubia (Hung. *Dunántúl*), the country west of the Danube, and (4) the Kisalföld or Little Plain.

FIG. 102.—Hungary: physical features and divisions. The numbers correspond with the regional divisions used in the text.

1. *The Great Plain, or Alföld*

More than half Hungary is occupied by the Great Plain. The Plain has a dead flat appearance. Slight rises like sand dunes are lost in its vast expanse, yet it increases in height gradually from about 300 ft above sea level near the Danube to 600 ft in the Nyírség in the far east.

The Alföld is divided by the river Tisza into two dissimilar parts. Between the Danube and the Tisza are extensive sand hills which, until recently, supported only a very sparse and tussocky grass. The area has now been reclaimed, although with difficulty, for the ground is too porous for surface irrigation. The water-table is near enough to the surface, however, for the long roots of vines and other fruit trees to reach it, and they serve also to bind the sands of the dunes. East of the Tisza the flatness is broken only by shallow river valleys, and its surface soil has developed from lacustrine deposits laid down in the ancient Pannonian Sea. Here and there are thin patches of loess, especially in the south-east. The eastern portion of the Plain is a type of steppe and like many other natural grasslands it has been ploughed, wherever suitable, for agriculture. The Great Plain extends beyond the boundaries of Hungary into Czechoslovakia, Yugoslavia and Rumania.

2. *The north central highland belt*

East of the Danube and north of the Great Plain stretch two series of hill ranges along the Czechoslovak and Soviet frontiers. The northern series, composed of karst limestones with caves and underground streams, rises in the Bükk hills to over 3000 ft. The southern ranges are volcanic, with intrusions of non-ferrous mineral ores such as gold, silver, copper and lead—none of which, however, is of economic importance. The highest of the volcanic rock masses are the Mátra and Zemplén ranges, which average about 3000 ft; but in general the volcanic hills are less than 1000 ft.

3. *Transdanubia*

Transdanubia covers the area stretching west from the Danube to the borders of Austria and Yugoslavia. It is divided in two by the parallel ranges of the Keszthely hills and the Bakony Forest, both of karst dolomite. The Bakony Forest is overlaid in the south-west by basaltic lava.

East and west of the hill ranges are undulating lowlands. Those of the west are a continuation of the Burgenland of Austria and have the same fertile, alluvial soils. On the east are the richest and most extensive deposits of loess in Hungary. They stretch to the Danube and drop to its valley by steep cliffs. The northern part of eastern Transdanubia is known as the Mesöföld, or Middle Plain. In the south of Transdanubia the granite massif of Mecsek rises like an island from the surrounding plain. On its southern flanks are coal-bearing Carboniferous strata.

4. *The Little Plain, or Kisalföld*

In the north-west of Hungary, drained to the Danube by the rivers Rabca and Raba, is the Little Plain, or Kisalföld. The lowland extends beyond the border of Hungary into the Vienna basin in Austria, and the plain of southern Slovakia. The Kisalföld, which is bounded on the north by the Danube, is flatter than Transdanubia, and has soils derived partly from the river silts and partly from lacustrine deposits. The latter were laid down when the area formed part of a lake of which Lake Balaton is a relic. As already noted, loess, which covered so much of Hungary, is lacking in the Kisalföld.

NATURAL VEGETATION AND SOILS

Hungary has a continental climate, with hot summers, cold winters and rain mainly in the summer half of the year. The temperature over most of the country is uniform—the result of the generally level surface—but rainfall shows some variation. The south-west is the wettest part, with from 27 to 35 in. a year; the driest areas are in the Tisza basin, with an annual average of 19 in. Most of the Great Plain has 23 in., with a maximum fall in June, when westerlies are drawn in from the Atlantic. There is a second rainy period in late September, the result of humid air coming from the Mediterranean. The intervening months often suffer parching droughts. Snow falls in winter on 20–30 days in the plains, but the total amount for the winter months is equal only to about three to five inches of rainfall. The annual rainfall is, however, sufficient everywhere for crop farming.

The soils of Hungary are classified as (a) chestnut-coloured and (b) sandy sub-groups. The chestnut-coloured type resembles the black earth of the Ukraine and is very fertile. Found mainly over loess, it covers many areas of the Great and Little Plains, and the lowlands south of the Bakony Forest. Sandy soils occur in small tracts between the Danube and Tisza, and in north-east Kisalföld. The original flood-plains of the rivers have a cover of clayey alluvium, difficult to work; but by careful cultivation and the addition of lime they have been recovered. In some parts, however, they have become alkaline and are being afforested.

The natural vegetation of the Hungarian basin is usually described as a steppe type of grassland, but Hungarian geographers say that, with the exception of a few desolate areas in the east, the whole region was at one time covered with forest: first of pines, then of oaks, and later of beech, according to variations in rainfall. The vegetation as it appears today is the result of the devastating Turkish occupation over hundreds of years, and of the more recent clearing of forests for pasture and agriculture. All the hilly regions have mixed coniferous and deciduous trees at lower levels, with pines and birch higher up. The total forest area, however, is small—only 13·6% of the country—and large amounts of timber have to be imported.

HUMAN GEOGRAPHY

HISTORICAL OUTLINE

The Magyars, a nomadic tribe who came from the steppes east of the Ural mountains, pushed like a wedge between the northern and southern

Slavs, and spread over the plains of Pannonia. Within a hundred years after the last wave of the great migration of peoples they founded the Hungarian state under Stephen I (892–896). The young kingdom had to face and fight threats on two fronts: against the Holy Roman Empire in the west and Byzantium in the east. In 1241, Hungary was overrun by Tartar hordes and complete destruction was averted only by withdrawal of the invaders, because of dynastic troubles at home, towards the end of the century. Hungary recovered, and for two centuries the country prospered under the Angevin kings and the Hungarian, Matthias Corvinus.

In the first half of the sixteenth century disaster came again, this time from the Ottoman Turks, who were spreading their empire westwards. The sultan's expansionist ambitions had been resisted in wars spread over the previous hundred years. Weakened by them and torn by factional strife among its own barons, Hungary collapsed in 1526 under the new Turkish onslaught, and became part of the Ottoman Empire. For over a century and a half the Hungarian plain and part of Transdanubia were occupied by the Turks, and Transylvania was only nominally independent. The plain, with its prosperous villages and rich agriculture, was almost depopulated, and marshland appeared again in its most fertile areas.

In the fourteenth century the Turks had invaded the mountain regions to the south. By 1481 they had conquered the whole of the peninsula to the south of the river Danube, with the exception of a small and difficult mountain region in Dalmatia, along the Adriatic Sea. With the fall of Hungary, they became overlords of the entire south-eastern corner of Europe.

The Ottoman rule was harsh and despotic, based on fear and savagery. For the five hundred years it lasted over much of the region, it saw little but cruel degradation of the native peoples, with results which persist even to the present day. The Turks penetrated as far as the gates of Vienna in 1683, but then the tide of victory in the plains began to turn. The Austrian empire of the Hapsburgs was expanding, and now looked towards the east. By 1699 the Turks were driven from the Hungarian plains by the Germanic forces and Hungary became part of the Austro-Hungarian Empire. The new rulers, however, did not allow much freedom to the Magyars. They were treated as serfs, and their country was made into a granary for the parts of the Empire which were becoming industrialised.

Time and again the people of Hungary tried unsuccessfully to achieve independence, notably in the revolt of 1848–49; but not until the breakdown of the Empire in 1918 did Hungary become once more a separate country, though with a much reduced area. Slovakia, Transylvania, the southern part of the Danubian plain, Croatia and Burgenland—territories inhabited mostly by non-Magyar peoples—claimed the right of self-determination and became parts of other countries. Hungary, now a republic, was predominantly in the hands of large estate owners and the

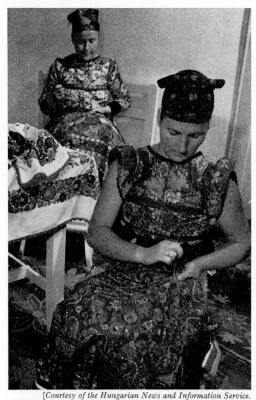

[*Courtesy of the Hungarian News and Information Service.*

FIG. 103.—Hungary: hand embroidery. Mezökövesd, in north-east Hungary, where this photograph was taken, has the most colourful folk costumes in the country. The craft industry of hand embroidery is carried on in all the countries of south central Europe.

great mass of the population continued to live in abject poverty and backwardness. The situation lasted until the end of the Second World War, when the country was occupied by Soviet armies.

Hungary, which had resisted Communist domination in the years between the war, became in 1945 a Communist or Workers' Republic controlled from Moscow. Agrarian reforms were begun immediately.

The large estates were liquidated and given to the peasants, co-operative and State farms were developed, and new impetus was given to the industries which were growing in the inter-war years.

POPULATION

Before the Second World War, in 1938, the population of Hungary was 9·2 million. War casualties did not reduce it much, and by 1961 it had risen to 10,054,000, with an average density of 279 persons a square mile, the highest in the whole of south-eastern Europe. Ninety-six per cent of the population is Hungarian, the remainder being composed of Slovaks, Germans, Rumanians and Serbo-Croats.

An interesting change is taking place in the proportion of urban to rural population. The urban population has risen in the years 1900–60 from 31·8 to 37·7% and the rural population fallen from 68·2 to 60·3%. This is a natural consequence of industrialisation. But whereas most of the urban growth was confined until 1945 to the Budapest district, there are rapid rises at present in the areas around Miskolc, Pécs and Dunauj-város.

THE ECONOMY

AGRICULTURE

Hungary is an agricultural country, 58% of its area being arable and 60·3% of its population rural. Post-war land reforms have followed the usual lines of splitting up large estates and either giving the land to peasant owners merged into co-operatives, or making it into State farms. There was, however, more opposition to co-operative farming in Hungary than in any other of the new Communist states. An all-out offensive by the peasants was launched against the co-operatives in the rising of 1956. It was put down with great cruelty by Soviet armed forces, and more lenient methods were introduced to speed up the process of co-operation. Today 90% of the peasants work on State farms or in co-operatives.

The chief crop is winter wheat, grown extensively in the Great Plain, but especially east of the Tisza. Large amounts come also from the Little Plain and southern Transdanubia. Rye is cultivated on sandy soils between the Danube and Tisza, and in the extreme east and west of the country. Barley, for brewing, is grown in the Little Plain, and in Northern Hungary round the Mátra and Bükk hills. By means of irrigation, rice is now produced over a large area of the lower Körös river basin. The area devoted to maize has increased rapidly, and is now greater than that devoted to wheat, the fertile soils, sufficient rainfall and sunny summers favouring its cultivation. It is grown everywhere south of an east–west line drawn through Budapest, particularly in the country east of Szeged, round Debrecen, and south of Pécs.

Sugar beet is important in all the wheat-growing areas, especially in the Little Plain and the east of the Great Plain. The chief areas for potatoes are the Nyírség, between the Danube and Tisza, and south of Lake Balaton. Other crops include grapes, peaches, apricots and vegetables such as paprika (for spices), tomatoes and melons. The chief vineyards

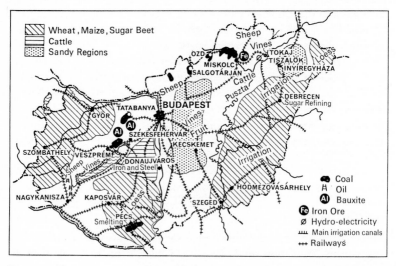

FIG. 104.—Hungary: economic. With the exception of the Pécs deposits, which are hard coal, the coalfields of Hungary produce lignite. Correlate this map with Fig. 102.

are on the slopes of the Mátra, Bükk and Zemplén hills, with Tokaj the wine centre. There are others along Lake Balaton and in south Transdanubia. The largest amount of wine is produced in the reclaimed sandy country between the Danube and Tisza and here too, around Kecskemét, is the main peach area.

Before the *tanyas* (isolated farmsteads) spread themselves over the Great Plain, the land between the cultivated fields which surrounded the large villages consisted of vast expanses of steppe (*puszta*), with meagre vegetation. On them roamed long-horned Hungarian cattle herded by nomadic Magyars. During the past century the steppe lands have been occupied by peasant arable farmers from the villages, the dispersion being made easier because the water table is never deep. Even where the surface seems driest, it is possible to reach water supplies by sinking shallow wells. By reason of this increase in arable farming, the numbers of cattle declined; but in recent years there has been a vigorous new development of livestock rearing as part of the agricultural economy.

This is not, however, on the Great Plain, where cattle and sheep used to roam in great numbers, but in Transdanubia, which possesses the majority of Hungary's 2 million cattle, providing Budapest with meat and dairy produce. Pigs are reared in the maize lands in the south of the country east of the Tisza, sheep on the slopes of the Bakony and Bükk highlands and on the alkaline lands east of the Tisza. Sheep rearing (2,155,000 in 1959) is on the increase.

REGIONAL ECONOMY

The economy of Hungary may be treated by regions corresponding with those outlined earlier and shown in Fig. 102. Budapest, the capital of the country, with nearly one-fifth of its population, lies astride the junction of three of the four regions, and is usually taken as a separate entity.

1. *The Great Plain*

The Danube–Tisza interfluve region in the west of the plain used to be one of shifting sand dunes. In the second half of the nineteenth century these were "bound" by planting vineyards, orchards and acacia plantations. In this way the Kiskunság, as the region is called, has been converted into a major fruit and wine producer. Its centre is Kecskemét (67,000), with flour milling and fruit and vegetable canning, and a new engineering works.

It should be noted that industry in Hungary hardly existed outside Budapest prior to the First World War, so that even the introduction of a single industrial establishment to most of its towns marks a great advance. Szeged (99,000), on the Tisza, is the largest town in the south-east. It is a market town with hemp and jute mills, tobacco works and paprika processing, to which have been added engineering and chemical works. East of the Tisza is the *puszta* or steppe, at one time the home of Magyar horsemen who herded cattle. Most of the land has been ploughed up to grow wheat, sugar beet, maize and fodder crops.

In the north of this region is the Hortobágy puszta, the last remaining part of Hungary where nomadic cattle and sheep grazing survive. On its infertile, alkaline land, pasture is still the chief occupation. It is the most backward part of Hungary but the Eastern Main Canal, which supplies it with water for irrigation, is helping to change its character. Farther east is a vast loess plateau, with intensive cultivation of wheat, maize, rye and sugar beet. The chief town is Debrecen (130,000), which besides being the market, with food processing and flour milling, now has engineering and the manufacture of pharmaceutical chemicals. In the north of the region is a tobacco and apple growing district round Nyíregyháza (57,000).

The whole of the Great Plain is dotted with isolated farmsteads (Hung. *tanya*), which have proved a hindrance to progress in co-operation and education. The towns of the plain, even the largest, have developed from giant villages built during the Turkish occupation as protection against marauding nomadic Magyar herdsmen. After the Turks were driven out, the growing populations of the villages began to build temporary summer residences from which to cultivate outlying fields, and this gave rise to the tanyas. As animal husbandry declined and more land was ploughed, the isolated farms increased in number and were more widespread. By building schools, shops and tractor stations in convenient positions, the Hungarian government is hoping to form the nuclei of new villages, and so bring many of the farming community into better contact with each other, thus reducing the backwardness of their economy.

2. *The north central highlands*

With the exception of the dry limestone platforms at higher levels in the karst hills, the whole of this region has fertile and productive soils. There are extensive vineyards on all the south-facing slopes, and Tokaj (Tokay), south of the Zemplén hills, is world-famous for its wine. Forests, which at one time covered the lower slopes and valleys of the highland belt, are found today on the limestone hills: the valleys have been cleared for wheat, rye, potatoes and fodder crops, the last being fed to cattle reared there. There are many mineral springs at the foot of the volcanic hills and, together with the mountainous character of the region in a country predominantly flat, they have made the highland belt a favourite holiday district for the Hungarians.

In many of the valleys opening to the south are deposits of lignite. The most important are in the Sajó valley, where Miskolc (143,000), the second city of Hungary, is the centre of a growing industrial region. Nearby, in the Hernád valley, is Hungary's only iron ore deposit, producing about 500,000 tons of ore annually. Based on this and the lignite, although it is of low calorific value, Miskolc has blast furnaces and iron and steel works; and Ozd (40,000) produces nearly a third of the country's pig-iron and crude steel. At Ozd and Salgótarján, there are engineering, glass and chemical works.

3. *Transdanubia*

Large deposits of lignite in the northern Bakony area have led to the growth of a heavy chemical industry round Veszprém (25,000). In other small towns such as Ajka (18,000) and Varpalota (26,000), aluminium is smelted from local bauxite. At Ajka, under a Soviet–Hungarian agreement by which Soviet foundries will turn Hungarian alumina into aluminium, the biggest alumina plant in Europe is to be built. Most of Hungary's lignite is used in thermal-electric power stations, which account for 99% of the country's generation of current.

Lake Balaton, in the heart of Transdanubia at the foot of the Bakony Forest, has an area of 231 square miles, but in most places is less than 12 ft deep. Its shallow waters become very warm in summer (75–80° F; 24–27° C) and because the entire shores of the lakes are carpeted by fine sands the Balaton region is the holiday playground of Hungary, with numerous resorts, the largest of which are Tata and Keszthely.

West of the highlands is Szombathely (54,000), a market town with textile and engineering works in the middle of a rich agricultural district. To the south, in the Zala valley, an oilfield with natural gas developed in the past twenty-five years, is connected by pipeline to Budapest. Nagy-kanisza (34,000) is the centre of the oilfields, and has glassworks and refineries.

Eastwards, Transdanubia is composed of flat or undulating plains, broken in the south by the Hercynian massif of Mecsek. On the southern flanks of the Mecsek is the Pécs coalfield, producing (1961) 2·7 million tons of coking coal and anthracite. Pécs (115,000) manufactures porcelain and clothing, and sends coal to the largest iron and steel works yet developed in Hungary, at Dunaujváros (31,000), on the Danube. This town has been built by the Soviet Union since 1945, and the ironworks are under Soviet control. Iron ore is brought from the Ukraine, shipped up the Danube. The eastern plains of Transdanubia have a thick layer of loess. The Mezöföld, flat plains between the northern tip of Lake Balaton and the Danube, is covered by co-operative farms, where large-scale methods yield big quantities of maize, wheat and sugar beet. There is intensive pig breeding, and sheep are reared in the less fertile parts. Székesfehérvár (56,000), in the north of the region, is a railway junction with an aluminium rolling mill and motor-cycle factory. Kaposvár (43,000) has sugar refineries and a cotton mill.

4. *The Little Plain*

The Kisalföld has the most equable climate in Hungary and, its soil being fertile as well, is the richest agricultural region in the country. The largest acreage is devoted to wheat, barley, rye and oats; maize, potatoes and sugar beet are also produced in quantity. In the middle of the Little Plain is the Györ basin, which is becoming an industrial district. Györ (71,000), its centre, has railway engineering, food processing, textile and furniture industries which were first developed under Austrian rule.

Budapest

Budapest (1,900,000) was founded at the most suitable crossing point of the Danube, at the junction of trade routes where the hills of Trans-danubia meet the Great Plain. There are really two towns, Buda on the right bank built in the shadow of a castle on the hills, and Pest, on the

[*Courtesy of the Hungarian News and Information Service.*

FIG. 105.—Hungary: a shipyard on the river Danube. Most of Hungary's ship-yards are near Budapest. They concentrate on sea-going freighters up to 1500 tons, tug-boats and floating cranes. The vessel shown, the *Sagastrand* (1400 tons), was built for a Norwegian firm, to be used on the fiords.

plain of the opposite bank. They were unified as a single city in 1873, to become the capital of Hungary. Budapest is the hub of Hungary's railway system and the heart of its industry: 60% of the country's manufactures are concentrated there. Buda is mainly residential, but has electrical engineer-ing, textiles and brickworks. Pest is larger and has the greater economic development. It has all the industries of a capital city, such as food processing, clothing, furniture and light engineering; and, especially to the south, there are breweries, chemical works, textile factories and more engineering, including the making of machine tools. Budapest is also a tourist and holiday centre, owing to the occurrence of mineral springs. Though it holds the same dominating position as Vienna in Austria, there is not the same imbalance in the economy of the country, for Hungary is more generally productive and has less waste land than its neighbour.

Budapest's position at the centre of a railway system which radiates from it (*see* Fig. 104) has meant that few provincial towns can communicate directly with each other without passing through the capital. This has helped industry in Budapest, but is a drawback to the rest of the country. The main roads, too, converge on the city; and over large parts of the country, villages can be approached only by earth roads or cart tracks which are impassable in wet weather. The Danube is the main trade artery, and Budapest is a major river port, with large docks. Its airport is one of the most important in south central Europe.

STUDY QUESTIONS

1. Attempt a division of Hungary into geographical regions and give a detailed account of *one* of the divisions named.

2. Write a short description of the characteristic agricultural activities of Hungary.

3. Analyse the factors which have influenced the site and development of Budapest.

4. Indicate the extent and the characteristics of the relief of the Carpathian mountains between the Vienna basin and the Iron Gate, and outline the principal economic activities of the peoples who live within their bounds. (J.M.B.)

5. Comment on the salient differences between the economic geography of Hungary and Belgium. (J.M.B.)

6. Show how the position and the relief of Hungary have affected the climate and the life of the people.

Chapter XXV

RUMANIA

PHYSICAL ASPECTS

STRUCTURAL DIVISIONS

Rumania (Roumania, Romania) has a far more complicated structure and relief than its neighbour, Hungary (*see* Fig. 106). (1) From the Soviet border in the north to the Iron Gate on the Danube, the great arc of the

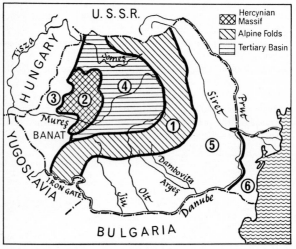

Fig. 106.—Rumania: physical divisions. The numbers correspond with those used in the text.

eastern Carpathians and Transylvanian Alps forms an axis around which the country is built. (2) Inside the arc is the ancient mass of the Bihor, with (3) the plains of the Banat to the west. (4) Between the Bihor massif and the mountain arc is the Transylvanian basin, and (5) to the south and east of the mountains, the plains of Walachia and Moldavia. (6) Bordering the Black Sea in the south-east of the country is the low plateau of the Dobrogea.

1. *The eastern Carpathians and Transylvanian Alps*

In the north of Rumania the eastern Carpathians are a wide series of ranges, folded, peneplained and again uplifted to form rounded mountains

416

rising to over 6000 ft. The system narrows southwards and becomes lower, with wider valleys, but in the south the Transylvanian Alps are high and rugged, with peaks over 8000 ft. The Carpathians and Transylvanian Alps are folded Alpine ranges, but the flattened tops of so many of the peaks suggest they are the results of the dissection of a peneplain. Glaciation has etched deep valleys and carved sharp peaks in parts of the Transylvanian Alps, which are more crystalline in formation. The softer sandstones and limestones of the Carpathians have retained their rounded outlines. The Transylvanian Alps are breached by several transverse valleys, the most notable being the Red Tower Pass, through which flows the river Olt (Oltul). The Olt provides a good example of river capture. It flows across the Transylvanian basin from the inner side of the Carpathians, as if to join the Mureş, then takes a sharp turn to the south through the pass. The change in direction must have taken place when the interior basin was at a much higher level than it is today.

2. *The Bihor mountains or massij*

Within the arc of the Carpathian system rises the ancient Hercynian or Variscan massif of the Bihor mountains, a plateau nearly 5000 ft in elevation, composed of crystalline and old sedimentary rocks, much faulted and dissected.

3. *The Banat*

West of the Bihor a belt of the Hungarian plain lies within the boundary of Rumania. It extends from Oradea southwards to the Danube and is known as the Banat, although strictly this name should be reserved for the wider southern portion of the plain. In the east of the plain there are vast alluvial fans washed from the mountains and cut by the valleys of the Mureş and other tributaries of the Hungarian river Tisza.

4. *The Transylvanian basin*

Between the Bihor and the encircling rim of mountains is the basin of Transylvania, a rolling upland between 1500 and 2000 ft in elevation. The basin slopes down to the west and is drained by the rivers Someş and Mureş, which flow respectively north and south of the Bihor to join the Tisza in Hungary. Transylvania is floored almost entirely by Tertiary sedimentary rocks, which have been deeply dissected by the rivers to produce a series of wide, subsidiary basins filled with alluvium. The course of the river Olt, which leaves the basin via the Red Tower Pass through the Transylvanian Alps, has already been noted.

5. *The plains of Walachia and Moldavia*

To the south of the Transylvanian Alps and sloping gently in a series of terraces towards the Danube is the Walachian plain, very like the southern part of the Hungarian plain. Along the northern edges are great fans of alluvium washed down from the mountains, and much of this has been spread over the Tertiary sands, marls and gravels of which the plain is composed. Loess, too, covers much of the area east of Craiova. The usually monotonous surface of the plain is broken by the deep valleys of streams flowing to join the Danube, the chief being the Jiu, Olt and Argeş. Adjoining the Danube is a belt of marshy country with lagoons and abandoned arms of the river. In consequence, although the Danube is wide and navigable, there are few towns on its banks in Walachia and none at all of any size, except Brăila. At the eastern end of the Walachian plain the Danube turns north into Rumania before entering the Black Sea by a delta. The delta is a maze of reed-covered swamps, salt lagoons and mud-flats which impede navigation of the river.

Moldavia, lying between the rivers Siret and Prut at the feet of the eastern Carpathians, is a low plateau of about 1000 ft in elevation rather than a plain.

6. *The Dobrogea*

The Dobrogea is a low plateau lying between the Danube and the Black Sea. It is covered with horizontal, undisturbed chalk strata, resting on Hercynian rocks, and with a top layer of loess. It is a flat dusty steppe, with little surface water, except for occasional valleys containing streams which dry up in late summer, though in the north there are tree-clad hills.

CLIMATE AND VEGETATION

The climate of Rumania is continental, with greatest annual extremes of temperature in the Carpathians and the Transylvanian basin. The winters in the basin are made more severe by its enclosed character and elevation, and by drainage of cold air from the surrounding mountains causing frequent frost pockets. The plains of the Banat, Walachia and Moldavia, and the plateau of the Dobrogea have hot summers, cold winters and low rainfall, the greatest precipitation being in summer. In this season, however, high temperatures cause rapid evaporation, so that many rivers crossing the plains dry up and water supply becomes a problem in the towns. As in Hungary, water shortage is not so serious in the rural areas, for the water-table is sufficiently near the surface to allow supplies to be drawn from shallow wells. The figures for Bucharest, centrally situated in Walachia, may be taken as typical of the lowlands. Bucharest has an average for January of 25° F (−3·9° C), and for July of 73° F (22·8° C); its annual precipitation is 23 in.

The eastern Carpathians and Transylvanian Alps are heavily forested, mainly with beech (34%), conifers (24%), and oak (20%). Similar but less dense forests cover the slopes of the Bihor massif and much of the Transylvanian basin. The zone of alluvial fans along the north of the plain of Walachia was also a deciduous forest region, but most of the trees have been cleared for cultivation. The natural vegetation of the Banat and other plains is steppe, but the grasses have been ploughed in and the lowlands transformed by grain production. The Dobrogea, too, once a dry area with patchy grasses, has been changed to arable land. The delta of the Danube is a marshy, reed-covered region, of little economic value.

HUMAN GEOGRAPHY

HISTORY AND PEOPLE

A "colony" of the Roman Empire was established on the Walachian plain as a defence against northern tribes, and the Slavs and Dacians who lived there were gradually Romanised. With the advance of the Magyars and, later, the Tartars and Ottoman Turks, the Rumanians sought refuge away from the plain and crossed the mountains into the Transylvanian basin, where they were joined by colonies of Germans, Magyars, gipsies and Jews. In the eighteenth and nineteenth centuries they reoccupied the plains and founded the modern state, assimilating the Slav, Turkish and Magyar elements already living there, to form the present language and people.

Walachia and Moldavia, north of the Danube, were not overrun by Turkey in the seventeenth century, but admitted its overlordship. In 1878, however, after a long period of enforced co-operation with the Ottoman Empire, the two provinces united to form the kingdom of Rumania. Transylvania and the Dobrogea were added to the new country, which became much larger in 1919, when it was given a piece of the Hungarian plain, Bessarabia and the Bukowina. Further changes in the boundaries took place after the Second World War, during the last months of which Rumania changed sides and joined the Western allies. The most important of these consisted in the return of Bessarabia and Bukowina to the Soviet Union, whose troops occupied Rumania. The king had fled the country during the war, and in 1945 Rumania became another Communist republic and was absorbed into the Soviet sphere.

The Rumanian people are basically Slavs, but with a considerable admixture of Dacian and Roman blood, the result of colonisation by these conquerors. Their language, a mixture of Slavonic and Low Latin, shows the influence of the diverse ethnic mixture; it is counted as a Romance language.

POPULATION

The population of Rumania is 18,750,000, of whom more than five-sixths are Rumanian-speaking. There are 1,5000,000 Hungarians (Magyars) in the Banat, upwards of 380,000 Germans and 100,000 gipsies in the Transylvanian basin, and 140,000 Jews, mainly in the towns of Walachia. Smaller numbers of Turks, Slovaks, Ukrainians, Ruthenians, Serbo-Croats and Bulgarians help to make up a most striking medley of races, languages and religions.

Rumania is an agricultural country, 67% of the population being classed in 1962 as rural. Thirty years ago nearly 80% of the people obtained their living from the land, so there has been a rapid move to the towns, indicative of a better use of the country's natural resources and the growth of industry. The greatest concentration of urban life is around Bucharest, with a population of nearly two millions in the city and surrounding districts; only Cluj of the remaining towns has more than 150,000 inhabitants. The average density of population in Rumania is 204 persons per square mile—but there are few people in the eastern mountain ranges, parts of Moldavia, and the Bihor massif.

THE ECONOMY

GENERAL CHARACTERISTICS

Until 1945, Rumania was classed as one of the most backward countries in Europe, with an economy based on inefficient agriculture. Since then it has made great strides in industrial development and agrarian reforms have revolutionised the use of the land. The reforms have been most in evidence on the Walachian plain, but have been enforced throughout the country. Forests and mineral resources are now nationalised, and the land is the property of the State.

In Rumania the farms are organised wherever possible into collectives and run on Soviet lines. A collective is worked as if it was a giant agricultural factory. Workers are banded by directors and managers into "production brigades," from which teams are drawn for the actual cultivation of the land, and everyone is paid in proportion to the total output of the farm. Each peasant family on the collective is provided with a house, a vegetable plot or orchard, arable land up to three-quarters of an acre for its own use, and a fixed number of livestock.

This system of large-scale farming is probably the best way of using the land of Walachia, for the peasant farmers before the reforms of 1952 could not afford machinery of any kind, crop yields were among the lowest in Europe, and there was little knowledge of modern methods of cultivation and marketing. Even as late as 1944, there were 25,000 wooden ploughs in Rumania, and the simplest of agricultural machines were a novelty. Today, over 80% of the Walachian farms are completely

[*Courtesy of the Rumanian Legation.*

FIG. 107.—Rumania: maize harvest. A State farm at Miriziceni, in Walachia. On State farms, maize is increasingly grown by irrigation, with higher yields and lower production costs. State farms occupy 12%, and collectives 62% of the total agricultural area of Rumania.

mechanised with up-to-date machines, there are experimental State farms, and fertiliser works have been built at Craiova.

The industrialisation of Rumania is proceeding rapidly, more rapidly perhaps than that of any of its neighbours; but it is easy to exaggerate the importance of even small advances in a country which only a few years ago was considered under-developed. There is a great danger that the "industrial revolution" in Rumania may be too rapid, that in trying to change in the short space of twenty-five years from a backward, illiterate country to a modern state with a balanced industrial economy, Rumania is creating for itself grave political and economic problems.

Rumania's economy, like that of most of the countries of east and south east central Europe, is being reorganised under Soviet domination and direction. Nearly half its foreign trade is with the Soviet Union and another sixth with other Communist countries. Rumania leans heavily on Soviet capital, technical equipment and scientific advisers, and in the years since 1945 has benefited greatly from introduction by the U.S.S.R. of new industries and of new methods in those already established. But this growth has been accompanied by an upsurge of national pride in the country's achievements, and a desire to be regarded by its powerful patron as more than a mere satellite. The Soviet Union's inordinate demands for excessive quantities of petroleum, forest products and cereal in return for industrial assistance have caused much resentment and even open opposition among the Rumanian peasantry, and a marked change for the worse can be seen in the relations between the two governments. Rumania is passing through a critical phase of transition from a purely agricultural economy. But its potentialities are great and its prospect bright.

REGIONAL ECONOMY

1. *The eastern Carpathians and Transylvanian Alps*

The mountain arc of Rumania is sparsely peopled. Villagers in isolated valleys and hollows among the ranges have been little affected by the Communist agrarian reforms or the growing industrial activity in the highlands, and practise a primitive cultivation of wheat, maize and vegetables. Cattle and sheep are taken in summer to high Alpine pastures, and much of the farmers' income comes from the sale of these animals in autumn in the towns of the plains, to which they are driven long distances along the roads.

Lumbering is widespread, with the greatest development on the inner slopes of the mountains, overlooking the Transylvanian basin. The timber industry exports large quantities of raw timber, and production of plywood and veneers is growing. The manufacture of pulp, paper and cellulose is still in its infancy. It is usually carried on in towns at some distance from the base of the mountains. The chief of these is Braşov where thermal-electricity is available. Pulp and paper mills will increase in number with the development of hydro-electricity. In Rumania it has been slow, largely because the country has such adequate alternative means of generating power as natural gas, petroleum and brown coal.

The total output of hydro-electric power in 1962 was 652 million kWh which is about the same as in East Germany and Poland, neither of which has anything like the area of mountains nor the number of fast-flowing

streams possessed by Rumania. The largest power station is at Piatra
Neamţ, on the river Bistrita, a tributary of the Siret. The Bicaz reservoir,
formed by damming the river, is the biggest freshwater lake in Rumania.
Piatra Neamţ has sawmills, plywood and furniture works, and pulp and
paper mills. Several new hydro-electric stations are planned in the
northern part of the Carpathians, along the headwaters of the Someş,
Mureş and Siret.

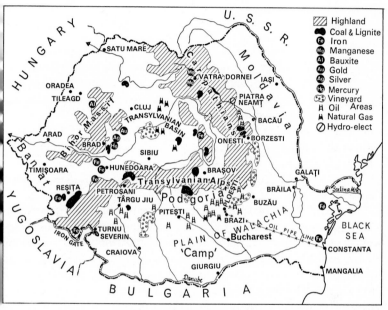

FIG. 108.—Rumania: minerals; chief towns. The map also shows the main vineyard
areas.

The mountains are rich in minerals, one part of the Transylvanian
Alps being called the Ore Mountains. There are deposits of copper, lead
and gold, but the greatest exploitation is of coal, iron ore and manganese.
Coal is found in two fields in the western Transylvanian Alps, around
Petroşani and Reşita, and the occurrence of iron ore near Reşita has led to
the growth there of smelting and steelworks. Manganese deposits are
worked around Vatra Dornei, in the northern Carpathians; most of the
ore is exported to the Soviet Union.

2. The Bihor massif

In its forested slopes, primitive farms, and transhumant rearing of cattle
and sheep, the Bihor is very like the Transylvanian Alps. Its relief, however, is different, for there are few real peaks, and villages may be found

high up on the flat plateaus which crown most of the massif. The Bihor is one of the chief sheep rearing regions in Rumania, the animals being kept for milk, cheese and wool, as well as for mutton. The ancient rocks of the Bihor contain important mineral deposits. Gold and silver-bearing ores, and some lignite and mercury, are mined in the vicinity of Brad. Southeast of Oradea are bauxite deposits, now nearly exhausted. The production of bauxite has fallen from 82,000 tons in 1959 to 15,000 tons at the present time.

3. *The Banat*

This region is here taken as the whole of the eastern portion of the Hungarian plain which is inside the Rumanian boundary, although as already noted the name applies strictly only to the southern part. The plain increases in elevation towards the east, where the change from the Carpathians, Bihor, and Transylvanian Alps is marked by vast alluvial fans, with an undulating surface. The loess soils of the west and the alluvium of the east are fertile, and covered by co-operatives growing maize, wheat and sugar beet; tobacco is grown extensively, and there are vineyards and mulberry groves (for sericulture) along the eastern margins. Cattle rearing is an essential part of this mixed farming economy.

The towns of the plain are all markets, with small food processing, textile and light engineering industries. The most important are Timişoara (148,000), Arad (114,000) and Oradea (109,000), which are among the largest towns in the country. Reşita (46,500), at the southern end of the Banat and near the coal and iron ore of the Transylvanian Alps, is growing rapidly, with blast furnaces, iron and steel works, and machine shops. The northern market is Satu Mare (62,500).

The Banat region was occupied by Rumanians in the nineteenth century, and became part of the country in 1920. There are, however, nearly 1,500,000 Magyar-speaking people living there, and the territory is still claimed by Hungary as rightfully hers. In its towns there are many ancient settlements of Jews, and their numbers were augmented in recent years by refugees from Germany and Poland.

4. *The Transylvanian basin*

Much of the Transylvanian basin is forested and the proportion of arable land is small. Yet, although the climate is severe in winter and farming is not easy, the basin has a denser population than might be expected. From time immemorial the region has been a place of refuge for people driven by invaders from the Danubian plains. It was here that the early Rumanians maintained their identity and independence; Magyar from the west penetrated to the upper Mureş basin and became known a

Szeklers; large numbers of nomad-like gipsies found safety and herded horses in its forest clearings; colonies of Germans settled in the south to found the towns of Braşov, Sibiu, and others, or remained in the shadow of the Bihor to build Cluj, on the Someş.

Rye is the usual food grain on the farms of the Transylvanian basin,

[*Courtesy of the Rumanian Legation.*]

FIG. 109.—Rumania: a tractor factory. The size of this tractor park at a factory in Brasov is indicative of the rapid mechanisation of Rumania's agriculture.

but wheat is grown in the centre. Sheep and cattle rearing is common everywhere, with some transhumance near the edges of the basin. Mineral deposits are abundant. Methane gas occurs a few miles east and south-east of Cluj; there are large deposits of iron ore around Hunedoara; lignite is found at several places in the east of the basin; common salt and gypsum are widespread.

Cluj (165,000), the largest town in the basin and the second in Rumania, has food processing, light engineering, textile manufacturing and the numerous small industries associated with a market town. As yet it has been little affected by the country's industrial advance. Nor has Sibiu (99,500), farther south, which has similar occupations. Braşov (131,200), however, situated in the upper Olt valley, is growing rapidly. Helped by beds of lignite west of the town, used to generate thermal-electricity, it has become the centre of a saw-milling, pulp and paper industry. Hunedoara (52,000), with large iron ore deposits near by, and salt from the centre of the basin, has developed engineering and chemical works.

5. The plains of Walachia and Moldavia

The Walachian plain contains a belt of foothills and alluvial fans at the foot of the Transylvanian Alps, known as the Podgoria ("piedmont"). South of this the wide, monotonous plain which stretches to the Black Sea shores is the Camp (open plain). The Podgoria is better watered than the Camp and is a land of forests, mixed agriculture and pasture, support-ing a denser population than the open plains to the south. Where the foothills meet the plain a line of towns and villages has grown of which Ploieşti (129,000), Buzău (53,200) and Piteşti (47,000) are the largest. Moldavia, east of the mountain ranges, is broken by low hills rising to about 1000 ft.

The plain of Walachia has loess soils and is fertile, but only in Moldavia has the loess developed into true black earth (chernozem). Both plains are a vast granary. Maize, the chief food grain of the people of the plains, and wheat, grown mostly for export, occupy two-thirds of the land. Fodder crops for cattle and horses are important, and oleaginous plants, such as sunflower, supply much-needed vegetable oils. The area under sugar beet is increasing, but potatoes, so useful in most European countries, are a minor crop in Rumania. Moldavia has vineyards and extensive fruit orchards, the latter producing plums, to be dried into prunes.

In the foothills of the mountain arc are large deposits of petroleum and natural gas. The oilfields are around Tirgu Jiu and north of Ploieşti, in the Walachian Podgoria, and west of Bacău, in Moldavia. Methane gas occurs south and west of Ploieşti. There are oil refineries in Walachia at Ploieşti and Brazi, and at Borzesti in Moldavia. A pipeline carries crude oil from Ploieşti to Constanţa, a port on the Black Sea. Rumania's annual production of petroleum is around 12 million tons, and of methane gas about 9000 million cubic metres—which makes it, outside the Soviet Union, Europe's greatest producer of oil and second producer of natural gas. A large proportion of Rumania's methane is used in the generation of thermal electricity. Ancillary to the oil industry are the chemical manu-factures of Ploieşti, Bucharest, Onesti and Constanţa.

Population in the Camp is fairly evenly distributed, except around

Bucharest in the east and Craiova in the west, where there are concentrations, and in a belt along the Danube, whose northern banks are fringed with marshland, liable to flood, and sparsely peopled. The chief towns on the Walachian Danube, which forms the southern boundary of Rumania for some distance, are Turnu Severin, near the Iron Gate, and Giurgiu. Turnu Severin is a river port which will increase in importance when a hydro-electric station, financed jointly by Rumania and Yugoslavia, is completed in the Iron Gate. Giurgiu is a ferry port connecting roads and railway to Ruse, in Bulgaria.

Bucharest (1,668,000), the capital, overshadows every other town in the country. The city grew in the middle of the plain, away from the Danube, at the crossing point of east–west roads and routes through the passes of the Transylvanian Alps. As the headquarters of the Walachian princes, it became the centre of trade and administration. Its importance grew with the development of grain exports and of the oilfields but, even with the great changes made under the Communist régime, Bucharest remains more an overgrown regional city than an industrial centre like Vienna or Budapest. Its food processing, machinery, light engineering industries, and newly established chemical works and oil refineries supply the needs of the agricultural plains, and have little significance beyond them. Craiova (115,700), the regional capital of the western end of the Camp, has light engineering and agricultural machinery works.

The lower course of the Danube (Dunarea in Rumania) lies entirely in Rumanian territory. It is extremely braided and the lands adjoining it are liable to flood. The river enters the Black Sea by a delta—the largest in Europe after that of the Volga—which is extending rapidly and contains lakes and reed-covered swamps. The delta has three main distributaries, but only the middle one, the Sulina, can take large ships, and then only by dint of constant dredging. To avoid the tedious passage through the delta, a ship canal is being constructed from Cernavodă on the Danube to Media, a tiny port north of Constanţa. Just above the delta are the ports of Brăila (116,400) and Galaţi (Galatz) (110,000), built to serve the needs of Walachia and Moldavia respectively, and the chief grain ports of Rumania. Brăila manufactures paper, cellulose and cardboard, using reeds from the delta as raw material.

There are very few towns in the interior of Moldavia besides those already mentioned near or in the mountains. Jassy (Iaşi) (125,000) is the largest, with linen manufacturing, and important quarries in its outskirts. It is also a hemp market. Flax is grown locally, and hemp cultivation is carried on throughout Moldavia and Walachia. After India and Yugoslavia, Rumania comes third in the world for production of hemp fibre.

6. *The Dobrogea*

The chalk plateau in the south-east of Rumania is structurally a part of the Bulgarian plateau. Until about fifty years ago semi-nomadic shepherds roamed its dry, dusty surface, but now it is largely under the plough. The southern half has a cover of loess, on which rye and barley are the chief crops; in the north, where the plateau is broken by deep valleys, there are clumps of trees, and a more general agriculture is possible. The Dobrogea region is sparsely peopled. The only concentration is at Constanța (Constantza) (117,000), an artificial port constructed on the Black Sea to serve as a port for Bucharest and to deal with petroleum exports from Ploieşti, to which it is connected by pipeline. The Dobrogea falls by cliffs to the sea, and where these are broken by valleys a number of holiday resorts have grown. The largest is Mangalia, near the southern boundary of the country.

STUDY QUESTIONS

1. Divide Rumania into natural regions and describe the important physical characteristics of each region.

2. Make a comparative study of the lower basins of the rivers Danube and Vistula.

3. What possibilities exist for the development of Rumania as an industrial country?

4. Give an account of major regional variations of population density in the basin of the river Danube. (J.M.B.)

5. Compare the economic activities of Transylvania with those of the Walachian and Moldavian plains.

Chapter XXVI

BULGARIA

PHYSICAL ASPECTS

BULGARIA, or the Bulgarian People's Republic, is structurally a part of the Balkan peninsula; but because the northern portion of the country is in the Danube basin, and because Bulgaria is orientated eastwards rather than to the rest of the Balkan peninsula, it is here included with the Danubian countries.

STRUCTURAL DIVISIONS

Bulgaria may be divided into four very different regions, (1) the Danubian plateau, (2) the Balkan mountains in the north, (3) the Rhodope mountains in the south, and (4) the basin of the Maritsa valley between the two mountain masses (*see* Fig. 110). The mountains of the north and

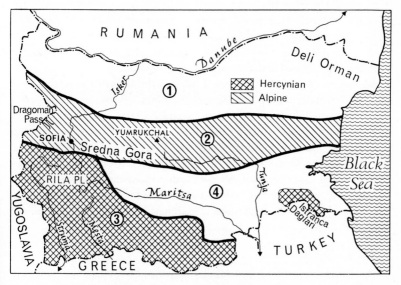

FIG. 110.—Bulgaria: physical divisions. The numbers refer to sections in the text. The areas shown on the map as "Hercynian" are regarded by some geologists as "median masses" of the Alpides system and, although composed of similar crystalline rocks, strictly not part of the Hercynian (Carbo–Permian) system.

south approach each other in the west of the country, so that they form a large **C**, opening to the Black Sea in the east.

1. *The Danubian plateau*

The Danubian or Bulgarian plateau lies immediately south of the river Danube. It appears to be a continuation of the Walachian plain of Rumania, but is at a higher altitude. Whereas the Rumanian bank of the Danube is low-lying, the Bulgarian side is often flanked by limestone cliffs. These are broken by passages to the river, along whose bank there are more small towns and villages than on the Rumanian side.

The plateau is composed of chalk, with a cover of loess, and because of its porous nature the surface is dry. Villages and towns are found in hollows or river valleys, where water is available. Over most of its area the plateau has a rolling surface, but towards the south it becomes hilly and ultimately merges into the Balkan mountains. Eastwards it rises to the low Deli Orman hills (Ludogorie), a dry chalk range which marks the southern boundary of the Dobruja, a continuation of the Rumanian Dobrogea (note the different spelling).

2. *The Balkan mountains*

The Balkan mountains, or Stara Planina, are a range of folded mountains which run from the Iron Gate to the Black Sea, decreasing eastwards in height. They are composed chiefly of limestones and sandstones, with a more elevated core of crystalline rocks in the middle portion, where the peak of Yumrukchal rises to 7822 ft. There are few precipitous slopes, the summits are rounded and the range is easy to cross.

Parallel to, and south of the main folds of the Balkan mountains, runs the low, crystalline range of the Sredna Gora. Between the two is a depression which is structurally a continuation of the "Diagonal Furrow" in Yugoslavia. At the western end of the country this Furrow lies between the "Alpine" Balkan mountains and the "Hercynian" Rhodope massif, and leads to the Morava valley, in Yugoslavia. Through the Bulgarian depression the river Tunja flows eastwards to join the Maritsa, its valley widening in places, in the basins around Klisura, Kazanlik and Sliven. The eastern end of the depression is represented by the plain behind the port of Burgas.

3. *The Rhodope mountains*

The Rhodope is a high and rugged massif of Hercynian age, covering the whole of southern Bulgaria and extending into Yugoslavia and Greece. It is highest in the west, in the Rila Planina, where Mount Mussalla rises to 9613 ft. The massif is much dissected; in the south-west, where there are areas of subsidence, deep, steep valleys have been carved by the rivers Struma and Mesta (Néstos). The central part of the Rhodope rarely falls below 6000 ft and forms a serious barrier to communications. Eastwards, the massif is lower and easier of access; some parts are composed of young volcanic rocks, through which flows the river Arda, a tributary of the Maritsa. In the extreme east of Bulgaria, but with its major portion in European Turkey, is the Istranca Dağlari, an outlier of the Rhodope.

4. The Maritsa valley

The river Maritsa rises in the Rila Planina and flows through the Plovdiv basin, one of the ancient dried-up lake basins of the Balkan peninsula. Below the basin the river takes a sharp turn to the south and flows ultimately to the Aegean Sea. East of the river bend the Maritsa lowlands narrow and are enclosed by the Sredna Gora and the Istranca Dağlari.

CLIMATE AND VEGETATION

The climate of the Danubian plateau is probably the most continental in peninsular Europe. In winter, bitterly cold winds blow from Russia, reducing the January mean temperatures to 5° F (−15° C) or less. Temperatures of −10° F (−23° C) have often been registered. The summers are hot, approaching a mean of 80° F (26° C) in July. Precipitation, which is mainly in summer, is rarely more than 15 in. annually. Much of the plateau is dry steppe; in valleys and nearer the Black Sea the grasslands have been ploughed for cereals.

The northern slopes of the Balkan mountains experience a climate even more severe than on the Danubian plateau, but the south-facing slopes are somewhat milder in winter: the basins at their feet, sheltered from the cold winds, have average temperatures in January of 30° F (−1·1° C) and in July of 72° F (22·2° C). Similar comparatively mild winters are found in the Maritsa valley. The Stara Planina and Sredna Gora are heavily forested, but the depression between the two ranges, with alluvial soils well watered by irrigation, is now cleared and intensively cultivated. The annual precipitation in all the lowlands drained to the Maritsa is less than 20 in. and has to be supplemented by irrigation. Where this is not possible in the Maritsa valley, there are stretches of steppe vegetation.

The Rhodope is cold in winter, mild in summer. It has an annual precipitation of over 40 in. on its western slopes, which are snow clad for weeks in winter. North of the Rila Planina there are some sheltered valleys and basins, in one of which Sofia is situated. Temperatures in

Sofia range from 27° F (−2·8° C) in January to 70° F (21·1° C) in July.
The annual precipitation is 26 in. In the valleys of the south-west Rhodope
the climate tends to be more Mediterranean, January temperatures averaging 36° F (2·2° C) and July 75° F (23·9° C), with an annual rainfall of
24 in. coming throughout the year but with maxima in May and November. The slopes of the Rhodope, especially of the Rila Planina, are covered
with dense virgin forests of conifers. Many parts of the plateau summits
are grasslands which are used as mountain pastures.

HUMAN GEOGRAPHY

HISTORY AND PEOPLE

The origin of the Bulgar people is uncertain. It is thought they derive
from a mid-Asian tribe, possibly akin to the Finns and Magyars, which
entered the southern side of the lower Danube basin before the Slav
migration. Their language (Bulgar) is now classified as Slavonic, with
Magyar influences; and the Bulgarians are mostly Slav in their culture
and outlook. Throughout history, however, they have preserved their
individuality as a people and when in 1878 the Turks withdrew from the
northern part of the present state, it was largely because of its community
of race and language that Bulgaria came into existence as a separate
country.

Russia was largely instrumental in obtaining Bulgaria's sovereignty, for
she hoped to use the country as an opening to the Aegean Sea. Thus she
made great efforts to have Macedonia added to the new state and so
complete her passage to the Mediterranean. In this she was thwarted in
1878 by Great Britain, which had no wish to see a powerful rival there.
However, when in the early years of the present century the Turks were
finally driven from the south of the Balkans, Macedonia was allotted to
Bulgaria by the Treaty of Bucharest in 1913. This precipitated the Second
Balkan War, for Greece and Serbia also laid claim to the disputed region.
Bulgaria was defeated and Macedonia divided between Greece and Serbia,
the latter receiving the larger portion. Small areas of Macedonia—principally isolated valleys near the south-western boundary of Bulgaria—
still remained in that country's hands, but in 1918 these fragments—
Timok, Tsaribrod, Basilegrad and Strumitsa—were annexed by Yugoslavia, which was incorporated as a sovereign state the same year.

The annexation resulted in thousands of "Bulgarised" Macedonian
refugees entering Bulgaria, where they settled around Sofia and in the
Burgas district. There they and their descendants form a dangerous
political minority, powerful enough to prevent any real *rapprochement*
between Bulgaria and Yugoslavia, who remain mutually hostile. Nor is

Rumania very friendly towards Bulgaria, for in 1940 she was forced to cede the southern part of the Dobruja to her neighbour.

In 1945, during the Second World War, the Soviet Union invaded and occupied Bulgaria. The following year the country was constrained to become a (Communist) People's Republic. It is now completely a satellite of the U.S.S.R., for whom it forms a western bastion and a spearhead directed towards its long-sought opening to the Mediterranean Sea.

POPULATION

The population of Bulgaria is 8,100,000 and is increasing rapidly. The average density is 183 persons a square mile, compared with 164 in Greece, 151 in Albania, and 190 in Yugoslavia, the last being much more industrialised than Bulgaria. The relatively large population is due to the fact that a larger proportion of the country's surface is available for cultivation than of its neighbours south of the Danube; and until recently its agriculture was mainly of the "garden cultivation" or "patch-farming" type which, although uneconomic, supports a denser rural population. Patch-farming has been abolished by the Communist government and replaced by co-operatives, which require less labour. The surplus of manpower has been directed into the towns to provide for the growing industries.

THE ECONOMY

GENERAL CHARACTERISTICS

Bulgaria is essentially and overwhelmingly an agricultural country, nor does it seem likely that any economic planning will much affect the position. There is certainly a great need to develop the present industries and introduce new ones. With the aid of Soviet capital and guidance, marked progress has in fact been made. But natural resources are few, deposits of mineral ores are small and the development of hydro-electric potential is slow, only 5% having so far been utilised. Great plans have been made to increase mineral output, to develop iron and steel industries, and to erect new hydro- and thermal-electric stations, but the programme is a long-term one. Industry in the modern sense is still in its infancy, dependent on Soviet help and goodwill. It is by no means certain that if Soviet support were withdrawn Bulgaria could maintain even the small industrial advance it has made in the past twenty years.

Manufactures are still linked mainly with agriculture, with flour milling, oilseed crushing, tobacco and leather manufacturing, and cotton and wool textiles, the last often hand-woven. The chief exports—in order of value—are textiles, fruit, tomatoes and tomato juice, cigarettes and raw tobacco. Mineral ores come very low in the list of exports. In total, the volume of trade per head of population is low—a sure sign of a backward economy.

For agriculture, however, the future seems brighter. Agrarian reforms were inaugurated in a two-year plan, 1947–48, when many large estates were broken up and re-assembled into co-operatives. Two five-

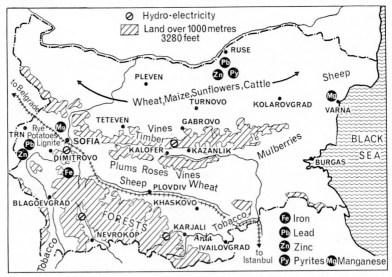

FIG. 111.—Bulgaria: economic. Correlate this map with Fig. 110. Note the extensive mineral exploitation in the west of the country, at heights of more than 1800 ft, which is the altitude of Sofia.

year plans followed, in which attention was given more to industries During this period a relatively big advance was made in the Sofia industrial region, in the Arda valley, and around Varna and Burgas. In 1961, an impressive twenty-year programme was published, which plans by 1980 the complete development of every branch of the country's economy. Primitive patch-farming disappeared during the five-year plans; today large-scale co-operative farms occupy 99% of all arable land. By the introduction of tractors, combine harvesters, etc., and the use of fertilisers, irrigation and modern methods, agricultural production has been nearly doubled, and with less manpower.

REGIONAL ECONOMY

1. *The Danubian plateau*

Much of the Danubian plateau is dry steppe used for sheep-rearing, but wheat and maize are grown wherever possible and on some of the valley slopes vines are cultivated. Sunflowers are an important crop; the oil from the seeds is used for cooking purposes. The plateau is Bulgaria's chief cereal and sunflower region. Most of its small towns have industries such as flour milling, oilseed crushing and the assembly and repair of agricultural machinery. They are also market towns. The largest is Ruse (91,700), a port on the Danube. In the middle of the plateau are Turnovo (46,000), Pleven (67,000) and Kolarovgrad (49,153); at the foot of the Balkan mountains, Teteven (35,000) and Gabrovo (45,000) have small wool textile industries.

The low Deli Orman hills in the east of the plateau are a southern extension of the Rumanian Dobrogea, here spelt Dobruja. Sheep rearing is almost the sole occupation in the hills, which have few inhabitants. This area was returned to Bulgaria from Rumania in 1940 and since that date Varna, a port at its south-east corner, has been developed as the main outlet to the Black Sea from the north of the country. Its population has grown to 123,830 and it has shipbuilding and chemical industries. Its chief exports are wheat and sunflower seeds. Small quantities of manganese, lead, zinc and pyrites are shipped, mainly to the Soviet Union. The manganese is mined near the port and the other minerals come from south-west of Ruse. Ruse also has a share in the mineral trade.

2. The Balkan mountains

This region is only sparsely populated. At one time the mountains supported far more people, but when the Turks left, many shepherds and farmer-lumbermen who had taken refuge there drifted to the better conditions in the towns to the south. The lower slopes of the Balkan mountains are densely forested; higher levels and the rounded summits have sheep pastures. Timber is carried to sawmills in the many river valleys, some of the mills being worked by small hydro-electric power stations on the south-flowing tributaries of the Tunja, which runs to the Maritsa. The dammed-up waters of the streams are also used for irrigation in the valley to the south.

In the depression between the Balkan mountains and the Sredna Gory the river Tunja widens its valley at several places. In the basins so formed, irrigation enables the fertile alluvial soils to support the intensive cultivation of wheat, maize, sunflowers, vegetables and vines. Plum orchards are found everywhere, and *slivovica*, an alcoholic spirit made from the fruit, is a staple drink. In the basins of Kazanlik and Kalofer, and extending southwards towards Plovdiv in the Maritsa valley, there are vast fields of roses, grown for their essence—attar of roses—which is an expensive perfume. The extraction industry, centred on Kazanlik, produces more than three tons of it a year.

P

Fig. 112.—Bulgaria: view of Plovdiv. The second city of Bulgaria, formerly
called Philippopolis, is centrally situated in the Maritsa basin. In the triangle
Plovdiv–Kalofer–Kazanlik, many square miles of rose fields produce annually nearly three tons of rose oil (attar of roses), a rich perfume, for which
Plovdiv is the market.

At its eastern end the depression widens into the plains of Burgas.
The town of Burgas (76,100) is the second port of Bulgaria, having been
outstripped in the past fifteen years by Varna. It has a shipbuilding industry and, in addition to being the outlet for the Tunja depression, serves
the Maritsa valley.

In the higher western end of the Bulgarian depression the river Isker,
which rises in the Rhodope and flows north through a gap in the Balkan
mountains to join the Danube, has widened its valley to form a basin. In
it, at an altitude of 1804 ft, is situated Sofia, the capital of Bulgaria. In
the cooler climate of this more elevated area, the chief crops are barley,
rye and potatoes, plus the ubiquitous plum orchards.

Sofia, very near the western frontier of the country and high in the
mountains, would appear to have an unusual site for a capital. The more
centrally placed Plovdiv would seem more suitable. Sofia, however, has
several advantages, chief of which are its strategic position and the fact
that around it are important mineral resources. The city lies at a crossroads in the mountains. Passes from its basin lead to the north, north-
west and south-west, and there is easy passage eastwards into the Maritsa

valley. The north-west passage is the Dragoman Pass, leading to the Morava valley. It is used by the railway—the Orient Express route—from western Europe to Istanbul, which passes through Sofia. The capital has become the focus of Bulgaria's railway system.

The Sofia region is becoming industrialised. Small amounts of bituminous coal are mined west of the capital, and of manganese to the north. There is iron ore in the Rila Planina (*planina*, "mountains"), south of Sofia; modern steelworks have been established in the city and at Dimitrovo, where hydro-electricity is available. Most of the raw material for Bulgaria's iron and steel industry must, however, be imported. Lead and zinc are mined around Trn, mainly for export, and Sofia is the market for the raw ores. Sofia has grown from a population of 16,000 in 1878 to 671,000 in 1963. This phenomenal increase is only partly due to the rise of industry; it has been helped by the large influx of refugees from Macedonia, which lies across the border. They have helped to make Sofia the chief textile, engineering and chemical centre in the country.

3. *The Rhodope mountains*

Grazing and lumbering are the chief occupations of the scanty population of most of the Rhodope; the outlier of the Istranca Dağlari, through which runs the boundary with European Turkey, is virtually uninhabited. The valleys of the rivers Mesta (Néstos) and Struma in the south-west, and of the Arda in the east of the massif are better peopled and some industries, based on hydro-electric power, are growing. From these three valleys comes the bulk of Bulgaria's tobacco exports.

The Arda has been harnessed for hydro-electric power near Karjal (Kurdjali), and lead and zinc smelters are using ores brought from Trn, near Sofia. Blagoevgrad, on the Struma, has textile works driven by electricity. Nevrokop, in the valley of the Mesta, has new iron and steel works. The Struma valley is an important thoroughfare, providing the main route from Sofia to the Aegean coastlands.

4. *The Maritsa valley*

Shut in on all sides by highlands, the valley of the Maritsa has milder winters than any other part of Bulgaria, except the southward-facing valleys of the south-west Rhodope. The rainfall is too small for agriculture and is supplemented by irrigation waters from the rivers flowing to the Maritsa. The irrigated areas are in the higher west of the valley, where wheat, maize, tomatoes, sunflowers and tobacco are grown. There are also vineyards, and orchards of peaches, apricots and plums. Some parts of the banks of the Maritsa are marshy; where the marshes have been reclaimed, rice is grown. In the east of the valley there are stretches of steppe, on which sheep are reared. From Khaskovo to Burgas the plains and low hills have scattered forests of oak, whose leaves support a small but thriving sericulture. The Maritsa bends southwards and flows through a gap between the main mass of the Rhodope and the Sakar Planina. In this valley tobacco is the chief crop, and Ivailovgrad, on the Arda, its market.

The only large town in the Maritsa valley is Plovdiv (Philippopolis) (171,391). Centrally situated in the lowlands, and in the middle of the irrigated region, it has flour mills, sugar refineries, tobacco factories, attar extraction plants and silk manufacture. Heavy industry, represented by steel and chemical works, has been introduced in the past ten years.

STUDY QUESTIONS

1. Examine the site, situation and development of Sofia.
2. Write a short account of the economic geography of Bulgaria.
3. Divide Bulgaria into natural geographical regions and give a detailed description of *one* of the divisions you make.

Chapter XXVII

YUGOSLAVIA

The Socialist Federal Republic of Yugoslavia came into existence in 1919 as a confederation of six small states: Serbia (with its autonomous provinces of Vojvodina and Kosovo-Metohija), Croatia, Slovenia, Bosnia-Hercegovina, Macedonia and Montenegro.

PHYSICAL ASPECTS

STRUCTURAL DIVISIONS

Three-quarters of Yugoslavia is mountainous, the highest ranges lying along the western, southern and eastern margins. In the north is the only extensive stretch of lowland in the country. The chief river of Yugoslavia is the Danube, which flows for 945 miles either across the northern plain or to form the boundary with Rumania. Its longest tributaries are the Sava, Drava and Morava. The Drava forms part of the Yugoslav–Hungarian boundary. Nearly 70% of the surface of Yugoslavia is drained to the Danube. The only important southward-flowing river is the Vardar, which passes through Greece to the Aegean Sea.

The physical—and mainly structural—divisions which may be distinguished in Yugoslavia are: (1) the Alpine zone, (2) the Dinaric ranges, (3) the Morava–Vardar "corridor" lands, and (4) the Danubian plains (*see* Fig. 113).

1. *The Alpine zone*

In the north-west of Yugoslavia the Karawanken Alps and the Julian Alps are continuations of the Alpine ranges of Austria. Mount Triglav (9393 ft), in the Julian Alps, is the highest peak in Yugoslavia. Away from the mountains the region is a high plateau cut by deep valleys, such as that of the Sava, which rises in the Karawanken Alps. In places the valleys have widened into extensive basins, the most important of which is around Ljubljana. This north-western Alpine zone constituted the old state and present republic of Slovenia.

2. *The Dinaric ranges*

The Dinaric Alps, the most extensive mountainous area in Yugoslavia, stretch from the Alpine zone in Slovenia to the river Drim and Lake

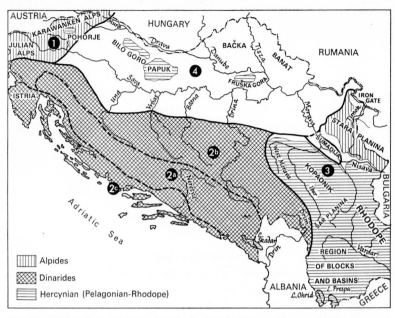

FIG. 113.—Yugoslavia: structural and physical divisions. The numbers correspond with those used in the text. *Note:* the Pelagonian-Rhodope massifs are sometimes regarded as a median mass (*see* caption to Fig. 110).

Skadar in the south, spreading eastwards, south of the Sava valley, to the West Morava river and the Field (or *polje*) of Kosovo. This mass of mountains and plateaus, one of the most rugged in Europe, comprises the republics of Bosnia-Hercegovina, Montenegro, and the southern part of Croatia. The region may be subdivided into three belts: (*a*) a central plateau dominated on its western edge by mountains which rise to over 8000 ft, (*b*) an eastern series of lower and less difficult ranges, with river valleys opening northwards, and (*c*) a still lower belt along the Adriatic Sea, known as Dalmatia.

(*a*) *The plateau and mountains* which fill western Bosnia-Hercegovina and the whole of Montenegro are composed of very permeable and soluble limestone. They are known as the Karst or High Karst. Although it has one of the heaviest precipitations in Europe, the surface of the region is dry, bare and inhospitable, for it allows rain and melting snows to soak or flow quickly through the outer strata to form underground streams and lakes. The Neretva is the only river to have its course entirely on the surface. This is because it has cut a very deep canyon, which takes its valley floor below the level of the water-table.

The peneplained limestone platforms on the plateau are deeply grooved and furrowed where solution has widened joints into grykes. There are many depressions or basins where the roofs of underground caverns have collapsed or where surface rocks of relatively greater solubility have been dissolved. The larger basins are known as *polja* (Serb. *polje*, "plain"), and may be many miles in diameter; smaller ones, *dolina* (Serb. *doline*, "hollow"), vary in diameter from hundreds of yards to a few feet. Polja and dolina are often floored with red earth, terra rossa, the insoluble quartz and clay impurities left as a residue by the dissolved limestone. The red colour derives from a long accumulation of minute traces of insoluble iron hydroxides. In some of the dolina there are fresh-water Tertiary deposits, suggesting that the area experienced epeirogenic uplift before the surface collapsed to form the depressions. Limestone regions in other parts of the world which, like the Karst, have a topography with grykes, sink-holes and broken river drainage with underground streams and caverns are said to have "karst" characteristics.

The High Karst, *i.e.* the mountainous western rim of the plateau, is a range high enough to form a climatic divide between the Mediterranean and continental influences. It is also a most difficult barrier to communications. There are only four passes through the High Karst, and all are at high altitudes. The highest peak in the range is Durmitor (8294 ft).

(b) *The mountain ranges east of the Karst*, though lower, are still rugged. They are composed partly of very soluble limestone similar to that of the Karst, partly of sandstones and crystalline rocks. The limestones, although in places they have dissolved to form polja, are not dry on the surface as in the Karst, and the whole of this sub-region usually has enough soil cover to support tree growth. The mountain ranges are traversed by numerous rivers whose deep, gorge-like valleys make communications difficult. The chief rivers are the Una, Vrbas, Bosna and Drina, which cut through the mountains on their way to the Sava in the north. Along their northern margin the mountain ranges decrease in height and the valleys widen, to form southern extensions of the plains of the Sava.

(c) *Dalmatia*. On the western side of the Dinaric region, the land falls in steep terraces from the High Karst to the cliff-lined Adriatic coast. On some of the lower terraces there are outcrops of flysch, with good soils; in the lower valleys of rivers which emerge from the base of the Karst there are alluvial flats and terra rossa. North of Sibenik a slight sinking of the land has resulted in a more continuous coastal plain. Southwards, the only lowlands are the river valleys mentioned above, and the narrow strip cut by the Neretva. The coast of Dalmatia is lined with strings of long, low, narrow islands, the remains of concordant limestone ranges which have subsided, and been drowned and partly dissolved by the sea. Parts of the

Dalmatian mainland have long, branching, rectangular inlets where depressions have been similarly invaded.

3. The Morava–Vardar "corridor" lands

East of the Dinaric region, Yugoslavia consists of a series of rugged, crystalline mountain blocks and enclosed basins, different in origin from the folded ranges of the west. They are parts of the Rhodope-Pelagonian massif, probably of Hercynian age, which was fractured and dislocated in mid-Tertiary times, the down-faulted areas being inundated by the waters of the Aegean Sea to form the "Aegean Lake." Later uplift broke the "Aegean Lake" into a number of separate small lakes, most of which have dried up, leaving basins floored with Tertiary rocks and a surface cover of lacustrine silts and alluvium. Two lakes which remain are Ohrid and Prespansço, on the Yugoslav–Albanian–Greek border.

The movements of uplift and subsidence were greatest in the south, in Macedonia. Here the mountain blocks rise to over 8500 ft in the massifs of Korab, Šar Planina and Borislaec, and several others have an altitude of 7000 ft. Between them are the basins of Bitola, Tetovo, Skopje and Strumica, interconnected by narrow defiles. The Macedonian mountains form the water-parting between the Danubian tributaries and the rivers flowing to the south. In the north of the region, where the uplift was not so great, the highest block, the Kapaonik, does not reach 5000 ft. The basins of Kosovo and Metohija, connected by a wide opening, are sufficiently extensive to form together an autonomous province of the republic of Serbia. In the north, the river valleys widen to form plains. The largest is along the lower Morava and called the Šumadija.

Some of the valleys of rivers flowing northwards to the Danubian plain and of those flowing southwards to the Aegean Sea are connected at their heads by low cols, and form continuous—if somewhat difficult—routes through the mountains. In the west, one of these "corridors" leads from the Ibar valley to the upper Vardar and the Tetovo and Skopje basins. East of this, the Morava and Vardar valleys are continuous and are known as the "Diagonal Furrow," the most important north–south "corridor" in the Balkans. A third route utilises the Struma valley, in Bulgaria. This is connected to the valley of the Nisava, a tributary of the Morava, which provides a passage eastwards from the Diagonal Furrow to the Sofia basin and thence to the Maritsa valley and Istanbul. This is the route taken by the Orient Express line. The two western corridors converge at their northern ends on Belgrade, and southwards they lead through Greece to the port of Salonica.

East of the Morava–Vardar corridor, the mountains in the south are the western edges of the Rhodope massif. North of the river Nisava are the Alpine folds of the western Balkan mountains, which swing north-wards to the Danube, where they are separated from the Transylvanian Alps of Rumania by the Iron Gate. The Yugoslav Rhodope is split into several blocks: the highest is Plackovica (5763 ft). The Balkan Mountains in Yugoslavia have a few lofty peaks in the south, such as Midzor (7172 ft), but towards the Danube they decrease in height to little more than hills. East of the Balkans, and shut off by them from the rest of the country, the Timok valley widens to the plain of Kladovo, near the Danube.

The "corridor" lands draining south to the Vardar form the republic of Macedonia. The first kingdom of Serbia grew in the western Ibar–Kosovo corridor, but the heart of the present republic is the Morava valley, the Šumadija.

4. The Danubian plain

Northern Yugoslavia forms part of the Pannonian basin, and is low-land. The eastern portion is a flat, monotonous plain, very similar to the adjoining Hungarian region. Through it flows the river Danube and the lower reaches of its tributaries, the Drava, Sava and Tisza. The Drava and Sava drain the western plain; the Tisza cuts the eastern portion in two. The rivers are flanked by broad belts of fertile alluvium, and east of the Danube there are extensive areas covered with loess. The western Danubian plain is undulating and broken by ancient crystalline rock masses which have been upthrust to form the forested hills of the Pohorje, Bilo Goro, Papuk and Fruška Gora, between the rivers Drava and Sava.

This hilly western region is Slavonia, a part of the republic of Croatia. The eastern plain, south of the Danube, is northern Serbia. Vojvodina, an autonomous province of Serbia, lies north of the Danube and is divided by the Tisza into the plains of the Bačka to the west, and of the Banat to the east. The latter are a continuation of the Banat of Rumania.

CLIMATE AND VEGETATION

The High Karst on the west and the mountain blocks of Macedonia in the south form a barrier between the Mediterranean and continental climates experienced in Yugoslavia. The Adriatic coastlands and the southern Vardar valley have the hot, dry summers and mild, wet winters associated with a Mediterranean climate, and occasionally these conditions penetrate to the interior of the country via the gaps in the mountains or along the valleys. The average January temperature for these "Mediter-ranean" areas is 41·5° F (5·3° C), and in July it is 79·5° F (26·4° C), with an annual rainfall of about 25 in.

The rest of the country has a continental climate—hot summers, cold winters and precipitation which falls mainly in summer. Temperatures range from January averages of 29° F (−1·7° C) to 73·5° F (23·1° C) in July. Annual precipitation varies considerably according to elevation, aspect or rainshadow effects. Mostar, for instance, in the valley of the Neretva, in the Dinaric Alps, has 55 in. annually, whereas Belgrade, in the northern plain, has only 18·5 in. Niš and Skopje, in sheltered valleys, have 17 in.

Precipitation in the Dinaric ranges overlooking the Adriatic Sea is strikingly high for a region so far removed from Atlantic influences. The district north of Titograd has registered 183 inches in a year, and Titograd itself has an annual precipitation of 52 in. The north-west Alpine region has about 70 inches in the mountains, and the Ljubljana basin 54 in. a year.

The Dalmatian coastlands are sometimes affected in winter by the *bora*, a cold wind blowing from the High Karst. During anticyclonic calms, cold air accumulates in the high valleys and, when a depression passes along the Adriatic it is drawn down to the coastlands as violent, icy winds which are a danger to shipping and greatly feared by fishermen. The high velocity of these winds is due to the steep thermal gradient caused by the presence of cold, high mountains near a warm sea.

A tenth of the surface of Yugoslavia consists of bare, high mountains or barren Karst. Of the remainder, the vegetation is almost equally divided between forests, pasture and arable land. Most of the mountains are forested, mainly with deciduous trees such as oak and walnut up to about 5000 ft, and with conifers, chiefly pines, at higher levels. Pasture land is found in the basins among the mountains or as Alpine pastures above the tree line. In the Bačka and Banat there remain areas of steppe vegetation which have not been ploughed for agriculture. The chief arable lands are in the Šumadija and the Danubian plain west of the Danube. The river valleys are cultivated, and in some of them two, or even three, successive harvests in the same year are not unusual.

HUMAN GEOGRAPHY

HISTORY AND PEOPLE

The people of Yugoslavia are classified as South Slavs. In the westward migrations of the early Slavs, various tribes at different times penetrated the mountains of Yugoslavia and settled in this most difficult environment. The Slovenes occupied the Alpine region, near the present Austrian and Italian borders. The Croats settled in the valley of the Sava and the hill ranges south of it. The Montenegrins and Macedonians took possession of the southern Dinarics and the southern "corridor" lands. The Serbs—the most powerful tribe—first occupied the eastern Dinarics, then spread towards the Morava valley and the eastern Danubian plain. These were the principal peoples, but there were in addition smaller communities in the fastnesses of Bosnia, Hercegovina and Pelagonia.

From the middle of the fifteenth century the whole of the Balkan peninsula was overrun by the Ottoman Turks, who spread their empire to the gates of Vienna. They were gradually driven back by the armies of the Holy Roman Emperor, and in 1699 Slovenia and Croatia became part of the Austrian possessions. In the course of time the inhabitants of these regions adopted a more Westernised culture than the other South Slavs. For nearly 400 years the Serbs and other mountain peoples lived under the domination of the Turks, who ruled with savage cruelty. The South Slavs, scattered in separate communities and isolated from each other by high mountain ranges, were unable to unite effectively against their oppressors. Their only defence against the armed retribution which invariably followed their refusal to pay the exorbitant taxes levied upon them was to withdraw to their mountain fastnesses and defy all Turkish attempts to crush them. There, living from hand to mouth, they developed an intense local patriotism and an unquenchable yearning for independence.

The first real chance of liberation came in the first part of the nineteenth century, when the Serbs rebelled against the hated Turks and achieved an uneasy kind of independence. Complete freedom came a step nearer after 1878, when the Ottoman Empire was defeated in a war with Russia. In 1881 the Niš region rebelled successfully, and all the rest of the mountain peoples became free when the Turks withdrew from southeastern Europe in 1912, keeping for themselves only a small area behind Constantinople (Istanbul). Freedom did not last long, however, for the Treaty of Bucharest in 1913, which terminated the Turkish war, gave Macedonia to Bulgaria and so precipitated the Second Balkan War. The result was that Macedonia was partitioned between Greece and Serbia, with the larger portion allotted to Serbia.

In the meantime, the Austrian-owned regions of Slovenia and Croatia were becoming restive and demanding independence; nationalist groups in the two provinces were fostering revolution, aided and abetted by Bosnia and Hercegovina, which had been annexed by Austria in 1908. The assassination of the Crown Prince of Austria in Sarajevo led to the invasion of Serbia by the Austro-Hungarian forces, and this campaign in turn precipitated the First World War.

In 1918, at the end of the war, the heterogeneous peoples of the northern Balkans became united as the Kingdom of the Serbs, Croats and Slovenes, under the king of Serbia. In 1929 the name of the new country was changed to Yugoslavia, as being the "land of the South Slavs." The frontiers, as fixed in 1919, included all the highlands to the east of the important Morava–Vardar corridor, and took from Bulgaria a portion of Macedonia it had retained.

In 1941, during the Second World War, Yugoslavia was invaded by the Italians and Germans. The country was partitioned between Germany, Italy, Hungary and Bulgaria. More than 10% of the population was killed, newly established industrial plants were left in ruins, towns and railways were destroyed and the countryside was a scene of desolation. In this period of tribulation the people of Yugoslavia ceased to be Serb, or Croat, or Bosnian, or Macedonian, and banded themselves into an "underground" Liberation Army to fight against the occupying forces; so that when, in 1945, the country was free again, Yugoslavia's peoples were more closely united than ever before. In 1947, a portion of Venezia Giulia, was taken from Italy and added to Yugoslavia, and the fragments of Macedonia still in Bulgarian hands were annexed.

At the end of the war Yugoslavia was under Soviet domination, with Marshal Tito, a leader of the wartime resistance against the Germans, in charge of government. Yugoslavia was proclaimed a Communist federal republic, within the Soviet zone of influence, which now stretched without a break from the Black Sea to the Adriatic. Tito, however, did not wholly accept the Soviet interpretation of Marxist Communism, and withdrew his country from the domination of Moscow. Yugoslavia is still Communist, but with differences from the ideology of the Soviet Union. The country is still friendly with Moscow; but, seeing itself in a position of balance between East and West, it maintains open relations with the Western powers, and is not behind the Iron Curtain. The Western powers, for their part, welcome the split in the Communist ranks, for it means that the Soviet Union is once more denied access to the Mediterranean.

POPULATION

The population of Yugoslavia totalled 19,064,000 in 1963, with an average density of 193 persons per square mile. The population is unevenly distributed. Some parts of the mountains in the west are almost uninhabited, whereas the agricultural plains of the north, especially the Vojvodina, are comparatively densely peopled. The greatest concentrations are around Belgrade and Zagreb, and in the Alpine region of Slovenia. The average numbers of people per square mile in the republics which comprise Yugoslavia are: Serbia 223, Slovenia 203, Croatia 190, Bosnia-Hercegovina 166, Macedonia 141 and Montenegro 88. With the increased mechanisation of agriculture in the northern plains, over-population is beginning to make itself felt, and the Government has introduced measures to attract surplus labour from the plains to the infant industries in the valleys of Bosnia-Hercegovina, Montenegro and Macedonia. Present trends show a distinct increase in Yugoslavia's population south of a line drawn across the country through Sarajevo and Skopje.

There are three official languages in Yugoslavia—Serbo-Croat, Slovene, and Macedonian. In addition there are at least six other "minority" languages, each spoken by considerable numbers. This assemblage of different tongues hindered the initial federation of Yugoslavia, and there are still political and economic tensions due to linguistic differences and the varying standards of cultural and living conditions found in the different republics. On the whole, however, the peoples of Yugoslavia have been united very effectively. The material advances made since 1919 have helped by raising the standard of living and increasing the general prosperity, but probably the tragic experiences of the Second World War had more effect.

THE ECONOMY

GENERAL CHARACTERISTICS

Before 1939, both industry and agriculture were backward. About 80% of the working population was engaged in inefficient or subsistence agriculture and only 7% in industry. At the present time, the number of agricultural workers has fallen to 52% of the total, yet production has increased, and the proportion of industrial workers has risen to 13%. The biggest increases are in the numbers engaged in building construction, transport and commerce. Moreover, the contribution of industry to the national income in the same period has risen from a paltry 9·5% to 47%.

Most of the advance came from developments in the Danubian plain and Slovenia, but the policy of the Government is to spread industry through the mountainous regions of the south, using the hydro-electric potential and the mineral deposits so abundant there. Since 1945, hundreds of factories have been built to produce goods such as diesel engines, automobiles, railway rolling stock, telephone exchanges, etc., which used to be imported. New agricultural techniques are releasing workers, not only for the factories, but for building roads and railways, the lack of which in some districts is a tremendous handicap.

Yugoslavia may be a Communist country, but it looks to the Western powers for capital and technical advice rather than to the Soviet Union. Its exports, mainly of foodstuffs, mineral ores and tobacco, go to Italy, West Germany, the U.S.A., the United Kingdom and the Soviet Union, in that order. Its imports of fuel (coal and petroleum), machinery and transport equipment, raw materials and foodstuffs come mainly from the

U.S.A., Italy, West Germany, the Soviet Union and the United Kingdom.

Post-war reconstruction, inaugurated and encouraged by the U.S.S.R., was taken over by the Western powers until Yugoslavia was able to continue independently. Today, the country shows promise of becoming a strong and progressive Mediterranean power.

MINERALS AND POWER

Yugoslavia ranks high among the countries of Europe in wealth of water power, as might be expected from its relief and ample rainfall in the higher regions. Yet the volume of hydro-electric power before 1945 was small. In 1946 it amounted to 478 million kWh, but by 1962 had increased phenomenally to 6851 million kWh; and this is still only a tenth of the estimated hydro-electric potential of the country. Hydro-electric power production surpasses the total of thermally generated energy, which in 1962 was 4424 kWh, and new hydro-electric stations continue to be built.

The chief hydro-electric power plants are in the wetter parts of the Dinaric Alps draining to the Adriatic Sea, at Split, Dubrovnik and

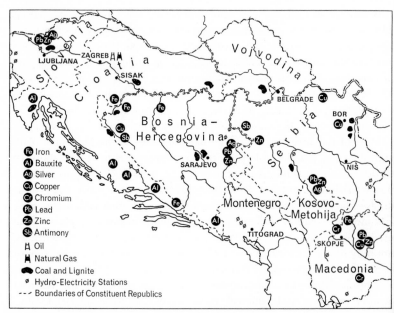

FIG. 114.—Yugoslavia: minerals and power. The map shows also the six republics—Bosnia-Hercegovina, Croatia, Macedonia, Montenegro, Serbia and Slovenia—which comprise the federal State of Yugoslavia. In the republic of Serbia there are two autonomous provinces, Vojvodina, with a large Hungarian minority population, and Kosovo-Metohija, with a population predominantly Albanian.

Jablanica. There is another large station at Maribor, in the Karawanken Alps. A large proportion of Yugoslavia's hydro-electric power potential is in the area drained by the right-bank tributaries of the Sava, and there are many stations along the valleys of the Vrbas, Bosna, Drina and Ibar (*see* Fig. 114).

Yugoslavia possesses considerable deposits of useful minerals. Hard coal is mined in the Timok and Ibar valleys in Serbia, but output amounts to only a million tons a year. Lignite and brown coal are more plentiful and widespread, the annual output being upwards of 23 million tons. The chief producing areas are in the Bosna valley near Sarajevo, around Ljubljana in Slovenia, north-west of Belgrade, and in the Istrian peninsula. A small oilfield south-east of Zagreb yields $1\frac{1}{2}$ million tons of petroleum a year, and there are deposits of natural gas in the same region.

Iron ore occurs in large quantities at Ljubija and in the Sava valley near Sisak, but is not yet fully exploited. Bauxite is found in the Dinaric karstlands and Istria. With an annual output of over one million tons, Yugoslavia is a major producer. Lead-zinc-silver ores occur in the Karawanken Alps, the Drina valley and at the southern end of the Kopaonik mountains. The yearly output of lead amounts to 98,000 tons, of zinc 39,000 tons and of silver 94 tons. There are extensive deposits of copper around Bor, in eastern Serbia, yielding annually 92,000 tons. Workable supplies of chromium and asbestos occur near Skopje, and there is mercury in the Julian Alps. The output of manganese and antimony in the Macedonian mountains is increasing, and uranium has been discovered in eastern Macedonia.

REGIONAL ECONOMY

1. *The Alpine zone*

The Julian and Karawanken Alps to the west and north of this region have deciduous forests far up their slopes, with conifers above. These have led to a lumbering industry, and to pulp and paper works in the Mura valley, where one of the largest hydro-electric power stations in Yugoslavia is situated. The plateau at the foot of the mountains, especially in the basins and along the rivers which cut its surface, has fertile soils and good farmland, producing wheat, maize and potatoes. Fodder crops are grown for cattle and pigs, and there is some transhumance to the mountain pastures in the Julian Alps. Vineyards and fruit orchards are found on all the lower slopes.

There are deposits of lead, zinc and mercury in the mountains, lignite in the plateau basins, petroleum and natural gas in the Mura valley. Along with the forest products and the hydro-electricity, they have made Slovenia (as this Alpine zone is called) an important industrial region, with a population density nearly as great as that of Serbia. Its towns have benefited, too, by the fact that the plateau is not difficult to cross, so that roads and railways from Austria lead through it to the ports of Trieste and Rijeka (Fiume).

Slovenia was for centuries under the rule of Austria, and its towns show little of the oriental architecture seen in most of Yugoslavia. The chief

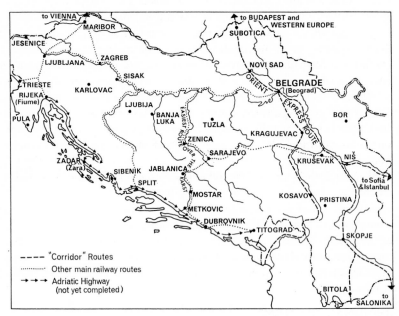

Fig. 115.—Yugoslavia: chief towns. Showing also the main railway routes through the mountains. Correlate this map with Figs. 113 and 114.

city is Ljubljana (160,000), in the centre of a fertile basin. It is a road and railway centre, with electrical engineering, wool textile factories, chemical and aluminium works. Maribor (89,000), in the north-east of Slovenia at the foot of the Karawanken Alps, supplies hydro-electric power to most of the plateau and has an oil refinery and light engineering works. Jesenice (18,000) until a few years ago was a tiny hamlet far up the Sava valley; newly constructed blast furnaces, steel works and rolling mills are encouraging a very rapid growth.

2. *The Dinaric ranges*

(a) *The plateau and mountains.* The mountains which fringe the western Karst are almost uninhabited, and the plateau itself has little use except for sheep and goat rearing on scattered patches of poor vegetation. Some of the polja, however, have fertile soils watered by streams flowing from the base of the slopes enclosing the depressions; and the Neretva valley is floored by alluvial deposits. The chief crops grown in the polja are wheat and maize, and there are tobacco fields, vineyards and plum orchards. Mostar (51,000) is the largest town in the Karst region. It is situated in the Neretva valley, which leads to the easiest route across the High Karst, and it serves as a market for the low-lying plains which surround the lower Neretva. In the south, lying astride the Yugoslav–Albanian frontier, is Lake Skadar, the flooded portion of a large polje. North of the lake, Titograd (35,000), the capital of Montenegro, has new light engineering works. Tobacco is an important cash crop in all the polja.

Yields of all crops are lower in the Karst region than elsewhere in Yugoslavia. Until recently there was a constant stream of emigrants to Serbia and abroad. It has been checked by the growth of industries, such as those of Titograd, and by work provided in the construction of new roads and improved railways in the region.

(b) *The mountains east of the Karst.* The mountainous region of central Yugoslavia is the most important source of timber in the country. More than half the area is forested, mainly with beech and pine. In the valleys which open to the north and the basins in the interior, wheat, maize and potatoes are the principal crops, though the cultivation of sugar beet and hemp is increasing. Cattle are reared in the lowlands and sheep in the mountains. Bosnia-Hercegovina is the chief sheep rearing part of Yugoslavia, with a current total of 2·3 million sheep. The manufacture of homespun and hand-loom woven woollen cloth is carried on in many of the mountain villages.

Central Yugoslavia is rich in minerals. In its middle course the river Bosna flows through a wide basin which, besides being a progressive agricultural district, contains several deposits of lignite, manganese and iron ore. Centred on Sarajevo, this basin is becoming an industrial region. Sarajevo (206,000), the capital of Bosnia-Hercegovina, has heavy engineering and a thriving chemical industry, encouraged by hydro-electricity developed at Jablanica, on the river Neretva. It is a busy commercial centre, and the third largest city in Yugoslavia. The architecture of Sarajevo and of most of the settlements in the mountains presents great contrasts to that of Slovenia, and shows the influence of centuries of Turkish domination. Flat-roofed houses of sun-dried mud bricks are common, and disused mosques and minarets stand side by side with Greek Orthodox churches.

Iron ore occurs in the valleys of the Una and Vrbas where they begin to widen in the north, and there are deposits of zinc and antimony in the

Drina valley. These mineral resources and the richer soils of the valley lowlands have given rise to a line of small towns along the northern margins of the central mountain region. Most of them are markets for the minerals and agricultural produce, but Banya Luka (53,000) has engineering works, using iron and steel from the blast furnaces and steel-rolling mills of Ljubija, which only a decade ago was a village.

Yugoslavia is making great efforts to improve the economy of its central mountain region, which for so long was the most backward part of the country. Mineral deposits previously neglected are being exploited, and new ones sought. Forest industries are being developed with the help of hydro-electricity. And, as already noted, numbers of power stations are being constructed along the valleys. In all this, communications are a paramount need. The railway from Belgrade to Dubrovnik, on the Adriatic, has been modernised. This line runs up the Morava valley to Stalac, turns west into the valleys of the Zap Morava (West Morava) and Drina to Sarajevo, then cuts through the Karst barrier via the upper Bosna and Neretva to Mostar and the coast. Recently it was extended to Titograd. In 1963, a new road was completed from Tuzla, in the lower Drina valley, to Mostar, passing through Sarajevo. This will be extended to join the Titograd–Dubrovnik section of the Adriatic Highway, and will give a much-needed motor transport route across the southern Karst.

(c) *Dalmatia*. The discontinuous lowlands of Dalmatia, on the western side of the High Karst and fringing the Adriatic coast, have long offered attractions for settlement. At various times they have been occupied by Greeks, Romans, Venetians and Italians. Today the great majority of the inhabitants are Yugoslav. The region has a Mediterranean climate, and the landscape is characteristic of the coastlands of that sea—terraced hillsides clothed with olive groves, vineyards and fig orchards; lime-washed cottages and hamlets clinging to the slopes, fields of wheat and maize, and irrigated groves of citrus fruits in the lowlands. Many of the inhabitants are fishermen-farmers: the Adriatic Sea provides seasonal catches of mackerel, sardines and lobsters (*see* Fig. 116).

The growth of towns is limited in Dalmatia to the occasional lowlands, so that each settlement developed as the centre of an agricultural district, isolated from its neighbours except by sea. Larger towns grew where there were good harbours backed by passages through the mountains behind, as at Rijeka, Sibenik, Split, Metkovic and Dubrovnik. In modern times the region has been helped by the discovery of large deposits of bauxite in the hinterlands of Split, Metkovic and Dubrovnik, and by hydro-electricity generated near Split, Jablanica and Rijeka. Salt, obtained by solar evaporation along the coast, has led to an electro-chemical industry at Sibenik.

FIG. 116.—Yugoslavia: Hvar, a fishing port. On an island of the same name in the Adriatic Sea. The harbour of Hvar is sheltered by an offshore string of limestone islands (the Infernal Isles), a characteristic feature of the Dalmatian coast.

The largest town in the region is Rijeka (Fiume) (106,000). Because of its easier connections across the Dinaric region with Slovenia and Austria to the north, and with the Danubian plain to the east, it is being developed as Yugoslavia's chief port, displacing Split (101,000), for centuries the centre of Dalmatian trade. Split remains the market for olive oil, grain and bauxite, and a large nylon factory has been built there. The two ports share most of Yugoslavia's shipbuilding industry. At places along the coast, near the hydro-electric plants, there are recently-built aluminium, ferro-alloy, cement and electro-chemical works.

The sheltered position of the Dalmatian lowlands, in the lee of the Dinaric Karst, has made them a holiday playground, especially in the north, where the more extensive and accessible stretches of beach are lined with small resorts. The tourist industry and the general industrial activity of Dalmatia will be further increased by the Adriatic Highway, a motor road from Rijeka to Titograd, which is nearing completion. When finished, it will link up with new motor roads to the interior. The growing towns of the Dalmatian coast, with their new industrial establishments and housing estates, have a decidedly "Western" appearance, but all contain areas of older buildings which in their Italianate and baroque architecture are quite different from the oriental appearance of settlements on the other side of the Dinaric Alps.

In the north of the Adriatic, the Istrian peninsula is a dry, limestone platform on which the chief occupation is sheep rearing. Lignite and bauxite occur in small deposits, and are sent either to Rijeka or to Karlovac, in Croatia. Pula (38,000), at the southern tip of the peninsula, is Yugoslavia's naval port and dockyard. In the north-west is the Italian port of Trieste, which was claimed by Yugoslavia in 1945 but was made a Free Territory instead, together with a narrow coastal strip on each side of the port. Gradually the eastern coastal strip was taken over by Yugoslavia, and the *fait accompli* was confirmed in 1954. Despite vigorous objections from Yugoslavia and the Soviet Union, the port and the western coastal strip were restored at the same time to Italy. Yugoslavia continues to use the port facilities of Trieste, but to a decreasing extent as Rijeka is further developed.

3. *The Morava–Vardar "corridor" lands*

The south of the region, draining to the river Vardar, is the republic of Macedonia. These southern "corridor" lands are more open to Mediterranean influences than the north, and most of their precipitation falls in winter. Macedonia consists of high massifs, separated by basins and valleys. The highlands are poorly forested; in fact, less than 4% of the total area of Macedonia is forest-clad, as compared with over 40% of Bosnia-Hercegovina, and 25% of Serbia. Sheep rearing is the chief occupation on the massifs, and there is domestic woollen industry in the mountain villages. The valleys and basins have fertile soils and an agricultural economy, but Macedonia, lacking mineral resources, remains under-developed. The lowlands, because of their approach to Mediterranean climatic conditions, grow more wheat than maize, and in the higher basins rye is cultivated. Tobacco is an important crop, and is the country's chief export. In some of the valleys, irrigation is necessary and where it has been introduced, as in the lower Vardar valley, there is production of citrus fruits, plums, cotton and rice.

An exception to the general backwardness of Macedonia is around Skopje (165,529), situated at the convergence of the Ibar and Morava–Vardar corridors. It is the largest town in southern Yugoslavia, a road and railway centre, with food, leather and wool textile industries. The other main towns in the south are Bitola (50,000) and Pristina (41,000), both collecting centres in basins.

Macedonia is a melting-pot of peoples, and is becoming more so as malarial swamps are drained, irrigation systems improved, new crops introduced and settlers invited from other parts of Yugoslavia. Most of its inhabitants are Macedonians, but in the course of history its "corridors" have been penetrated and settled by Romans, Greeks, Serbians, Vlachs, Albanians, Bulgars and Turks. Skopje still has an important Turkish and Bulgar minority and, with its bazaars and mosques, presents a definitely oriental appearance. Macedonia remains an area of dispute between Yugoslavia and Bulgaria; its present allocation to Yugoslavia was mainly intended to deny to Bulgaria the use of the southern end of the very important Morava–Vardar corridor.

North of Macedonia the corridor lands fall within the republic of Serbia, which had its birth in the Ibar valley and the Kosovo basin. When the region was invaded by the Turks, the Serbs withdrew into the mountains of this central region. After the expulsion of the Turks the Serbs moved into the lower valley of the Morava, leaving their original home virtually uninhabited. Since 1912, however, it has begun to develop again. In the highlands live transhumant shepherds, and the valleys produce maize, wheat, hemp and potatoes. Industry has as yet scarcely appeared in the small market towns of the region, and the population, though increasing, remains sparse. The Ibar corridor, which traverses the mountains of western Serbia, is continued by the valley of the Drim. The lower course of this river (Alb. Drin) is in Albania, and so the corridor to the Adriatic is not much used by Yugoslavia.

The Morava, which rises near the Skopje basin, has a valley which widens towards the north, where it is known as Šumadija. Fertile soil and a humid climate support a dense agricultural population, but there are few large towns. Maize, wheat, sugar beet and hemp are the chief crops; and here are the largest mulberry groves (sericulture) and plum orchards in Yugoslavia. Plums are made into jam, dried as prunes or used for the manufacture of plum brandy (*slivovitz*), the Serbian national beverage.

The largest town in the Morava valley is Niš (81,250), at the confluence of the river with the Nisava. It is a commercial and route centre, where the Nisava valley leads from the main north–south corridor to the Bulgarian depression and Istanbul. It is a junction for railways from the north to Salonica, and eastwards to the Bosphorus. Kruševak is a small town near the confluence of the Morava and West Morava; it has lead and zinc smelters, using ores from the nearby Kapaonik mountains. Kragujevac (55,000), at the northern end of the Ibar valley, manufactures cottons and silk, and has an engineering industry.

East of the Morava, the corridor lands are little developed. South of Niš the Rhodope has very few people, and north of the town the western ranges of the Balkan mountains support sheep rearing and a little lumbering. To the west of the Timok, which cuts through the Balkan mountains to join the Danube, there are important deposits of copper and pyrites

at Bor. At the northern end of the mountains the Danube runs through a
narrow gorge, the Iron Gate (Fig. 117), and its swiftly-flowing waters are
a hindrance to up-river shipping. A deep channel has been blasted to
improve navigation, and although the swift current remains a disadvantage, the Danube is a main artery of Yugoslavia's foreign trade to

[*Courtesy of the Yugoslav Embassy.*

FIG. 117.—Yugoslavia: the Iron Gate. A gorge cut by the river Danube between
the Transylvanian Alps and the Balkan mountains. Note the road cut into
the base of the cliffs on the far side of the river.

eastern Europe. A hydro-electric power station is being completed on
the Iron Gate, its construction being financed jointly by Yugoslavia and
Rumania. The plain of the lower Timok, isolated from the rest of Yugoslavia by the mountains, has little share in the general economic advance
of the country, and depends on primitive agriculture and sheep rearing.
Its outlet is the small river port of Kladovo.

4. *The Danubian plain*

   The northern plains of Yugoslavia have the richest farms in the country,
and co-operative methods are showing impressive increases in the yields
of maize—the chief crop—wheat, sugar beet and potatoes. The rearing of
fat cattle and pigs is an important part of the rural economy. Croatia and
northern Serbia, including Vojvodina, have the highest density of population in Yugoslavia, and many parts of the purely agricultural areas have
more than 200 persons per square mile. Sugar refineries, flour mills and

distilleries are scattered throughout the region, and there are leather, tobacco and food-processing factories in all the large towns.

The Danubian plain is also the most industrialised part of Yugoslavia. It is the seat of the textile industry and has rapidly developing heavy engineering and chemical works. The largest industrial concentrations are around Belgrade and Zagreb, at the eastern and western ends of the plain. Belgrade (Serb. Beograd) is built on a hill site overlooking the confluence of the Danube and Sava, where the two western corridors to the south converge and enter the plain. Easy routes in every direction make the city a good commercial focus. It was originally the market for the agricultural produce of Šumadija, and when the rich farmlands of Voyvodina were added to Serbia it became an agricultural engineering centre. As the capital of Serbia, Belgrade was only a small town, with a population in 1918 of 112,000. As capital of the federated Yugoslavia, it grew rapidly to 240,000 by 1931, 470,000 by 1953 and 585,234 today. More and more industries were attracted to it. The chief are food processing, tobacco manufacture, electrical engineering, chemical and cotton textile industries.

At the western end of the plain is Zagreb (430,802), the capital of Croatia and the second city of Yugoslavia. It is the textile metropolis, manufacturing wool, cotton, silk and rayon. Zagreb has heavy engineering and machine tool works, makes electrical apparatus, paper, glass and chinaware, and is a banking centre. In the plains of Vojvodina, north of the Danube, the economy is based on farming produce in the Bačka, and pasture in the Banat. Throughout the western part of the region there are flour mills, sugar refineries and agricultural engineering works and repair shops. The Bačka is densely peopled, but with only two large towns, Novi Sad (102,469), at a bridge point over the Danube, and Subotica (75,036) serving the north. Both are collecting centres and markets, with light industries. The Banat has large areas of steppe, with sheep rearing. Its market is Zrenjanin, in the middle of arable farms.

STUDY QUESTIONS

1. Write an account of the natural resources of Yugoslavia. (O. & C.)

2. Examine the economic and political consequences of the fact that the Adriatic coast of Yugoslavia is bordered by a range of high and in parts impassable mountains. (O. & C.)

3. Make a comparative study of Belgrade and Bucharest. (J.M.B.)

4. Examine the extent to which Yugoslavia possesses resources for the development of manufacturing industries. (J.M.B.)

5. Discuss the physical character of the coastlands of Yugoslavia. (J.M.B.)

6. Divide Yugoslavia into natural regions and give an account of the division you consider the most important in the country's economy.

Chapter XXVIII

SOUTHERN EUROPE

SOUTHERN EUROPE may be said to comprise the three great peninsulas of Iberia, Italy and the Balkans, which project southwards into the Mediterranean Sea, and the islands which lie off their coasts. It includes the countries of Portugal, Spain, Italy, Greece, Albania, Turkey-in-Europe and the minor political units of Andorra, Gibraltar, San Marino, the Vatican State and Malta. The three peninsulas differ in their geological structure and political development, but they have many similarities of climate, vegetation and ways of life, which may be summed up as "Mediterranean." Something has already been said in earlier chapters of the mountain-building movements which formed the Mediterranean basin, and of the sea which resulted; and the general characteristics of the "Mediterranean" climate have been examined. Here are described in brief the topography of the northern margins of the Mediterranean, the importance of the region in early history and its gradual decline to the comparative backwardness of today.

TOPOGRAPHY

The mountains which form so much of the southern edges of Europe are young and recently folded. In consequence they are high and rugged. The islands, which in the main are upstanding fragments of submerged ranges, are also mountainous. At the continental end of the peninsulas the mountains form a climatic barrier, limiting "Mediterranean" influences to a narrow coastal belt and causing such variations from the winter rain/summer drought type of climate as occur in the plain of Lombardy, Turkey-in-Europe, northern Greece and parts of the Meseta in Iberia.

The landscape of southern Europe, viewed from the sea, is invariably of mountains rising steeply from the shores, with here and there small stretches of lowland nestling at their feet. Agriculture is necessarily discontinuous in extent and specialised in type, since it can be practised only in the plains or on slopes which are gentle enough to allow terracing. Terraces are found in every southern European country, stone walls holding up the soil, which otherwise would be washed down by the sudden torrential rains characteristic of Mediterranean lands. The landscape is almost entirely man-made, even where it consists of bare rock, for when deforestation has occurred soil erosion has exposed the brilliantly white limestone of which most of the mountains are composed.

On the terraced slopes arable farming is difficult and often primitive: tree crops, with roots which can penetrate the stony mountain sides, become of first importance. Vines, olives, peaches, apricots, figs, citrus fruits, almonds and other nut-bearing trees thrive in the Mediterranean climate; but it should be noted that citrus fruits such as oranges and lemons require so much water that they are usually confined to lowlands, where they can be irrigated. On the upper slopes of the highlands, where trees have been cut down, are large areas of tangled, thorny bushes, known as *maquis* in French-speaking lands and *macchia* in Italian. Brightly painted or whitewashed houses may be seen in clusters down to the water's edge— for the Mediterranean is almost tideless—or perched precariously among the terraces on the slopes.

The clear atmosphere and the blue skies of summer, reflected in the blue waters of the Mediterranean, add to the scenic beauty. Where the narrow coastal plains are sheltered from westerlies, as in the various *rivieras*, the tourist and holiday industry has developed enormously, especially in winter, when the rest of Europe is cloud-covered, cold and uninviting.

Many of the small plains are alluvial flats built up by the silt-laden torrents pouring in winter from soil-eroded mountains to a tideless sea. The lower courses of rivers are impeded by accumulations of water-borne alluvium or by lateral drifting of marine muds along the shores, and many marshlands developed just inland from the coasts. In the warm atmosphere mosquitoes bred rapidly, among them the *Anopheles*, which carries malaria. The disease-ridden swamps of Italy, Greece and Albania prevented development until it was learnt how to drain them and destroy the mosquito threat. In recent years reclamation has turned many of them into fruitful agricultural lands, so that the sadly over-populated countries of southern Europe are finding new space on which to expand. The swamps, where they existed, were a factor in forcing the Mediterranean peoples to develop a way of life which involved adaptation to a mountainous environment and difficult agriculture.

The mountains, too, because they broke the coastlands into a great number of pockets isolated from each other, were responsible for the number of political units, large and small, which have developed in history along the north of the Mediterranean. Only in the past two centuries have Italy and Greece emerged as unified states and Albania and European Turkey are political creations of the present century.

MEDITERRANEAN CIVILISATIONS

The Mediterranean basin is the cradle of Western civilisation, but why this should be so has not yet been satisfactorily answered. In the riverine lands of the Middle East grew the cultures of Assyria and Babylon, and in the lower Nile valley that of Egypt. These were land empires, but they spread their influences along the south-eastern coast of the Mediterranean and thence to Crete and Greece. Little is known of the Cretan (Minoan) civilisation, but it seems very probable that Crete was a stepping-stone from Egypt to Greece, and that Greek culture owed some part of its early development to both Crete and Egypt. In the ancient land empires a knowledge of primitive cultivation of food crops was augmented by the discovery of irrigation, canal construction and bridge building. Most important of all, their peoples had learnt to live in towns, for these discoveries meant the rural population was able to produce enough surplus foodstuffs to support urban communities and could exchange them for services from the town-dwellers.

It has been said that the growth of civilisation was favoured in these eastern Mediterranean lands by the annual renewal of fertile silts by flooding rivers and by the climate. In terms of human geography they are "regions of increment," where man's labours on flooded fields or during winter rains gave him sufficient food to last during periods of drought, and sufficient leisure to develop a knowledge of science, philosophy, literature and the arts, at a time when the rest of Europe, in "regions of effort," was striving to exist in a harsher and more difficult environment. This, however, can be only one factor in the extraordinary rise of ancient Greece. It does not explain the first development of city life, which became a feature not only in that country but throughout the Mediterranean. Indeed, this crowding into cities continues, even in countries which are predominantly agricultural.

From the city-states Greek civilisation spread to Sicily, Italy and southern France, eastwards to Asia Minor and south to Libya, in the form of trading colonies. The Mediterranean, in which ships are rarely out of sight of land, was at once a unifying factor and a challenge to the first mariners and traders. The Greeks, however, were not colonists in the modern sense. They confined their overseas activities mainly to coastal settlements, which they occupied primarily for commercial purposes. The Romans, on the other hand, were settlers, either by occupation or by conquest, and they imposed their civilisation on the whole of the Mediterranean basin. For the only time in history the Mediterranean lands were united as a single political unit, and once more the sea was a unifying factor. The Roman Empire was *thalassic*, that is, based upon a sea which

was, as its name implies, in "the middle of the lands." All routes, by land
and sea, led to Rome. Along them passed the grain and other foodstuffs
the capital required. In return the Romans endowed their dominions with
good roads, aqueducts and buildings—some of them still exist—and with
a system of law and order which in some countries became the basis of

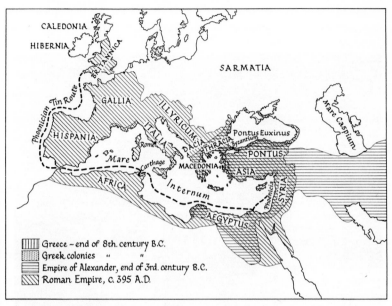

FIG. 118.—The spread of Greek and Roman civilisations. The empire of Alexander
spreads eastwards as far as the Indus basin in India.

their present mode of government. At the beginning of the Christian
era, Rome was at its zenith and the Mediterranean Sea had reached a
degree of importance which, comparatively, it has never achieved since.

DECLINE AND RE-AWAKENING

The Roman Empire began to break up with the barbarian invasion
of the fifth and sixth centuries, but it was the Arab expansion of the eighth
century that finally brought to an end the unity Rome had given to the
Mediterranean. It should be noted that three great religions—Judaism,
Christianity and Mohammedanism—were all born in the eastern Mediterranean; and that the Arab peoples, almost without exception, became
followers of Mohammed. With fanatical missionary zeal they invaded
and occupied the eastern and southern coastlands of the Mediterranean,
overran most of the Iberian peninsula in Europe and penetrated even into

southern France. Their rule was savage, but not without advantages, for it brought a revived knowledge of irrigation and water-supply, a new type of architecture and products such as citrus fruits, sugar-cane and cotton, not previously grown in Europe.

The Mediterranean basin was now divided between two opposing camps, Christians and Mohammedans. Commerce, which had been its life-blood, came to a standstill. It is true that in the Middle Ages some cities, notably Venice and Genoa, had maintained a trade with the East,

[*Courtesy of the Turkish Embassy.*

Fig. 119.—Turkey: Istanbul, Suleymaniye mosque. This was originally the Christian cathedral of Santa Sophia, and is now used as a museum.

principally in silks, jewels and spices. This continued even during the wars of the Crusades. But with the rise of the Turkish Empire, and especially after the fall of Constantinople in 1453, overland trade links between east and west were severed. The Renaissance period saw the spread of Mediterranean culture to western Europe, but it was a time too when new routes were discovered to the Far East, via the Cape of Good Hope and, later, round Cape Horn. The Mediterranean ceased to be a mercantile highway in the face of the new ocean routes, although, it must be noted, Mediterranean ships and men were foremost among the maritime adventurers who rounded the Cape of Good Hope, discovered the New World and circumnavigated the Globe. Spain and Portugal became the richest countries of Europe, but their glories did not last long and in common with all the other lands around the Mediterranean they began to decline.

The results of the general lapse into backwardness are easy to find. Trading cities were turned into fortresses to repel invaders or ward off pirates. Forests were burnt by advancing Turks or by retreating defenders who withdrew into mountain fastnesses, with resultant soil erosion and swamp formation in the lowlands. Abandoned cities were left to fall into ruins; and the lowlands, with the spread of malaria, became almost depopulated. These were results; it is not so easy to find causes. Certainly constant wars and unrest, with disruption of trade and interference with the normal way of life, were a major factor in the eastern half of the Mediterranean; but they do not account for the wretchedness and misery of the peoples of southern Italy and the Iberian peninsula. Here the psychological effects of an outdated feudal system, with landless peasants dependent on an absentee landlord, are apparent; an ever-increasing population had to feed itself on insufficient acreage, leaving no time for anything but a struggle for mere existence. Alternatively, it may be that the whole of the Mediterranean basin found itself unable to compete with the developing trading nations of western Europe—Great Britain, France, Holland—and more or less gave up the struggle.

With the discoveries of large coal and iron fields in western Europe, and the Industrial Revolution, the Mediterranean lands sank further into the background, for they possess negligible amounts of these minerals; and the Agrarian Revolution had little effect on their limited agricultural lands. But with the opening of the nineteenth century the situation began to improve.

The Turkish Empire had begun to crumble, and new states appeared on the map. Napoleon had attempted to invade Egypt and had been repelled by Great Britain, which thus gained a footing in north-east Africa. France began to colonise Algeria; Britain had a string of fortified stations in Gibraltar, Malta, Cyprus and Port Said, and trade began to flow again, guarded by the Royal Navy and the French fleet.

The opening of the Suez Canal in 1869 was of major importance. Ships forsook the long voyage round the Cape of Good Hope or the Horn to south-eastern Asia and Australasia; and the Suez route brought the Mediterranean countries back to commercial and political prominence. Greece and Italy were already independent states during the nineteenth century; Bulgaria, Yugoslavia and Albania were created in the twentieth.

The new countries, and also Spain and Portugal, which are much older, found they had considerable resources of water power for hydro-electricity and valuable deposits of non-ferrous minerals such as bauxite, mercury, copper, etc., to help them in their economic recovery. By drainage and irrigation they could increase their opportunities of exploiting modern methods in agriculture. The Mediterranean lands were at the beginning of a new prosperity. They have a long way to go, for the neglect and backwardness of centuries cannot be remedied in a couple of decades. Moreover, under the new and improved conditions the population of every Mediterranean country is rising rapidly. In the past twenty-five years the total population of the Iberian peninsula, Italy and the Balkan peninsula has risen from 104 to 120 millions, despite the large loss of life in the Second World War and emigration from Iberia and the Balkans. This increase, averaging two-thirds of a million a year, is too great for the available food resources; nor is industrial development as yet big enough to absorb the surplus. This over-population is probably the greatest problem in the Mediterranean countries of Europe.

STUDY QUESTIONS

1. Comment on the role the Mediterranean Sea has played in the development of civilisation in Europe.

2. Discuss, with specific examples, the characteristic physical features of the Mediterranean coast of Europe.

Chapter XXIX

SPAIN

INTRODUCTION: THE IBERIAN PENINSULA

CLINGING to the south-west of Europe is the Iberian peninsula, a rectangular land mass separated from the rest of the continent by the Pyrenees, a continuous chain of rugged, high-peaked mountains through which no more than ten passes allow of road communications. The Iberian peninsula has an area of 231,000 square miles—nearly twice that of the British Isles—and is divided into Spain and Portugal. Spain is almost six times as large as Portugal.

The peninsula is so shut off by the Pyrenees from its neighbour to the north that Louis XIV of France, towards the end of the seventeenth century, was led to declare that "Europe ends at the Pyrenees." Pedro Lain, a Spanish historian, called the peninsula "Marginal Europe." One would certainly disagree with the French king, but Lain's definition is very apt, since the Iberian peninsula is distinct from the rest of Europe in its climatic types, its geographical outlook and the development of its peoples—the last especially so in modern times.

PHYSICAL ASPECTS

STRUCTURAL DEVELOPMENT OF IBERIA

The complicated structure of the Iberian peninsula has led to much speculation about its development. It will be useful, therefore, to examine its geological history as a preliminary to the more detailed treatment of the structural divisions of Spain and Portugal.

In the north-west of the Iberian peninsula—in Galicia, north Portugal and much of the Central Sierras—there are rocks of pre-Cambrian age, similar in type to those in the Baltic Shield; and traces of Caledonian folding have been found. According to one hypothesis, these were folded in late Carboniferous times in high Hercynian mountain ranges, running from east to west across the present area of the peninsula. The ranges were then eroded almost to their stumps, and submerged and covered by Mesozoic and Tertiary deposits. Towards the end of the Tertiary period the Alpine orogenesis buckled the sedimentaries on the floor of the Tethys Sea, which covered the area, so lifting and folding the Betic

Cordillera across the south and south-east of the present peninsula. At the same time the Pyrenees and Cantabrians were being uplifted in the north. Between the northern and southern systems the ancient Hercynian platform was forced upwards as a great horst, to form the plateau of the Meseta which now occupies most of the peninsula.

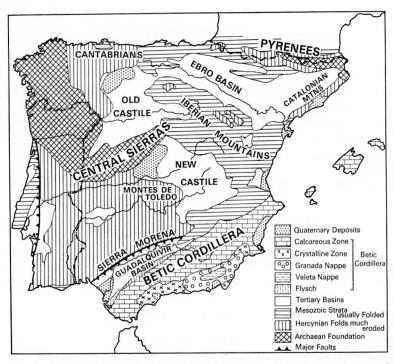

Fig. 120.—Iberian peninsula: structure. The boundary between Spain and Portugal is shown by a chain line. The Hercynian formations are continued under the Tertiary basins of Old and New Castile.

The Cantabrian mountains and Pyrenees are usually regarded as part of the Alpine system, but the presence in them of so many rocks of Carbo-Permian age suggests that strictly speaking they are Hercynian folds rejuvenated in the "Alpine storm." To the same period belong the Catalonian mountains and the ranges which fringe the Meseta in the north-east. It seems likely, too, that the Central Sierras, the Sierra Toledo and the Sierra Morena were uplifted across the surface of the Meseta by thrusts from the south late in the Alpine-building period, and that they are the results, not of folding, but of faulting.

The Betic Cordillera, on the other hand, are true Alpine ranges in structure. To the north there is a narrow belt of flysch, similar to that north of the Alps in central Europe. It is followed by an outer limestone zone. Nappe formation in Granada has resulted in the Sierra Nevada, the highest part of the Cordillera, in which crystalline rocks come to the surface in the Veleta "window." The southern ranges are mostly of limestone. There are only faint traces of nappe formation in the Pyrenees and none at all in the Cantabrians. Fundamentally, the greater part of the Iberian peninsula is of Hercynian rocks.

Pressures exerted on the horst of the Meseta caused faulting on its northern and southern margins. Between the Meseta and the Pyrenees was formed the trough of the Ebro basin, and in the south the Guadalquivir basin lies between the Meseta and the Betic Cordillera. The same pressures, which resulted in the "horsts within a horst" of the plateau sierras, caused down-faulting north and south of these block ranges, and a series of transverse troughs or depressions. The northernmost includes the basin of Old Castile; south of the Central Sierras are the basins of New Castile and the middle Tagus, the latter in Portugal. The upper Guadiana basin in Extremadura is in a third series. All these depressions are floored by Tertiary sands, marls and clays. A great fault running from the mouth of the river Douro to Cape St Vincent resulted in the downthrow of the Meseta west of it, and produced the lowlands of Portugal.

The south-west of the Iberian peninsula is still unstable: in recent centuries Portugal has suffered many disastrous earthquakes, probably because of earth movement along the great fault. This fault may have been formed in an epeirogenic upheaval of Pliocene times, when the whole peninsula, except in the south-west, was uplifted, resulting in the steep edges of the Meseta, which make access to the interior difficult, except from Portugal. In the same uplift the rivers of the Meseta were rejuvenated. Their deeply-incised, gulley-like valleys constitute serious obstacles to north–south communications on the plateau.

There are few traces of the existence of the Ice Age in Iberia. The Pyrenees, Cantabrians and Sierra Nevada show signs of valley glaciation, such as U-shaped valleys, but nowhere in the peninsula was there an extensive ice sheet. Probably the climate was too dry.

STRUCTURAL DIVISIONS OF SPAIN

From the foregoing it is seen that Spain may be divided into the plateau of the Meseta, around which are the pseudo-Alpine ranges of the Pyrenees, Cantabrians and Galicia in the north, and the truly Alpine Betic Cordillera in the south, separated from the Meseta by the troughs of the Ebro and Guadalquivir. But this simple division into plateau, mountain ranges, and lowland river basins, is not really satisfactory in examining Spain's

Q

geography. For besides being distinguished from each other by accidents
of geology, the regions are further differentiated by climates which range
from wet to very dry, and by peoples who in different parts of the country
are so unlike each other in language, culture and economic development
as almost to give the impression they belong to separate nations. Moreover, this "compartmentalism" of Spain (as it has been called) is encountered even within the major structural divisions, so that, to obtain a

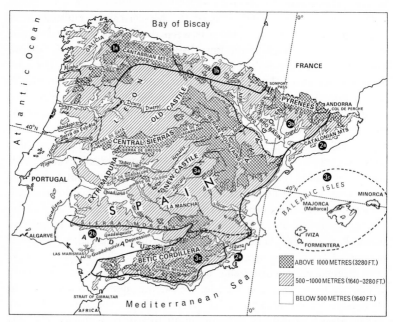

FIG. 121.—Iberian peninsula physical features. The numbers correspond with the
regional divisions of Spain used in the text.

true picture of the country's geography, each must be sub-divided into
minor regions. The whole country is better grouped according to
physical, climatic and economic rather than purely structural considerations.

In this chapter, therefore, Spain is divided initially into: (1) the Atlantic
coastlands, (2) the Mediterranean coastlands, and (3) the remainder of the
country. These are further subdivided into 1(a) Galicia, the Cantabrian
mountains and the coastal plain of the Asturias, 1(b) the province of
Santander, the Basque provinces and the western Pyrenees. The Mediterranean coastlands include 2(a) the eastern Pyrenees and the series of
isolated coastal plains which occur along the east and south coasts of
Spain, 2(b) the basin of the river Guadalquivir, which although outside the

Mediterranean is related in its development to the coastal plains along it. The remaining regions are 3(*a*) the Meseta, 3(*b*) the central Pyrenees and the basin of the river Ebro, 3(*c*) the Betic Cordillera and the Balearic islands. The divisions are shown in Fig. 121.

1. *The Atlantic coastlands*

(a) *Galicia; the Cantabrian mountains; the Asturian plain.* Galicia, in the north-west of Spain, is a low undulating plateau of pre-Cambrian granites. The region was severely fractured when the Cantabrian mountains were being formed and, in the intervals between the resultant horsts, swift, short rivers have carved deep valleys. Slight sinking of their lower courses has led to invasion by the sea and the formation of a ria coastline, similar to that in Brittany and south-west England. The soils of Galicia, derived from igneous rocks, are poor.

East of Galicia the quartzites and limestones of the Cantabrian mountains rise to over 7000 ft. The range forms a high barrier between the coast and the interior, pierced by only one main road and one railway. From the southern slopes of the Galician and Cantabrian highlands flow the headwaters of the Minho (Miño), and of the Esla and its tributaries which flow to the Douro (Duero). These are important because of the hydro-electric power stations recently constructed on them. North of the Cantabrians is the narrow but well-developed coastal plain of the Asturias. Its soils are not much better than those of Galicia, but careful cultivation has made them very productive.

(b) *The province of Santander; the Basque provinces; the western Pyrenees.* The Cantabrian mountains east of Asturias decrease in height and the ranges are more broken. They are largely covered by Mesozoic sandstones and limestones. These have developed into good soils, so that the province of Santander and the rolling, hilly Basque provinces which succeed it eastwards are agriculturally the most favoured parts of Spain.

The undulating lowlands continue to the French boundary, and communications to the interior in this region, though not easy, are much better than farther west.

The western Pyrenees are included here because they have a population which is closely related to that of the Basque provinces. They form the lowest part of the Pyrenees, rarely rising to more than 7000 ft. The western Pyrenees lie west of the Somport Pass (5310 ft), which is traversed by a road and railway. There are several other passes, notably that of Roncesvalles (3435 ft). On the French side the western Pyrenees have steep slopes, but in Spain they descend in steps to low sierras and intermontane basins floored by Mesozoic deposits similar to those of the Basque provinces.

2. *The Mediterranean coastlands*

(a) *The eastern Pyrenees; the coastal plains.* East of the Col de la Perche (5120 ft), the Pyrenees are broken into a number of ranges, the highest of which, with many peaks over 8000 ft, are in France. On the Spanish side, although there are occasional high mountains, such as Puigmal (9460 ft), the ranges are lower and enclose several longitudinal depressions. The eastern Pyrenees are pierced by roads and railways. One road crosses by the Col de la Perche, another by an easier route nearer the coast. A railway from Barcelona to Toulouse makes use of the valley leading to the Col de la Perche, then tunnels under the Carlotta massif. Coastal roads and the railway between Spain and France pass along the narrow gap between the Pyrenees and the Mediterranean coast.

The eastern and southern coasts of Spain are rugged and often cliff-lined, and there is very little lowland. North of the river Ebro, the sub-Pyrenean sierras are flanked by narrow coastal plains; south of the river the lowlands are chiefly the result of delta formation by the short, swift streams flowing from the Meseta or the Betic Cordillera to the Mediterranean. North of the Ebro, the plains of Catalonia include those of Gerona, Barcelona and Tarragona, which have a flooring of Tertiary sands and river alluvium. They are separated from each other by granite outliers of the eastern Pyrenees, or by the Mesozoic formations of the Catalonian mountains. In between the ranges are further small lowlands, parallel to the coast.

Southwards along the coast are the plains of Castellón de la Plana and Valencia, completely isolated by the steep edge of the Meseta from western climatic influences. At the south-east corner of Spain, hemmed in by the Betic Cordillera, are the plains of Alicante and Murcia, which form a continuous lowland. Along the south coast, the mountains are so near the sea there is little room for coastal plains. The only ones of any size lie behind Almería and Málaga, where water for irrigation is available. At the western end of the coast a tiny strip of lowland lies behind the narrow, rocky peninsula of Gibraltar. This small plain serves as a kind of "no man's land" between British and Spanish territory.

(b) *The basin of the river Guadalquivir.* The province of Andalusia includes the southern slopes of the Meseta—Sierra Morena—the basin of the river Guadalquivir, the Betic Cordillera and the southern coastal plains. Here attention is confined to the wedge-shaped lowland opening westwards to the Atlantic and drained by the Guadalquivir (Arab. *wadi al kabir*, "the great river"). It is a trough let down between the Meseta and the folded Cordilleran ranges, with limestone hills in its eastern section, Tertiary clays in the middle stretch, and alluvium and muds in the area nearer the sea. It is included with the Mediterranean coastlands because it has a Mediterranean climate; but because it is open to the west it receives oceanic winds which bring more rain than to the plains on the east and south of Spain.

3. *The Meseta; the central Pyrenees; the Ebro basin; the Betic Cordillera*

(a) *The Meseta.* Geologically, the term "meseta" is applied to the whole of the region of Iberia and north-west Africa involved in pre-Cambrian flexing and Hercynian folding. In its geographical sense the Meseta is the vast tableland of Spain, which stretches from the Cantabrians in the north to the Guadalquivir basin in the south, and from the borders of Portugal to the Mediterranean coast. It is a horst, originally part of the Hercynian mountain system, peneplained, submerged beneath the water of the Tethys Sea, uplifted again in Tertiary times, and tilted downwards towards the west. The level of the tableland falls from about 3200 ft in the east to less than 1500 ft near Portugal, but it is traversed by three series of mountain ranges which in places exceed 8000 ft.

The northern series, the Central Sierras, includes the Sierra de Guadarrama, Sierra de Gredos, Sierra de Avila and Sierra de Gata. It continues into Portugal as the Serra da Estrêla. These ranges are composed largely of the granites and schists of the pre-Cambrian Meseta platform, broken into horsts and massifs packed tightly against one another, with rounded tops or high plateaus. They are a formidable barrier between the northern and southern Meseta.

The second series is known collectively as the Mountains of Toledo, and includes the Sierra de Guadalupe and Sierra de San Pedro. They are similar in origin and rock structure to the Central Sierras, but are neither as high nor as difficult to cross. The Sierra Morena, forming the southern margin of the Meseta, are the third series. Viewed from the plateau, they are not really mountains, but rather the warped edge of the Meseta. They fall steeply to the Andalusian basin of the Guadalquivir, but are not a serious obstacle to communications.

North of the Central Sierras is the basin of Old Castile (Castilla la Vieja) and León, at an average height of about 2500 ft. South of the ranges the depression of New Castile (Castilla la Nueva) is about 300 ft lower. These hollows in the surface of the Meseta were once salt-water lakes, in which were deposited Tertiary and later sediments which now floor the basins. In the north-east of the Meseta are the Iberian mountains, a confused area of folded ranges. They are mainly of Mesozoic limestones formed in Tertiary times and greatly eroded, so that the region is more plateau-like than mountainous.

Before its final uplift the Meseta was covered by Tertiary sedimentaries.

Large areas of these remain in the plateau basins and in the basin of the Ebro to the north. Over most of the plateau they have disappeared; where denudation has been extensive, the older and more resistant rocks thus disclosed have given rise to a broken relief. Differential erosion of the original Tertiaries has resulted in a great number of low, flat-topped plateaus rising above the general level of the Meseta, sometimes to a height of 400 ft. The flat tops of the *paramos*, as the low plateaus are called, represent the original level. Denudation has lowered the floor of the Meseta, leaving the paramos as cliff-lined blocks of limestone, fit only for poor sheep pasture.

The Meseta is crossed from east to west by the rivers Douro, Tagus (Tajo) and Guadiana. They flow in deeply entrenched valleys and, in Spain, are unnavigable. A marked seasonal régime makes them of little value for hydro-electric development, and their waters are too far below the general level of the plateau to be used for irrigation, except locally. The tributaries of the Tagus, for instance, fed by melting snows on the Central Sierras, are more valuable than the main stream: they are dammed for power, domestic water supplies for Madrid, and irrigation.

(b) *The central Pyrenees; the Ebro basin.* These two regions are taken together because historically they constitute the ancient kingdom of Aragon, and are geographically complementary.

The central Pyrenees, lying between the Somport Pass and the Col de la Perche, are a massive barrier of folded mountains, rarely falling below 5000 ft and rising in Maladetta to 11,174 ft. In the main, they are composed of crystalline rocks. Most of the valleys leading into the mountains from the south finish blindly, and only three of them are continued by poor roads across the range. One road goes to Andorra, a tiny republic of 191 square miles, which lies in interconnected valleys at an altitude of more than 6500 ft. At the foot of the central Pyrenees is a broad belt of less elevated sierras which present steep scarp slopes to the Ebro lowlands south of them.

The river Ebro flows through a long, triangular basin, which is almost enclosed between the Pyrenees and the Meseta. The upper course of the river is in the Basque provinces, and it enters its plain tract below Miranda. The surface of the basin is far from being level. The almost horizontal Tertiary beds which floor it have been scored into deep valleys by the Ebro and its tributaries. Differential erosion has resulted in many flat-topped, isolated plateaus, not high enough to be called paramos nor to make much difference to the general monotony of the arid-looking landscape. The Ebro leaves its basin by a gorge through the Catalonian mountains and enters the Mediterranean by a delta. It is of negligible value for navigation. Its volume varies too much; its speed in the gorge is too great; and its delta channels are constantly in process of silting.

(c) *The Betic Cordillera; the Balearic islands.* The Betic Cordillera lie across southern Spain, with an east-north-east to west-south-west trend. The Cordillera are divided into two parallel belts of highland, separated by a narrow depression which widens into a number of distinct basins. The northern belt, the sub-Betic region, is composed (among other ranges) of the Sierra de Lucena, Sierra del Pozo, Sierra de Segura and Sierra de Tiabilla. They are all mainly of limestones, with clays and sandstones in the valleys. Their average height is less than 6500 ft. The southern belt is largely of crystalline rocks, and reaches much greater altitudes. It runs from the Sierra Bermeja in the west to the Sierra de las Estancias in the east, and is highest in the centre, in the Sierra Nevada, with the peak of Mulhacen (11,420 ft). The high basins strung along the central depression include Loja, Granada, Moreda, Braza and Lorca.

East of the Betic Cordillera, and separated by a channel about fifty miles wide, are the Balearic islands. Folds of Jurassic limestone, topped by Tertiary strata, suggest they are continuations of the northern belt of the cordillera. The largest islands are Majorca (Mallorca), Minorca (Menorca) and Iviza (Ibiza). There are nearly twenty other islets, some too small to be inhabited.

CLIMATE AND VEGETATION

The Iberian peninsula, of which Spain forms the major portion, is situated between 36 and $43\frac{1}{2}$ degrees N., *i.e.* in summer it falls within the normal anticyclonic belt of the Mediterranean, and in winter under the influence of the westerlies. The climate of the peninsula, however, shows great variations from the conditions which usually follow from this position. Although Iberia is almost surrounded by sea, maritime influences play only a minor part in determining its climate. The peninsula is like a miniature continent, in winter developing a high pressure system in its interior, with accompanying cold, frosty days and nights, and some snow. It is often possible to enjoy open-air skating in Madrid during January and February. In winter, when the Mediterranean region has its maximum precipitation, the interior and east of Iberia are still dry, so that much of the peninsula has little rain at any season. Parts of the Ebro basin, for instance, have only 12 in. a year.

The depressions which move along the Mediterranean in winter bring rain to the north, north-west and west of Iberia, where the mountain ranges and the western edge of the Meseta form a screen, leaving the rest of the peninsula in their rain-shadow. The high Betic Cordillera is also well watered in winter. The outer slopes of the Cantabrians and the

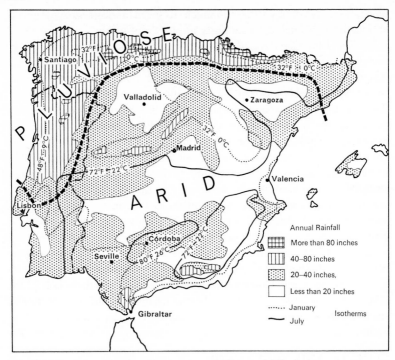

Fig. 122.—Iberian peninsula: climate. Note (*a*) the rapid fall of winter temperatures away from the coast, and the large area in the north of the Meseta below freezing point (unique in western and southern Europe), (*b*) the extensive areas with less than 20 in. of rainfall annually, (*c*) the favourable climate of Portugal in comparison with that of Spain.

north-west corner of Iberia have maximum precipitation in winter, but they have sufficient rainfall in summer to justify their inclusion in the region of west European marginal climate. Santiago has an annual rainfall of 65 in., of which 23 in. fall in summer. This region is also the most equable in Spain, with mean temperatures ranging from 45° F (7·2° C) in January to 66° F (18·9° C) in July. Atlantic influences are felt farther south in Portugal, whose lowlands, open to the sea, may receive up to 30 in. rainfall annually (the climate of Portugal is treated more fully in the next chapter). The rocky peninsula of Gibraltar, at the western end of the Betic Cordillera, has an annual rainfall of 35 in. and, farther east, the Sierra Nevada may have up to 45 in., falling as snow in winter. The Sierra Nevada are the only Mediterranean mountains to retain a capping of snow in summer.

Away from these highland regions, the peninsula's annual rainfall is low. Valladolid, in the north-west of the Meseta and under the lee of the mountains, receives only 13 in. a year; Zaragoza, in the Ebro basin, $11\frac{1}{2}$ in. Few districts of the Meseta have an annual precipitation of more than 20 in., and these are in the higher parts of the plateau sierras. Madrid, near the Sierra de Guadarrama and at an altitude of 2168 ft, has a yearly rainfall of $16\frac{1}{2}$ in.—rather more than the average on the plateau. One of the driest regions of the Meseta is La Mancha (Arab. *al mancha*, "the thirsty land"), in New Castile. Rain on the Meseta comes in heavy showers of short duration but great erosive power. Before it has had time to soak into the surface or increase the volume of the plateau rivers to any extent, it is dried up by evaporation. Consequently, the plateau has normally a scorched appearance. In the southern half it may approach semi-desert conditions.

The coastlands of the east and south have, in general, slightly more rain than the Meseta, with a definite winter maximum. The Mediterranean coastal plains in the north, owing to their proximity to the Pyrenees, have the highest precipitation, around 20 in. a year. Barcelona, however, only 69 ft above sea level, has a mere 15 in. The driest of the coastal plains are Murcia and Alicante, where, in the shelter of the Betic Cordillera, the annual rainfall is $14\frac{1}{2}$ in.

The annual rainfall is taken as a basis for dividing Spain into two regions, a *pluviose* (rainy) and an *arid* sector, using the 25-in. isohyet as the line of demarcation. The pluviose sector includes the north-west corner, the Biscayan coastlands and the Pyrenees; the arid sector, the rest of the country.

The anticyclonic conditions which obtain over arid Spain both in winter and summer tend to give continental extremes of temperature, annual and diurnal. Winter temperatures do not on average fall below freezing point for any considerable periods, although snow is not uncommon on the northern plateau and frost may be experienced for days on end. Night frosts are frequent in January and February. January mean temperatures increase from north to south, from 39° F (3·9° C) in Valladolid and 41° F (5° C) in Madrid, to 50° F (10° C) in Seville. Summer temperatures range from 66° F (18·9° C) in Valladolid to 84° F (28·9° C) in Seville. Summers in the Guadalquivir valley are perhaps the hottest in Europe. Madrid's July average is 78° F (25·6° C).

The coastal plains of the east and south are more typically Mediterranean in their temperatures. Barcelona ranges from a mean of 46° F (7·8° C) in January to 74° F (23·3° C) in July, Valencia from 51° F (10·6° C) to 76° F (24·4° C), and Murcia from 50° F (10° C) to 79° F (26·1° C).

From the foregoing, it will be seen that Spain offers two sets of climatic contrasts: (*a*) between the pluviose and arid sectors of the country, and (*b*) between the coastlands and the interior. These contrasts are evident also in the natural vegetation, which varies from the forested and verdant mountains of the north-west to the parched, arid plains of La Mancha.

North-west Spain has a natural cover of forests of oak and chestnut, with pines at higher levels, and these are continued into the western Pyrenees. The central and eastern Pyrenees are clothed with cork oak and pine in the wetter parts, and Mediterranean shrubs such as gorse and broom in the drier, and on the limestone platforms at their base there is an extensive cover of garrigue. Forests of cork oak and pine are found also in the Betic Cordillera, and on some of the plateau sierras. Over most of the Meseta and the coastal plains the natural vegetation is grass, richer in the wetter parts but descending to poor steppe in La Mancha, the Ebro basin and the eastern Guadalquivir basin. Much of the grass is esparto, valuable for sheep rearing and as a raw material for paper.

HUMAN GEOGRAPHY

HISTORY AND PEOPLE

It is believed that human habitation of the Iberian peninsula began in the eleventh century B.C., when Cro-Magnon man migrated from Africa to settle in caves near Murcia and Andalusia, and along the Cantabrian coast. In the caves of Altamira, near Santander, he has left well-preserved red and black drawings of bison, horses, boar and deer. He was followed by the Iberians, who landed on the east coast and penetrated to the interior. In the sixth century B.C. the Celts came in by the same route as the Iberians, and after much fighting merged with them to form the Celtiberians. It was part of this Celtic migration which peopled the west of Ireland and Scotland.

Meanwhile the Phoenicians, seafaring merchants from the eastern Mediterranean, set up trading posts and small settlements on the south and west coasts. The chief of these was Agadir, where Cadiz now stands. The Greeks, too, had coastal trading stations. The Carthaginians were called in to help the Phoenicians repel the attacks of barbarians from the north; they moved inland and took over much of the interior, directing operations from their headquarters, New Carthage, now Cartagena.

In the third century B.C. the Romans invaded the peninsula, and retained control for more than 500 years. They called the peninsula Iberia and the eastern portion Hispania—hence the name of Spain. The region to the west, the present Portugal, was called Lusitania. The Romans introduced their language and culture, constructed roads, aqueducts and bridges, and built beautiful villas. The aqueducts of Segovia and Mérida, and the bridges at Alcantara, Salamanca and Mérida date from Roman times. The beneficent rule of the Romans, who met with little resistance from the inhabitants at any time, became very relaxed, so that when the Visigoths invaded the peninsula from the north in the fifth century A.D. they found it easy to conquer. Visigoth domination began in A.D. 414 and lasted 300 years, during which most of the benefits the Romans bestowed were lost. In the latter years of their rule, the country was threatened by Moorish inroads from the south.

The Moors landed from North Africa in 710. After a harsh and vigorous seven-year campaign they commanded the whole peninsula except for the wild, rugged highlands of the Asturias and north of the river Douro in Portugal. For seven centuries the Iberian peninsula was divided between the Moslem Moors and the Christian Visigoth-Iberians, and all the time the conquerors were harassed by guerrilla bands from the north. Although they were cruel masters, the Moors introduced not only their religion but also laws and customs derived from the civilisations of Egypt and Persia, and there are still signs of the long period of occupation. Place-names derived from Arabic are very common in the south; much of the architecture has Moslem characteristics; irrigation systems like those in North Africa were constructed wherever possible; and plants such as citrus fruits, cotton and sugar cane were imported. Some of their laws of water usage are still in force.

By the eleventh century, easy conquest, luxury and internal squabbles were loosening the Moors' grip on the country. They were gradually driven from the north of the peninsula by the tough, mountain-bred, fanatical Christians. The little kingdom of the Asturias spread over the mountains to become the larger kingdom of León; Castile and Aragon became Christian again; by 1085 the Moors were compelled to retreat south of the Sierra Morena. This was the period of Spain's legendary hero, El Cid Campeador, whose name struck terror into the hearts of the Moors. It saw too the birth of Portugal as a separate country. By the beginning of the thirteenth century the Moors had lost Córdoba and Seville, and were encircled in Granada and the Portuguese Algarve. In 1474, the year the kingdoms of León, Castile and Aragon were united by the marriage of Isabella of Castile and Ferdinand of Aragon, the end of the long struggle was in sight. Granada, the last Moorish stronghold, was captured in 1492 and the hated occupiers finally expelled from the peninsula.

The reign of Ferdinand and Isabella marks a turning point in the history of Spain. In the same year that Granada surrendered, Christopher Columbus, a Genoese sailing in the service of Spain, discovered the New World. Spanish *conquistadores* soon followed in his wake. Adventurers such as Pizarro, Cortes and de Soto brought back from the Americas vast stores of gold and added new territories to the Spanish crown. Spain became a leading power in exploration and colonisation.

This "Golden Age," during which Spain was the richest and one of the most powerful states in Europe, lasted until the death of Philip II in 1598. Afterwards, decline set in. Philip's father, Charles I, was an Austrian Hapsburg, who came to the throne of Spain by marriage and ruled from 1516 to 1556. He was elected Holy Roman Emperor in 1519 and Spain was immediately embroiled in the wars and politics of the rest of Europe. At the same time as the conquistadores were extending her empire in the New World, the country was dragged into wars with England, France and the Netherlands. Her increasing exhaustion at home was demonstrated in 1588 by the ruinous defeat of the great Armada. The Hapsburg successors of Philip II were ineffective rulers in Spain— they were more interested in Austria—and when the last of them died in 1700, the gold brought back from America had been squandered, and Spain was almost bankrupt. Dispute about who should succeed the Hapsburgs led to the War of the Spanish Succession, and when it ended in 1713 the Spanish throne was given to the Bourbons (Borbóns). With two short intermissions they ruled Spain until 1931.

The Bourbon monarchy proved to be as effete as the later Hapsburgs. There were many uprisings by the Spanish peasants against the harshness of the aristocracy and the squalor in which they were forced to live. Matters became worse after 1833, when rival claimants to the throne precipitated the Carlist Wars, civil warfare which continued inter-mittently for forty-three years and left many parts of the country in ruins. General discontent and labour troubles were prolonged into the present century. In 1931 the king was dethroned, exiled and a republic proclaimed. Political and economic turmoil ensued; in 1936 civil war broke out again, and continued for three years. Armed forces under General Franco rose successfully against the official republican govern-ment in Madrid and seized power, but not before one of the bitterest conflicts in history had been fought. In 1939 Franco became Chief of State and ruler of Spain, a position he still holds today.

Under his leadership the country has made considerable social and economic advances. It has even returned to its monarchist traditions. In 1947 a public referendum ratified the Act of Succession, which proclaimed Spain a kingdom, with Franco (Francisco Franco Bahamonde) Chief of State. On his death he is to be succeeded by a person of royal blood, but up to the present the Council of the Realm has not designated an heir. Spain, therefore, has a peculiar political status: it is a kingdom without a king.

History offers few contrasts so striking as between Spain during the sixteenth century and at the present time. Less than four hundred years ago Spain was a great power, claiming dominion over a large portion of the world and drawing vast riches from the exploits of its seamen and exploring adventurers. Today it is economically backward and politically unstable. Only the Canary Islands and the two tiny African enclaves of Rio de Oro and Rio Muni remain of its empire. Much of its decline was undoubtedly due to the ineptitude or indifference of its rulers during the past three centuries, but this is only part of the explanation. We must search in geography for other important reasons.

In the first place Spain, unlike Portugal, is not really a maritime nation. Its coasts, except at the entrance to the Guadalquivir basin, are shut off from the interior of the country by the wall-like edges of the Meseta; it is noteworthy that Cádiz, its greatest port in past times, is near the mouth of the Guadalquivir. It is a reasonable supposition that Spain was encouraged to maritime adventure by the successful exploits of Portugal; her own victory over the Moors had aroused feelings of national pride and confidence. But as we have seen, the "Golden Age" lasted only a hundred years, and in any case it brought little benefit to the great mass of the people. Wealth and land ownership were concentrated in the hands of the Crown, the Church and the nobility, and the position is only slightly changed today.

A second factor was Spain's isolation from the rest of Europe by the barrier of the Pyrenees. It was underlined by the adoption of a broad gauge for the railways which approached the French frontier. With the memory of several invasions still fresh, Spain deliberately chose a different gauge from its neighbour in order to restrict the easy passage of troops, but it just as effectively slowed down commercial transport and hindered industrial development.

Spain's present internal political troubles also have geographical causes. At the beginning of the century the country had virtually no industrial activity, except the mining and export of mineral ores, the iron and steel production of the Biscayan region and the textile manufactures of Barcelona. A very large proportion of this was in the hands of Basques and Catalans—peoples who lived in "compartments" outside the main mass of the country and were different in ethnic origin, language, culture and ways of thinking, as well as material well-being. Catalonia and the Basque provinces became increasingly separatist in politics, and demanded self-determination. Their demands precipitated the civil war of 1936–39, in which the rebels were joined by many of the working classes of the plateau, whose condition, especially after the world economic crisis of 1929, was wretched in the extreme.

The civil war destroyed whatever economic advance had been made in the early part of the century. In addition to heavy loss of life, the transport system was crippled, the industries in Catalonia and the Basque lands were brought to a standstill, livestock was decimated, and a large proportion of the best agricultural land in the country was laid waste.

During the Second World War, Spain was unable to take advantage of her uneasy neutrality to improve her trading position with any of the combatants. She was much too occupied in attempting to rebuild her own shattered economy. Moreover, because the opposing sides in the civil war had been helped by Fascist, Nazi and Communist men and arms, the country was ostracised by the Western powers after the Second World War, and excluded from the help given to other countries of western Europe to rehabilitate themselves. Not until 1954 was any assistance given to Spain, and then the U.S.A. came to her aid. Only since that date has she shown signs of real economic advance; even now it is very slow and laboured.

The people of Spain are the result of invasion and settlement from the south, east and north. The true Spaniard, if any one type can be regarded as such, is found in Old Castile, and Castilian is the basis of the present Spanish language. There are, however, in Galicia, the Basque provinces and Catalonia, peoples who differ markedly in origin and tongue from the Castilians and have their own culture and traditions. In the south, too, the long occupation by the Moors has left its mark on the physical characteristics and temperament of the people of Andalusia. Their dialect is tempered with a large number of Arabic derivatives. It will be noted that the inhabitants of the Meseta seem to be the descendants of the original Spanish people, and that the various sub-peoples are around its edges. The Basques live at the eastern end of the Biscay coastlands, and are found also in south-western France. The Catalans live in north-eastern Spain and appear to be the same people as the Provençals of southern France, the dialects being very much akin. The Galicians are of the same racial stock as the old inhabitants of Brittany, south-west Ireland and some parts of west Scotland. They may be offshoots of a Celtic migration.

POPULATION

Spain, with a population of 30,430,000, has an average density of 156 persons per square mile, which is low compared with its neighbour Portugal's 254 per square mile. It must be remembered, however, that a far larger proportion of Spain is mountain or dry plateau, whereas Portugal has wide plains open to the sea.

The greatest concentration of population, outside the Meseta, is in the north. Catalonia and the Biscayan lands are the regions of industrial development, with a total of 10·5 million inhabitants: more than a third of the population in less than a quarter of the country's surface area. Catalonia has 262 persons a square mile, and some provinces along the

Bay of Biscay 218. The density of 232 in the province of Galicia is noteworthy, for the region is one of fishermen-farmers and has little industry. The coastal plain of Valencia has a density of 252 but Murcia, the largest of the other coastal lowlands, has only 114. Away from the north, the greatest density is in the lowlands of Andalusia, where it is 166 a square mile.

The most densely peopled region of the Meseta is New Castile, with an

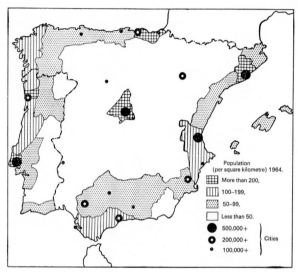

Fig. 123.—Iberian peninsula: population density (per square kilometre). Of the cities shown, Madrid has more than 2 million inhabitants, and Barcelona and Lisbon 1 million each. Note that the figure in the text gives density per square mile.

average of 123 persons a square mile; but this includes well over 2 millions in Madrid alone, and the average distribution outside the city is around 80. Over the plateau as a whole the average density never exceeds 85 and in some areas, such as La Mancha and Extremadura, there are very few inhabitants. The sparsest population is in Aragon, which includes the central Pyrenees, the Ebro basin and the mountains of the north-east Meseta. Here the average is 57 persons a square mile.

THE ECONOMY

GENERAL FEATURES

Spain is one of the best endowed of all Mediterranean countries in agricultural potential and mineral resources, but so far she has lacked the national unity essential for their full development.

Agriculture, which employs at least half the working population, is backward and often at subsistence level. The outstanding characteristic of the rural population is its poverty. Conditions along the north coast and in the Mediterranean *huertas* are somewhat better, but rarely are there signs of true agricultural prosperity. A much more serious policy of

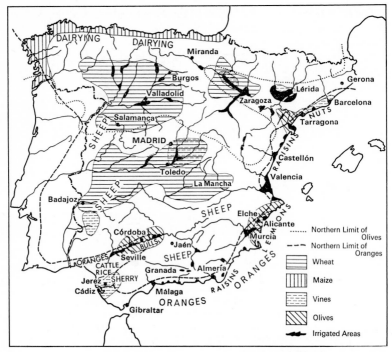

Fig. 124.—Spain: agriculture. The northern limit of olive cultivation is often taken as the boundary of the Mediterranean type of climate in Europe, but there are large areas of the southern Meseta in which the climate is not typically Mediterranean.

agrarian reform is needed. The large *latifundia* of southern Spain must be split into smaller and more productive units, and the uneconomic "patch-farming" of the north and north-west requires the stimulus of co-operative methods. In all parts of the country there is a woeful lack of farm machinery, fertilisers and knowledge of modern techniques.

Wheat is the most important field crop and covers large areas of the Meseta. The total output varies considerably from year to year, according to the vagaries of the weather, and in some years Spain has had to import wheat. It is doubtful, too, whether the area under *secano* wheat can be increased, again for reasons of climate. In other parts of the country, however, where irrigation can be further developed, larger acreages are already being devoted to sugar beet (in the north) and to sugar cane, tobacco, cotton and tomatoes (in the south). Equally important, yields per acre are increasing. Spain already ranks first in the world in the production of olive oil and cork, and in exports of oranges and orange juice, and she is third in output of wine.

Spain is one of the most important European producers of lead, copper, mercury, silver, zinc, manganese and iron ores. In each case the output could be greater, but the Spanish peasant, with his long tradition of work on the land, regards labour in the mines as degrading. The Oviedo coalfields, for instance, are always short of miners. The minerals so essential to the development of the country's own industries are largely exported, though during the last decade home consumption has been growing, helped by a phenomenal increase in the generation of hydro-electricity. Developed hydro-electric power has risen in the past twenty years from 5 million to nearly 20 million kWh, mainly in State-owned schemes. Not only has it enabled the industrial regions of Barcelona and the northern coastlands to extend their activities, but it has also made possible the dispersal of manufacturing industry to regions previously without any. Coal production amounts to about 13 million tons a year, but as far as the interior of the country is concerned the coalfields are badly situated; and the coal is mostly of poor quality.

Communications are another weak point in Spain's economy. Both road and railway systems were constructed so as to centre on Madrid. This concentration on the capital city has made the development of manufacturing industries in the rest of the plateau very difficult. Any improvement is hampered by the deep valleys which cut across the Meseta; and as time goes on, Madrid's predominance tends to become more permanent. Three-quarters of the railways are broad gauge, the remainder narrow gauge—another disadvantage—and much of the track and rolling stock was damaged or destroyed during the civil war. It has not yet been fully repaired or restored, and the same is true of the roads.

In many ways it appears that Spain is only just awakening after centuries of lethargy and mismanagement by its rulers, centuries in which its ordinary people, hard-working, frugal and fanatically attached to their country and religion, were given little or no opportunity to improve their lot. Today things are changing. The conservative Castilian, the energetic Basque and the progressive Catalan are being brought together. Slowly and often reluctantly they are beginning to appreciate that Spain's complete economic recovery will be achieved, not through internal jealousies and conflict, but by unity.

REGIONAL ECONOMY

1. *The Atlantic coastlands*

(a) *Galicia; the Cantabrian mountains; the Asturian plain.* The mountainous north-west of Spain has the highest rainfall in the country. On its rivers, the Minho (Miño) and Sil in Galicia, and the Esla from the western Cantabrians, hydro-electric power stations have recently been constructed. The current generated amounts to about one-tenth of Spain's total hydro-electricity, and it may lead to the development of industry in this otherwise poorly endowed region. Already there are fertiliser factories at Puenteareas and a pulp and paper mill at Pontevedra, the latter making use of timber from the forest-clad mountains. Probably of greater immediate importance, however, is the water made available for irrigation on the Meseta south of the Cantabrians.

The soils of Galicia are poor, and those of the Asturias not much better, but by dint of careful cultivation good crops of maize, vegetables and orchard fruit are obtained. The wet grasslands have made north-west Spain the country's most important cattle rearing region, supplying milk and dairy produce to the towns of the Biscay coast. The farms of Galicia have been so fragmented by the laws of inheritance that they are too small to support a family reasonably, and there has been constant emigration to the towns of the Basque country. The farms of the Asturias are larger and more prosperous. In both Galicia and the plain of Asturias the coastal districts have more people than the interior, for many farmers there are fishermen too and thus can supplement their income.

The chief fishing ports are Corunna (La Coruña) (177,502), Vigo (158,550), in Galicia, and Gijón (124,714), in the Asturias. A fifth of Spain's catch comes into these ports, principally sardines from near the coast and cod from the Newfoundland Grand Banks. The value of the Galician ports is reduced by their distance from the more developed parts of Spain and by the fact that there is no railway to connect them directly with the rest of the Biscayan coast. In spite of this, they have important sardine canning and cod drying factories.

Galicia has no mineral resources, but the coastal plain of Asturias is the most highly mineralised part of Spain. Between Gijón and Oviedo is the largest coalfield in the country, producing bituminous and anthracite coal, though not of the best quality. South-west of Avilés are extensive deposits of iron ore which have led to smelting and steelworks at Oviedo and Avilés. Zinc occurs near Avilés, mercury a few miles south of Oviedo. Industrial activity is increasing in the region, and less of the mineral ores is being exported in the raw state than was the case only a few years ago. Oviedo (127,058), the largest town, has iron and steel, chemical and glass works, coke ovens and zinc smelting. Some of its power supplies come from the hydro-electric stations on the south side of the Cantabrian mountains. The industrial development of Asturias is proceeding so rapidly that there is a labour shortage despite the influx of surplus population from Galicia.

(b) *Santander; the Basque provinces; the western Pyrenees.* The coastal plains and the wide valleys of the rivers that flow to the Bay of Biscay are

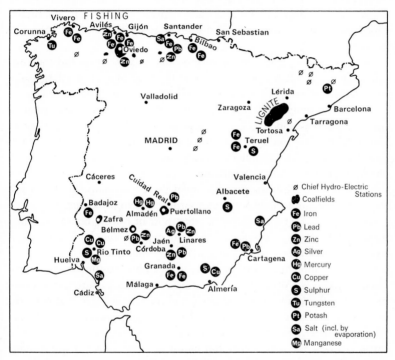

Fig. 125.—Spain: minerals. Although Spain is richly endowed in mineral resources, the only real industrial development is in the north of the country.

agriculturally the most favoured part of Spain. Maize, fruit, vegetables and dairy products find ready markets in the numerous towns of Santander and the Basque provinces. Vineyards are found on many southward-facing slopes.

Santander is historically a part of the kingdom of Old Castile, and its people are Castilian, but its economic development is so bound up with that of the Basque provinces that it is always included with them. The Basques are a virile mountain people; they accepted industrialism earlier than the more easy-going Castilians. The Basque provinces are Vizcaya,

Alava and Guipúzcoa, known collectively as Vascongadas. With Santander they form the most extensive industrial region in Spain.

Industrialisation was helped by the existence in the hinterland of Santander and Bilbao of the largest deposits of hematite iron ore in the
country. Santander is also the chief producer of zinc ore, and lead and
lignite occur in minor quantities. Until recent years most of the iron ore
was exported via Santander and Bilbao to South Wales, which in return
sent coking coal for a smelting and iron and steel industry at Bilbao.
Today this reciprocal trade is very small, although it continues;
more and more of the mineral output is being smelted and processed
locally.

Bilbao (298,000) is the largest city on the Atlantic coast and the chief
industrial centre. It is a port, situated at the head of a ria, but large ships
must use its outport of Portugalete. The iron and steel industry is paramount: the province of Vizcaya produces about 60% of Spain's total, in
spite of the new and larger steelworks being built at Avilés in Asturias.
Based on the steel industry are shipbuilding, engineering, boiler works
and the making of machinery. There are coke ovens, cement works,
chemicals and glass manufacture and paper mills. The raw material for
the paper comes from the pine forests of the Cantabrians. Bilbao is also
a commercial and fishing port, with sardine and tunny canneries.

Santander (118,435) has industries like those of Bilbao, but on a smaller
scale. Both towns smelt lead, zinc and copper, and both give comparatively easy access from the coast to the interior. Reinosa, a small
town in the mountains, near the source of the Ebro, has important hydro-
electricity works. With electro-smelting, glass manufacture and a school
of naval architecture, it is a growing industrial centre. It is also in the
middle of a dairy cattle region and has a dairying industry which uses
electrical power. San Sebastian (135,149), at the eastern end of the Biscayan coast, is not only a port and industrial centre but a major holiday
resort—the most popular in Spain. It has food processing, textile and paper
industries; in its hinterland are many small towns with metalliferous,
chemical, glass and engineering works. It has also some strategic importance, commanding as it does the narrow lowland route from France,
west of the Pyrenees.

The western Pyrenees, though well-watered on their outer slopes,
are poorly peopled. The inhabitants, largely Basque in origin, are
engaged in lumbering in the pine forests which clothe the mountains in
the wetter parts or in poor transhumant farming and pasture in the valleys.
Dairy cattle are reared in forest clearings and maize is the chief food crop.
Rainfall decreases rapidly eastwards in the sub-Pyrenean zone and, with
the greater aridity, wheat takes the place of maize and olive groves begin

to appear. This sub-Pyrenean area presents a great contrast in fruitfulness to the lands facing the Bay of Biscay.

The largest towns of the western Pyrenees region are Pamplona (97,880) and Jaca. Both are market towns. Pamplona has textile factories and Jaca is a crossroads, commanding the Somport Pass.

2. *The Mediterranean coastlands*

(a) *The eastern Pyrenees; the Mediterranean coastal plains.* The eastern Pyrenees are a valuable source of hydro-electric power (*see* Fig. 125). The Segre, a tributary of the Ebro, and the Ter, which flows directly to the Mediterranean, have been harnessed and current is sent to the industrial region of Catalonia to the south. The economy of the eastern Pyrenees is pastoral, but with sheep rather than cattle. In the valleys and depressions, wheat is the chief crop. Population is scanty, though with the general increase of industry in the district north of Barcelona, and with larger numbers of people using the eastern route from France into Spain, villages at the foot of the mountains are growing in size, especially near the power stations.

The best developed of the Mediterranean coastal plains are those of Catalonia and Valencia. The Catalonian plains include Gerona, Barcelona and Tarragona, which are separated by the northern ranges of the Catalonian mountains and well watered by streams from the eastern Pyrenees. Much of the mountain area is forested, while the lower slopes are terraced for vines, olives and nut-trees. Cork from the forests north of Barcelona is sent out from the small ports of Palamos and San Felíu.

The plain of Gerona in the north, with more rainfall, has mixed farming—maize, wheat, fodder crops, dairying and pig rearing. Farther south there are market-gardens supplying the city of Barcelona with fruit and vegetables. In the plain of Tarragona the vine is dominant. Throughout the Catalonian lowlands there are irrigation networks, so that every piece of potentially productive land is used. Even on the Ebro delta, until recent years a marsh in winter and a dried-up plain in summer, rice is grown in exportable quantities by means of a carefully regulated system of drainage and irrigation canals.

The Catalans are much more businesslike than the Castilian Spaniards, and had developed trading and industrial activities while the rest of Spain was still fighting the Moors. The Catalan language seems to be a debased version of the French Languedoc dialect, and in many ways the culture is more closely related to southern France than to Spain. The people of Catalonia have also been greatly influenced by long-continued contacts with merchants from the eastern Mediterranean. Very early in history Barcelona became a major trading port.

[*Courtesy of British European Airways.*

FIG. 126.—Gradas de Santiago, Barcelona. The Steps of St James, leading to the
church in the Spanish Village, a district in the city. Note the name
"Spanish" Village, many of the inhabitants of which are Castilian, as distinct
from the Catalans, who inhabit this region of Spain.

Barcelona (1,558,000) is the second city and foremost port of Spain.
On an excellent harbour, and facing the trade routes of the Mediterranean, it was a focus of shipping and commerce as early as the fifteenth
century. With the Industrial Revolution, it developed cotton and silk
manufactures, using imported raw materials and fuel. Today it is overwhelmingly the textile capital of Spain, manufacturing woollens, linen,
jute and synthetic fibres. The textile industry, encouraged by hydro-
electricity, has spread into the north of the plain. Barcelona has the
largest paper mills in Spain, and is the chief engineering city as well;
it specialises in marine engines, railway locomotives and rolling stock,
motor cars, heavy machinery, electrical apparatus and ship-building.
In its northern suburbs is a heavy chemical industry, using pyrites from
other parts of Spain, phosphates from North Africa and potash salts

from large deposits in the interior valleys of the province. Barcelona's food-processing industry rivals Madrid's.

Tarragona (42,100) is the market and outlet for the wine trade of the northern region. It exports hazel nuts, medlars, almonds and other fruit. Maize and rice are the main cereals; and in the *huertas* (kitchen gardens or irrigated lands) peas, beans, lentils, onions and other vegetables are grown. Along the coast of Catalonia is a growing tourist and holiday industry, especially north and south of the city of Barcelona. The resorts of the Costa de Levante and Costa Brava are now competing with those of the French Riviera.

Southwards along the coast are the plains of Castellón de la Plana and Valencia. Sheltered by the Meseta behind them, they have scorchingly hot summers and low winter rainfall, but by sinking wells and making use of the waters of the numerous streams flowing from the plateau rim they have been transformed into huertas of the highest fertility. Maize and rice are again of first importance, with wheat and barley as secondary crops. Valencia is the chief rice growing province in Spain. Olive groves and vineyards occur everywhere, and in the best irrigated areas are orange and lemon groves, apricots, carob beans, peaches, pomegranates and fig trees. The province of Valencia provides the finest example of *huerta* cultivation in the country. It supports Spain's third largest city, Valencia (505,000), and one of the densest populations in the country. On a good harbour at the mouth of the river Guadalaviar, Valencia is the chief port for raisins (sun-dried grapes). It is also a manufacturing city, with textiles and engineering, chemicals and shipbuilding.

Lying at the south-east corner of Spain, hemmed in by the ranges of the Betic Cordillera, are the plains of Alicante and Murcia, forming a continuous stretch. This is the driest part of the Mediterranean coastlands, and water for irrigation is brought by a complex canal system from the mountains. On lands too high to be watered in this way there are vines, olives, fig trees and almonds, which can withstand drought because of their long roots. On the irrigated areas crops can be grown without intermission, for the winters are warm enough for the cultivation of onions, peas, beans and tomatoes. Wheat is grown side by side with tropical produce such as cotton and groundnuts; and along with the usual Mediterranean fruits may be seen bananas and sugar cane. At Elche there are groves of date palms, more reminiscent of an African oasis than of Europe. On the inner edges of the plains sheep rearing is the chief occupation, the animals being taken on to the Meseta during the winter, when the rains come.

Alicante (122,200) is the chief port for grapes, and is the outlet for the industries of Murcia (249,700), which manufactures linen, paper and explosives. The province of Murcia has deposits of iron ore and lead in the Sierra de Cartagena; there are smaller amounts of zinc, copper and tin. These minerals are all exported raw from Alicante and Cartagena. Salt is evaporated from lagoons along the coast south of the town of Alicante.

The south coast of Spain is backed so closely by the Betic Cordillera

FIG. 127.—Spain: Málaga, the harbour. A general view, taken from Gibralfaro Hill, of the excellent though small harbour. Note the size of the bull-ring, a characteristic feature of most Spanish towns.

that there is little room for lowlands. The only plains are behind Almería and Málaga, where water is available for irrigation. Here are grown citrus fruits, cotton, tobacco, figs, vines and early vegetables, especially potatoes. Sugar cane and dates show the nearness of Africa. Almería (86,808) exports table grapes, iron ore, lead, silver, esparto grass, citrus fruits and salt. Málaga (301,000) has an important wine trade, sugar refineries, soapworks, textiles and engineering. After Barcelona, it is the main exporter of Spain's Mediterranean produce (*see* Fig. 127).

At the western end of south Spain is the narrow, rocky peninsula of Gibraltar which, though territorially a part of Spain, belongs to Great Britain. The Rock, as it is called, is nearly 1400 ft in height, and serves as a fortress commanding the entrance to the Mediterranean. It is consequently a military and naval base, a refuelling point and supply depot; but all supplies have to be imported, as there is no area suitable for cultivation. Water for its population of 25,000 and for such simple industries as olive oil pressing, sardine canning and tobacco processing, comes from rainwater stored in enormous underground reservoirs hewn out of the rock. Since the loss of control of the Suez Canal the strategic value of Gibraltar to Great Britain has declined, but it is still of importance to the Western powers as a strong-point against the growing ambitions of the Arab nations of North Africa and the Soviet Union. This is one reason why the Spanish claim to it has so far been denied.

The Mediterranean coastlands of Spain, though they occupy in total area only a small part of the country, contain a large proportion of the population, with one city of over 1,500,000 people and another with more than 500,000. The fact that every one of the lowlands strung along the Mediterranean littoral supports a large concentration of people gives ample proof of their collective agricultural productivity. Two points are worthy of note: the value and success of irrigation throughout the region, and the growth of industry in the northern portion, based largely on the development of hydro-electric power in the Pyrenees. Industry is now spreading southwards from the Barcelona area, helped by the new power stations constructed on the lower river Ebro where it passes through a gorge near the southern end of the Catalonian mountains.

(b) *The Guadalquivir basin.* This river basin is included with the Mediterranean coastlands because it has a Mediterranean climate; but because it lies open to the west it receives more rain than the south and east coasts. Even so, the total precipitation in the eastern basin is scanty, and much of the surface there is esparto steppe.

Andalusia, which includes the Guadalquivir basin, was the last part of Spain to be reconquered from the Moors. It shows the most obvious signs of their long occupation—in place-names, architecture, aqueducts, irrigation systems, etc., and in the variety of plants they introduced, some of which, such as citrus fruits, sugar cane and cotton have already been noted in the coastal huertas. Under Moorish rule, Andalusia was the most productive region in Spain; when the Moors were driven out, the province declined.

For this the aristocracy and the Church were largely to blame. As a reward for their assistance in the reconquest they were given large grants of land. The dispossessed peasants were forced to work on the extensive estates (Sp. *latifundia*) as labourers or to become share-croppers on small-holdings. In the course of time the latifundia passed into the hands of landlords who lived in Madrid or Seville. They left the running of their estates in the hands of managers and in a majority of cases this is still the case. The absentee landlords are little interested in new, scientific methods of farming; large areas are left fallow every third year; implements are primitive and machinery rarely seen; and too much land is devoted to wheat and olives, which, in the climate of Andalusia, require a minimum of labour but give a good cash return. There is little doubt that with reforms in land ownership and farming techniques, and better use of water which flows down both sides of the Guadalquivir, the basin would become a vast huerta. Measures for improvement have been decided upon by the Government, but few so far have been put into operation.

The exceptions are in the alluvial valleys and on the irrigated clay soils of the region between Seville and Córdoba, where sugar cane, tobacco, cotton, groundnuts, rice and vegetables are successfully cultivated, as well as the ubiquitous wheat and olives. But the yields are small compared with those of the east coast huertas. The best conditions are in the Seville district, where irrigation enables enormous quantities of bitter oranges to be produced for export, to be used in making marmalade.

The growing of vines is of greatest importance around Jerez and Jaén, but viticulture is found on all hill slopes. Jerez has been noted for centuries for the production of sherry: the wine takes its name from the town. Young bulls are bred south of Córdoba and sent to the Marismas, below Seville, to be prepared for use in bullfights (Sp. *corridas*) all over the country. The Marismas are a marshy wilderness on both sides of the Guadalquivir below Seville. On the north side are vast water meadows where the bulls are reared; on the south, where there has been some reclamation, rice is grown.

The Sierra Morena, which form the northern boundary of the Andalusian basin, are rich in minerals. On their gentle slopes are wheatfields and cork oak forests, with maquis in the poorer parts. Goat rearing is part of the economy, as it is throughout Andalusia. Copper and cupriferous pyrites are mined at Rio Tinto and exported through Huelva. Mercury, of which Spain is the world's leading producer, is found at Almadén. Lead–zinc–silver ores occur at Linares and near Jaén on the south side of the river valley. Spain comes ninth in the world for lead output, twelfth for zinc and twelfth for silver. Near Bélmez and Puertollano are two small coalfields of poor quality. The many streams which flow from the Sierra Morena to the Guadalquivir have been dammed for irrigation and power, but the irrigation systems could be greatly improved, and the power generated is at present negligible.

Seville (443,000) is the largest town of the basin. It is situated at the head of navigation and lowest bridge point of the Guadalquivir; the river, which is tidal, is kept open only by dredging. Seville has textile manufactures and light engineering, but its chief function is as the collecting centre and exporting port for the wine, oranges, minerals and olive oil of the basin. It is the regional capital. Córdoba (198,148) was once a stronghold of the Moors and contains many examples of their architecture. In the centre of wheatlands and cattle farms, it is a market and has fast-developing electrical and light engineering industries too. Cádiz (117,871), on a narrow harbour south of the Guadalquivir mouth, exports sherry and olive oil. It was once the chief port of Spain but has declined considerably in importance. It can accommodate larger ships than Seville and competes for trade to the Canaries and South America, besides being a naval dockyard.

3. The Meseta, central Pyrenees, Ebro basin and Betic Cordillera

(a) *The Meseta*. In consequence of its elevated, isolated character and continental climate, the Meseta has a backward economy. The northern Meseta, that is, north of the Central Sierras, is the basin of Old Castile. It is slightly more favoured than the south as far as rainfall is concerned, and large areas are devoted to the growth of wheat without irrigation—a method known as *secano* (Sp. "non-irrigated land"). In the better-watered districts, fodder crops, peas and beans are grown in rotation with secano wheat and, in the poorer districts, potatoes and rye. Where irrigation is possible, flax and hemp are cultivated, and vines appear on the lower slopes of valleys. Where the soil is too porous for agriculture the basin of Old Castile is covered by garrigue and steppe, on which sheep are reared, mainly on the flat tops of the *paramos*. Old Castile was the original home of the Merino sheep, which was taken to South Africa and Australia, and produces the finest quality wools. The amount of wool exported from Spain is, however, small.

The basin of Old Castile is thinly populated. There are only two towns of any size, Valladolid and Burgos. Both are railway foci for the northern half of Spain, and wheat markets for the basin, which is the granary of the country. Valladolid (151,807) is a flour-milling centre and has railway and automobile engineering; and Burgos (82,177), nearer to the Basque industrial region and with easy access to it, has paper, chemical and agricultural engineering industries. It is also a tourist centre.

South of the Central Sierras lies the basin of New Castile. It is not so obviously a basin as Old Castile: the western portion is broken by the mountains of Toledo and the granite plateaus of Extremadura, across which flow the Tagus and Guadiana. Extremadura and New Castile are drier than the northern basin and have more "Mediterranean" characteristics; the olive, absent in Old Castile, makes its appearance. Secano wheat is again the main crop, but aridity and poor facilities for irrigation make sheep rearing the chief occupation, especially in Extremadura, which has the largest flocks of Merino sheep in the country. Here, and over large areas in the south-east of the New Castile basin, transhumance is common, the sheep being driven up the mountains in summer and brought down to the plateau level in winter. In the south-east is the basin of La Mancha (Arab. *al mancha*, "the thirsty land"), a vast, arid plain covered with drought-resisting shrubs (Sp. *matorral* "undergrowth") or esparto grass, which is used for paper making as well as fodder. The southern basin is more scantily peopled than north of the Sierras. Only Badajos (96,152) and Toledo (46,500) are of any size. Toledo at one time had a reputation for the quality of the steel swords made there, but this ancient craft has completely disappeared.

Although the basins of the Meseta are poorly populated, the southern foot of the Sierra de Guadarrama holds the largest concentration of people in Spain, in Madrid, the capital. Madrid (2,260,000) is an artificial creation: the site was chosen solely because it is geographically in the centre of the country. It has nothing else to commend it, since the region is arid and unproductive. Nor is it in easy communication with all parts of the country, except by dint of heavy engineering projects. Although it has been made the focus of Spain's road and railway systems, and great efforts have been made to increase industrial activity, it is hard pressed to compete with Barcelona and the Basque coast, where there are more raw materials and better facilities for overseas trade.

Madrid is the administrative and commercial centre of Spain, and its industries are mainly concerned with consumer goods, such as foodstuffs, furniture, clothing, footwear and leather goods, glassware and pottery, and pharmaceutical chemicals. In the past twenty years its population has grown by over half a million, and new industries connected with electricity, gas, cement and machinery have been helped by hydro-electric power; but it appears unlikely that Madrid will ever become a great industrial city. Its water supply comes from streams to the north, as already noted, and from the huge reservoirs of Buendia and Alocén, impounded in the upper Tagus basin. Some miles north of Madrid is the famous palace of the Escorial, part of which has now been turned into a monastery.

(b) *The central Pyrenees; the Ebro basin.* The high central Pyrenees have only slight economic value. There is a little lumbering, and sheep are reared in clearings up to 5000 ft. In a few high valleys approached by a difficult road is the tiny republic of Andorra (190 sq miles), whose 5000 inhabitants live by a precarious subsistence agriculture of rye, potatoes and vegetables, by transhumant pasture of cattle and sheep, and—more recently—by tourism. This last, however, has been developed more by entry from the French side of the Pyrenees than from Spain. Andorra is a remarkable example in modern times of how a mountain people can preserve its independence. At the foot of the central Pyrenees a series of low limestone sierras is too dry for any vegetation except garrigue, on which sheep are reared. Wheat, rye and vines are cultivated very near the rivers, but considerable areas are "badland," of no use at all.

Shut off from rain-bearing winds, the Ebro basin is one of the driest regions of Spain. Its winters, too, are decidedly cool for a Mediterranean land. Zaragoza, for instance, in the middle of the basin, has an average January temperature of 42° F (5·6° C) and an annual precipitation of $11\frac{1}{2}$ in. During the winter, when cold air drains down the slopes of the central Pyrenees, the basin may experience frost at night. Away from the river Ebro and its tributary valleys, vegetation is maquis or garrigue on hills and steppe on lowlands. East of Zaragoza, the district of Los Manegros is by nature almost semi-desert, but irrigation has succeeded in making parts of it productive. The middle section of the river basin has occasional surface encrustations of salt or gypsum; in such places irrigation is either useless or too expensive. On the garrigue and steppe the chief occupation is sheep rearing.

Below Logroño the river Ebro has been tapped for irrigation, and from there to Zaragoza two major canals—the Canal Imperial de Aragon along the left bank and the Canal de Tauste along the right—provide water to a narrow belt of land. South of the Ebro, the valleys of the Jalon and Guadalope are partially irrigated. Further east the left bank tributaries, notably the Cinca, Esera, Noguera Ribagorzana, Noguera Pallaresa and Segre, are more completely controlled, so that a large portion of the eastern basin north of the parent river is fully irrigated. This includes the Llanos (Sp. "plains") de Urgel and part of Los Manegros. In the upper Segre valley, hydro-electricity is generated and sent to the Barcelona district and to Lérida, lower down the valley. The irrigated areas are the only parts of the Ebro basin which are more than scantily populated. Large crops of wheat and sugar beet are grown in them and onions, vines, olives and tree crops such as almonds, apricots, peaches and plums are cultivated. Peas, beans, tomatoes, pimento and alfalfa (grass) are other crops. In the western end of the basin, nearer to the wetter Cantabrian sierras, cattle rearing is important.

The chief town in the Ebro basin is Zaragoza (Saragossa) (326,316). It is well placed in the centre of the basin, where the Ebro can be bridged and where routes round both ends of the Pyrenees converge towards the

Jalon Gap, which leads through the Iberian mountains to Madrid. Its industries are concerned mainly with the products of the irrigated lands—flour milling, sugar refining, oil pressing, wine making and jam manufacture—but it has also modern iron and steel works, railway and electrical engineering, cement manufacture and machine tool making. After Madrid, it is the largest city in "arid" Spain. Lerida (63,850) has grown rapidly in the eastern irrigated region, benefiting from the hydro-electric power developed on the river Segre. Logroño (61,292) is the market for the western basin, where irrigation is less necessary.

The Ebro is of little value for navigation, as its volume is too variable and its speed too great in the gorge by which it passes to its delta. Hydroelectric power stations have been built in the gorge, above Tortosa, and current is sent to the towns of the coastal plain.

(c) *The Betic Cordillera; the Balearic Isles.* In the west of the Betic Cordillera the rainfall is sufficient for secano cultivation of cereals, vines and olives, and the mountain slopes have forests of cork oak. Farther east the landscape becomes increasingly barren and there are large areas of esparto grass, which supports transhumant sheep rearing. Only in the basins between the northern and southern mountain belts is there any considerable population, for only here is it possible to harness the numerous mountain streams for irrigation.

The chief basin, around Granada, is watered by snow-melt from the Sierra Nevada and has been transformed into a *vega*, the name given in southern Spain to fertile lowland plains—although these mountain basins are only low in comparison to the surrounding heights. In the Granada basin the chief products are maize, wheat, sugar beet and fodder crops, with vines and olives climbing up the lower slopes. Granada (157,178) has flour mills, sugar refineries, paper mills and a woollen industry. It is also a tourist centre, for it contains the Alhambra, a magnificent castle and palace built by the Moors, typifying the high degree of civilisation they reached in their last stronghold in Spain. The other intermontane basins, Loja, Moreda, Lorca and Braza, have similar agricultural products to Granada.

In the Balearic islands, agriculture is possible only by irrigation. This is well developed, and the same crops are grown as in the huertas of the east coast of the mainland. Fishing for sardines and anchovies occupies many of the coastal population but is of only local importance. The largest islands—Majorca, Minorca and Iviza—have become favourite holiday resorts, largely because of the reliable Mediterranean climate, which here is tempered by the surrounding sea. The chief towns are Palma (159,084), on Majorca, and Mahon (19,000), on Minorca.

STUDY QUESTIONS

1. Make a division of Spain into geographical regions. Describe the relief and drainage of each region and show how these have influenced communications through the whole area of the country. (O. & C.)

2. Contrast the climate of the Meseta with that of the south coast of Spain and that of the northern coastal region. (O. & C.)

3. Account for the regional differences in economic development to be found in Spain. (J.M.B.)

4. Discuss the bearing of physical factors upon the economic development of two contrasted regions in Spain.

5. Outline the geographical background of the main politico-economic problems of Spain. (J.M.B.)

6. Write a comprehensive account of the Meseta of Spain. (J.M.B.)

7. Discuss the characteristic features of agriculture in the Mediterranean coastlands of Spain. (J.M.B.)

8. Describe the distribution of population in Spain, pointing out reasons for variations in regional densities.

Chapter XXX

PORTUGAL

PHYSICAL ASPECTS

PORTUGAL, on the western side of the Iberian peninsula, is rectangular in shape, about 300 miles from north to south and rarely more than 100 miles wide. Most of the country lies outside the Meseta and is at a lower elevation. Because its surface is broken in such a way as to form extensive coastal plains penetrating the interior, the whole of Portugal is open to the sea, allowing the free entry of rain-bearing, cooling winds from the Atlantic. To the north and east it is bounded by Spain, but the frontier is historical rather than physical.

Portugal was born in the land immediately to the south of the river Minho, which was given originally to the Count of Portugal. Its boundaries were extended southwards during the drive to expel the Moors from the west of the peninsula. This campaign was accompanied by a parallel movement southwards of the Spanish forces, but the two Christian armies did not mix. The regions they took by conquest were settled, on the west by the Portuguese, on the east by the Spaniards; so that gradually, by the process of occupation, the line of demarcation between the two peoples became the frontier. As it passed through a region which even today has a scanty population, there have been singularly few arguments about its position. In fact, with one minor exception, it has remained unaltered since the thirteenth century. It is also a natural linguistic frontier, for Portuguese, though akin to Castilian, is a separate Romance language.

Physically, the Portuguese are much like the Spaniards, though on average slightly taller. But there are ethnic differences between the peoples of north and south Portugal. In the north they resemble their Galician neighbours; south of the Serra da Estrêla they are a mixture of Iberian with Moorish, Berber, Jewish and Negro strains. This last is found mainly in the south of the Algarve, and is attributed variously to a prehistoric negroid population and to imported slave labour in the days of colonial expansion.

East of the fault-zone which runs southwards from the mouth of the river Douro is the worn-down western edge of the Meseta, composed of ancient granites and other crystalline rocks. The plateau ranges of the

498

Meseta in Spain are continued into Portugal, and the lowlands are extensions of the down-warpings in the Spanish plateau (*see* Fig. 120). The Central Sierras of Spain have their counterpart in the Serra da Estrêla and Serra da Guardunha; the Sierra de Guadalupe is continued into the Serra d'Ossa; and the Serra do Caldeirão and Serra de Monchique, which run towards the rocky Cape St Vincent, are extensions of the Sierra Morena. West of the fault-zone the Serra da Estrêla is continued into hill ranges of Mesozoic age. These are chiefly of limestone, and form the northern slopes of the lower Tagus basin, finishing in the cliffs of Cape Roca. Similar Mesozoic limestones occur also in the extreme south of the Algarve. The first of the lowlands stretches to the north and south of the river Mondego, and represents the westernmost part of the basin of Old Castile. It is at a much lower level, however, and is floored by Tertiary sands and clays, with alluvium near the rivers. The more extensive plain in the lower Tagus and Sado basins may be regarded as an extension of the Spanish Extremadura or Badajoz basin. In this plain of central Portugal the Tertiaries conceal the line of faults and extend on to the ancient platform in the east.

STRUCTURAL DIVISIONS

Portugal may be divided physically (and economically) into (1) the north, (2) the centre, and (3) the south (*see* Fig. 128). Northern Portugal— the provinces of Minho, Douro, Tras os Montes, Beira Alta, Beira Baixa and Beira Litoral—is predominantly mountainous or hilly, and extends from the northern boundary southwards, to include the Serra da Estrêla. Central Portugal comprises the hilly country of Estremadura, the plain of the Tagus in Ribatejo (*riba Tejo*, "bank of the Tagus"), the plain of the Sado and the hilly basin of the Guadiana in Alentejo. Southern Portugal is the Algarve, a small province shut off by mountains from the rest of the country and turned geographically more towards Africa.

1. *Northern Portugal*

The northern provinces of Portugal consist of a number of small horsts separated by steep-sided valleys, so arranged that oceanic influences penetrate inland. The highland massifs, such as the Serra da Cabreira, Serra de Villarelha, Serra de Nogueira, and Serra da Lapa, are parts of the ancient Meseta platform, broken by severe fracturing in Tertiary times. Two series of intersecting faults split the region into horsts, which are about 4000 ft high in the west, in Minho, and somewhat lower in the east, in Tras os Montes. Along the fault valleys flow the rivers Minho, Limia, Cavado, and the right-bank tributaries of the lower Douro. North of the Douro the highlands approach the coast, and some of them terminate

R

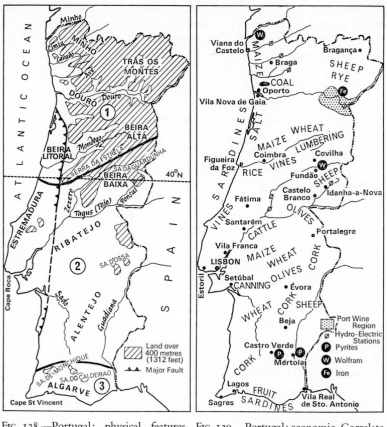

FIG. 128.—Portugal: physical features and divisions. The numbers refer to sections in the text. The names of provinces are shown. *See also* Figs 120 and 122.

FIG. 129.—Portugal: economic. Correlate with the distribution of population shown in Fig. 123.

in cliffs. The coastline is straight, a contrast to the rias of Galicia to the north. Between the mouths of the Limia and Douro there is a narrow coastal plain of alluvial silts brought down by the rivers.

In the south of northern Portugal the granite massifs of the Serra da Estrêla rise to over 6500 ft. They are an extension of the Central Sierras of Spain. As in the more northern highlands, they are split into a number of horsts, among which are the Serra de Lousa, Serra Guardunha and Serra do Moradal. Along the northern and southern flanks of the Serra da Estrêla flow the rivers Mondego and Zezere. The Zezere has been harnessed for hydro-electricity at Castelo do Bode, Cabril, and Bouca to supply Lisbon with power. West of the highlands of northern Portugal a major fault, stretching north–south from the mouth of the Douro to Cape St Vincent, has allowed the land to subside on the seaward side, to form a low coastal plain backed by low hills. The coast of this lowland is straight and lined with sand-hills, behind which are lagoons and swamps.

2. Central Portugal

Central Portugal may be taken as comprising the provinces of Estremadura, Ribatejo and Alentejo. Estremadura lies along the coast north and south of the river Tagus (Tejo). The northern portion has a backbone of folded Mesozoic and Tertiary hills, in which Jurassic limestones and sandstones predominate. The limestone exposures are dry and karstlike, the sandstones fertile and productive. Ribatejo consists of plains which encompass the lower Tagus; these lowlands widen south of the river, and continue southwards into western Alentejo. The central Portuguese lowlands are covered by Tertiary marls and loams, with alluvium near the rivers. The latter flood annually in winter. Eastwards, the plains rise to a series of low horsts, of which the Serra d'Ossa is the highest. These horsts are similar in origin to those of northern Portugal, being derived from the fracturing of the Meseta margins, and having soils which are not very fertile.

The plains of Alentejo are drained by the river Sado. The highlands in the east of the province (known collectively as the Alentejo plateau) form the lower basin of the Guadiana, which in parts acts as the boundary with Spain.

3. Southern Portugal

South of Alentejo a series of barren mountain ranges of crystalline rock, such as the Serra de Monchique, Serra da Mezquita and Serra do Caldeirão, form the northern boundary of the Algarve, a province unlike any other in Portugal. The mountains are a continuation of the Sierra Morena in Spain. South of the mountain rim, Algarve slopes towards the coast as lowlands, which are composed of Mesozoic sandstones. The slope to the south and east gives the region a definite southern or "African" aspect. This region was the last part of the country to be reconquered from the Moors. Its long occupation is reflected in the lower stature, the dark skins and dark eyes of its inhabitants, many of whom have inherited Moorish blood.

CLIMATE

Much about the climate of Portugal may be gathered from what has already been noted about that of Spain (*see* Fig. 122). No part of Portugal, however, has less than 25 in. of rainfall annually, since the country is more open than Spain to the moist westerlies. Temperatures, too, are tempered by nearness to the sea, so that annual ranges are less than in the neighbouring country. Lisbon, for instance, ranges from an average of 51° F (10·6° C) in January to 71° F (21·7° C) in August—the hottest month—and has an annual rainfall of 27 in., three-quarters of which comes in the winter half of the year. The southern aspect of the Algarve produces higher temperatures, average ranges being from 55° F (12·8° C) in January to 75° F (23·9° C) in July. Rainfall in the Algarve is about 26 in. annually.

The mountains of northern Portugal are the wettest part of the country, annual precipitation of 50 in. being common in the Minho province; and over most of the region there is rarely less than 40 in. In northern Portugal a larger proportion of the precipitation comes in summer than in the rest of the country, but there is still a winter maximum. In that season there may be snow on the Serra da Estrêla and some of the northernmost horsts. A notable feature of the climate of northern Portugal is the very high temperatures experienced in summer in the deep, sheltered valleys of Tras os Montes, where the thermometer occasionally registers 104° F (40° C) in the shade.

HUMAN GEOGRAPHY

HISTORICAL OUTLINE

Until the middle of the eleventh century the history of the area now covered by Portugal was common with that of Spain, except that there was always some difference between the peoples of Lusitania, as the western portion of the peninsula was called, and those of Iberia. During the Moorish occupation, the entire population of the Iberian peninsula was united against the heathens, and the inhabitants of the first Spanish kingdom of León included both Lusitanians and Iberians.

At the beginning of the eleventh century a young Burgundian count so distinguished himself in the service of the king of León that he was given in marriage a princess whose dowry was the land between the rivers Minho and Douro. His son, Afonso (Alfonso) Henriques, rebelled against the Leonese and proclaimed his little domain a kingdom. He routed the Leonese army sent to subdue him, then advanced to the south, driving the Moors before him. He added to his kingdom all the territory as far as Évora, in Alentejo. In the following centuries the Moors were pushed farther south, and encircled in the Algarve, which they held only with difficulty. In the early fifteenth century the last Moor was expelled from the south-west of the peninsula, and Portugal assumed almost its present shape.

The country's boundaries were more or less fortuitous. The Portuguese and Spanish forces followed the retreating Moors southwards, but remained distinct from each other, separated by a belt of rough country. Through this inhospitable region, which even now is sparsely peopled, the frontier between the two countries was tacitly recognised from the very first and, with only slight changes in the upper Douro and Tagus basins in Portugal, it retains its original shape.

Prominent among the early rulers of Portugal was John (João) I, who in 1385 made an alliance with England which has never been broken; in 1387 he married Philippa of Lancaster, daughter of John of Gaunt, thus cementing the alliance. One of John's sons was Prince Henry, called the Navigator, who from his school of navigation at Sagres sent out expeditions which discovered Madeira, the Azores and the Canary Islands, and made extended reconnaissance of the west coast of Africa. It was largely as a result of Prince Henry's enthusiasm that Portugal was responsible in later years for opening up many parts of the world as yet unknown.

In 1487 Bartholomew Diaz rounded the Cape of Good Hope and in 1498 Vasco da Gama reached India. In 1500 Cabral discovered Brazil, in 1501 Corte Real landed in Greenland; in 1541 Cabrillo explored the coast of California, and Martins the coast of Alaska. The Portuguese were the first to land in the Moluccas, China, Japan and Australia. In 1520 Magellan was the first to circumnavigate the globe. Portugal laid claim to an enormous empire; and because of the gold, precious stones, silks and spices brought back by her ships she became fabulously rich.

The wealth which came from distant lands proved in the long run to be the country's undoing. Its rulers became corrupt and incompetent until, about the middle of the sixteenth century, Philip II of Spain invaded Portugal and added the country to his crown. For sixty years it was ruled by Spain. Drawn into wars with France and England, Portugal, like Spain, lost much of its overseas empire. In the following century the Portuguese rose against Spain and, with English help, regained their independence in 1640. To reinforce the English alliance, the new king, John IV, gave his daughter in marriage to Charles II.

Portugal now began to exploit Brazil more fully, and a period of renewed prosperity commenced. But it was apparent rather than real; for although many beautiful churches and palaces were built and furnished with magnificent ornaments of gold, silver and precious stones, the ordinary people of Portugal—especially in overcrowded Lisbon—were wretchedly poor. Throughout the country, agriculture was of the most primitive type and industry virtually non-existent. To make matters worse, an earthquake shook the country in 1755 and destroyed most of the capital. During the Napoleonic wars, Portugal was invaded three times and its countryside laid waste. Such were the conditions when the king abdicated, to become Emperor of Brazil. By so doing, he cut the motherland off from the wealth of this colony.

Throughout the nineteenth century there was discontent among the people. Successive kings were blamed for the poverty-stricken state of the country and the monarchy became increasingly unpopular. Peasant uprisings were frequent. In 1908 they culminated in the assassination of King Carlos and his heir. The new king, Manuel, was dethroned in 1910 and Portugal proclaimed a republic.

Since then, the country has had to face constant internal difficulties, principally concerned with the condition of its working classes. After the First World War, civil strife so convulsed the country that the military took charge of the Government in order to restore peace. Oliveira Salazar, professor of economics at Coimbra University, was made President of the Council in 1928, and given a free hand to reorganise the country's economy. Salazar is still in power, and under his beneficent dictatorship Portugal has made substantial industrial and agricultural advance.

POPULATION

Portugal has a population of 8,889,000 and an average density of 255 persons per square mile. Its people are unevenly distributed, the greatest concentrations being around Lisbon and Oporto (see Fig. 123). In general, the density of population decreases with distance from the coast. The large estates of Alentejo, especially in the east of the province, are sparsely peopled, but mountainous northern Portugal, with its tiny farm-holdings, is severely overcrowded. The whole country may be said to be over-populated, and the pressure of too many people has led to large-scale emigration, mainly to Brazil. Unfortunately for Portugal, the emigrants include many of the more progressive and better educated of its people.

THE ECONOMY

Portugal's economy is almost entirely agricultural and forestal, plus an important contribution from sardine fishing. Only a quarter of the working population is engaged in industry, and this concerned mainly with the preparation for export of the products of field, forest and sea. Manufacturing industries were already expanding around Lisbon and Oporto before 1928; since then, under Salazar's wise if somewhat autocratic administration, they are spreading to other parts of the country. But shortage of fuel, poor supplies of minerals, insufficient capital and the very low standard of literacy are great drawbacks. The fact that Portugal's chief products—cork, wine, sardines, olive oil—have only minor significance in world commerce has been another factor in her slow industrial advance.

MINERALS AND POWER

Mineral wealth consists mainly of wolfram and pyrites. The chief wolfram deposits, yielding about 3000 tons of ore a year, are in the Fundão district of the upper Zezere basin, and in the lower Minho valley. Cupriferous pyrites occur around Mértola and Castro Verde, in southern

[*Courtesy of the Portuguese State Office.*

FIG. 130.—Portugal: hydro-electricity station, Venda Nova. A small power station on the Rio de Ocreza, a tributary of the Tagus. Part of Lisbon's supply of current comes from this station in Beira Alta.

Alentejo. Small amounts of iron ore are mined near Moncorvo, in the upper Douro basin; and there are a few seams of poor coal east of Oporto.

Outside the larger towns, charcoal is used for domestic heating and cooking. Coal for industrial purposes and for the railways must be imported. In the past few years, however, there has been a notable development of hydro-electric power. The greatest scope for this is in northern Portugal, with its mountains, its more reliable rainfall, and swift rivers. Power stations have been constructed in two areas: in Beira Baixa along the river Zezere; and in the Minho province on the rivers

Lima, Cavado and Ave. These schemes serve respectively Lisbon and Oporto, where most of Portugal's industry is concentrated, but they also give power to new and modernised factories and workshops in Fundão, Covilha, Coimbra and Santarém. The Zezere scheme in addition provides irrigation water to the Tagus plains.

AGRICULTURE

Improvement in Portugal's agricultural economy has been slower than in industry. The chief problems are connected with irrigation and education. In the south of the country there are large areas still virtually unproductive because of lack of water, but irrigation schemes are slowed down by difficulties of level. Most of the rivers flow in narrow valleys, whose floors are far below the surface of the surrounding plateau; the Guadiana, for instance, because of its gorge-like valley, is so far of little value for irrigation. This part of Portugal, too—and in fact the whole of the eastern half of the country—needs a good road system.

Perhaps the greatest need in Portugal today is for a revolution in agricultural methods, which are often primitive. Knowledge of fertilisers and modern scientific farming is scanty, and difficult to improve, for the greatest degree of illiteracy occurs among the rural population. The small farmers of the north, living from hand to mouth, have neither the time nor the capital necessary for improvement; the absentee landlords of the south are satisfied with present conditions and their tenants are given little opportunity to improve themselves. Nevertheless, the economic measures introduced by Salazar are slowly bearing fruit and, if the advance Portugal has made in the last thirty years has been slow, it is on sound lines.

REGIONAL ECONOMY

1. *Northern Portugal*

The mountainous region of northern Portugal is better watered than the rest of the country, and for the most part has a denser population. Every available square inch of cultivable land is utilised, yet despite considerable emigration to other parts of Portugal and overseas there are too many people for its meagre resources. Farms are so small and fragmented that some families have to exist on a piece of land hardly large enough to produce cabbages for their soup or maize for their bread—these being their staple foodstuffs.

In the valleys of the provinces of Minho and coastal Douro, with an adequate rainfall assisted by irrigation from wells, maize is the chief crop; cattle and oxen are reared for dairy produce and as draught animals. Flax is grown in lower, wetter areas near rivers. In the uplands, rye is the chief food crop, and sheep and goats are reared for wool, hair, milk and cheese.

The higher slopes are clothed with edible-chestnut trees; in the tiny fields which cling to the mountains, potatoes are grown.

In the provinces of Tras os Montes ("the region beyond the mountains") and Douro Alto is the most difficult part of northern Portugal, with its people concentrated into isolated villages. Here wheat is commoner than maize, but rye is the chief cereal and black bread the staple food. In Beira the mountain dwellers in the Serra da Estrêla work as shepherds, charcoal burners or lumberers in the chestnut and oak forests which cover the slopes; and in the wild region of Beira Baixa (Lower Beira), the foothills of the desolate *serras* support olive trees, especially around Castelo Branco, which is noted for olive oil. In Beira Alta (Upper Beira) and Beira Baixa there is still a domestic woollen industry, using local supplies of wool; but as a result of hydro-electric power developed on the rivers Zezere and Ponsul, tributaries of the Tagus, factories for woollens and linen have been built at Covilhã, Fundão and Idanha-a-Nova.

The vine is cultivated throughout northern Portugal, but except in the Douro valley, in Tras os Montes, the grapes do not ripen properly, and produce a rather acid *vinho verde* ("green wine") which is drunk locally. In the Upper Douro, however, are the vines that yield port wine. Here, in a soil which is more like rubble broken down from the granites and mica schists of the steep valley slopes, the long-rooted vine thrives. The summer heat—in gulleys as much as 104° F (40° C)—gives an excellent balance of alcohol and sugar, as is required in the best wines. The vineyards climb up 120 miles of valleys, on terraces supported by low, dry walls, to the limit where the grape runs the risk of drying up before it ripens. Work in the vineyard region is restricted to growing the grapes and producing the *must*, that is, the unfermented juice. This is carried in casks on flat-bottomed boats along the Douro to storehouses in Vila Nova de Gaia (45,739), a small town opposite Oporto, near the mouth of the river. Here by careful fermentation the wine is made ready for export.

The vines for port wine were introduced from Burgundy early in Portugal's history, but not until 1703 did an increasing demand from England cause a rapid extension of the vineyards. Since that date, when English exporters began to settle in Oporto, much of the trade has remained in English hands, and many of the inhabitants of the Lower Douro have English-sounding names. The export of port wine is today Portugal's main source of income, and Great Britain the chief customer.

South of the Douro estuary is a low coastal plain backed by hilly country. The coast itself is straight and lined with sandhills, behind which are lagoons and swamps. The inhabitants of this littoral zone are often fishermen-farmers, the chief catch off the coast being sardines. Salt is obtained by evaporation in salt pans. Inland, in Beira Litoral, the area is fertile, especially in the flood-plain of the river Mondego, where maize and rice are grown. Higher up the valley are wheatfields and vineyards; in the hills to the east, olive oil is an important product.

The chief town of northern Portugal, and the second in the country, is Oporto (310,000), on the river Douro where it cuts through the hills and begins to widen to its estuary. Access to its harbour is impeded for ocean-going vessels by a bar across the mouth of the river. Most large ships now use the outport of Leixões, an artificial port 3 miles north of the estuary. Oporto is the centre of the wine trade; it also has flour mills, food industries, fish canning, iron and steel works, engineering, and wool textile and silk industries. It is helped by hydro-electric power developed in the river valleys to the north. Other towns in northern Portugal are small and are chiefly agricultural markets. They include Coimbra (45,508) and Braga (41,043), both ancient regional capitals; Viana do Castelo, a naval dockyard; Figueira da Foz, a market for fish; and Fátima, a hill village in the south of the region. Fátima is growing rapidly as a religious pilgrimage centre.

2. *Central Portugal*

This region consists of the hilly province of Estremadura, the plains of Ribatejo, and the large province of Alentejo; this last is divided into lowlands near the coast, and the broken horst country of the Alentejo plateau further inland. The valleys among the hills of Estremadura have fertile soils, and so have the alluvial Ribatejo flood-plains. The soils of Baixo Alentejo are fertile too but are not well used; those of the highlands of Alto Alentejo, derived from crystalline rocks, are infertile.

The plains of central Portugal, especially in Estremadura and Ribatejo, produce heavy crops of maize, wheat, rice and fodder. Between Santarém and Vila Franca, cattle rearing is outstanding. Here and farther up the Tagus plain are bred the bulls used in Portugal's special type of bull-fighting, in which the animals are not killed. Vines are grown extensively, and olive groves appear on the drier sides of hills. Farms in the Alentejo lowlands, in contrast to those in northern Portugal, are large—some of them up to 1300 acres; in fact, some might be called villages. They are very like the *latifundia* of southern Spain. Around the owner's and steward's houses are store rooms, wine presses, oil presses, barns, silos, cheese dairies, bakeries, carpenters' and wheelwrights' workshops and the smaller houses of the employees, as well as dormitories for seasonal workers. Near by there are roofed shelters for the piles of cork awaiting transport to Lisbon. The owner, a rich man, is often an absentee landlord who leaves the running of the estate in the hands of the steward.

The mountains of inner Alentejo are clothed with cultivated forests of cork-oak. The region is the main source of cork, which, after pine (used for pit-props and for its resin), is the most important forest product of Portugal. The cork-oak forests occupy roughly a quarter of the forested area of the country. They are carefully tended; the cork, which is the bark of the tree, is stripped off at intervals of nine years, the time taken to grow new layers. The chief centres for cork collection are Portalegre,

[*Courtesy of the Portuguese State Office.*]

FIG. 131.—Portugal: small-holdings in the Sado valley. Some of the large estates in central Portugal have been broken up and the land leased to small-holders, who are organised on a co-operative basis. The crop in the foreground is tomatoes. Nearer to the houses, which are of uniform pattern and size, wheat, maize and vegetables are separated by rows of young olives and fruit trees. There is a complete absence of mechanisation. The woods in the background are of cork-oak.

Évora (24,144) and Beja. Lisbon is the port of export. The cork-oak also yields tannin, used in the leather-tanning industry; and large numbers of pigs are reared in the forests, where they feed on acorns.

In eastern Alentejo, agriculture is at subsistence level and confined to small areas. The wide, flat stretches between the horsts, the *campos*, are used more for sheep rearing than for arable farming.

Situated on hills on the north banks of the Tagus, about 8 miles from the sea, is Lisbon (Lisboa), the capital of Portugal, with a population of 1,397,000. Here the river widens into a basin which forms one of the best harbours in the world (*see* Fig. 132). The earthquake of 1755, which destroyed the old city, enabled Lisbon to be replanned and rebuilt in grandiose style; and the more modern additions of the present century have been equally well-planned. Lisbon has doubled in size in the past twenty years, but eighteenth- and twentieth-century architectural styles have blended in a most harmonious and satisfying way.

As the outlet of fertile central Portugal, and being on the best harbour in western Iberia, Lisbon has developed a large variety of industries, in

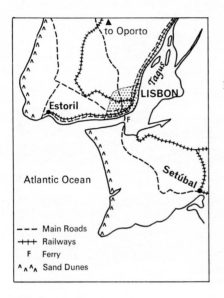

Fig. 132.—Portugal: Lisbon. The bottle-necked estuary of the Tagus encloses one of the best harbours in the world, 12 miles long and 7 miles wide. The southern margins are swampy, so most settlement is on the northern side. Note the absence of a bridge. The nearest bridge-point is nearly 40 miles up the Tagus.

addition to its entrepôt trade and to being a port of call for ships. To the old industries connected with wine, cork, sardines and olive oil have been added shipbuilding, textiles (mainly cottons), oil refining, oilseed crushing and chemical manufacture (chiefly of fertilisers). It is also the headquarters of the Portuguese long-distance cod-fishing fleet and of steamship lines to Africa and South America. It is an important airport; and last, but not least, it has extended along the banks of the Tagus in a series of holiday resorts, among which Estoril has reached international fame.

Below the mouth of the Tagus, and connected to Lisbon by ferry, is the peninsula of Setúbal, largely pine- or heath-covered. In the south of the peninsula, on the wide estuary of the river Sado and protected by a long sandspit, is the town of Setúbal (44,605), the chief sardine-canning centre, and one of the ports for the pyrites of south Alentejo. In the Sado lowlands south of the peninsula, rice growing is important.

In the mountains which separate central Portugal from the Algarve in the south, a mineralised area produces pyrites containing copper. The deposits are similar to those of the Rio Tinto in the Sierra Morena. The chief fields are around Mértola and Castro Verde.

3. Southern Portugal

The Algarve is potentially a rich land of wheat, vines, olives, figs, almonds and even sugar cane and sweet potatoes; but its farmers, though hardworking, are handicapped by lack of surface water. They inherited from the Moors a knowledge of irrigation, but it is employed only on a small scale. A big extension of the irrigation system is needed before full measure can be taken of the Algarve's agricultural potential.

Off the coasts are the richest fishing grounds of Portugal, the chief catch being sardines and tunny, which are canned at Vila Real de Santo Antonio and Lagos. Most of the fishermen are also part-time workers in the canning factories. Lagos was the starting point for the seafaring explorers sent out by Henry the Navigator; today it has an airport on some of the European routes to West Africa and South America. Sagres, on the south-western tip of Europe, is a fishing port; here was situated Prince Henry's school of navigation.

STUDY QUESTIONS

1. From the points of view of (a) climate, (b) natural resources, (c) economic development, contrast the regions of Portugal which lie north and south of Lisbon.

2. Illustrate the influence of relief and climate upon the people of Portugal.

3. Show how geographical conditions have influenced the location and importance of Lisbon and Oporto.

4. Describe the distribution of population in Portugal and analyse the chief factors upon which this distribution depends.

Chapter XXXI

ITALY

ITALY is physically a well-defined geographical entity, centrally situated in the Mediterranean Sea, which it divides into two basins, east and west. The country has been described as a long pier jutting into the sea, or as a leg, terminating in a heel and toe; but descriptions of this kind are incomplete. Besides the familiar peninsula, Italy includes in the north a continental portion. This comprises a share of the Alpine arc of mountains, and the alluvial Plain of Lombardy, which is the most extensive continuous stretch of lowland in Mediterranean Europe. In addition, the large islands of Sicily and Sardinia are part of Italy.

PHYSICAL ASPECTS

STRUCTURAL DIVISIONS

The major physical features of Italy are the Alps and the Plain of Lombardy in the north; and the Apennines, which run the length of the peninsula. For purposes of study, however, it is more convenient to divide the country into: (1) northern, (2) central, (3) southern and (4) insular Italy (*see* Fig. 133). Northern Italy is taken as that part of the country north of 44 degrees latitude; a second line drawn across the peninsula south of Rome and the Abruzzi mountains marks off central Italy; and southern Italy is the remainder of the peninsula. Insular Italy is self-explanatory. One advantage of dividing Italy in this way is that each division differs in structure, climate, and economic and cultural development. Northern Italy includes two of the major physical features; and the Apennines, running through northern, central and southern Italy, fall naturally by the above divisions into three distinct parts.

1. *Northern Italy*

The region may be sub-divided into (*a*) the Italian Alps, (*b*) the Plain of Lombardy and (*c*) the northern Apennines. The plains of Venetia are regarded as part of the Plain of Lombardy, and the coastal plain of Liguria is included with the Apennines (*see* Fig. 134).

(*a*) *The Italian Alps.* Across the north of Italy, rising like a wall above the valley of the river Po, stands the arc of the Alps. The ranges may be

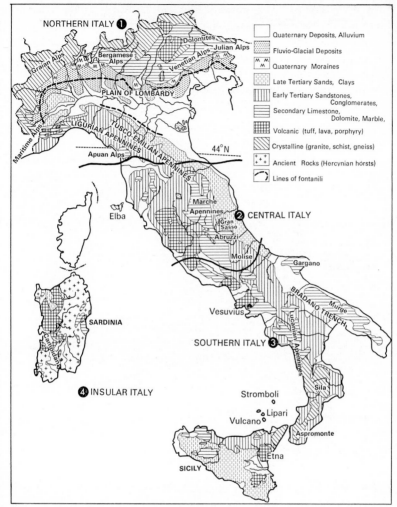

Fig. 133.—Italy: structure (much simplified). The numbers refer to the physical divisions used in the text.

divided into: the western Alps, from the coast to the Valle d'Aosta; the central Alps to the river Oglio and Lake d'Iseo; and the eastern Alps to the Julian Alps on the eastern border.

The western Alps rise to over 10,000 ft, but just across the French border the ranges reach over 14,000 ft. The valleys are orientated mainly in an east–west direction and provide good routes to the Mont Cenis, Little St Bernard and de Tende passes. The valleys of the headwaters of the Po —the Dora Riparia and the Dora Baltea—are followed by roads and

railways to France. The western Alps fall eastwards to the Plain of
Lombardy by the series of low ranges of Piedmont.

The central Alps are narrow in Italy and, along the Swiss border, have
the highest peaks, such as Monte Rosa (15,217 ft). The valleys through
the crystalline mountains of this section are deep and narrow, but towards
the south some of them widen and contain lakes dammed back by
moraines. The largest lakes are Maggiore, Lugano, Como and d'Iseo. The

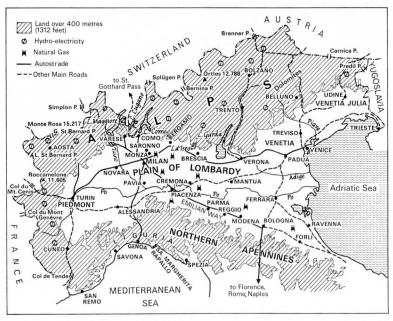

FIG. 134.—Italy: northern. Sub-divisions are (a) Alps, (b) Plain of Lombardy, (c)
northern Apennines.

central Alps are pierced by the important Simplon, St Gotthard, Splügen
and Maloja passes. The St Gotthard's southern exit leads to Milan and
Genoa.

The central Alps continue beyond Lake Como to Lake d'Iseo, but
crystalline rocks give way to limestone, and the ranges are lower and
wider. East of d'Iseo, the eastern Alps are lower still and reach their
widest, extending up to 100 miles from north to south. They are cut by
many broad valleys in this direction, and these in turn are crossed by
longitudinal valleys giving east–west connections, so that the mountain
mass does not form a serious obstacle. The river Adige leads to the Brenner Pass (4495 ft) on the boundary between Italy and Austria, the Piave
gives access to the Comelico Pass, and the Tagliamento to the Carnico

Pass. All these river valleys are followed by roads and railways. Lake Garda, almost 1000 ft deep, in the west of the region, lies in a fault valley which was dammed by a moraine.

One of the eastern ranges, the Dolomites, is composed of dolomitic or magnesian limestone and has been eroded into fantastic shapes. Dolomite is the double carbonate of magnesium and calcium. The calcium carbonate is dissolved by rainwater and washed away, leaving the insoluble magnesium carbonate behind: sometimes in strange, twisted shapes, sometimes in step-like terraces. The Dolomites have become a great attraction to tourists.

The easternmost ranges of the Italian Alps—the Venetian and Julian Alps—are plateaus rather than mountains, and in parts have all the characteristics of karst. The area they cover was at one time known as "Italia Irredenta" and was a subject of dispute between Italy and Austria (which claimed it because it was German-speaking). It was finally given to Italy in 1919. The boundary between Italy and Yugoslavia, which runs through the Julian Alps, was also for long in dispute until its present position was agreed.

The Italian Alps have never been a serious obstacle to communication. The many passes mentioned, to which should be added the Great St Bernard and the Stelvio, have been used for commerce since the Middle Ages. Through most of them invaders have entered Italy, but not since Roman times have Italians been very successful in penetrating northwards. This is largely because the passes converge on the Plain of Lombardy, allowing invading armies to concentrate, whereas forces moving to the north become widely dispersed. Easy movement through the passes has also resulted in similar peoples being found on both sides of the mountains. Italian-speaking cantons occur on the Swiss side of the boundary north of Lombardy; and in the north-west, in Piedmont, there is a French-speaking population on the Italian side.

(b) *The Plain of Lombardy*. Between the Alps and the northern Apennines is a great triangular depression known as the Plain of Lombardy, although its eastern portion lies in Venetia. It was originally an arm of the Adriatic Sea, but it was filled in by alluvial deposits washed down mainly from the Alps. The surface of the Plain slopes gently from the north and south towards the river Po, which has been forced to the south of the depression by the greater quantity of silts brought from the Alps as compared with those from the northern Apennines. The Plain of Lombardy is, in consequence, a huge asymmetrical valley.

The deposits north of the Po have been "sorted" so as to form three belts lying roughly east–west. At the foot of the sub-Alpine moraines is a belt of coarse sands and gravel, in a series of fans. This belt is too porous for much surface water and therefore is of minor importance for agriculture, except where irrigation is possible. From the southern face of the gravel zone, water issues in a line of springs (*fontanili*), to flow across the second belt, which is composed of fertile alluvium. Nearer the Po, the third belt consists of muddy marshland with occasional patches of drier alluvium. There are similar belts, including fontanili, south of the Po, but they are narrower and less well defined.

The Po enters the Adriatic by a large delta, which is growing rapidly. The town of Adria, a coastal port in Roman times, is now nearly 15 miles inland. South of the delta a number of lagoons (Valli di Comacchio) have been shut off from the sea by extensive sandbanks.

With the Plain of Lombardy are usually included the narrow, coastal lowlands which lie between the Ligurian Apennines and the Gulf of Genoa. They are connected to the Lombardian plain by the easy Bochetta and Altare passes.

(c) *The northern Apennines*. The dominant feature of the Italian peninsula is the Apennine mountains, which extend in a great curve from the Ligurian Apennines in the north to the Strait of Messina in the south, trending first from north-west to south-east towards the Adriatic coast, and then turning back to form the "toe" of Italy. The Apennines fall naturally into three sections: the northern Apennines extend from the Maritime Alps nearly to Ancona and include the Ligurian, Etruscan and Emilian Apennines; the central Apennines are composed of the highest parts of the mountain range, in the provinces of Marche, Abruzzi and Molise; and the southern Apennines continue southwards in lower and less distinct ranges, terminating in the massifs of Calabria.

The northern Apennines—which form the southern boundary of the Plain of Lombardy—are a series of short ranges composed of easily eroded sandstones, chalky marls and clays, very much dissected by narrow, deep valleys and troubled by landslides. In the west, the Ligurian Apennines are linked to the Maritime Alps and, like them, are close to the sea. The Ligurian Apennines, which are nowhere very high (Mount Ebro, 5581 ft, is the highest peak), are pierced by several passes, of which the chief are the Bochetta (Giovi) and the Altare (Cadibona), leading respectively from the coast to Milan and Turin.

The eastern ranges of the northern Apennines, the Etruscan-Emilian Apennines, are higher than those of Liguria (Mount Cimone, 7095 ft), but in general are not difficult to cross. They are pierced by several roads but few railways, for the passes are high and necessitate expensive tunnels. Between Bologna and Florence, for instance, the railway runs under the mountains by a tunnel $11\frac{1}{2}$ miles long. West of the main ranges of the northern Apennines are the Apuan Alps, composed of metamorphosed

[*Courtesy of Information Service, Rome.*

Fig. 135.—Italy: hauling marble, Carrara. The quarries of Carrara and Massa, on the edges of the Apuan Alps, are renowned for their pure, white marble. The photograph shows blocks amounting to several tons being hauled from the bottom of a quarry. The marble is used principally for statuary.

limestone. Quarries on their lower slopes produce the famous white marble of Carrara and Massa (*see* Fig. 135).

2. *Central Italy*

This region is the northern half of the Italian peninsula; it extends from the northern Apennines to a line drawn south of the city of Rome and curving round the southern end of the mountains of Abruzzi to the mouth of the river Sangro. Central Italy may be divided into (*a*) the central Apennines, (*b*) the plains and hills of Tuscany and Umbria, and (*c*) the basin of the lower Tiber (*see* Fig. 136).

(*a*) *The central Apennines*, higher and wider than those of the north, are composed predominantly of limestones, which in places have been eroded to steep-sided peaks, in others to flat-topped, barren plateaus. The Gran Sasso d'Italia, which rises in Monte Corno to 9584 ft, is the highest part of the Apennines; it is a broad plateau, from which rise jagged peaks. Much of the limestone of the central Apennines, especially in Abruzzi and Molise, is karst, with little surface drainage. At best, except in a few faulted basins, it supports only a scanty sheep rearing population. Here and there among the ranges are longitudinal depressions, caused by faulting. Some of them are ill-drained and marshy; others have a flooring of alluvium. The chief of these basin depressions are drained by the rivers Aquila and Sulmona to the Adriatic Sea. On the eastern side of the central

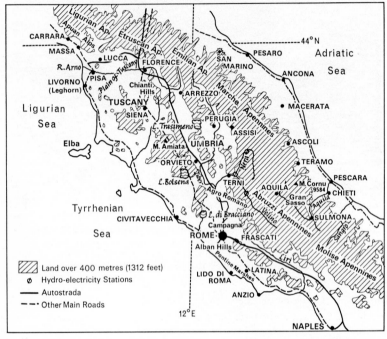

FIG. 136.—Italy: central. The region may be sub-divided into (*a*) central Apennines and Adriatic coastlands, (*b*) hills and plains of Tuscany and Umbria, (*c*) lower Tiber basin.

Apennines, the Adriatic coastlands are made up of sands and clays washed from the mountains to the floor of the sea, and later uplifted. These narrow coastal lowlands are greatly dissected by the mountain torrents which cross them. The Adriatic coast is of recent emergence and very straight, with few harbours.

(*b*) *Tuscany and Umbria.* Within the curve of the central Apennines, and bounded on the west by the Ligurian and Tyrrhenian Seas, is a region of plateaus and low hills, with intervening alluvial basins and valleys which are drained mainly by the rivers Arno and upper Tiber. The northern portion is Tuscany, which comprises the Arno basin and the adjacent coastal lowlands. The Arno rises in the northern Apennines and when it leaves the mountains flows through the Plain of Tuscany, an undulating lowland broken by low hills. Near the river the plain is flat and liable to flooding, but successful control and drainage have made it productive. The coast of Tuscany, in common with the whole of the western coast of central and southern Italy as far south as Naples, is being silted. The blockage of drainage to the Tyrrhenian Sea has resulted in coastal marshes in several places. The most extensive in central Italy are the Maremma marshes, south of the mouth of the Arno.

South of the Arno basin are the hills and valleys of south Tuscany and of Umbria. This is a region of Tertiary sands and clays in the valleys, above which rise sandstone plateaus and the cones and calderas of an ancient and extinct vulcanicity. The most impressive of the extinct cones is Monte Amiata (5687 ft). Many of the calderas contain lakes, the largest of which is Lake Bolzano. Nearer to the central Apennines and north of Lake Bolzano is situated Lake Trasimeno, which by association might erroneously be taken to be a crater lake. It lies in a limestone hollow and has no surface outlet; its waters escape to the river Tiber by an underground channel.

(c) *The Tiber basin.* South of the Umbrian hill country, the river Tiber flows through the Agro Romano, a lowland which opens to the Campagna, the name given to the coastal plains and the Tiber delta. The Agro Romano, although predominantly a plain, is dotted with many low hills of volcanic origin. The Alban Hills, for example, which run along the south of the Agro Romano and the Campagna, are composed of volcanic rocks that have weathered into very fertile soils. Until fifty years ago the plains of the lower Tiber were a stretch of rough pasture or malarial swamp. The swamps were continued south of the Tiber delta in the Pontine marshes. Most of the marshy area has now been reclaimed.

3. *Southern Italy*

Southern Italy consists of (a) the southern Apennines, with which are included the plains of Apulia, and (b) Campania (*see* Fig. 137).

(a) *The southern Apennines* may be said to begin south of the river Sangro, where the mountains swing from the Adriatic littoral to form the "toe" of Italy. They lose their folded character and, instead of lying in well-defined ranges, are faulted and dislocated into isolated blocks separated by lowlands. During the Tertiary period these lowlands were invaded by the sea. Most of the blocks are of Cretaceous limestone, covered in places by Pliocene clays, marls and sands, which are found also in the lowlands and valleys. Vertical displacement has lifted some of the limestone platforms to over 3000 ft; in the Lucanian Apennines, Monte Pollino rises to 7448 ft, Monte Cervati to 6228 ft and Volturino to 6022 ft.

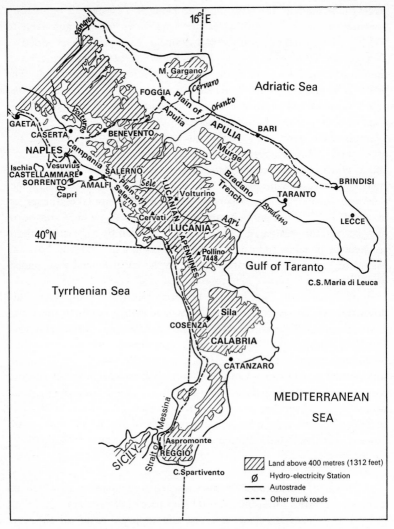

FIG. 137.—Italy: southern. The region may be sub-divided into (*a*) southern Apennines, (*b*) plains of Apulia, (*c*) massifs and lowlands of Calabria, (*d*) Campania.

Farther south, the limestone Apennines give place in Calabria to a
succession of ancient crystalline horsts of Hercynian age, the chief of
which are the Sila and Aspromonte massifs. The Sila is an immense granite
plateau, rising to 6327 ft. For most of the year it has a fairly heavy precipitation, with snow in winter. In hollows in its surface, large reservoirs
(Lake di Cécita, Lake Arvo, Lake Ampollino) have been constructed for

hydro-electric power. Aspromonte, in the extreme south of the peninsula, is composed of schists.

On the Adriatic side of south Italy, in Apulia, there are two limestone
plateaus, Monte Gargano and the Murge; the former is separated from
the Campanian Apennines by the Plain of Apulia (Tavoliere di Puglia),
and the latter from the Lucanian Apennines by the trench of the river
Bradano. Both plateaus, which rarely rise to more than the 2000 ft of
Monte Gargano or the 1200 ft of the Murge, are karst and usually
without surface water: the water-table is too low, except in hollows
eroded in the limestone. Here, and in valleys, there are deposits of terra
rossa, which is fertile if water is available.

(b) *Campania.* Southwards from Gaeta, where the spurs of the Apennines reach the coast of the Tyrrhenian Sea, is the plain of Campania, the
name also of the province, and not to be confused with the Campagna of
central Italy. Campania is divided by the rocky Sorrento peninsula into
the Plain of Naples in the north, and the Plain of Salerno in the south.

The Plain of Naples, with its extensions into the lower valleys of the
rivers Volturno and Liri, is the result of subsidence and of subsequent in-
filling by volcanic activity, which still continues. In the north of the
plain is the extinct cone of Roccamonfina, and at the southern end,
towering over Naples, is Vesuvius, an active volcano. North-west of
Naples are the Phlegraean Fields (Campi Flegrei), the wreck of an
immense volcano, where hot, sulphurous springs (*solfatare*) are still active
and molten lava occasionally spurts through the surface in places. In
historical times the eruptions of Vesuvius have been very destructive. The
most violent was in A.D. 79, when the Roman town of Pompeii was
covered by mud washed from the slopes of the volcano and Herculaneum
(Ercolano) was buried in hot ash.

All the soils of the Plain of Naples are derived from basaltic lavas, basic
tuffs, or alluvium deposited by the rivers—especially the Volturno—but
their productivity varies with their age. In a belt on the eastern side, from
the Volturno southwards to Nocera and extending up the slopes of the
hills enclosing the plain on that side, the soils are old, well developed and
very fertile. In the areas more recently covered by volcanic activity, the
decomposition of the surface deposits is not yet sufficiently advanced to
give the maximum results, and agriculture is limited to wheat, maize,
sugar beet and hemp. The delta of the Volturno has marshes built up in
the same way as the Maremma and Pontine marshes; they are now largely
reclaimed.

To the south of the Plain of Naples, and separating it from the Plain of
Salerno, is the Sorrento peninsula, a spur of the southern Apennines composed of limestone. The isle of Capri is a broken-off piece of the peninsula.

The Plain of Salerno is made up of Tertiary clays and sandstones covered by alluvium brought down by the river Sele, which drains it.

4. *Insular Italy*

The name "insular" should strictly include all the islands around the coasts of Italy, but is usually confined to the large islands of Sicily and Sardinia. Small islands, such as Elba, Ischia, Capri, the Lipari islands, etc., are included with the regions nearest to them.

(a) *Sicily.* Separated from the "toe" of Italy by the narrow Strait of Messina is the island of Sicily (9925 square miles). The north of Sicily is

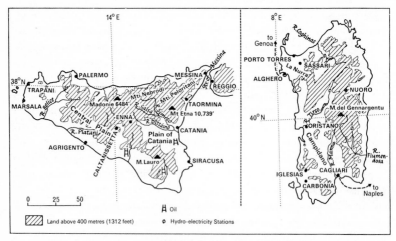

FIG. 138.—Sicily; Sardinia. Together these are known as Insular Italy, and economically they are regarded as part of Italy's Mezzogiorno.

mountainous. The ranges, a continuation of the Apennines, rise in the Madonie to 6484 ft. Nearer to the Strait of Messina, the Monti Peloritani have horsts of gneisses and schists similar to those in Calabria; westwards, the ranges are of Mesozoic limestones and Tertiary sandstones. To the south of the Monti Peloritani is Mount Etna (10,739 ft), an active volcano. Most of the remainder of Sicily consists of high, rolling plains of Tertiary marls, clays and sandstones, at an average height of more than 600 ft. These rise in the south-east and south-west to low limestone plateaus, the one in the south-east having a cover of basic lavas and tuffs. The only real lowland is the Plain of Catania, in the east of the island.

(b) *Sardinia.* Roughly 200 miles west of central Italy is the island of Sardinia (9300 square miles), nearly as large as Sicily.

In structure Sardinia is very like Corsica, from which it is separated by a narrow strait; it is mainly a horst of Hercynian age, uplifted, tilted and fractured during the Alpine orogeny. Most of the eastern half of Sardinia is a plateau of granites and quartzites, at an average elevation of over 3000 ft, and rising to 6000 ft in the Monti del Gennargentu. In the northwest of the plateau there is a cover of Tertiary lavas and tuffs, extruded when the island was uplifted and faulted. The plateau slopes towards the west, terminating in low cliffs along the west and south-west. The western part of the plateau has patches of Mesozoic limestones and Tertiary sedimentaries. These originally covered the entire surface of crystalline rocks but have been eroded except in hollows and valleys. Cutting across the south-west of the plateau is the wide low-lying depression of the Campidano, a plain floored with alluvium; there are other alluvial deposits at intervals around the coast.

CLIMATE

There are great climatic differences between the continental portion of the country and the remainder. In the north, the Alps and the Plain of Lombardy have a climate classed as continental; the peninsula and the islands have a Mediterranean climate. This broad classification, however, has to be modified because of (a) the shelter given by the Alps to the Plain of Lombardy, which is also shut off from most Mediterranean influences by the Maritime Alps and northern Apennines, and (b) the north–south trend of the peninsula, lying athwart the depression tracks of the westerlies and acting as a rain-barrier. The western side of the peninsula is protected against cold northerly winds by the Apennines; the eastern side is in the rain-shadow of the mountain backbone.

Climate in the Alps, as might be expected, varies with altitude and aspect. Precipitation is heavy, and greater in summer than in winter. But no season is dry, and snow lies on the peaks of the western ranges all the year. During the winter, when depressions move from west to east in the north of the Mediterranean, cold air may be drawn from the Alpine region to affect the lands to the south. The violent, icy winds which as a result blow over the Ligurian Sea to Corsica and Sardinia are the *maestrale* (cf. *mistral* in France); those in the north of the Adriatic, affecting the Italian coastlands as far south as Ancona, are the *bora* (*see also* Chapter XXVII).

The southward-facing valleys and foothills along the southern flanks of the Alps are sheltered and have summers in which the mean temperature for the hottest month is from 70° F to 75° F (21° C to 24° C). The winters are cool, ranging in January from 35° F to 38° F (1·7° C to 3·3° C). Annual precipitation is heavy—Como, for instance, having 66 in.

The Plain of Lombardy has a climate best described as continental, with cool winters, hot summers and rainfall mainly in summer; but south of the river Po, and in the northern Apennines, such Mediterranean characteristics as milder winters and less summer rainfall begin to appear. Winters in the Plain of Lombardy are generally short but sometimes severe, especially when cold air drains from the Alps and settles in hollows (temperature inversion). Frosts are common and foggy weather frequent. The mean January temperature for Milan is 32° F (0° C), for Piacenza the same, and for Alessandria 31° F (−0·6° C). Venice, more open to Mediterranean influences, has a January mean temperature of 39° F (4° C) and Bologna, in the south of the Plain, 36° F (2·2° C). July temperatures everywhere are around 75° F (24° C).

Rainfall in the Plain of Lombardy decreases from west to east and from north to south, but on an average is over 20 in. annually. Milan has an annual precipitation of 33·9 in., well distributed throughout the year but with a slight summer maximum. Eastwards the amount decreases to 29·3 in. in Venice; southwards, to 25·5 in. in Alessandria, and 22 in. in Bologna. Most of the rain in Bologna comes in the winter half of the year.

The climate of the Italian peninsula varies with position west or east of the Apennines, and there are considerable differences between the north and south. In the north of the western side, the coastal plain of Liguria, sheltered by mountains and open to the warm Ligurian Sea, has very mild winters and hot summers. Genoa, for example, has a mean in January of 47° F (8·3° C), and in August (the hottest month) of 77° F (25° C). Its annual rainfall amounts to 44 in., of which over 30 in. falls in the six months of winter.

In the coastlands west of the Apennines, south of Liguria, winter temperatures are lower than might be expected: the January mean for Leghorn is 45° F (7·2° C) and for Viterbo 42° F (5·6° C). This is largely due to the influence of the depressions which pass over them in that season. From Naples southwards, January temperatures are higher—usually over 47° F (8·3° C). Summers along the coast are hot: Leghorn 76° F (24·4° C), Naples 75° F (24° C) and Viterbo, slightly inland, 73° F (22·8° C). Annual rainfall, with a definite winter maximum, ranges from 35 in. in Florence and 33 in. in Rome to 32 in. in Naples. These totals contrast with those on the eastern side of the peninsula.

The Adriatic coastlands lie in the rain-shadow of the Apennines and are open to cold winds in winter from the north-east. Rainfall at Foggia amounts to 19 in. a year, and the January mean temperature is 43° F (6° C). The January mean for Ancona is 42° F (5·6° C) and for Chieti 39° F (3·9° C). July temperatures on the whole are higher than on the west coast, Foggia having in that month an average of 80° F (26·7° C), Ancona 78° F (25·6° C) and Chieti 73° F (22·8° C). The Apennines have mountain variants of the east and west coast climates, according to altitude and aspect. Winters in the Abruzzi are severe, with heavy snowfall; temperatures are below freezing point for over a month on the high plateaus, and are not much above it even in the low valleys enclosed by the mountains. Aquila, for instance, at a height of 2390 ft, has a January average of 36° F (2·2 °C). July temperatures at high levels are around 60° F (15·6° C) and in valleys 70° F (21·1° C).

The "toe" of Italy, and Sicily, are distinguished by an almost complete absence of frost; a long, sunny and droughty summer; a short period of rainfall in winter, and high average temperatures in that season. Reggio, in Calabria, ranges from 53° F (11·7° C) in January to 79° F (26·1° C) in July and has an annual rainfall of 29·5 in. The Calabrian massifs have rainfalls of over 40 in. but some of the valleys between them receive less than 20 in. Rainfall comes in short but heavy showers, and large areas are gullied by soil erosion. Winter temperatures in Sicily are much the same as in Calabria, i.e. around 53° F, and summers about 77° F (25° C); rainfall varies from 30 in. in the mountains in the north of the island to 25 in. in the south. The months from May to August are virtually rainless. Much of the rainfall in both Calabria and Sicily is lost by rapid run-off in the crystalline areas and by evaporation. Sicily is affected in summer by the *sirocco*, a dry sand-laden wind from the Sahara, which results in scorchingly hot days.

The climate of Sardinia is Mediterranean, tempered by altitude, but, as is so often the case around the Mediterranean basin, there are big differences in temperature and annual rainfall between regions very close together. The exposed western side of the island has an annual precipitation of 25–30 in. and on the highest plateaus it reaches 45 in.; but the sheltered east coast may have less than 20 in. and around Cape Monte Santo only 16 in. All these totals are average amounts, but the rainfall in Sardinia is unreliable, and in some years the island suffers from prolonged droughts. Sassari, in the north-west of Sardinia, ranges from 47° F (8·3° C) in January to 77° F (25° C) in July, and has an annual rainfall of 24 in. Caltanissetta, in the south, has means of 44° F (6·7° C) in January and 76° F (24·4° C) in July, with 24 in. of rainfall. The effectiveness of the precipitation in Sardinia is reduced by the sirocco in summer and the maestrale in winter, which cause rapid evaporation.

HUMAN GEOGRAPHY

HISTORICAL OUTLINE

The first "cities" in Italy were undoubtedly founded by Greeks and Etruscans, but the history of the country may be said to date from the settlement of groups of Latins on the Palatine Hill, which is within the walls of present-day Rome. By the end of the second century B.C., Rome was a State of soldiers and farmers. It had become master of the Italian peninsula and most of the Po basin, with dominion over territory stretching from Spain to Greece and Asia Minor, and along the north coast of Africa. Further successful invasions of France, Belgium, Britain and part of Germany took place under such famous soldiers as Marius, Sulla, Julius Caesar, Pompey, Antony and Octavian. In 44 B.C. the last-named was elected Emperor of the newly proclaimed Roman Empire. The Empire lasted four centuries before it finally disintegrated; then it took 1500 years for Italy to emerge once more as a unified and sovereign state.

During the Middle Ages, Italy was invaded by barbarians from the north. The invaders were rarely strong enough to defend their conquered territories, so for several centuries the country lay at the mercy of first one and then another set of marauders. This was especially the case with southern Italy and Sicily. First the Byzantines, then the Arabs and finally the Normans controlled southern Italy without serious opposition. In northern Italy the Lombards, a fierce Germanic tribe, reigned for two centuries, with Pavia as their capital. Meanwhile, other parts of the country began to emerge as separate States under individual rulers. These were all united under Charlemagne, who in 800 was crowned in Rome as the first Emperor of the Holy Roman Empire. It looked as though Imperial Rome was being re-born, but after his death Italy began to divide again. In Rome the Papal State was created, and Berengarius became king of the "Kingdom of Italy," which was composed of Lombardy, Tuscany and Umbria. The kingdom was short-lived, and in the tenth century northern Italy was invaded and subjugated by the German Holy Roman Emperor. The final phase of the Middle Ages saw a struggle for power between the Papacy and German or Austrian Emperors. One of the latter, Frederick II, was born in Italy and had his court at Palermo in Sicily.

During this period of strife, many Italian cities took the opportunity of organising themselves into small independent States. They lay in the more vigorous north; and under democratic administrations, the arts, law and education began to flourish and foreign trade grew in strength. The Scaligeri family in Verona, the Gonzagas in Mantua, the Estes in Emilia and the Medici in Florence became rulers of city states. Pisa, Genoa and Venice were the headquarters of successful seafaring and trading republics, and grew extremely prosperous. The great Italian authors, Dante, Petrarch and Boccaccio, belong to this period; Marco Polo, a Venetian, at the end of the thirteenth century travelled through central Asia to China and Tibet, returning to Venice via India and Persia.

Two centuries later, in 1492, Christopher Columbus, a Genoese sailing in the service of Spain, discovered the Americas anew. A few years later Amerigo Vespucci, a Florentine, made further voyages and gave his name to the new lands. These explorations turned the course of history, for the Mediterranean ceased to be the centre of the civilised world. The countries with direct contact with the Atlantic Ocean—Spain, Portugal, France, England and the Netherlands—acquired new power and overseas possessions. The Mediterranean became a political and economic backwater, and Italy a weak, disunited country. In 1559, Naples, Sicily, Sardinia and the Duchy of Milan passed under Spanish rule; they remained so for 150 years. By the eighteenth century two other foreign dynasties were ruling in Italy—the Hapsburgs in Tuscany, and French Bourbons in Parma and Piacenza. Towards the end of the period, the Duke of Savoy, ruler of a mountain-girt province which had early proclaimed its independence, took possession of Sardinia.

The possibility of a free and united Italy, so long an apparently unattainable ideal, emerged after the Napoleonic wars (Napoleon himself had been king of Italy for a short time after 1805). In 1820 there arose a movement known as the Risorgimento, or "re-arising," aimed at uniting all Italy under one government. Its leaders were great statesmen or soldiers—Cavour, Mazzini, Garibaldi. In 1861 the Duke of Savoy, head of the oldest ruling house in Italy, became king, with the "Mezzogiorno" (southern Italy, Sicily and Sardinia) and Lombardy part of his kingdom. Venetia was annexed in 1866. In 1870 the Pope, giving up his political power in Rome and Latium, retired to the Vatican Palace, and Rome was made capital of the new Italy. The northern provinces of the Trentino, Trieste, Venetia Giulia and Istria, which had remained in Austrian hands, were joined to Italy after the First World War; and for the first time in fifteen centuries the country was restored to the sovereign dignity of Roman times.

But unification did not bring prosperity. The country was divided into a progressive and rapidly developing north, and an overpopulated, illiterate, poverty-stricken south. During the years 1924–39, Mussolini's Fascist régime tried to remedy the imbalance but the economic and social problems of the Mezzogiorno persist to this day. Fascist policy aimed at putting Italy on equal terms with the world's great political and economic powers, by building up industrial output, improving communications, draining swamps, increasing agricultural production and acquiring an overseas empire. It laid the foundations of future development, but proved too aggressive, causing hardship to the people it purported to benefit. It tried to move too fast in a country whose climate and topography demand slow progress, and whose people, in the Mezzogiorno, were far behind western Europe in standard of living, education and ways of thought. In southern Italy, too, the limit placed on emigration by the Fascist government accentuated the problem of over-population.

In the years 1943–45, Italy was a huge battlefield and most of the Fascist achievements were destroyed. Railways, bridges, viaducts, hydro-electric power stations and harbour works were blown up, the countryside devastated and many of the cities left in ruins. After the Second World War and the defeat of Fascism, Italy was faced with the task of rebuilding the country and feeding its population, which in 1951 amounted to 47 million people. But industrial incentive and agricultural hopes were at a low ebb; the standard of living declined; and there was a steady rise in unemployment. In 1948 Italy ceased to be a kingdom and voted for a republic.

Since then the worst problems of industrial stagnation and hunger have been mitigated and most of the war damage repaired, so that the diplomatic and economic position is better today than at any time before 1939. The population has risen to 50,464,000; and in spite of the still unsolved problem of the depressed areas of the south, the general standard of living has risen.

POPULATION

The population of Italy at the last census (October 1961) was, as noted above, 50,464,000; but as it is increasing by 400,000 a year the current estimate would be nearly 52 million, which would give an average density of 448 persons a square mile. Italy is not a rich country. It is relatively poor in raw materials and mineral resources, and its agriculture is limited by lack of rainfall and the mountainous character of much of its surface, so that it cannot support this large population at a reasonable standard of living. In other words, it is heavily over-populated.

The greatest concentrations of people are in the better-endowed industrial regions of northern Italy. Most parts of the Plain of Lombardy have densities of over 400 per square mile; in the Milan conurbation and along the Ligurian Plain there are nearly 900 persons per square mile. Similar densities are found in the Agro Romano and the Plain of Naples, where there are fewer opportunities for industrial development and where, in consequence, the cities contain large numbers of unemployed. The Plain of Lombardy has a textile industry which ranks fifth in the world for the production of cotton and woollen fabrics; in it are located world-famous firms such as Vespa and Lambretta (motor scooters), Alfa Romeo, Ferrari and Maserati (motor cars), Guzzi and Gilera (motor cycles); and its engineering firms provide experts in the construction of roads, bridges and dams. The Kariba dam in Africa is an achievement of

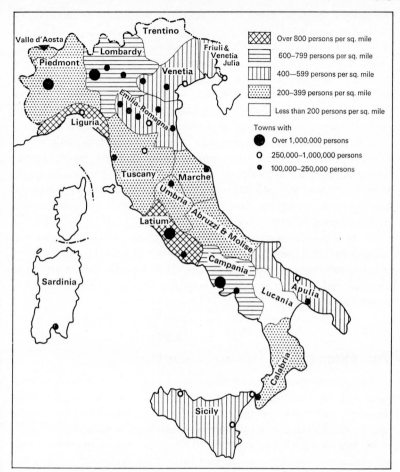

FIG. 139.—Italy: distribution of population, 1961 (by provinces). Maps showing distribution and density of population should be read with due regard given to relief and other factors such as the existence of very large cities. Lombardy, for instance, has an average density of 787 persons per square mile; but a large proportion of its area is Alpine, and scantily peopled. Its lowlands, which include the large city of Milan, have an average density of over 900 persons per square mile. Similarly, Lucania, with a small density, is actually over-populated.

northern Italy. The south of the country has no openings for industrial employment in any way comparable, and its universally poverty-stricken appearance presents a sad contrast to the north.

South of Rome, including Sicily and Sardinia, lies the Mezzogiorno, whose dense population is Italy's most serious problem. This is accentuated by the high reproduction rate, *i.e.* the excess of births over deaths per 1000 of the population. In southern Italy it averages 15 and in Sicily 13, as compared with less than 5 in northern Italy. The "toe" and "heel" of Italy—Calabria and Apulia—have population densities of 520 per square mile; in pockets in Campania there are over 900 per square mile in rural areas, a density which in northern Italy would be found only in the cities. There are few possibilities for extensive absorption of surplus population by industrialisation of the Mezzogiorno, and the solution to over-population for the immediate future seems to lie either in emigration or in some policy of birth restriction. The first is not easy: Italy has no overseas possessions, most other countries have restricting quota systems for immigrants, and industrial northern Italy has reached saturation point. Birth restriction, too, presents religious difficulties, for the people of the Mezzogiorno are fervent Roman Catholics and thus forbidden to use artificial means of birth prevention.

The least populated regions in Italy are in the Alps, central Apennines, volcanic hills of Umbria, the limestone massifs of Lucania, and Sardinia; but even here only the northern ranges of the Alps, the caldera region of Umbria, and the high plateaus of northern Sardinia have less than 120 persons per square mile.

THE ECONOMY

THE PROBLEM OF THE MEZZOGIORNO

Before examining the regional economy of Italy, it is well to look further at the contrasts that exist between the north and south of the country. The native peoples of the Plain of Lombardy have a long history of achievement and prosperity, engendered to some degree by the more stimulating climate experienced there, in spite of resources which are really only meagre. In the past forty years, industrial advance has been phenomenal. Large numbers of immigrants have come from the south to share the new prosperity and to swell the population. Northern Italy has now 21 million inhabitants in an area which—including the sparsely populated Alps—is less than a quarter of the whole country. Both industrially and agriculturally, saturation point has been reached; yet the flood of immigrants continues, and unemployment is increasing. Nevertheless, to southern Italians the north is a picture of wealth and opportunity, in contrast to the poverty, overcrowding and under-development they see around them.

The economic geography of southern Italy is most depressing. Although there has been some amelioration in recent years, centuries of struggle in an adverse environment have reduced the spirit of enterprise and the desire to rise above the generally low standard of living. The same applies to Sicily and Sardinia, though to a lesser extent. The reasons for this backwardness must be sought in both history and geography.

Geographically, a large proportion of southern Italy is mountainous. Much of it is composed of soft limestones, easily eroded and liable to landslides. Valleys and coastal plains are blocked by mud and pebbles washed from the highlands, and may turn into marshes. Soil erosion is a common feature of a landscape which is often bare and dry, and many hill slopes have no soil at all. Southern Italy is subject to destructive earthquakes, and vulcanicity in the Campania is still active. It should be noted, however, that the fertile soils of the volcanic district support the densest rural population in the country. Farms are found far up the slopes of Vesuvius, where streams of lava may destroy their fields and crops. South of Rome, the summers become hotter and more arid, and many of the streams dry up; the karst areas are without surface water at any season.

Much of Sicily is porous limestone and poorly watered on the surface; and the rain which falls on the crystalline mountains in the north runs off too quickly or is dried up. Sardinia is composed largely of crystalline plateaus with thin soils which cannot support a dense population and offer only a scanty living to shepherds and subsistence farmers. Sicily is far more productive than Sardinia and has over three times as many people. This number, however, is too great for its economic capacity, and both islands will remain badly over-populated unless industry can be increased and agriculture improved.

Historical factors in the deterioration of southern Italy are possibly of greater importance than geography, although in some cases it is hard to distinguish between them. They date from the third century B.C., when Greek and Carthaginian trading stations and colonies flourished on the coasts of southern Italy and Sicily. They were expelled by the Romans, their agricultural settlements depopulated, and the land was split into large parcels and given to Roman patricians. These wide estates (*latifundia*), supervised by stewards and worked by slaves, produced the wheat and wool required by Rome. They formed the pattern of farming in southern Italy for the next two thousand years. Even in the nineteenth century, over most of the region, the peasants (*braccianti*) were landless or at best had insufficient land to support a family and had to supplement their income by working for a landlord at extremely low wages.

The latifundia system continued until the 1930s, when the *latifondi* (the modern equivalent) were appropriated by the Government, split into small farms and leased to peasants. At the same time, the grazing rights of the "sheep barons" of the Apulian plain, which had been reduced late in the nineteenth century, were terminated and much of the better-

s

watered grasslands ploughed up. There are still a few wheat-producing latifondi in Calabria and Sicily, but they will disappear soon. Agrarian reforms are being introduced, but the standard of life in much of rural Mezzogiorno has not yet shown any striking change, chiefly because of inadequate water supplies and the enormous cost of improving them.

Other adverse historical factors have included war, piracy and mal-administration. The Mezzogiorno's central position in the Mediterranean and the vulnerability of its coastal plains invited invasion by Goths, Vandals, Arabs, Byzantines, Lombards, Franks and Aragonese. None, except the last, remained for long, but all left a trail of devastation in the most fertile parts. The coasts, too, were harassed by pirates from Barbary, Tripoli and Turkey, who forced the southern Italians into the mountains so that the neglected lowlands became still more marshy and malarial.

In 1559, southern Italy, Sicily, Sardinia and the Duchy of Milan passed into the hands of the Spanish Bourbons, to become the "Kingdom of the Two Sicilies." It remained in their possession for 150 years; one short intermission aside, it was a period of misrule, corruption and oppression, with the latifondi system at its worst. The court of Naples presented all the signs of prosperity and grandiose magnificence, but the city itself and the rest of the Mezzogiorno were reduced to misery and abject poverty.

The psychological effects of centuries of oppression have been lasting. The people, especially the rural population, are distrustful of officials who seek to introduce reforms. They have little use for education, and resent interference with their old-fashioned and inefficient farming methods, appearing content with a way of life that perpetuates their poverty. In Sicily, especially, the succession of foreign overlords engendered a resistance to authority and legislation which is reflected today in the corruption of officials and the power of lawless secret societies such as the Mafia. The problem is made worse by the dense populations in those regions least able to support them and by the rate at which they are increasing (*see* p. 530).

The "Cassa." Such was the alarming position the Republican government faced when it came to power after the Second World War. To try to find a solution it inaugurated in 1950 the *Cassa per il Mezzogiorno*, the Fund for the Development of the South, usually known as the "Cassa." Its purpose is to undertake or encourage public works like land reclamation, flood and erosion control, the provision of aqueducts, sewers, roads, railways and ferry boats; it gives help in the building of vocational schools, fosters tourism and provides additional capital for the setting up of private industry. Before the war the Fascist government had begun to tackle the problem with schemes of reclamation and agrarian improvement, and had tried to relieve the pressure of population by planned settlement of colonists in North Africa. Its efforts met with little success, however, and the Cassa of 1950 appears to have wider vision and more promise.

In southern Italy the results are decidedly encouraging, although it must be said that up to the present the Cassa's endeavours have been concerned rather with laying the foundations of future progress than with immediate returns. Priority has been given to water control, land reclamation and road-making; but at the same time, factories have been built for food processing and manufacturing paper, cement, tyres and textiles. Iron and steel works are already in existence. Thousands of people in the Mezzogiorno are now employed on the new Cassa schemes, electricity and water have been made available for new industries, soil erosion and flooding are being combated, and co-operative farming introduced. But the problem of overcrowding still remains!

REGIONAL ECONOMY

1. *Northern Italy*

(a) *The Italian Alps.* Precipitation throughout the Alps is heavy and comes at all seasons. In the western Alps, the northern sides of the valleys receive the most sunshine. They have vineyards on the lower slopes and oats, barley and hay above, up to about 3500 ft. Higher still, and on the north-facing slopes, there are forests of pines. In the valleys, maize is the chief crop and dairying the main occupation. The Piedmont is the most important region in Italy for dairy cattle, and produces butter and cheese.

The greatest asset of the western Alps is their water power, which is gradually changing the economy of the region (*see* Fig. 134). The rivers have been harnessed to provide a fifth of Italy's hydro-electricity, principally for the Turin district, but it is also helping the development of light engineering industries far up the valleys. Near Aosta, in the Dora Baltea valley, are a small coalfield and some deposits of magnetite; these, helped by hydro-electricity and imports of scrap iron, are the basis of steel and chemical industries in the town. The people of Valle d'Aosta are mostly French-speaking. The tourist industry is also developing in the western Alps, not so much because of the Italian resorts but because the northern passes lead to well-known French winter sports centres such as Chamonix.

The winter climate in the wider valleys and around the lakes of the central Alps is mild because of their sheltered position. Maize, vines, peaches, apricots and fodder crops are grown. The occasional appearance of olives here and around the lakes of the eastern Alps is evidence of the favourable climatic conditions. The mild winters and hot summers tempered by the waters of the lakes have made the southern margins of

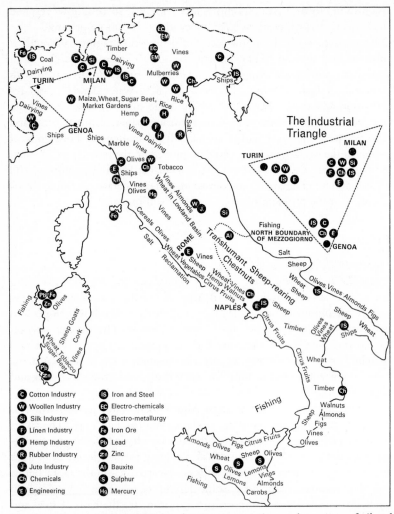

FIG. 140.—Italy: economic. Hydro-electric power stations and resources of oil and natural gas are omitted from this map in order to avoid overcrowding. They will be found on the regional maps, Figs. 134, 136, 137 and 138.

the region a favourite with holiday-makers, especially around lakes Lugano and Como.

The first hydro-electric power station in Italy was built in the Val Tellina, in the central Alps. Today almost every suitable river is harnessed, so that more than half Italy's hydro-electricity comes from this region. The Alps as a whole produce three-quarters of Italy's total current. With an output of over 46,000 million kWh annually, the country is

Europe's largest generator of hydro-electricity, 70% of the potential resources being utilised. An important result of the construction of dams is that water is made available for irrigation in the dry limestone sub-Alpine zone.

The eastern Alpine region is more forested and has more summer mountain pastures than the central and western Alps. Lumbering is important, and transhumant cattle rearing occupies many of the people in the higher valleys, where agriculture is confined mainly to fodder, potatoes, rye and barley. In the more open valleys, and especially around Lake Garda, maize, tobacco, vines and fruit are grown; along the western shores of the lake there are olive and lemon groves. Lemons are particularly susceptible to frost, and special protective measures are taken when temperatures are low. Many of the people of the eastern Alps are German-speaking, for the ease with which the mountains are penetrated has led to occupation at various times by Austrians, Swiss and Yugoslavs, as well as Italians.

On the whole, the Alps of Italy are poorly peopled, compared with the rest of the country. Except in the eastern Alps, industry has hardly penetrated the mountains; and the hydro-electric power stations, unlike those of France, lie mostly in areas of scanty population. The eastern Alps have power stations in the upper valleys of the Adige, Piave and Tagliamento, generating roughly as much current as the western Alps. The more open character of the region has encouraged the growth of electro-chemical, electro-metallurgical, engineering and paper industries in the Adige valley at Bolzano (88,000) and Trento (75,000), the largest towns in the interior of the Italian Alps. The Dolomites, which lie between the Adige and Piave valleys, have a prosperous tourist industry.

The greatest concentrations of people in the Alpine zone are along the southern flanks of the mountains, and more and more they are becoming centres of industry, helped by hydro-electricity. Varese (67,000), Como (82,000), Bergamo (115,000) and Brescia (172,000) have wool textile and engineering industries. Como and Trento are major tourist centres. Much of the raw wool for the textile industry comes from sheep reared in the sub-Alpine hills, where transhumance, once common, has largely disappeared.

(b) *The Plain of Lombardy*, south of the Alpine region, has a belt from east to west of sandy, gravelly outwash, followed by another of alluvial fans. Between the two is a line of springs (*fontanili*) from waters which have soaked through the gravels. The northern zone is generally too dry for agriculture, and sheep-rearing is important, but a highly organised system of irrigation both there and in the alluvial belt has led to a great variety of crops, including maize, wheat, clover and other fodder crops, sugar beet, rice, flax and hemp. Scattered through the north of the Plain of Lombardy are groves of mulberry trees, on the leaves of which silk-worms are reared; but sericulture is a declining occupation, most raw silk now being imported. Vineyards producing the well-known Asti wines cover the slopes at the western end of the plain, and in the east the terra rossa of Venetia supports olive groves. The Plain of Lombardy is the most important agricultural region in Italy.

The marshy riverine belt, where the river Po has built its banks higher than the level of the plain, is subject to flooding, so that extensive and costly reclamation has been necessary. Most farmers are engaged in dairying and rice cultivation. Because of the flood danger there are few towns on the banks of the river. The Po enters the Adriatic by a delta, where there are dyked fields reminiscent of the Dutch polders.

Most of the towns of the agricultural belt lie in two lines, north and south of the river. The northern line includes Pavia (74,000), Cremona (73,000), Mantua (62,000), Verona (210,000), Padua (197,000), Treviso (75,000) and Udine (86,000). They are all essentially market towns, but with the growth of industry in northern Italy they have shared in the development of modern food processing, textile manufactures, engineering and chemical industries. The southern line of towns contains Alessandria (92,000), Parma (141,000), Reggio (116,000), Modena (139,000), Bologna (444,000) and Forli (91,000). The road connecting these southern towns is known as the Emilian Way. They are larger than the northern towns, for in addition to having the industries already mentioned their sites command routes through the northern Apennines. The only large town of the plain actually on the river Po is Piacenza (88,000), to the west, where flooding is uncommon. Ferrara (152,000) and Ravenna (115,000) lie in the middle of the plain, in a hemp-producing and manufacturing district.

In the west of the Plain of Lombardy the greatest supplies of hydro-electric power are available from the Alps, and in 1945 enormous deposits of methane gas were discovered at Caviaga, east of Milan. Hence it is the most highly industrialised region in Italy. Further deposits of methane gas have been found underlying most of the plain south of the Po, as far east as Ravenna, where the gas is used as a raw material in the making of synthetic rubber. Methane is distributed by pipeline or in cylinders throughout northern Italy, where it is utilised as fuel in thermal-electric stations, industrial plants and for household purposes. In a country with negligible coal resources, the gas has been of inestimable value, not only as a fuel but as the basis of the manufacture of nitrogenous fertilisers and other chemicals.

The focus of the industrial region is Milan (Milano), the second city of Italy, with a population of 1,528,000. Situated at the convergence of Alpine routes, it was already a trading and craft centre in the Middle Ages. Today it is the chief industrial and commercial city in the country, the centre of most of the great manufacturing groups. It has all kinds of engineering, and it manufactures cottons, woollens and worsteds, silk and man-made fibres. It is the focus of the most intensive railway network in Italy. Around it are a number of satellite towns, such as Monza and Saronno, which have chemical, metallurgical and textile industries, for which Milan is the market.

Turin (Torino) (1,025,000), the second city of the Plain, is at the meeting point of routes through the western Alps with the west–east route of the Po, on which the city stands. The Dora Baltea leads to the St Bernard Pass, the Dora Riparia to the Mont Cenis Pass and tunnel, the Col de Tende to Mediterranean France, and the Altare Pass to the coast. Turin has cotton and rayon industries, but these are giving way to motor engineering; the giant Fiat works and the smaller Lancia plant are world famous. Turin has also railway and aeronautical engineering; and sheet steel is produced in electric furnaces, using imported scrap. Novara (87,000), midway between Milan and Turin, and Cuneo (46,000), in the south-west of the Piedmont, are overgrown market towns, with textile, chemical, engineering and food industries.

Lying outside the Plain of Lombardy, but linked to its industrial and commercial life by gaps through the Ligurian Alps, is a narrow and discontinuous coastal plain which enjoys a Mediterranean climate, in contrast to the continental characteristics of Lombardy. In the west along the Riviera di Ponente are the holiday resorts of San Remo, Santa Margherita and Rapallo. The amount of lowland available for cultivation is limited, as the mountains are near the coast, which in places is cliff-lined. On the small plains, oranges, pomegranates, flowers, and early vegetables are cultivated. The surrounding slopes are terraced for vines, olives and figs. Only small amounts of cereals are grown; and in general the people of Liguria are concerned with tourism or with industry and commerce in the ports.

The chief of these is Genoa (Genova) (784,000), the second port of Italy, situated on a good harbour. Behind it the Bochetta Pass leads to Milan and, via the St Gotthard tunnel, to Switzerland and West Germany, for which countries Genoa has become the Mediterranean outlet. Besides its function as a port, Genoa has shipyards, steelworks, engineering, and chemical manufactures, soapworks and textile industries. Helped by hydro-electricity from the Alps and methane gas piped from the Plain of Lombardy, and using imported scrap iron, a large integrated iron and steel works has been established west of the city. There are oil refineries too. Since 1945, Genoa has more than doubled its population, and its industries have grown fourfold. It is at the southern tip of Italy's "industrial triangle," with Milan and Turin at the other two corners. Savona (72,000), to the west of Genoa, is the port for Turin and the western Piedmont; it has industries similar to Genoa but on a much smaller scale. Spezia (121,000) is a naval base and dockyard, with jute manufacture and oil refineries.

The eastern outlet of the Plain of Lombardy is the port of Venice (Venezia) (347,000). Built on a number of islands in lagoons north of the Po delta and shut off from the Adriatic by the Lido, a line of sand dunes which have become a holiday resort, Venice was originally simply a refuge against the attacks of the Huns. Gradually it developed into a trading centre and one of the richest cities of Europe. Its commercial importance declined with the opening of the Suez Canal, when the Adriatic became little more than a backwater; but its picturesque position and the romantic association of canals, gondolas and beautiful buildings encouraged a tourist industry, on which the city still largely depends. Here its craft industries, such as the making of lace, silk, glassware and silver filigree, have been of great assistance. In recent years, the increase of industry in northern Italy has given Venice new life. In its mainland suburbs of Mestre and Porto Marghera there are shipyards, oil refineries, chemical works, zinc and bauxite processing plants and engineering works. With the improvement of its harbour facilities, Venice is once again a premier port in the Mediterranean. Trieste (270,000), the northernmost major port in the Adriatic, has shipbuilding, steel and paper works, and oil refining; and it serves as a transit port for Austria and Yugoslavia rather than as an outlet of the Plain of Lombardy, for it lies on the extreme eastern edge of the lowland.

(c) *The northern Apennines.* These form the southern boundary of the Plain of Lombardy. They have considerable forest cover, with oak, beech and chestnut at lower levels, and scattered conifers above. The higher parts are used mainly for grazing sheep and goats. The valleys are cultivated for wheat, maize and vegetables, while vineyards and olive groves cover the terraced slopes. Cattle are reared on the northern slopes overlooking the Plain, providing the cities of the Emilian Way with milk, butter, cheese and meat. The northern Apennines are the best-developed part of the mountain backbone of Italy.

With its large cities, high agricultural yields, hydro-electric power and methane gas, northern Italy is economically the most important part of the country. The big industrial concerns are found there. Montecatini is a chemical, mining, metallurgical and electrical giant. Fiat is Italy's largest company, best known perhaps for its cars but with equally important naval, aircraft and electro-chemical branches. The Italian Edison company is responsible for a third of all electrical power. Snia Viscosa produces about two-thirds of the country's man-made fibres and tissues. Pirelli and Michelin's Italian subsidiary make high-tension cables and rubber products as well as the tyres for which they are best known.

The Plain of Lombardy is also one of the most densely peopled regions in Italy (*see* Fig. 139). Its phenomenal industrial growth during the past forty years has attracted a flood of immigrants from the Mezzogiorno. The better social and economic conditions have proved such a magnet that there is now a surplus of labour and consequent unemployment, notably in the "industrial triangle." It is imperative that the flow of population from the south be halted, possibly by removing some of the industrial "bulge" to the Mezzogiorno.

2. *Central Italy*

(a) *The central Apennines*, composed mainly of limestone, are high and karst-like, with little surface water except in depressions and valleys. They support only a sparse population, which is engaged principally in sheep rearing and subsistence agriculture. The larger depressions are drained by the rivers Aquila and Sulmona; in them, assisted by irrigation, wheat, sugar beet and almonds are cash crops. The upper Nera and Velino rivers have been harnessed for hydro-electric power, which is supplied to Rome (*see* Fig. 136). Most of the people of the central Apennines live in villages built high up the mountain slopes and approached by difficult and winding roads. The village sites were chosen mainly for defence, but sometimes merely to avoid building on cultivable land in the valleys below. The best known of these hillside villages is Assisi, a pilgrimage centre associated with St Francis.

In the north-eastern corner of the central Apennines is the tiny independent republic of San Marino, only 24 square miles in area. It has managed to preserve its independence partly by political expediency, partly because of its position on the slopes of Monte Titano, an isolated mountain, 2437 ft high, which has little attraction for outsiders. The Sammarinesi, as the people of the republic are called, live by subsistence agriculture, quarrying, olive oil pressing, cheese making, and the tourist industry. San Marino (4000) is the only town. It has a small silk industry.

The eastern slopes of the central Apennines have been deforested and the land is cut by deep gullies, the result of soil erosion. The better alluvial areas have been reclaimed and on them cereals and olives are the chief products. In the wider parts of the coastal plain are the market towns of Macerata (38,340), Ascoli (50,000), Teramo (41,000) and Chieti (47,000)—

all surprisingly large in view of the comparative poverty of the region. The Adriatic coast is straight, with few harbours. Most of the coastal towns are fishing ports which, in the north, are developing also a tourist trade. The chief are Ancona (100,000), Pesaro (66,000) and Pescara (87,000), which serve in addition as markets for their agricultural hinterlands.

(b) *Tuscany and Umbria*. In its rich polyculture and way of life, the region which lies within the curve of the central Apennines and the Ligurian and Tyrrhenian Seas presents a marked contrast to the harsh landscape of the neighbouring mountain ranges. In the north, the Plain of Tuscany, *i.e.* of the lower Arno, is intensely cultivated, with wheat, maize, sugar beet and fodder crops. Dairy cattle are reared in the middle of the Plain, and all the hill slopes are covered with vineyards and olive groves. The Chianti hills in the east are famous for their wines. Lucca (88,000), the chief town of the olive-growing district, has oil crushing mills.

At the point where the river Arno enters the Plain of Tuscany stands the city of Florence (Firenze) (436,000). Situated on the Flaminian Way from Rome and commanding routes through the northern Apennines, Florence has a strong strategic position. Under the powerful Medici family it became the capital of Tuscany and a centre of Renaissance art and architecture. It still retains its craft industries—leather and metal working, lace making and jewellery—and its museums and cathedral draw thousands of tourists annually; but it is more important today as an industrial city. There are chemical and machine tool works, railway and electrical engineering, woollen manufacturing and food-processing, the last concerned principally with making macaroni and other *pasta*.

The main outlets of the Tuscan Plain are the ports of Leghorn (161,000) and Pisa (90,000). Leghorn (Livorno), on a good harbour, is the more important and has shipbuilding and heavy engineering. Pisa, on the Arno eight miles from the sea, was the chief port in medieval times but the river silted and Leghorn took over its port functions. During the past twenty years, navigation of the Arno has been improved by dredging and Pisa is once more a major port, with chemical and iron and steel industries. Iron ore is imported from the island of Elba, which lies off the Tuscan coast. The Leaning Tower is of course the city's best-known feature.

The coast of Tuscany, in common with the whole coastline as far south as Naples, is being silted and the blockage of drainage to the Tyrrhenian Sea has resulted in coastal marshes at several points. The most extensive are the Maremma marshes, south of the mouth of the Arno. Until 1950, they could be used only as winter pasture for sheep, but since that date large-scale drainage and reclamation under State supervision have transformed the area into smallholdings which are leased to landless peasants and farmed as co-operatives. The Maremma, once a malarial swamp, is a fine example of the merits of reclamation and re-settlement (*see* Fig. 141). The crops produced and marketed are principally wheat, maize and vegetables, especially tomatoes. There are as yet no large towns in this part of Tuscany. The rocky isle of Elba produces iron ore, which is sent to Genoa, Pisa and Civitavecchia.

South of the Arno plain, the hills and valleys of Tuscany and Umbria are covered with soils derived either from sandstones or, in south Tuscany,

[*Courtesy of the Italian Embassy.*

Fig. 141.—Italy: the Maremma. The coastal strip of Tuscany, previously malarial marsh, has been drained and colonised. The photograph shows a newly completed house on a small-holding. Note (*a*) the freshly planted fruit trees, probably almonds, near the road, (*b*) the typical shape of the bell-tower on the church, (*c*) the community centre and offices with a row of motor cars, (*d*) the short-distance service bus at the right-hand corner, (*e*) the beginning of the Tuscan hills in the background.

from volcanic extrusions. Farmlands cover the Tuscan valleys and extend even to the tops of some of the hills. Everywhere fields of wheat, barley and maize mingle with orchards of peaches and apricots. Olives, vines and mulberries are grown throughout the region. In the less fertile parts sheep are reared, especially in Umbria, where there are considerable areas of macchia. On the upper slopes of the higher cones are patchy forests of oak and chestnut.

The largest town of the Tuscan hill country is Siena (61,000), a market, tourist and route centre. Farther east, in basins or troughs between the

Tuscan and Umbrian hills and the high central Apennines, the towns are
larger, for they lie along the Flaminian Way, the route along the Tiber
valley from Rome to Florence and the north, and each commands a road
through the mountains. The chief of these focal points are Arezzo (75,000),
Perugia (112,000) and Terni (95,000). All have wool textile manufactures,
and at Terni is a hydro-electric power station, chemical and engineering
works. Orvieto, on a more direct route from Rome to the north, is the
centre of a wine-producing district.

[*Courtesy of the Italian State Tourist Department.*

FIG. 142.—Italy: a farm near Rome. The machinery used for threshing is comparatively old-fashioned. In the background, cattle may be seen grazing on
the hill slope. The type of cattle yoked in pairs for draught purposes is to be
found also in Portugal, south Spain and Greece.

(c) *The Lower Tiber basin.* Until fifty years ago the plains of the lower
Tiber were a stretch of rough pasture or malarial swamp. The landlords
of the vast estates into which the plain was divided were content with the
income from sheep rearing, and did little to improve the land. Irrigation
was almost non-existent. Agrarian reform was imposed on them by the
Fascist government, especially after 1928. Today, irrigation schemes feed
wheatfields, dairy farms and vineyards in most of the Agro Romano, and
the malarial swamps of the Campagna have been drained and made into
smallholdings. On the rich, volcanic soils of the Alban hills, south of the
Campagna, the vineyards around Frascati are noted for their wines.

The reclamation of the Pontine marshes, which lie south of the Tiber
delta, was part of the same scheme. Many attempts to reclaim these
swamps had been made in the past two centuries, for they were a barrier

to communications and a source of disease. The name "malaria," it should be noted, is derived from the Italian *mal'aria*, which means "bad air"; for early medical science blamed the disease on the stench of rotting vegetation in the marshes. In the years 1926–32 the marshlands were cut by intersecting canals, whose waters were pumped into the Mussolini Canal and carried to the sea, thus draining the stagnant pools cut off by coastal silting. The Pontine marshes became an area of re-settlement, farms of 20–60 acres being leased to peasants. The smallholdings, separated from the sea by salt lagoons and a line of sand dunes, extend in a belt 60 miles long and 20 miles wide. Among them are several settlements with agricultural schools and depots, commenced by the Government. Some of them have developed into large towns; Latina, founded only in 1932, now has over 200,000 inhabitants. The erstwhile Pontine marshes are today a major producer of cereals, vegetables, vines and tree crops.

Along the coast have grown holiday resorts for the people of Rome. Civitavecchia, a small port north of the coastal plain, serves the capital, though only to a minor extent; it is becoming better known for its steel-works. Anzio is a fishing port and the maritime outlet for the produce of the reclaimed Pontine area.

Dominating the whole of the lower Tiber region is the city of Rome, built on seven volcanic hills on the left bank of the river and in the middle of the Campagna. Its central position in the Italian peninsula—and indeed in the Mediterranean basin—made it an excellent capital for the Roman Empire, for to it were easily brought from conquered territories the food and other products the metropolitan region could not supply. With the fall of the Roman Empire, and after the partial disintegration of the Holy Roman Empire, the Popes became rulers of Rome and the city lost much of its political and military importance. At no time, however, did it cease to be a metropolis; it merely exchanged secular for ecclesiastical leadership, for the Pope is the head of the Roman Catholic Church. The city retained this status in a disunited Italy until 1870, when the country became once more a sovereign state and Rome was chosen as capital.

Rome has grown from a population of 244,000 in 1870 to 2,188,000 in 1961. Despite its size, it is not a great industrial city. It has railway, electrical and various branches of light engineering, and some textile, clothing and chemical works. But its main industrial activities are connected with food processing, luxury goods, camera and cinematograph manufactures, radio and television, furniture and the assembly of machinery from components provided by the Lombardy industrial region. Rome derives its chief source of income from the ruins of its ancient civilisation and from being the greatest religious centre in the world, drawing millions of pilgrims and tourists annually. Within its walls the ruins of the Coliseum, the Forum, the arches of Titus and Constantine, stand side by side with the magnificent statuary of the Renaissance and hundreds of churches and basilicas, of which St Peter's is the most famous. As the political capital, it is the administrative centre of Italy. It is the chief railway focus in the peninsula, and its airport is an international route centre.

Vatican City, or the Vatican State, is an independent political unit, covering 109 acres in the south of Rome. When the Papal States were incorporated in 1870 into the Italian state, the Pope retired to the Vatican Palace. There he and his successors remained, virtually in house custody, until 1929. In that year, by treaty, the Pope was given sovereignty over the newly-defined Vatican City, which included some other buildings in Rome, and a summer villa and estate at Castel Gondolfo on the shores of Lake Albano. The Vatican City has its own administration, postage system, coinage, and radio and television station.

3. *Southern Italy*

(a) *The southern Apennines and plains of Apulia.* The southern Apennines have already been described as a series of limestone or crystalline horsts separated by areas of subsidence. In general, the limestone heights are karst, and in spite of higher rainfall have little surface water. At best they are suitable only for sheep rearing. In solution hollows and on benches on their slopes, where Tertiary clays and marls have been preserved and springs provide water, subsistence farming is carried on. The crystalline horsts of the Sila and Aspromonte have similar occupations, but their impervious rocks provide an excellent catchment area for the heavy winter rainfall; several lakes on the surface of the Sila have been transformed into reservoirs for hydro-electric power stations and for irrigation in the valleys and coastal plains (*see* Fig. 137). All the horsts have a scattered cover of forests of beech and Mediterranean pine, but deforestation in the past has caused widespread soil erosion. The limestone is easily worn away, and in winter torrential showers, often of hail, cause landslides when the protecting forest cover is removed. Piles of mud and pebbles are swept from the highlands into the deep, narrow valleys and on to the coastal plains, leaving the upper surfaces bare and sterile. The transported sediments block the drainage, and turn the coastal plains into swamps, which become malarial and able to support only a sprinkling of inhabitants.

The provinces of Lucania (Basilicata) and Calabria, which are composed almost entirely of the Apennine highlands, are the poorest in Italy, yet they contain nearly 3 million people. Most of these, however, live in the small coastal plains of Calabria. The plains are intensively cultivated for wheat and vegetables, and have olives, vines, figs, oranges and lemons in irrigated huertas. Citrus fruits are the main wealth of Calabria: orange and lemon groves cover much of the area around Reggio (153,000), Cosenza (78,000) and Catanzaro (74,000). The crystalline plateaus in the interior of Calabria supply water for irrigation, and their power stations generate about 3% of Italy's hydro-electric power, but the development of industry in the "toe" of Italy is not commensurate with this total. Calabria remains the most over-populated province in the country.

Textile, chemical and iron and steel works have been established in Reggio, Cosenza and Catanzaro, with the help of the Cassa, and the harbour facilities of Reggio, the ferry port to Sicily, have been improved, but these can absorb only a tiny fraction of the ever-growing mass of people along the coasts. In the mountainous interior of Lucania and Calabria the position is even worse, for there are fewer resources and the birthrate is among the highest in the world. Here Italy's "Problem of the Mezzogiorno" is at its worst.

On the eastern side of southern Italy is the province of Apulia (Puglia), with two areas of lowland fringing the Adriatic Sea. The first is the Plain of Apulia, between the Campanian Apennines and the limestone plateau of the Murge. It is a plain of recent emergence, and has a thin cover of marine clays and sands overlying impure limestone. In some parts the limestone has dissolved and its residual deposits have formed a thick, impermeable layer below the surface silts, producing malarial swamps; in other places the limestone is very porous, making irrigation difficult. The Apulian Plain is watered by streams from the base of the limestone Apennines; but in summer it is the hottest part of Italy, average July temperatures being 85° F (29° C). The rivers dry up and there is a shortage of water for household purposes.

In these conditions, the plain was given over to sheep rearing. The wretchedly poor shepherds were employed by landowners who lived in Naples or Rome and who resisted any use of the plain for arable farming. In the 1930s the grazing rights of the sheep barons were terminated, and sheep rearing confined to the worst parts of the plain. In 1939 the Apulian Aqueduct was completed after 30 years' work, to feed water to the plain. The westward-flowing river Sele was diverted through tunnels pierced in the Apennines to an aqueduct over 150 miles long, and its waters directed to irrigation channels in the Apulian Plain, and to supply systems in the towns. The Cassa is increasing the scope of the aqueduct, so that more land is constantly brought into use, chiefly for wheat and vegetable production. In the middle of the plain is Foggia (118,000), which has grown rapidly because of the aqueduct; in it the Cassa has built new dairies, grain warehouses and a co-operative olive oil processing works.

In the "heel" of Italy is another plain, with a cover of terra rossa, and here, as in the Apulian Plain, the provision and control of water supplies is the chief problem. The principal products are olives and olive oil, of which Apulia is a major exporter. The chief towns are Brindisi (70,000), Taranto (194,000) and Lecce (75,000), each surrounded by irrigation systems and rich agriculture, and acting as markets for olive oil, wine and fruit. Brindisi, on a good harbour, was a growing mail port for the East until the advent of air travel, but has now declined in importance. Taranto's functions as a naval, shipbuilding and fishing port have been augmented by new iron and steel works.

In contrast to the dry plains, the narrow coastal plain and terraced slopes north and south of Bari, on the east coast, are one vast orchard. The soil, enriched by phosphatic deposits and irrigated by streams from the Murge plateau, supports vines, olives, figs, oranges, lemons and almonds. Bari (312,000), the centre of this fruitful huerta, is the chief Adriatic port south of Venice. It exports olive oil, wine and fruit. New industries started by the Cassa include rubber, metal pipe and marble works. Elsewhere on the Apulian coasts, the Cassa is building new aqueducts for the better distribution of irrigation waters to the huertas, and improving the roads on the difficult slopes.

(b) *Campania.* The Plain of Naples, in the north of Campania, is the most fertile of the Tyrrhenian lowlands, its productivity being attributable in a large degree to the breakdown of basaltic lavas and volcanic tuffs, especially in the east of the plain. The rich soils have long supported a full range of Mediterranean polyculture, with crops of wheat, maize, vegetables, flax, hemp and tree crops such as peaches, apricots, mulberries and vines, all on small farms. On hill slopes are more vineyards, olive groves and fig trees; at their feet are orange groves. On the limestone hills bounding the eastern plain, sheep are reared. In the west and north there were coastal swamps around the river mouths but most of them have been reclaimed and re-settled, as in the Pontine and Maremma marshes; the land now produces wheat, vegetables, flax and hemp. The Campanian lowlands, after the Plain of Lombardy, are the most productive part of Italy, yet many of the inhabitants live in a state of dire poverty belied by the rich landscape, and the pressure of rural population is great.

The largest city of Campania is Naples (Napoli), with a population of 1,182,000. It is a major port on a first-class harbour, with good routes through its agricultural hinterland to Rome and, via Benevento, to the Adriatic coast. Its importance as a port is increased by the absence of good harbours on the Tyrrhenian coast until Leghorn is reached in the north. Naples is in a position of great scenic beauty—"See Naples and die!"—but within the city itself, although there are magnificent buildings and a prosperous industrial area, parts are filthy overcrowded slums, teeming with hordes of immigrants from the poverty-stricken rural areas of southern Italy and with the city's own surplus of unemployed.

Naples is Italy's greatest industrial city outside the north. It has ship-building, chemical, leather, cotton and rayon manufactures, railway engineering and food processing; as part of the Cassa developments, light

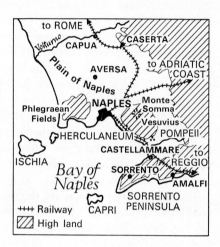

FIG. 143.—Italy: Naples. The Plain of Naples is the most intensively cultivated region in Italy, with vines, peaches, apricots, olives, figs and mulberries on hill slopes, and wheat, maize, vegetables, flax, hemp and oranges at lower levels.

industries of all kinds are being introduced. At Bagnoli, a southern suburb, is a new iron and steel works using imported fuel and raw materials.

Among other Cassa projects scattered through the plain are hotels—for Pompeii, Capri, etc., attract many tourists—tobacco works, paper and cardboard factories, and food processing plants, especially for the making of macaroni. At Caserta (50,000) there are glass, paper and plastics factories. In the Phlegraean Fields region, new thermo-electric stations supply power to motor, electrical and mechanical engineering works.

South of the Plain of Naples, a spur of the Apennines forms the rocky Sorrento peninsula. In little bays at the foot of its cliffs there are holiday resorts such as Sorrento and Amalfi; Castellammare is a naval base. Capri, a beautiful island off this picturesque coast, attracts thousands of tourists from Naples.

The southern part of Campania is the Plain of Salerno, through which flows the river Sele. Its products are the same as those of the Plain of Naples, but farming methods are more primitive and yields smaller.

The chief town is Salerno (117,000), whose industries are concerned mainly
with the agricultural products of the Sele basin. Hydro-electricity generated in the upper Sele valley has led to electrical engineering in Salerno
and is helping Cassa projects—macaroni making, tobacco and paper
works—throughout the plain.

4. *Insular Italy*

(a) *Sicily.* The economy is essentially agricultural, and its industries are
mainly connected with farm products. It has a population of 4,712,000
and the very high density of 475 persons per square mile, which is far
beyond the island's capacity to support. Much of the area is over-
populated, and large numbers emigrate to northern Italy. The climate is
typically Mediterranean, with rainfall chiefly in winter. But the total
precipitation is not great—Palermo has 25 in. a year—and much is lost by
rapid run-off and by evaporation. Sicily needs a complete reorganisation
of its water supplies, so as to increase its agricultural yields and reduce the
pressure of population. This is one of the objects of the Cassa, which has
already brought into operation the Palermo Aqueduct to distribute irrigation water to the central plain. Other dams have been constructed in the
upper valleys of the Salso and Simeto rivers to feed the extended irrigation
systems of the Plain of Catania.

The richest farming areas are the small coastal plains along the north
coast, which are watered by streams from the limestone heights behind
(*see* Fig. 138). Their chief crop is lemons, followed by oranges and tan-
gerines, and there is a big output of vegetables, which can be grown all the
year round. The plains of the centre and south are wheat-lands, with olive
groves and sheep on the higher areas. The Plain of Catania, thanks to the
new irrigation systems, is the most improved region of Sicily, producing
all the crops of the northern huertas, together with vines, olives and
almonds. One of the most fruitful districts is on the lower slopes of Etna,
which have fertile volcanic soils in places; other parts of the mountain are
covered with a mass of broken lavas and pumice.

Sicily has deposits of sulphur near Caltanisetta, Agrigento and Catania
(*see* Fig. 140), but the competition of larger and more easily exploited
supplies from Louisiana has robbed it of its former pre-eminence in the
export of this mineral.

In view of the absence of any outstanding manufacturing industries,
the cities of Sicily are surprisingly large—an indication of the island's over-
population. Palermo, the capital, has a population of 588,000. Situated
on a good harbour and in the centre of a rich huerta, it is Sicily's chief
port. Its industries include shipbuilding, chemical works, mechanical
and naval engineering, and food processing. Catania (363,900) exports

the products of its hinterland, and has glass and pottery works, and paper mills. Messina (254,000), on the strait, exports oranges from the groves which surround it and is the ferry port for Reggio, on the mainland. Taormina, a small town on a limestone bluff overlooking the Mediterranean, is a holiday resort famous for its ruins of a Greek theatre and for its view of Mount Etna. Other large towns of Sicily are Siracusa (90,000), Agrigento (48,000) and Trapani (77,000), all in fertile huertas, and Caltanissetta (63,000), a wheat and sulphur market in the central plain. Trapani exports the wine of Marsala. On the whole Sicily is better endowed with resources than most of southern Italy, but much further attention by the Cassa is needed.

To the north of Sicily are the volcanic Lipari isles, with Stromboli, a volcano in constant activity and known as the "lighthouse of the Mediterranean." Another of the group is Vulcano, which has given its name to all volcanoes.

Centrally situated in the Mediterranean, Sicily has attracted a succession of invaders during its history, nearly every southern European and north African people having attempted to occupy and govern it at one time or another. Each invasion in turn left its mark. The Greeks developed city states and trading colonies; the Romans used the island as a granary and left a legacy of latifondi; the Arabs introduced irrigation, citrus fruits and cotton; the Bourbons exploited it and left it in a state of destitution. Under this succession of foreign overlords, the Sicilians—hardworking, frugal, clannish, hot-blooded, fiery—developed a resistance to authority and legislation which has made the work of the Cassa very difficult. Past experience of corruption among Government officials has made them suspicious of the Cassa experts; but the reforms and improvements of the past ten years have done much, not only to increase the economic capacity of Sicily, but to convert its people to an acceptance of outside interference and an acquiescence to agrarian reforms.

(b) *Sardinia*. Although Sardinia is not much smaller than Sicily, its population, 1,413,300, is less than one-third of the larger island's. The density is 152 persons a square mile; although this is small compared with other parts of the Mezzogiorno, Sardinia is overcrowded and is one of the poorest provinces in Italy. The plateaus are largely unproductive, with bare rocks dotted with patches of macchia and occasional cork-oaks, but they serve as catchment areas for the water needed in the lower-lying areas. The Cassa has constructed dams in the upper valleys of the rivers Coghinas, Tirso and Flumendosa, and the impounded waters are used for hydro-electricity and to feed irrigation systems (*see* Fig. 138). The Cassa has been responsible too for the drainage of malarial swamps which dotted the coasts, and for the reafforestation of some of the plateau slopes. The rearing of sheep and goats is the chief occupation throughout the highlands of Sardinia, and wool and cheese are staple products.

The best agricultural areas lie at the two ends of the Campidano, where, with irrigation, the chief crops are wheat, maize, rice, tobacco, beans and sugar beet. Olives, vines and almonds grow on slopes, and there is some sheep rearing. In the centre of the plain there are large wheat farms. The largest town in Sardinia, Cagliari (183,000), is situated at the southern end of the Campidano. It is the island's chief port, trading mainly with Naples; it has salt pans, woollen manufacture and cement works. At the northern end of the plain is Oristano, a small market town.

The crystalline rocks of the south-western plateau are highly mineralised, yielding lead and zinc near Iglesias and coal at Carbonia (see Fig. 140). The peninsula of La Nurra in the west of Sardinia has deposits of lead, zinc, iron and antimony. Sassari (90,000) concentrates the minerals of the La Nurra district, and is in the chief olive-growing region. The concentrated ores are exported to Italy through Alghero and Porto Tórres, which are also small tunny- and sardine-fishing ports. The coal of Carbonia is sent to Italy from Cagliari; nearly all Italy's coal comes from Sardinia.

The poverty of Sardinia is visible in most parts of the island. Although the Cassa is very active in its schemes of reconstruction and rehabilitation, many years must elapse before Sardinia has a standard of living comparable even with that of the southern Apennines.

STUDY QUESTIONS

1. Make a division of peninsular Italy into geographical regions. Describe the relief and drainage of each region and show how these have influenced communications through the whole peninsula. (O. & C.)

2. Compare the agriculture of the Lombardy Plain with that of Italy south of Naples. (O. & C.)

3. Write a concise geographical account of *either* Sicily *or* Sardinia. (O. & C.)

4. Make a comparative geographical study of the Plain of Lombardy and Lower Saxony. (J.M.B.)

5. Account for regional contrasts in economic development in Italy. (J.M.B.)

6. Suggest a division of Italy into natural regions. Discuss the bearing of physical factors upon economic activities in any *two* of the regions recognised. (J.M.B.)

7. Poverty is more prevalent among the rural population of southern Italy and Sicily than among the rural population of the Plain of Lombardy. Discuss the influence of geographical conditions on this state of affairs. (J.M.B.)

8. Describe the position, chief manufactures and commercial activities of *either* Milan *or* Naples.

9. Compare the industrial activities of Italy with those of the Scandinavian peninsula. (J.M.B.)

10. Describe the distribution of population in Italy and account for any regional differences in density you may note.

Chapter XXXII

GREECE

PHYSICAL ASPECTS

GREECE has been described variously as "a bare country with all its ribs showing" and "the skeleton of a worn-out country from which all the good land has been stripped." The southern part, with its long finger-like projections southwards into the Mediterranean Sea and its thousands of islands, certainly gives this impression, but it must be remembered that there is also a continental portion of Greece which is quite different from the rest of the country.

STRUCTURAL DIVISIONS

The heart of Greece lies in the southern part of the Balkan peninsula and is a peninsula itself. It is almost divided in two by the Gulf of Corinth, so that the southern third of the area forms a separate peninsula, the Peloponnesus or Morea, usually treated as a distinct region; the northern two-thirds of the peninsula is called Peninsular Greece. Northwards, the country widens to the hills and plains of Macedonia and Thrace, which extend eastwards to the border of European Turkey. Around the coasts are several archipelagoes containing islands which range in size from mere dots to hundreds of square miles. Greece can thus be divided into: (1) peninsular Greece, (2) Peloponnesus, (3) Macedonia and Thrace, and (4) insular Greece (*see* Fig. 144).

1. *Peninsular Greece*

The middle of peninsular Greece is a mass of high mountain ranges, to the east and west of which the country, though still mountainous, is more open. It is convenient, therefore, to divide the region into (*a*) central, (*b*) western, and (*c*) eastern peninsular Greece.

(a) *Western peninsular Greece.* This is the region generally known as Epirus (Ipiros). It consists of a number of folded ranges running parallel to the coast and rarely rising to more than 4500 ft, the highest point being Psili Korifi (5187 ft). There is less limestone and more sandstone than in the central peninsular ranges, and in the valleys and small plains the soil is productive. The most extensive plain is that of Árta, around the shallow Gulf of Amvrakía. Elsewhere the west coast has steep, rocky shores, with few openings. The Ionian islands, of which the largest are Corfu (Kérkira), Levkás, Cephalonia (Kefallinía) and Zante (Zákinthos), form a festoon archipelago; they are the upstanding portions of a foundered mountain range. The Ionian islands are usually included with western peninsular Greece rather than with insular Greece, since they are more closely

FIG. 144.—Greece: physical features and divisions. The numbers correspond with the regional divisions used in the text.

associated with the economy of the mainland than are the archipelagoes of the Aegean Sea.

(b) *Central peninsular Greece.* The centre of peninsular Greece is occupied by a series of folded mountain ranges, which are a continuation of the Dinaric Alps of Albania and Yugoslavia. In the north, near those countries, the ranges are broken into high, rugged blocks, separated by depressions containing lakes. The highest of the blocks is Smólikas (8636 ft), and the largest lake is Prespa (Prespansço) (104 square miles). Most of the lake lies within the Yugoslav and Albanian frontiers. Southwards the Pindus mountains are a high and more continuous range, in which several peaks are more than 7000 ft above sea level. The highest are Tzoumérka (7851 ft), Timfristós (7609 ft), and Peristéri (7530 ft). The Pindus form a difficult barrier between the east and west of peninsular Greece; there is no railway across them and only two good roads, one of which rises at the Métsovon Pass to 5087 ft.

At the southern end of the Pindus, east–west ranges cut across the main mountain mass. In one of them, Mount Parnassus rises to 8064 ft. Along their southern flanks, bordering the Gulf of Corinth, are the small plains of Agrínion and Phokís. All the central mountains are composed mainly of limestones, which are often karst, barren and reminiscent of the Karst of Yugoslavia.

(c) *Eastern peninsular Greece.* East of the central mountains a number of ranges run towards the Aegean Sea, and between them are alluvial lowlands. There are some high peaks in the ranges but, on the whole, eastern Greece is lower than the remainder of the peninsula; the lowlands are more extensive and the coast more broken, with many good harbours. The chief lowlands are the plains of Thessaly, Boeotia and Attica. The Plain of Thessaly is mainly the basin of the river Piniós. It is overlooked by Mounts Olympus (9571 ft), Ossa (6409 ft) and Pelion (Pílion) (5308 ft), all famous in Greek history and mythology. The Plain of Boeotia at one time contained Lake Copais (Kopaís), but this has now been drained and its bed is rich farmland. The Plain of Attica lies behind Athens. Boeotia and Attica, with the citadels of Thebes (Thívai) and Athens, were the heart of Ancient Greece. Another productive lowland in the east is the lower valley of the river Sperkhiós, known as the Plain of Phthiótis (Fthiótis). Off the coast is the long, narrow island of Euboea (Évvoia), separated from the mainland by a shallow strait; it is usually included for study purposes with the mainland, of which it is structurally a part.

2. *Peloponnesus*

Southern Greece is the peninsula of Peloponnesus or Morea, joined to peninsular Greece by the Isthmus of Corinth. Peloponnesus is entirely mountainous: folded ranges follow the north–south Dinaric trend and splay out at their extremities into four "fingers," with intervening deep gulfs. The mountains rise in places to over 6000 ft, *e.g.* Sikionía (7789 ft), Párnon (6855 ft), and Ponakhaïkón (6322 ft). Within the mountains are several enclosed basins of good soil, such as those around Trípolis and Megalópolis. Around the coasts, and more especially at the heads of the southern gulfs, are small alluvial plains, isolated from each other by high mountain ridges. The gulf plains are Argos, Sparta (Spárti) and Messene (Messíni); on the west coast, in the lower basin of the river Ládhon, is the Plain of Olympia. On these plains grew the original city states of Ancient Greece. On the north-east and north-west corners of Peloponnesus are narrow coastal plains around Corinth and Patras (Pátrai).

3. *Macedonia and Thrace*

North of peninsular Greece is western Macedonia, known also as High Macedonia to distinguish it from eastern Macedonia, which is mostly lowland. High Macedonia lies among mountain blocks which seem to run from the Pindus to the Aegean shores but are in fact similar to the faulted and dislocated Pelagonian massifs of Yugoslav Macedonia. In Greek Macedonia they are rarely more than 4000 ft high. Within the mountains are two large basins, a northern one which contains Lake Vegorrítis (Ostrovo) and extends southwards to Ptolemaís, and one in the south around the upper Aliákmon river.

The north-east of Greece is a region of coastal plains and low hills, bordering the northern Aegean Sea and backed by the foothills of the Rhodope massif. It is divided by the river Néstos (Mesta) into eastern Macedonia to the west and Thrace to the east. Here are the most extensive lowlands in Greece. They are widest in the west in the Plain of Thessaloníki (Salonica), across which flows the lower river Vardar. The western end of the plain, Campania, was once occupied by Lake Yiannitsá but is now completely drained.

East of the Plain of Thessaloníki is the limestone plateau of Chalcidice (Khalkidhikí), a peninsula which terminates in three cliff-girt prongs. Beyond are the Plain of Seres in the lower Struma valley, and the Plain of Philippi west of the Néstos. All these plains have alluvial soils and are the most fertile in Greece. Lake Tachinos, which lay in the Struma valley, has now been drained like Yiannitsá and is rich farmland. Farther east, the plains of Thrace are narrower and more hilly than those of Macedonia, and they rise gradually to the foothills of the crystalline Rhodope. Only a tiny portion of this massif is in Greece, but it contains Mount Koulá (7143 ft), one of the highest points in the Rhodope.

No part of the mainland of Greece is more than 60 miles from the sea, and so there are no long rivers with their courses entirely Greek. In the north, only the lowest parts of the courses of the Vardar (Axios), Struma, Néstos and Maritsa (Évros) are in Greece. The Maritsa forms part of the boundary between Greece and Turkey. The longest entirely Greek river is the Aliákmon in High Macedonia. None of the rivers is navigable, and their volume varies so much that opportunities for hydro-power development are limited. They may, however, be useful for irrigation.

4. *Insular Greece*

The islands which are considered under this heading lie on the eastern side of Greece, in what is usually called the Aegean Sea but which in the south is known also as the Mirtoan Sea and the Sea of Crete. The islands may be grouped as follows:

(i) A northern group includes the Northern Sporadhes (Voríai Sporádhes), an archipelago of small islands off the coast of peninsular Greece,

[*Courtesy of the Greek Embassy.*

FIG. 145.—Greece: the harbour of Firra on the island of Thíra, in the Cyclades. Many of the islands, which are hard crystalline rock, rise to over 2500 ft. Note the steep, winding, stepped mule-tracks which climb from the harbour to the villages above. The Cyclades have little economic importance, except for the emery and wine of Náxos, and a small output of iron ore in Sériphos and four other islands.

and the larger islands of Thásos, Samothrace (Samothráki) and Lemnos (Límnos). Thásos is an outlier of the Rhodope massif; Samothrace and Lemnos are composed mainly of limestone.

(ii) In the south of the Aegean are the Cyclades (Kikládhes), fragments of a fractured crustal block which was topped by limestone and pierced by volcanoes, all of which are now extinct. Signs of former volcanic activity are to be seen in the crater harbour of Mílos and the lava soils of Thíra.

(iii) In the east, and structurally a part of Asia Minor, are the islands of Lesbos (Lésvos), Chios (Khíos), Sámos and the Dodecanese (Southern Sporádhes) archipelago, which includes the larger islands of Rhodes (Ródhos) and Kárpathos.

(iv) Crete, over 150 miles long, 8–20 miles wide and with an area of 3000 square miles, is the largest island in the Aegean. It appears to be a continuation of the Dinarides of the Peloponnesus, but with an east–west trend. It has a mountainous backbone which rises to 8193 ft in Mount Ídhi, 7904 ft in the Iévka Ori and 7166 ft in Áyios Nikólaus. The range, which is composed of limestone, is broken into three distinct blocks. On the south of the island the mountains are so close to the sea that there is little room for lowland, and most of the coast has steep, bare cliffs. On the north there are small coastal plains in the centre and west.

CLIMATE

Although the situation of Greece is truly Mediterranean, its climate varies from the Mediterranean norm. Three distinct climatic types may be distinguished, and they can be further divided into local sub-types.

(i) The true Mediterranean climate is found in the coastal regions of the peninsula and in the islands. Here the summers are hot and dry; the winters mild, wet and windy. Temperatures range from 45° F (7° C) in January to 80° F (26° C) in July. Rainfall, however, is much greater on the west coast than on the more sheltered east. Corfu, for instance, has an annual precipitation of 50·4 in., 39·7 in. of which falls in the six winter months; whereas Athens has an annual rainfall of only 15·4 in., 12 in. of it in winter.

(ii) Away from the coast, the mountainous peninsula has a climate which is basically Mediterranean but is much affected by altitude. Summer temperatures, except in valleys, rarely rise above 60° F (15° C) and the winters may be severe, with snow lying for several months. Precipitation may amount to 70 or 80 in. annually and, although most comes in winter, there is sufficient in summer to keep a constant flow in the rivers.

(iii) The third climatic type is found in Macedonia and Thrace, where there is a definite tendency to continental conditions in the seasonal distribution of rainfall and in the occurrence of winter frosts on the plains.

Salonica, for example, ranges from an average of 40·6° F (4·7° C) in January to 78·6° F (25·8° C) in July; its annual precipitation amounts to 21·5 in., which falls at all seasons but with maxima in May and November.

Temperature on all the Aegean coasts may rise on occasions to over 100° F (37·8° C) in the shade, setting up strong sea breezes which temper the sultriness. Noteworthy, too, are the Etesian winds which blow in winter from the north-west. They are pulled from the high-pressure regions of eastern Europe to the lower pressure areas in the Mediterranean and affect the northern Aegean Sea and its adjacent lands. They are invigorating winds, but they may bring spells of cold weather with frost, and as they advance to the south may reach gale force.

NATURAL VEGETATION

Of the total area of Greece, 17% consists of bare mountains or un-cultivated marshland, 15% of forest, 39% of pasture and 27% of culti-vated land. The remaining 2% includes lakes, towns and roads.

The forests, which occur mainly in the Pindus mountains and the Arcadian Highlands (in Peloponnesus), are of pines and oaks at higher levels and of wild olives on the lower slopes. Olives are not found where frosts are at all frequent. Much of the forest was cut down when the country was ruled by Turkey. The result was soil erosion and the forma-tion of coastal swamps, which became malarial. At least a quarter of the remaining forest was destroyed during the Second World War. Since 1945, serious efforts have been made to re-forest the country; but, since rural Greece depends to a large extent on firewood as fuel, the authorities in some parts are fighting a losing battle. Much of the deforested areas are covered with maquis or garrigue, on which goats find a meagre sustenance; and a large proportion of the pastoral lands consists of Mediterranean shrubs and patchy grasses which are green only in winter.

The beauty of the Greek landscape lies more in the craggy, limestone heights, often brilliantly white, which rise along the Aegean and in the islands from an azure blue sea, than from the vegetation which may clothe them.

HUMAN GEOGRAPHY

HISTORICAL OUTLINE

The Homeric age may be regarded as the starting point of Greek history. There were earlier civilisations in the region—the Minoan in Crete and the Mycenaean in the Peloponnesus—but not much is known about them and they seem to have come to a sudden end. How much the civilisation of the ancient Greeks owes to Crete and Mycenae, and who were the indigenous inhabitants of the country, are still open questions.

Ancient Greece as it was known to Homer some 3000 years ago lay south of a line drawn roughly from the mouth of the river Piniós to the Gulf of Amvrakía (Árta). From the shores of this small and difficult mountain country spread a civilisation that has had a lasting influence on the whole world. Around its southern peninsulas grew city states, each on a coastal plain enclosed by mountains. Their inhabitants, although essentially agriculturists, developed also a love of city life and showed it by erecting magnificent buildings and temples, and by depicting it in literature and philosophic discussions. Ancient Greece was swallowed by the Roman Empire, but not before it had spread its civilisation to all parts of the Mediterranean. Even in those far-off times, Greece was sadly over-peopled and colonies were founded in Asia Minor, Sicily, Italy, Libya, southern France and Iberia, each based on the city state pattern. Greek influences penetrated Rome, which became "Hellenised" (Hellas, Εελλας, is the name of the country in Greek, and the people are Hellenes). As the bounds of the Roman Empire were extended, Greek-style archi-tecture, temples and sports arenas were imposed on the conquered terri-tories and the Greek language, rather than Latin, was the usual means of communication in the eastern Mediterranean.

The glories of classical Greece were eclipsed on the fall of the Roman Empire. The history of the country for several centuries is more a record of barbarian invasions, occasional plagues (chiefly malaria) and frequent earthquakes, all of which helped to undermine the prosperity of the late Roman Empire. Sporadic raids by Vandal and Ostrogoth pirates in the fifth century had little lasting effect, but in the sixth century Slavonic tribes (Wends, Slovenes) invaded from the north and occupied the mountainous inland; after 1084 nomad Vlachs took possession of Thessaly. The dissolution in 1204 of the Byzantine empire—of which Greece formed part—brought in its train a series of invasions by Frankish barons and Venetian and Catalan merchant adventurers, eager for new territory. For over two centuries Greece consisted of a number of small states, many of them governed by "despots" (rulers with absolute power). From the beginning of the fourteenth century the mutual quarrels of these petty princes led to conquest by the Turks. Some of the despots had employed Turkish pirates as auxiliaries, and these, augmented by Ottoman Turkish forces, took over the lands they conquered and then turned on their employers. By 1460 the Turks had complete control of the country, having conquered it piecemeal, and they remained in power until the nineteenth century. Hellas sank into poverty and wretchedness which have lasted to the present time.

The people of Ancient and medieval Greece generally lived near the coasts, and much of their prosperity depended on the sea. With the advent of the Turkish invaders, they were driven inland, to meet with opposition from the mountain dwellers. The lowlands they vacated became malarial. Decimated by wars, weakened by disease and malnutrition, and living in a mountain environment where hardship was a constant companion, the Greeks nevertheless looked to a return of the days of ancient glory, and after centuries of oppression they were among the first to welcome the liberal ideas which developed in Europe during the eighteenth and nineteenth centuries.

In the years 1821–29 they rose against the Turks and, in 1830, the Greeks were the first Balkan people to become independent of the Sultanate. This was the rebellion in which Lord Byron, the English poet, fought for Greek liberation; it resulted in the Kingdom of the Hellenes. It was the beginning of modern Greece, but the country was small in area, being confined to the region south of the river Sperkhiós.

With the gradual expulsion of the Turks from the Balkans, the little kingdom acquired more territory. The Ionian islands became Greek in 1863 and Thessaly in 1881; in 1913, with the final downfall of the Turks, Epirus, Macedonia, western Thrace, Crete and most of the larger Aegean islands were added. In 1918, eastern Thrace was occupied and in 1947 Greek ownership of Kárpathos, Rhodes and the Dodecanese islands was confirmed.

Greece attempted in 1920 to occupy all the eastern shores of the Aegean so as to make it an entirely Hellenic sea. Their reasons were that over a million Greeks lived in the coastlands of Asia Minor and that Smyrna (now called Izmir) was overwhelmingly Greek in population. The Turks, however, had recovered from their defeat in the First World War and, inspired by Kemal Ataturk, they drove the Greeks from the mainland of Asia Minor. To obviate further incursion by either country into the other's territory, Greece and Turkey agreed, by the Treaty of Lausanne in 1924, to the present boundaries and arranged for an exchange of peoples. Upwards of 1,300,000 Greeks were expatriated from Asia Minor; about half that number of Turks living in Greece, mainly in eastern Thrace, were moved to Turkey. The huge incursion of Greeks, especially into Macedonia and Thrace, upset the economy of the country and caused much poverty and suffering. But it had the effect of making the population of Greece more homogeneous than it had been for centuries and of introducing much-needed new blood. One less desirable result was that many of the immigrants who could not find land to settle on moved into the cities, adding to already overcrowded slums.

During the Second World War, Greece was torn asunder once again, first by the Italians and later by the Germans, yet despite the ravages of war, famine and disease, the country has made remarkable progress since 1945. It is still very poor, and living conditions in the mountains near the Yugoslav border are so miserable that many of the inhabitants are attracted to Communism as a cure for their troubles. In the cities, too, in the slums which grew inevitably as a result of overcrowding and unemployment, Communism has gained a foothold.

Since 1960, relations between Greece and Turkey have become strained once more, largely because of conditions in Cyprus. Most of the inhabitants of this island, which is independent, are Greek Cypriots. The minority are Turkish Cypriots. Many Greek Cypriots desire *Enosis*, that is, complete union with Greece, and all of them demand a larger share in the government of their island than the Turkish Cypriots are willing to admit. The two peoples' mutual distrust led to a sporadic and bitter civil war, and to attempts first by Great Britain and later by the United Nations to restore peace and tranquillity. The quarrel was taken up by Greece and Turkey; Turkey is alleged to have introduced economic sanctions against Greece. Among them was a new expulsion of Greeks who still lived in European Turkey. In 1964, 2346 Greeks were expelled across the river Évros (Maritsa), whereas Greece claims that no action has been taken against Turkish nationals living in Greek territory. The position of Cyprus in the economy of Greece, and the future relations of Greece and Turkey, remain to be settled.

POPULATION

The population of Greece is 8,388,500, with an average density of 166 persons a square mile. As four-fifths of the surface of the country is mountainous and can support only a very sparse population, densities in most of the lowlands are high—too high, indeed, for their food-producing capacity.

The greatest numbers of people live in the plains of Attica and Boeotia (*see* Fig. 146), with the largest concentration around Athens–Piraeus. Here the density rises to nearly 450 persons a square mile. It is the most industrialised part of the country. In the remainder of Greece only the plains of Thessaloníki and the island of Corfu have more than 100 persons per square mile, and many of these are gathered in the towns of Thessaloníki (Salonica) and Kérkira. A map showing distribution of population in Greece is often misleading, for in many of the lowlands there are pockets of dense population surrounded by poorly peopled farming areas. The Pindus mountains, the limestone prongs of Chalcidice, and the high blocks near the Albanian border have very few inhabitants. Some of the mountainous regions of western and eastern peninsular Greece, south-eastern Peloponnesus, and eastern Crete are not much better.

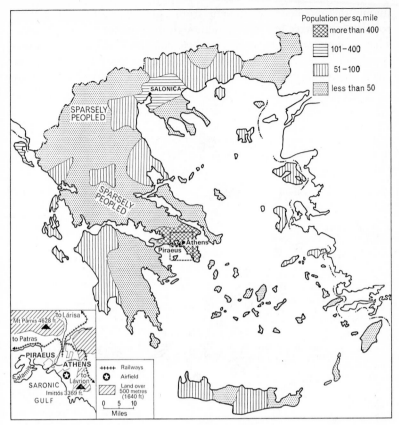

FIG. 146.—Greece: population. The rural and semi-urban population (living in communes of less than 10,000 people) is 4,747,000 (census 1961), 56% of the total population. The metropolitan area of Athens, which includes a number of boroughs under their own mayors, has a population of 1,900,000 (*see* inset map), nearly one-fifth the country's total.

THE ECONOMY

GENERAL CHARACTERISTICS

Greece is an agricultural country. Just under half the working popula-tion is engaged on the land and responsible for the chief exports (currants, olives, olive oil, tobacco, grapes, citrus fruits, cotton) of the country. Of these, tobacco is the most important. Greece is a country of small farms. Over 90% are less than 10 acres in size, and their owners cannot afford modern machinery or fertilisers, so that yields are low. The Government is encouraging co-operation, with good results on the larger plains, but many of the farms in the interior are too tiny and too scattered among the mountains to benefit from agrarian reforms. The rural population is increasing rapidly; although the pressure is relieved somewhat by emigration, the small farms are constantly adding to the overpopulation of the countryside. There is no easy solution to this problem, but it is obvious that if Greece is to achieve a more balanced economy

FIG. 147.—Greece: chief towns; minerals. Greece's mineral resources, although limited, are varied. Output (in thousand metric tons) of main ores amounts annually to: lignite, 2550; bauxite (aluminium), 884; iron, 297; pyrites, 164; manganese, 126. Mineral oil has been discovered north-east of Dráma.

than it has at present, there must be a great development of industry to attract the surplus workers from the land.

The Government is conscious of this problem but is handicapped by lack of capital and natural resources. The extensive highlands have poorly distributed and inadequate possibilities for hydro-electric power developments; soil erosion is serious, in spite of the great efforts made to combat it; minerals are present in large variety but rarely in sufficient quantity for successful exploitation; and communications over large areas, especially of central peninsular Greece, are almost non-existent. Some so-called main roads are little more than rough, boulder-strewn tracks. Great numbers of the inhabitants are illiterate, and one of the major elements in the Government's social policy is an educational programme aimed at improving the cultural standards of the people and raising the quality of the labour force.

Industrial development is slow, but it is proceeding along well-planned lines. Existing food processing, textile, chemical and light engineering industries are being extended and modernised, notably in the regions of densest population, and new industrial areas are growing in Western Macedonia and Euboea. The export of mineral ores has fallen, since they are used more and more at home. In agriculture, the policy is to reduce the cultivation of wheat in favour of cotton, animal feeding stuffs, fruit, vegetables, meat and dairy produce. Extensive investment is under way in irrigation and land reclamation projects. The tourist industry is under review, and new hotels and better facilities are being provided. The merchnat fleet, especially passenger liners, has been increased enormously. In the period 1950–63 the average annual rate of growth of the gross national product, that is, of all branches of Greek economy, was 6·4%, one of the highest in the world. In 1964, industrial production alone increased by over 12%. Official figures show also that today Greece ranks fifth as a world passenger shipping owner, after Great Britain, Italy, France and the U.S.A.

These great efforts to bring Greece's economy more in line with that of Western countries have attracted enormous amounts of capital and material assistance from abroad, in particular from the U.S.A. But the motives of the Western powers are not entirely altruistic. Greece forms a natural barrier or buffer between the Western world and the Soviet Communist bloc. The Western countries hope that, by building up the Greek economy and helping the country to develop its resources, Communist influence and infiltration will be minimised. So far their efforts have been effective, and official Greek political sympathies lie with the West.

1. *Peninsular Greece*

(a) *Western peninsular Greece*. In general, Epirus is a poor, highland region. Agriculture occupies 82% of its population, of whom the vast majority live in the coastal plains of Árta and Yannina (Ioánnina). The chief crops in the lowlands and valleys are maize, barley, rye, tobacco and a little wheat. Walnuts, chestnuts and figs are grown everywhere in

T

Epirus, and the Plain of Árta has citrus fruits and olives. There is as yet no industrial development. The largest towns, Yannina (35,000), Árta (16,900) and Préveza (11,200) are little more than straggling villages. The Loúros hydro-electricity station, which generates 10 million kWh annually, may lead to the growth of industry in Yannina.

Off the coast are the Ionian islands, of which the chief are Corfu (Kérkira), Sta Maura (Levkás), Cephalonia (Kefallinía) and Zante (Zákinthos). The largest and most important island is Corfu, which has fertile soils and one of the densest populations of all the Greek islands. Two-thirds of its area is cultivated for vines, olives, citrus fruits, vegetables and maize. Similar crops are found in the other islands of the group. The Ionian islands are noted for their olive oil, reputed to be the best in Greece; and grapes, as well as being used for wine, are dried as raisins. Corfu (27,000) is the chief port and the centre of a growing tourist trade.

(b) *Central peninsular Greece.* The Pindus and other mountains in the centre of peninsular Greece are well wooded, but have only a very sparse population and no towns. Some lumbering is carried on, and the making of charcoal and gathering of acorns have local importance. The chief occupation is sheep rearing, especially in the north, where Vlach shepherds live almost isolated from the rest of Greece. At the southern end of the central region, lying along the coast of the Gulf of Corinth, are the small plains of Agrínion and Phokís, which grow good crops of wheat, maize and tobacco. Both plains have extensive vineyards, and Phokís is noted for olives and olive oil.

(c) *Eastern peninsular Greece.* The eastern side of the Greek peninsula contains a large proportion of the richest agricultural land and almost all the industry of Greece. From north to south there is a succession of coastal plains, some only very small. The largest are the Plain of Thessaly, which is broken by hills into the basins of Tríkkala, Kardhítsa and Lárisa; the Plain of Phthiótis, which is really the river Sperkhiós valley; and the Plains of Boeotia and Attica. All the plains grow wheat, maize, tobacco, vines and olives. The Plain of Thessaly has mulberry groves and cotton fields, and the latter cover an increasing area in Boeotia. Sericulture in Thessaly gives promise of a future silk industry, but at present most of the crop is exported. In Thessaly, too, cattle-rearing and cheese making are prominent. The Plain of Attica has large market gardens and fruit orchards, to supply the demands of Athens.

In the east of the peninsula there is a varied, though as yet small, mineral production. Large deposits of lignite occur on the island of Euboea, around Kími and Alivérion. In the latter town is the largest thermo-electric power plant in Greece, supplying half the current used in Athens–Piraeus. Lignite occurs also outside Athens. Iron ore and nickel are mined in Phthiótis, and lead and zinc at Lávrion, in Attica. Chromium occurs in Phthiótis and Thessaly, and widespread deposits of bauxite have been found eastwards from Mount Parnassus.

In Thessaly, a power station on the Mégdhova, a tributary of the Achelóos, generates 250 million kWh per annum. Plans are well advanced for another station on the Achelóos itself. The impounded waters will serve irrigation systems in the Plains of Agrínion and Thessaly.

[*Courtesy of the Greek Embassy.*

FIG. 148.—Greece: hydro-electric power plant, Tavropos, Thessaly. Most of the hydro-electricity of Greece is generated along the rivers Achelóos and Piniós, in the Pindus mountains, and supplies the plains of Thessaly and Epirus. The Ládhon hydro-electricity plant supplies part of the Peloponnesus.

Small industries, such as cigarette making in Agrínion and Lárisa (55,400), olive oil processing at Eleusís and many other towns, and fish drying and salting at Missolonghi (Mesolóngion), are scattered through eastern Greece and along the plains north of the Gulf of Corinth; but there are only two real industrial regions: a small one in the Plain of Thessaly, and a much larger one around Athens and Piraeus. The capital of Thessaly is Lárisa, which makes textiles, farm implements and matches, but the centre of industry is Vólos (49,200), its chief port, which has growing shipbuilding and chemical industries.

Athens was sited nearly 1000 years B.C. on the slopes of a hill in Attica where it could be protected by the Acropolis, a citadel built on the

T 2

summit. In the course of time Athens spread to the surrounding plain, and was linked by roads to the port of Piraeus. Today the capital and port form one city, with a population of 1,852,700. Prior to 1830, when Greece became an independent kingdom, Athens was only a small town but, like Rome, when it was made capital of the country it grew at a phenomenal rate. It is in consequence a modern city and only a few fragments, such as the Acropolis, tell of its antiquity. (*See* inset, Fig. 146.)

Athens itself is concerned mainly with administration, commerce, banking and tourism. Its chief industrial area lies south-west of the city and extends to Piraeus. Here are food processing, chemical and textile manufactures, agricultural and railway engineering, and the making of electrical apparatus. Piraeus has shipbuilding and oil refining. It is the chief port of Greece, dealing with 44% of its exports and 66% of its imports.

2. *The Peloponnesus*

The name Peloponnesus means "the island of Pelops," because the ancient Greeks thought this southern peninsula was an island. The Peloponnesus, also called Morea, is joined to peninsular Greece by the narrow Isthmus of Corinth, which has been pierced by a canal. The Corinth Canal, constructed in the nineteenth century, is too narrow and shallow for modern vessels and it is planned to deepen and widen it in the near future. The Peloponnesus has played a most important role in the history of Greece, for in it grew the famous city states of Corinth, Sparta, Argos, Messene and Olympia. Set well back from the sea in fertile, sheltered lowlands, they were safe from attack by sea-rovers and were clear of the malarial swamps which fringed the river mouths. From them sailed the Greek traders and pioneers who carried the influence of Greece to all parts of the Mediterranean basin.

The mountains which cover most of the Peloponnesus run in four finger-like ranges from north to south. They enclose several plains, some in high hollows in the interior of the peninsula, others along the south coast. On the west coast, in the lower basin of the river Ládhon, is the Plain of Olympia. The highlands have forests of pine, oak, cedar and wild olive, but there has been much wasteful cutting, and large areas are covered with garrigue, on which sheep and goats are reared. The largest of the enclosed basins is around Trípolis (18,500), which lies in a kind of polje, with no outlet for surface waters. The marshes that used to cover the basin have been drained; wheat and maize are grown on its floor, vines and fruit on the surrounding slopes. The absence of olive groves denotes a variation from the typical Mediterranean climate.

As in peninsular Greece, the chief products of the lowlands of Peloponnesus are wheat, maize, rice, barley, grapes and olives. The coastal plains of Argos and Messene are noted for citrus fruits, figs and vegetables, while cotton and tobacco are of increasing importance. In recent years, large irrigation and drainage schemes in all the plains have increased the cultivable area, almost eliminating malaria; and the hydro-electric power station on the river Ládhon, besides providing current for the growing industries of Patras and Pírgos, serves as flood control for the Olympian plain, where an extensive coastal marsh has been reclaimed and then irrigated.

Deposits of lignite have been found in the plains of Patras, Olympia and Messene. South-west of Corinth, iron ore has been discovered, and iron pyrites south of the city, but there has been little exploitation as yet. Red and yellow marble is quarried in the easternmost mountain ridge.

The outstanding product of the Peloponnesus is currants, the dried fruit of vines which produce small, black grapes. The vineyards cover the narrow plain of Patras and all the surrounding slopes. The word "currant" derives from "Corinth," which was once the chief exporter but has been superseded by Patras. Currants are still known in France as *raisins de Corinthe*, *i.e.* dried grapes from Corinth. Today Corinth is a decayed port, with 15,900 inhabitants, and Patras (95,400) has become not only the chief port of the Peloponnesus but the third largest in Greece. Its industries include the making of machinery, cotton goods, paper and wine.

Other towns in the Peloponnesus are Kalámai (38,200), the outlet of the Messene plain, with machinery and soap works, olive oil presses, and cigarette and tile manufacturing; Pírgos (20,500), in Olympia, with flour mills, soap and chemical works; and Argos and Návplion, little more than villages, with flour milling and fruit and vegetable canning.

3. *Macedonia and Thrace*

These are the newest additions to Greece, having been acquired in 1913 and 1919 respectively. Before then they were most backward in their economies. Only since 1922, when the Greeks expelled from Turkey were settled in the region in exchange for repatriated Turks, has there been any considerable industrial and agricultural advance. Thrace is still completely agricultural, except for a small metallurgical industry which has developed near Didymótichon (Dimotika) as a result of asphalt deposits and a few veins of uranium and thorium. Macedonia, with better soils and resources, has become one of the most prosperous parts of Greece.

Western (or High) Macedonia lies among mountain ranges running from the Pindus towards the Aegean Sea. Within the mountains are two large basins, around the upper Aliákmon river in the south, and a more northerly one which contains Lake Vegorrítis (Ostrovo) and extends southwards to Ptolemaís. Only a few years ago these basins were almost deserted, the only inhabitants a few Vlach herdsmen tending their sheep. They were then developed in much the same way as the intermontane basins of Yugoslavia, being drained and re-settled. Today they support wheat, maize, plums and vines. Kozáni (21,500) has become the market for an important wheat region and has a leather industry based on local hides. Édhessa (15,500), in the northern basin, has a flourishing textile industry.

Western Macedonia is undergoing an industrial transformation. In 1954 the construction of dams began on the Aliákmon river. When completed they will supply water to thousands of acres of new cultivable land in the Kozáni basin. The Agra hydro-electric scheme, using the waters of a tributary of the Aliákmon, is already in operation and the Ptolemaís thermo-electric power station, the most ambitious of its kind in Greece, was opened in 1959. The Ptolemaís scheme is based on deposits of lignite found within the Flórina–Ptolemaís–Kozáni triangle, estimated to total upwards of 9000 million tons. The coalfield, besides supplying fuel for the power station, will provide processed lignite for the railways, and for industrial and domestic use throughout Greece. Already there is an output of nitrogenous products, especially fertilisers, and there are plans for a major chemical industry.

In eastern Macedonia, the plains of Campania (the lower Vardar), Seres (the lower Struma) and Philippi are among the most fertile in Greece, especially since rivers have been controlled, reservoirs constructed, irrigation and drainage schemes well advanced, and delta swamps minimised. Lake Yiannitsá in the Vardar flood-plain and Lake Tachinos in the Struma valley have been completely drained, and their beds turned into rich farmland. The lowlands of eastern Macedonia have been transformed within the past twenty years and are producing ever-increasing crops of wheat, maize, rice, sesame, tobacco and cotton. In the older lowlands— that is, those already under cultivation before 1913—there are mulberry trees (for sericulture), vines and orchards, but in the reclaimed areas there is a notable absence of trees. Except in the limestone peninsula of Chalcidice, the olive is rarely found in Macedonia.

The number of areas growing cotton should be noted. Greece is the only country in Europe which can grow and export a surplus of raw cotton, and it is the policy of the Government to increase output at the expense of the ubiquitous wheat and maize. Dairy farming, too, for which the Macedonian plains are well suited, is being encouraged.

Besides the lignite in western Macedonia there are deposits of iron ore and pyrites in Chalcidice, chromite and asbestos in Kozáni and manganese and uranium in Dráma.

The plains of Thrace grow the same products as the Macedonian plains, but methods are still often primitive. The chief crop is tobacco of the "oriental" variety, of which Thrace has almost a monopoly; there are olive groves and cotton fields near the coast. Behind Alexandroúpolis (Dedéagach) is a small lignite deposit, and in north-west Thrace borings are being made for oil.

The chief city of Macedonia is Salonica (Thessaloníki), the second port of Greece, with a population of 251,000. Situated near the mouth of the river Vardar, it is also the outlet for southern Yugoslavia, and its hinterland extends northwards beyond Belgrade. Its function as an international port was reduced for some years following the Second World War because of political claims and counter-claims but, with the easing of tension between Greece and Yugoslavia, Salonica is recovering its former role as the chief port of the northern Aegean. It is also the most important industrial centre in Greece, after Athens–Piraeus. Its activities in food processing, cotton and silk textiles, agricultural engineering, chemicals, leather, soap and shipbuilding are likely to be increased with the development of the Ptolemaís scheme.

Dráma (32,200) and the port of Kaválla (44,500) are the chief towns of the Plain of Philippi, and are markets for the Macedonian tobacco crop. The largest towns in Thrace are Komotiní (28,350) and Alexandroúpolis (18,700), its port.

4. Insular Greece

Although the Greek islands are noted for their scenic beauty, they are with few exceptions backward in their economy, poorly peopled and of minor importance.

(i) The islands of the northern Aegean—Thásos, Samothrace, Lemnos and the Northern Sporádhes—are all unproductive.

(ii) The eastern group of islands includes Lesbos, Chios, Sámos and the Dodecanese. The first three are mountainous but they include stretches of fertile lowland, which produce cereals, tobacco, cotton, citrus fruits, vegetables and olives. Lesbos produces one-fifth of Greece's olive oil and Mytilene (Mitilíni) (25,750), its chief town, has oil pressing, soap and cotton thread factories.

The Dodecanese, known also as the Southern Sporádhes, were Italian possessions until 1945. Since that date, land reclamation projects on a large scale have resulted in marked agricultural progress, especially in the yield of wheat, cotton, water-melons, sesame and fruit. Sponge diving is important off the islands of Kálimnos and Sími: an average of 60 tons of sponges is gathered yearly.

(iii) Life in the high, limestone islands of the Cyclades (Kikládhes) in the south of the Aegean is difficult and backward, and many of the people emigrate. The chief occupations outside subsidence farming are the production of wine and mineral ores. Emery is mined in Náxos, iron ore in Sériphos and manganese in Andros, but the total output is small.

(iv) *Crete*. The mountainous backbone of Crete (Kríti) has been largely deforested. In the cleared areas and on the upper slopes there is much garrigue, on which sheep and goats are reared by transhumant shepherds. In the forests there is some lumbering and, as in the Peloponnesus, reafforestation schemes are helping to preserve timber resources, at the same time combating soil erosion and reducing the encroaching garrigue. Crete is often quoted as the type example of Mediterranean climate and polyculture, but the importance of its production of wheat, maize, vines, olives, tobacco and citrus fruits in the economy of Greece is easily exaggerated. Cattle are reared in the coastal lowlands, and a dairying industry, subsidised by the Government, is developing. The only mineral exploited in Crete is iron ore, which occurs at Kastélli.

Crete has a population of about half a million, mostly crowded into the plains in the centre and west of the north coast. The largest towns and ports are Iráklion (Candia) (63,500) and Khaniá (Canea) (38,500). Both have industries dependent on agricultural activities, *e.g.* olive oil processing, tanning, soap manufacture and wine production. Crete is the south-eastern outpost of Europe, and its strategic position in the eastern Mediterranean has given the island a stormy history. In ancient days it was the home of the little-known Minoan civilisation. Before it became part of Greece in 1913, it had been successively under Arab, Venetian and Turkish domination. In the Second World War it was invaded by Germany, which hoped to use it as a stepping-stone to the Middle East. The devastation which resulted has only just been repaired.

STUDY QUESTIONS

1. Make a geographical comparison between the Adriatic and Aegean Seas. (O. & C.)

2. Only a small proportion of the land area of Greece is capable of cultivation. What are the main restrictions on agriculture in this region and what are the main products of the farming carried on there? (O. & C.)

3. Divide Greece into its natural regions and give an account of *two* of them. (O. & C.)

4. Give a reasoned comparative account of economic development in Greece and Austria. (J.M.B.)

5. Comment upon the salient differences between the human geography of Greece and Denmark. (J.M.B.)

6. What are the geographical factors which have contributed to the growth of Athens and Salonica?

7. Describe, and suggest reasons for, the distribution of population in Greece.

Chapter XXXIII

MALTA, ALBANIA AND TURKEY-IN-EUROPE

ALTHOUGH the countries of Malta, Albania and Turkey-in-Europe are distinct European states and lie at some distance from each other, they are dealt with here in one chapter because they are among the least important Mediterranean countries and are too small to warrant separate chapters.

MALTA

The Maltese islands rise from a submarine shelf which extends southwards from Sicily, and include Malta (95 square miles), Gozo (26 square miles) and Comino (1 square mile). The islands are composed mainly of Tertiary limestones, which rise in western Malta to the Rabat plateau,

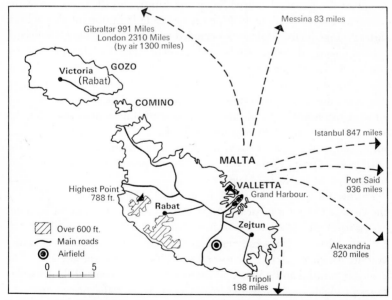

FIG. 149.—The Maltese islands: the strategic value of Malta at the "crossroads of the Mediterranean" is best seen from an atlas map of the Mediterranean Sea. In their small area (about 121 square miles) the islands have a population of 329,000: an average density of 2700 persons per square mile, which is far too great for the total amount of foodstuffs grown.

571

whose highest point is about 700 ft in altitude. The west coasts of all the islands are cliff-girt and inhospitable, but the east coasts are lower and have some good harbours. On the eastern sides of the islands occasional patches of sandstones overlie the limestone, and these have broken down to form a thin but fertile soil.

The climate of the Maltese islands is typically Mediterranean, but the porosity of the limestone surface has resulted in a parched, almost treeless landscape and an agricultural economy in which goat-rearing predominates. Irrigation is possible in a few small areas, where wheat, vegetables and cotton are the chief crops, and potatoes and onions are grown for export. Away from the industrial region which has developed around Valletta, the chief occupation everywhere is agriculture. But the Maltese islands in their tiny space have a population of 329,000 and an average density of over 2700 persons per square mile; the amount of food produced on the small (rarely more than 5 acres) farms is totally inadequate. The islands are overcrowded, and there is large-scale emigration, principally to London, Canada and Australia. Between 1948 and 1962 over 80,000 Maltese settled overseas.

The central position in the Mediterranean of the island group, commanding the passage between Sicily and Libya, and the existence of the excellent Grand Harbour in Malta have made it important throughout history. Like Sicily, Malta was occupied successively by the Phoenicians, Carthaginians, Romans, Arabs and French. The Knights of St John owned the islands for over 200 years until they were expelled by Napoleon. In 1814 the Maltese asked to be annexed to the British Crown and Malta became a British fortress, the whole of its economy being directed later in the nineteenth century towards maintaining and protecting its strategic value on the Suez route to the East. The Grand Harbour was improved, and around it grew the naval base and dockyard of Valletta. The great majority of the town's inhabitants were dependent in one way or another on the Royal Navy.

During the Second World War, in which Malta *en bloc* was awarded the George Cross for its steadfastness and courage in the face of constant attack from sea and air, it was realised that the strategic value of the islands had diminished. Ships can travel farther without refuelling and aerial warfare has changed strategic values. For these reasons, and because of the changed political and military situation at the eastern end of the Mediterranean, which resulted in the loss of control over the Suez Canal, the British Government decided to close the naval base and dockyard. This was a serious blow to Malta's economy, for most of its workers were employed by the defence services and there was no alternative demand for labour.

Civilian industries were concerned with the processing of foodstuffs and the manufacture of cigarettes, or with crafts such as lace-making and glove manufacture. Further opportunities of increasing work on the land were very limited. To ease the situation, the British authorities assisted in the conversion of the dockyard to civilian use, and built docks and wharves to accommodate large cargo vessels. British firms were encouraged to introduce light engineering, and twenty new factories are producing fibres, textiles, paint, furniture, plastics and other goods. Great efforts are being made to encourage the growing and export of flowers, and tourism is increasing. In both these new developments, rapid air transport is a big advantage. The success of the new ventures—especially shipbuilding—will depend on how far the Maltese can compete in the world market with rivals already well established.

In 1964, Malta was given its independence within the British Commonwealth. Some of its political leaders, however, wish to form a republic outside the Commonwealth and the uneasy internal political situation is complicated by tensions between these leaders and the Church, which opposes them. The Church in Malta is powerful, for the great majority of the inhabitants are Roman Catholics.

Most of the people of the Maltese islands live in small towns or large villages, built on defensive sites. The chief town is Valletta, on the Grand Harbour. Originally a naval port and dockyard, it is now attempting to become an entrepôt port by extending its wharf and warehouse capacity. It has shipbuilding, light engineering, iron pipe manufacture and food processing, and exports the products of the craft industries. In the interior of the island of Malta is Rabat, situated where springs from the limestone hills provide water for irrigation; it is a market town with a light engineering industry. The island of Gozo has proportionately more good soil than Malta. Its largest town is Victoria (also called Rabat), many of whose inhabitants are farmers owning land outside its boundaries but living in the town for defensive purposes.

ALBANIA

PHYSICAL ASPECTS AND CLIMATE

Albania lies between Yugoslavia and Greece. One of the smallest countries in Europe, it consists of a coastal plain hemmed in by high mountain ranges. The plain is narrow in the north and widens southwards to its termination near Vlonë (Valona). It is crossed by low, limestone ridges which sometimes extend from the interior mountains to the coast, where they form headlands (see Fig. 150a). Between these ridges there are flat, alluvial stretches, often ill-drained, liable to floods and malarial. In the east of the plain, near the foot of the mountains, better-drained alluvial fans provide good farmland and sites for settlement. The coastline from the river Drin in the north to Vlonë is low-lying and discordant, but from Vlonë southwards it resumes the usual Dinaric concordance, with a mountain range parallel to the coast.

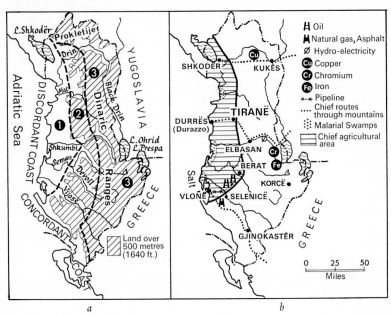

FIG. 150.—Albania: (*a*) physical features and divisions, (*b*) economic. The numbers in (*a*) refer to the divisions used in the text. For continuations of the chief routes through the mountains, *see* Fig. 114.

The interior of Albania consists in the south of four, and in one area five, parallel mountain ranges. In the north, the number is reduced to two but they are higher and more impenetrable. The Prokletije range, which rises to over 8000 ft, forms an almost impassable barrier between Albania and Yugoslavia. The southern mountains, although still difficult, are pierced by passes from the upper valleys of the rivers Drin, Shkumbi and Vijosë; the Shkumbi valley leads to the upper Vardar valley and to Skopje, in Yugoslavia.

Between the southern ranges are longitudinal valleys, in one of which are Lakes Ohrid (Okhrida) and Prespa (Prespansço), lying astride the international boundary. Other intermontane depressions include the basins of Korcë (Koritsa) and Kukës. The mountains, especially in the north, are deeply dissected and their inhabitants are isolated not only from the outside world but often from each other. It was this factor which was

largely responsible for their long-continued backwardness and—when
one community attempted to penetrate the territory of another—for the
blood feuds known as *vendette*.

Albania has a Mediterranean climate, modified in the interior by
altitude or by rain-shadow effects. On the whole, the country forms part
of the eastern Adriatic region of high rainfall: the plains in the north have
a rainfall of over 40 in. annually, most of it in winter. The mountains in
that season are often snow-covered.

HISTORY AND PEOPLE

The Albanians are the descendants of Illyrian peoples who were
pushed westwards by the successive advances of Greeks, Slavs and Turks,
and who took refuge in the difficult Dinaric mountains. Many of the
invaders intermarried with the Illyrians. There were incursions also of
Romans and, more recently, of Italians. The present Albanians are a
mixture of all these, but two distinct types have emerged: the Ghegs
north of the river Seman, and the Tosks to the south. The Ghegs are
taller, more backward and of purer Illyrian blood; the Tosks are shorter
in stature and more influenced by Greek culture, many of them belonging
to the Greek Orthodox Church. Near the northern borders of Albania,
a minority of the Ghegs are Roman Catholics. Two-thirds of the total
population are nominally Mohammedans converted to Islam by the Turks,
who ruled Albania from 1477 to 1912. The Albanians speak various
dialects of a language called Skipetar, which is derived from Thraco-
Illyrian—the original language of the Balkans—and has borrowed from
Latin, Greek, Slav and Turkish. There was no written Albanian language
until late in the nineteenth century.

Albania came into existence as a separate state in 1913, and then only
because Italy would not agree to the region becoming part of Greece or
Yugoslavia. The reason was that Italy did not want either country to
control the main routes which pass through the Albanian mountains and
give land connections between the Adriatic and Aegean seas. The country
remained disunited and in a state of anarchy until 1925, when it was
proclaimed a republic under President Zog, who later had himself elected
king. He looked to Italy for financial help to develop Albania's economy,
and in 1927 allied his country with Italy. Mussolini, however, proved to
be a false friend. In 1939 his army invaded Albania, expelled the king and
occupied the country. In 1945, after the defeat of the Italians in the Second
World War, Albania became an independent state once more, but the
Communists took control and the country was proclaimed a People's
Republic.

Worn out by war, its resources undeveloped, Albania was in no
U

position to improve its economy single-handed. The Communists allied themselves to Yugoslavia, another Communist country, in the hope of obtaining economic assistance. When Yugoslavia abandoned Soviet Communism and dissociated itself from Moscow they had to turn to the Soviet Union for help. But the Albanian people, especially those in the mountainous parts of the country, are unsatisfactory co-operators. There are intense local rivalries and jealousies which used to lead to blood feuds and still cause political disruption; religious differences between Christians and Mohammedans are a source of friction; large numbers of Albanians cling to the traditions and oriental way of life which have existed for centuries, and show no wish to change.

The Soviet Union was very ready to assist Albania, for she was anxious to obtain a foothold in the Mediterranean, and her initial efforts were directed to building naval strong points and bases along the Albanian coastline. These did not help the country's agricultural economy and so in 1964 Albania began to look farther afield, to Communist China, for economic aid. In consequence, the Soviet Union has abandoned some of its building schemes and has withdrawn many of its experts and most of its financial assistance. Soviet policy, as other satellite countries have found, seems to have aimed at exploitation rather than assistance. The exports of oil, grain and timber demanded from Albania in return for aid in building up the country's economy were so exorbitant as to foster intense resentment and to bring about political re-alignment which is a source of anxiety both to the Soviet Union and to the Western world. The advent of Communist China in the sphere of European politics may have far-reaching results.

THE ECONOMY

More than 90% of Albania's population of 1,665,000 are engaged in some form of agriculture, yet the area under cultivation amounts to not more than 12% of the country's surface. The inhabitants of the mountains live by subsistence farming and by transhumant sheep and goat rearing. Their villages lie on narrow strips of alluvium in deep river gorges. In the wider intermontane basins, maize, wheat, barley and vegetables are cultivated; and the small towns of Korcë, Kukës and Gjinokastër serve as markets (see Fig. 150b).

The coastal plains are being drained and reclaimed, but there are still malarial swamps in the lower river valleys and along the lagoon-lined coast. The reclaimed lands, and the alluvial fans at the foot of the mountains in the east and south, have fertile soils and produce good crops of wheat, maize, barley, rice, tobacco and cotton. Vines, olives and mulberries thrive on slopes throughout the plains. Most of the larger towns are situated near the junction of mountains and plain. The chief are Tiranë (130,000), the capital, Shkodër (41,000), Elbasan (26,000) and Berat. On two of the very few good harbours along the coast are the ports of Durrës (Durazzo) (32,000) and Vlonë (33,000). Durrës is the main port of Albania and is connected to Tiranë by the country's only railway.

Albania has mineral resources which may lead to future industrial activity, but most of them have as yet been little exploited. Two small oilfields south-west of Berat produce about 500,000 tons of oil annually. The output is sent by pipeline to Vlonë, where there is a small refinery. Most of the oil is exported, mainly to the U.S.S.R. and China. Albania has sufficient oil for its own present small requirements. There is considerable water power potential in the mountains, and two hydro-electric plants have been constructed to feed Tiranë. Copper is mined in the Drin valley and chromium near Lake Ohrid; salt is obtained by evaporation at Vlonë. There are natural gas and asphalt deposits at Selenicë, and a large field of hematite iron ore near Lake Ohrid, but exploitation of these has only just begun.

The industries of Albania are still in their infancy. They are concerned with oil refining, food processing and hydro-electric plant upkeep. There are a few textile factories, but textile manufacture is still a craft industry carried on in homes throughout the country. Albania has at present the least promising economy of any European country, and any future advance appears to be dependent on outside help.

TURKEY-IN-EUROPE

"Turkey-in-Europe" consists of the lands on the western side of the Bosphorus, the Sea of Marmara and the Dardanelles (collectively known as the Straits), which separate Europe from Asia. It comprises about 3% of the total area of Turkey and is all that is left of Turkey's European possessions, which at one time included the whole of the Balkan peninsula. It remains a part of the Turkish republic more or less as an accident of history, as is explained later.

STRUCTURAL DIVISIONS AND REGIONAL ECONOMY

European Turkey forms part of the basin of the lower river Maritsa, being drained by the Ergene, one of its tributaries. It may be divided into (1) the plain of Thrace, with its enclosing highlands, and (2) the Straits. The Straits are treated separately more because of their strategic significance than because they form a distinct physical region.

1. *The plain of Thrace*

Most of European Turkey consists of the plain of Thrace, through which flow the river Ergene and its tributaries to join the Maritsa, which forms the whole of the Turko-Greek boundary. North of the plain, and running in part along the Black Sea coast, are the Strandja Dag (Istranca Dağlari), a mountain range composed of Palaeozoic rocks similar to those

FIG. 151.—Turkey-in-Europe: physical. Turkish Thrace, as Turkey-in-Europe may be called, is of strategic value only to Turkey. It serves rather as an agricultural supplier to Istanbul than as a contributor to the economy of the country as a whole.

in the Rhodope massif and rising in Mount Mahya to 3396 ft. To the south, shutting off the lowlands from the Sea of Marmara, are the Tekir Dag, lower in altitude than the northern mountains but sufficiently high to exclude most Mediterranean climatic influences. The Strandja Dag have been eroded into knobs rather than peaks. They have considerable areas of forest, but only a sparse population. All the mountains have suffered deforestation, and rapid run-off of the rainfall, which amounts to over 40 in. annually in the northern ranges, has resulted in soil erosion and coastal swamps. The lowlands have a climate which tends to be continental, the winters being bleak and the summers hot. The rainfall, which comes at all seasons but with a maximum in winter, is not sufficient for tree growth, and the natural vegetation of the plain of Thrace is steppe.

Much of the plain is used for sheep and cattle pasture, or for extensive wheat cultivation with low yields. Near the rivers or where artesian wells have been sunk for irrigation there are better crops of wheat, barley and vegetables, for the soil of the plain of Thrace is alluvial and naturally fertile if water is available. Cattle rearing for milk is important and supplies the needs of the large population of Istanbul. Rainfall increases towards the mountains and, besides the crops already mentioned, maize, hemp, sunflowers, tobacco and sugar beet are grown. There are also orchards of plums, which are dried as prunes. Tree crops, however, are few and there is an almost complete absence of Mediterranean arboriculture, except along the short stretch of Aegean coastline. The swamps of the lower Maritsa have been drained and rice is grown on the reclaimed lands.

The plain of Thrace is gradually becoming one of the best cultivated regions in Turkey; but it is more important as the food-producing hinterland of Istanbul and as a boundary zone protecting the European side of the Straits than as a part of Turkey's economy. The only town of note in the plain of Thrace is Edirne (Adrianople), with a population of 31,900.

2. The Straits

The Straits consist of the Bosphorus, the Sea of Marmara and the Dardanelles. The Sea of Marmara is an area of subsidence which is permanently flooded by the waters of the Black Sea. The Bosphorus and the Dardanelles are drowned river valleys but, although they have roughly the same alignment, it is not certain they belonged to the same river. The Bosphorus, a strait cut into hard rocks between the Black Sea and the Sea of Marmara, is 20 miles long and varies in width from 800 yards to $2\frac{3}{4}$ miles. The Dardanelles—known to the ancient world as the Hellespont—joins the Sea of Marmara to the Aegean Sea. It is a strait 40 miles long and up to 4 miles wide, carved in soft Cretaceous and Tertiary rocks, which also overlie parts of the Tekir Dag. The magnificent harbour of the Golden Horn, around which Istanbul is built, is a drowned tributary valley.

The Straits are the most important north–south passage in southern Europe east of the Rhône–Saône corridor but, since they belong in part to Asia as well, any consideration of their political and strategic importance must take account of this. The Straits form a natural gateway from the Soviet Union to the Mediterranean, and on several occasions Russia has attempted to control the narrow passage. Since Russia became a Communist State, it has been the policy of the Western powers to support Turkey's ownership of both sides of the Straits and, by giving Turkey

FIG. 152.—Turkey-in-Europe: general view of the Bosphorus. Taken from a hill near Istanbul, looking south. This narrow passage separates Europe (*right*) from Asia (*left*). Along its shores are fishing villages, holiday resorts and pine woods. The trees in the foreground are Mediterranean pines.

financial and political aid, to minimise any close co-operation between that country and the Soviet Union. They are, in any case, enemies of long standing. In a sense, Turkey is being subsidised to act as guardian of this most important gateway and its economic value, although still great, is secondary to its political status. The Soviet Union, with little hope at present of controlling the Straits, has adopted a policy of penetration towards the Mediterranean by dominating Bulgaria and befriending Albania. A completely Soviet-controlled land route from the Black Sea to the Mediterranean is broken, however, by Yugoslavia, which although Communist is not in full accord with Moscow.

For over 1500 years the Straits have been guarded by Istanbul (Byzantium; Constantinople), a key point where land routes are crossed by sea routes (*see* Figs. 119 and 153). The ancient Greek colony of Byzantium was chosen in 330 by Constantine as the site of the capital of the Roman Empire of the East. His new city, Constantinople, on the harbour of the Golden Horn, protected to the south by cliffs and to the west by strong walls, was an almost impregnable fortress. The Byzantine Empire remained the eastern bastion of Christendom for over a thousand years until at last, after two long sieges and the failure of the West to come to its aid, the city fell to the Turks in 1453—one of the most critical victories in European history, for it led to the domination of south-eastern Europe by the Ottoman Turks. Constantinople was made capital of the Ottoman Empire and held that function until 1924, when Kemal Ataturk moved his capital to Ankara.

When Constantinople was the Turkish capital, the overland trade route from Central Europe to Asia Minor was important, but the removal of

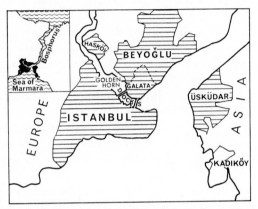

FIG. 153.—Turkey-in-Europe: the site of Istanbul. Built astride two continents some twenty-six centuries ago, the city commands the entrance to the Black Sea. From A.D. 330 to 1453 it was capital of the Eastern Roman Empire, until Sultan Mehmet II captured it and made it capital of the new Turkish Empire. After the revolution of 1919–22, modern Turkey chose the ancient Hittite city of Ankara as capital.

the capital and the Turkish withdrawal from the Balkan peninsula reduced its value. Renamed Istanbul, the city lost much of its economic pre-eminence. Fifty years ago it had a population of over a million but when it lost metropolitan status this fell to about 700,000. Since 1924 the city has been modernised and is today an industrial centre. Besides acting as an entrepôt for the whole of northern Turkey, it has cotton and woollen textile and carpet manufactures, light engineering, leather, pottery, paper, cement, food-processing and shipbuilding industries. The population of Istanbul—including the suburbs of Galata and Beyoğlu on the northern side of the Golden Horn, and Üsküdar on the Asiatic side of the Bosphorus —had grown to 1,459,500 in 1964 and is still increasing. It is now more than twice the size of Ankara.

HISTORICAL OUTLINE

As a reward for entering the First World War on the side of the United Kingdom and France, Russia in 1914 was promised a strip of Turkish territory which was to include the Turkish Black Sea coastlands and the Bosphorus, with Constantinople. Russia, however, was itself torn by revolution in 1917 and was unable to take part in the negotiations which followed the Allied victory in 1918. This was the "accident of history" referred to earlier in the chapter. By the negotiations, the Aegean coastlands of Turkey were given to Greece, the southern coastlands to Italy, and the Straits became a "special zone," for the time being not allocated to any country. Turkey was to be reduced to a tiny state in the middle of Anatolia.

These arrangements were upset by Kemal Ataturk, the "father of the Turks," who came to power in 1922, dethroned the Sultan, set up a republic and began to transform the whole social, religious and political economy of his country. Taking absolute political power, he led his people against the Greeks and drove them from the Aegean coastlands of Turkey. In 1923 he forced the occupying troops of Britain, France and Italy to withdraw from the whole of Anatolia. By the Treaty of Lausanne, Turkey's sovereignty over Asia Minor was recognised and she was given control of the Straits, as well as of the small hinterland now known as Turkey-in-Europe.

By the same treaty it was agreed that an exchange of populations should take place between Greece and Turkey, so as to make the two countries more homogeneous in race. Exceptions were made for many of the Turkish tobacco farmers of Eastern Thrace and for Greek merchants in Constantinople. About 1½ million Greeks were moved from Turkish Thrace and Anatolia to Macedonia and replaced by 700,000 Turks, an exchange more favourable in numbers to Turkey. In both countries, however, the movement of homeless people caused great misery and distress. The effect of Ataturk's reforms in European Turkey was to reduce Istanbul's political and economic importance by transferring its administrative functions to Ankara. But, situated as it is at probably the finest "cross-roads" position in the world, it was inevitable that Istanbul should become once more the greatest industrial centre in the Near East and that its strategic value would be maintained.

STUDY QUESTIONS

1. Write a short essay on the position and strategic importance of the Maltese Islands.

2. Describe the position and trade of the following ports: Naples; Valletta; Trieste. Sketch-maps are essential. (O. & C.)

3. Write a concise account of the geography of Albania.

4. Make a geographical study of the Adriatic coastlands of the Balkan peninsula. (J.M.B.)

5. Discuss the influence of the position and relief of Albania on the life and trade of its inhabitants.

6. Analyse the factors which have influenced the site and importance of Istanbul.

7. Write an account of the use of irrigation in the agriculture of the Mediterranean region of Europe. (O. & C.)

8. Give an account of transhumance in Southern Europe.

9. Indicate the relationships which exist between rainfall and land use in the Mediterranean coastlands of Europe. (J.M.B.)

10. Illustrate the truth of the following: "The pattern of the political map of the Scandinavian peninsula is very different from that of the Balkan peninsula; any attempt to explain this must take a variety of features into account."

Chapter XXXIV

EUROPE: A POLITICAL AND ECONOMIC SUMMARY

PRESENT-DAY Europe occupies less than 10% of the habitable area of the world, yet within its boundaries lie a disproportionate number of the political units known as independent or sovereign states or nations. Throughout European history, communities possessed of common traditions and ways of life have tended to think of themselves as distinct from their neighbours and have striven to achieve some kind of independence. In the past, most of them were unsuccessful in doing so for any length of time and were grouped into empires such as the Holy Roman Empire and its successors, the Austro-Hungarian and German empires, or the vast Ottoman Turkish régime. Since 1800, however, and more especially during the present century, historical events have led to an acute nationalistic self-consciousness in many such states, and to a profound desire for "self-determination," *i.e.* for sovereign status.

In the nineteenth century—excluding developments in Germany and Austria, which countries already existed in some form—there came into being Greece, Italy, Serbia, Bulgaria and others. After 1918, Finland, Poland, Latvia, Estonia, Lithuania and Hungary were given sovereign status. Latvia, Lithuania and Estonia have since been forcibly incorporated into the Soviet Union, but there still remains in them, and in the Ukraine, a strong desire for independence; in each there are well-developed separatist movements.

Most of the new countries were brought into existence with a common language as a unifying factor, but language cannot always be regarded as a reliable guide to nationality. In Switzerland, for instance, where German, French and Italian are spoken, as well as the indigenous Romansch, different languages have never been a bar to national unity. Tradition rather than language decided the boundaries of Czechoslovakia (where Czech and Slovak are spoken) and Yugoslavia (with Serbo-Croat, Slovene and Macedonian languages). In the latter two countries, however, the different language groups are not yet as mutually amicable as the Swiss, and separatist agitations have occurred in both.

However, language seems in the present century to be the dominant factor in the plea for self-determination, and where linguistic "minorities" have formed important economic communities they have often been the cause of political unrest and even bloodshed in the countries housing them. German-speaking peoples, for instance, live in Austria (where German is the national tongue) and Switzerland; there are German minorities in Italy, eastern France, Luxembourg, Belgium and Hungary. Today they do not present a political problem, but it must be remembered that it was the German minority in the Sudetenland of Czechoslovakia that was a factor in the outbreak of the Second World War. Catalans and Basques form disquieting linguistic minorities in Spain; so do Macedonians in Yugoslavia, Greece and Bulgaria. Even in Belgium, where French- and Flemish-speaking peoples are in a ratio of (roughly) 3 to 5 and have the same political rights, there are tensions. These, however, are based only incidentally on language: economics are a more potent factor, as we saw in Chapter XIII.

Minority problems are most numerous in south-eastern Europe, where the complexity of peoples, languages and cultures has led to the region being called the "Shatter Belt." On both sides of the frontiers between Rumania and Hungary, Rumania and Bulgaria, Greece and Turkey, Greece and Yugoslavia, Greece and Bulgaria, and Yugoslavia and Bulgaria, there are zones of "mixed" languages which have been the cause of political quarrels, boundary disputes and frequent changes of frontiers. These have been minimised in recent years by exchanges of population—compulsory or voluntary—which will increase homogeneity of language in all these countries.

In the past fifty years, movements of population have been a notable feature in Europe. Some were the direct result of war, others were caused by economic pressure. In the years 1914–21 they were small and sometimes only temporary. Belgian refugees, for instance, came to the British Isles in large numbers during the First World War, but most of them returned to their homeland on the cessation of hostilities. There were more permanent migrations during this period of Poles, Lithuanians and "White" Russians to the United Kingdom, France and U.S.A., of Macedonians from Yugoslavia to Bulgaria, and of Greeks from Asiatic Turkey. The movements during and after the Second World War were more extensive. During the war hundreds of thousands were carried off from occupied lands by Germany and Russia to work in labour camps and on military and industrial projects; most of these were able to return to their homes after the war, but large numbers of the survivors were left homeless and destitute in foreign lands.

Of greater impact on the economy of Western Europe were the crowds of anti-Communist "displaced" Poles, Hungarians, Lithuanians and Ukrainians who escaped through the closing Iron Curtain and sought refuge in the countries of the "free" world, where they are now more or less integrated in their new homes. Jews, who suffered almost complete extermination in Nazi Germany, were among the worst sufferers in these migrations from central Europe, and large numbers fled to Israel, Rumania and the Americas. Finns were driven by the Soviet Union from the Viipuri and Petsamo regions to settle elsewhere in Finland or to emigrate to Sweden or the U.S.A. About $1\frac{1}{2}$ million Greeks were expelled from Turkish Thrace and Anatolia in exchange for approximately half that number of Turks. Perhaps the greatest number of migrants were Germans. They were expelled from East Prussia and the Polish-occupied region east of the Oder–Neisse line, and from Czechoslovakia. More Germans, amounting to millions, fled from Communist rule in East Germany and East Berlin, mainly to West Germany. Poles from the Soviet-annexed eastern half of the country were settled in Germany's lost Eastern Territories.

In addition to the movements which were an aftermath of war, more than a million workers from southern Europe migrate annually to western Europe, to meet the labour needs of industrial countries. Up to 1961 about half were from Italy, but since then the Italian economy has improved and the numbers leaving that country have fallen. Nevertheless, Italy remains the greatest exporter of labour, having sent about 300,000 workers to West Germany and nearly as many to Switzerland. Italians go to France, too—another major importer of workers, receiving annually in addition an average of 140,000 Spaniards, 60,000 Portuguese and many Moroccans and Tunisians. Greece and Turkey are the other main suppliers of labour to the west. 115,000 Greeks and 85,000 Turks are at present working in West Germany, but the flow of emigrants from these countries is being discouraged in view of improvements planned in their own industrial and agricultural economies. On the other hand, against this loss of manpower by the under-developed countries must be placed the return of hundreds of thousands of foreign emigrants after a couple of years abroad, bringing back to their mother countries new industrial skills which may be used to advance economic expansion.

Political boundaries did not alter much as a result of the Second World War, that is, after 1945, but what did emerge was a division into Western and Eastern Europe, into non-Communist and Communist countries, separated by the so-called Iron Curtain. The chief Communist country is the U.S.S.R., which dominates all the states on its western borders from the Baltic to the Black Sea. These satellites—Eastern Germany, Poland, Czechoslovakia, Hungary, Rumania and Bulgaria—have become buffer states, forming a strategic barrier between the U.S.S.R. and the west; they are organised by the Soviet Union both for mutual military assistance (by the Warsaw Pact, 1955) and for economic and commercial development. Albania is also a signatory of the Warsaw Pact but is separated from the U.S.S.R. by Yugoslavia, which although a Communist country has less close ties with Moscow and is not behind the Iron Curtain.

Faced by this powerful Soviet *bloc*, the non-Communist countries of the Western world began to consider ways and means of amalgamation,

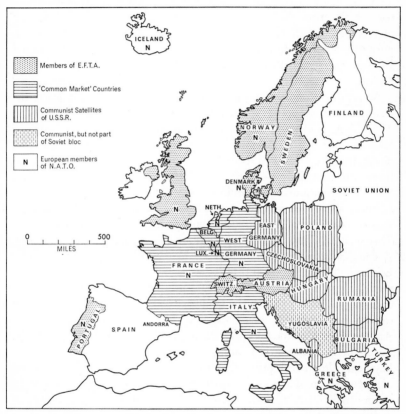

Fig. 154.—Europe: political. Showing also political and economic groupings.

militarily, politically and commercially, but in such a manner as not to destroy their independence or sovereignty. In 1948 the Brussels Treaty was signed by the United Kingdom, France and the Benelux countries, to last for 50 years. The Brussels Treaty Organisation, as it was called, ensured "collaboration in economic, social and cultural matters and for collective self-defence." In the following year, 1949, as a result of a pact between the same three signatories together with the United States, Canada, Denmark, Italy, Norway, Portugal and Iceland, the North

Atlantic Treaty Organisation (NATO) came into existence and set up an integrated defence force for Western Europe. This organisation has its headquarters—Supreme Headquarteers, Allied Powers in Europe (SHAPE)—in Paris. It is noteworthy because for the first occasion in history the United States allied itself in peace time for defensive purposes with Europe. Greece and Turkey were admitted to NATO in 1951 and West Germany in 1954. In 1950, NATO took over the defensive function of the Brussels Treaty Organisation and some of its economic objects were transferred to other organisations set up specifically for the purpose (*see below*). In 1954, Italy and West Germany signed the amended Brussels Treaty and the organisation changed its name to the Western Union.

As regards economic co-operation, the first point to be noted is the changed attitude of the United States after the Second World War. The U.S.A. not only abandoned its isolationist policy but also began to take the initiative in planning a programme of recovery for the war-devastated, impoverished countries of non-Communist Europe, and helped to carry it out. In the immediate post-war years, the United States poured thousands of millions of dollars into Europe, along with technical advice and assistance; and this had wonderful results in helping those countries participating in the European Recovery Programme (the "Marshall Plan") to begin rehabilitation.

The work in Europe was supervised by the Organisation for European Economic Co-operation (OEEC), set up in 1948. When Marshall Aid was discontinued in 1952, the OEEC turned its attention more fully to encouraging trade between the countries of Western Europe and began to act as a co-ordinating body, setting up further economic organisations. Among them were the European Payments Union (EPU) in 1950 and the European Coal and Steel Community (ECSC) in 1952. The European Payments Union dealt primarily with currency problems and the balance of payments in and between participating countries. It has helped to restore trade relations among Marshall Aid countries and between them and the rest of the world.

The background of the European Coal and Steel Community needs some explanation. Coal, iron and steel are vitally important for industrial development: any country that has adequate supplies of coal and iron ore of the right quality is fortunate. But in western Europe the two are seldom located close together within one country in large enough quantities and of the necessary quality, as we have seen in earlier chapters. Either the coal is not of great value for coking or the iron ore content is low and uneconomic to smelt. France, for instance, although a large coal producer, has to import metallurgical coke from Germany for her blast furnaces and steel works in Lorraine. West Germany, on the other hand, has some of the best deposits of coking coal in Europe, but is short of iron ore to feed the Ruhr industrial region. Luxembourg needs coal but has large amounts of iron; Belgium and the Netherlands have coking coal but little iron ore. In all these countries, too, there were variations in the cost of extraction and processing; in general, the price of steel in countries which had to import iron ore was greater than in those rich in coal.

In order to achieve some degree of integration between the producing countries so that the cost of steel would be reduced, Robert Schuman, Foreign Minister of France, proposed in 1950 what is now called the Schuman Plan. From it evolved in 1952 the European Coal and Steel Community, composed of France, West Germany, Benelux and—later— Italy. The ECSC is the central authority which pools raw materials and finished steel, and fixes prices. It works reasonably smoothly, although it has entailed some surrender of national sovereignty and of individual control; and it has had a beneficent result on Franco-German political relations.

Of greater economic importance is the fact that the six countries of ECSC decided in 1959 to extend their agreement so as to cover all trade between them. This European Economic Community (EEC; the Common Market) intends to remove all customs and tariff barriers between its members by 1970, so building up a powerful trading *bloc*. This will be an enormous step forward on the road to a United States of Western Europe, a concept that has been advanced by many statesmen but which still hangs fire because of the persistent fear that sovereignty and national status will be curtailed.

In 1962 the United Kingdom applied to join the Common Market but was refused permission, just as in 1950 it had been excluded from participation in the Schuman Plan. In the meantime Britain organised the European Free Trade Association (EFTA) in partnership with Norway, Sweden, Denmark, Austria, Switzerland and Portugal, but this association ("The Outer Seven") bears little comparison in wealth or productivity with the Common Market countries ("The Inner Six"). Efforts are now being made to bring EFTA and EEC into closer economic association. Finland, Spain, Greece and Eire have so far remained unallied to either of the trading groups.

Although the EPU and the ECSC—and to some extent the Common Market—were offshoots of OEEC, some of the credit must be given to the Council of Europe. This organisation was set up in 1949 with headquarters at Strasbourg to examine the possibility of political integration in Europe, that is, of the "United States of Europe" mentioned above.

Fifteen countries are represented on the Council, whose members are all from parliaments or legislative assemblies. The Council has no controlling or directive authority over its constituent countries, but acts as a centre for information and debate. Another post-war development is the General Agreement on Tariffs and Trade (GATT), with headquarters in Geneva. It was set up to try to reduce tariffs on a world-wide basis and has been very effective in increasing international trade. GATT was sponsored by the United States and is intended to serve the whole world, not just Western Europe.

This summary of the politico-economic organisations that have been set up in Europe leads to a consideration of the significant changes taking place in the industrial and agricultural development of the continent, and particularly in the under-developed ("backward") countries. Two-thirds of the countries of Europe are agricultural, and they lie mainly to the east and south of the continent. The Iron Curtain, besides being a political and ideological barrier, divides Europe into an industrial West and an agricultural East—remembering always that in the industrial countries of the West there are extensive areas of highly mechanised and efficient agriculture, and that in the East there are important industrial regions in the U.S.S.R., East Germany, Czechoslovakia and Poland. Southern Europe, with the exception of north and north-east Spain, northern Italy and part of Yugoslavia, is predominantly agricultural. Standards of living in all these eastern and southern countries are far below those in western Europe: in general, the less industrial activity there is, the lower the standard. Unfortunately, this has led to the concept that purely agricultural countries are somehow "inferior," and that to improve themselves they must become industrialised.

It is true that successful industrialisation makes a country less dependent on imported manufactured goods and in the long run raises the standard of living; and we have seen how many under-developed countries in Europe are introducing industry with this end in view. Many of them, however, have neither the fuel nor the raw materials to do so effectively. Their first efforts have led to a wasteful use of available resources and a struggling economy. Moreover, their infant industries are in competition with the older and more highly developed industrial regions of the west, and to obtain a share in the world's markets their products must be sold at competitive prices. Some countries have attempted to do it by subsidies, but such methods lay a heavy burden on the whole community and delay improvements in the standard of living. Even in the Soviet Union, where the natural resources are enormous, the emphasis placed on the development of heavy industry and manufacturing has led to unrest in the agricultural sector of the population, which has been required to supply ever greater quantities of foodstuffs to feed the growing towns, but with no substantial reward for its labours.

In the west, Denmark, recognising the futility of trying to compete with industrial countries, "industrialised" its agriculture. A similar development would appear to be the economic solution for countries like Hungary, Rumania, and large parts of Poland, Greece and other states, where efforts to introduce heavy industry are being made. The first objective of such countries should be to bring their agriculture up to date and limit their industrial development to the furtherance of this policy, with manufacturing industry concerned primarily with processing the products of the field. Many of the new enterprises in the Iron Curtain countries, such as the steel works on the Danube in Hungary, established and maintained by imports of fuel, raw materials and technical help from the Soviet Union, have an uncertain future. In Greece, the ambitious Ptolemaís scheme depends on imported machinery at present and on imported mineral ores in the future, but because there are large fuel resources it has much better prospects.

A more enlightened agrarian policy in the under-developed countries would ensure that exports of agricultural produce paid for imports of heavy machinery, engineering products of all kinds and increased quantities of consumer goods. It would mean, too, that industrial and agricultural countries could fulfil their respective functions more effectively, and that the interdependence of states would be more clearly realised. The standard of living in agricultural countries might not equal that of the industrial communities, but it would be improved more rapidly than by their own problematical industrialisation.

The industrial west and the agricultural east and south of Europe, though differing in culture and social advancement, are economically complementary. Each needs the other. Despite the Iron Curtain and the "cold war," trade has been maintained between east and west, and is increasing. More important, the distinction between the economies of the countries on opposite sides of the Iron Curtain is gradually being blurred; the richer West and the Soviet Union are each actively concerned with effecting improvements in the other's sphere of influence. For example, a new oil refinery being built at Szazhalombatta, 15 miles south of Budapest in Hungary, will have machinery from the Soviet Union, distillation plant from Czechoslovakia and automation equipment from France. A paper mill in Budapest will be equipped with machinery from London and stapling machines from Sweden. It is significant that at the international Budapest Trade Fair in 1965, there were 150 exhibitors from West Germany, 90 from the U.S.A. and 50 from the United Kingdom.

In industry, Europe remains a great "workshop of the world." In agriculture, the potential is great. Increased yields and productivity are being achieved everywhere, including the under-developed countries. Developments in hydro-electric power resources; the growth of light industries; the spread of irrigation and drainage schemes; the exploitation of mineral deposits; the introduction of much-needed mechanisation and modern scientific methods into agriculture, are all bringing new hope to backward economies and reducing political enmities. The economic future of Europe may not be dazzling but it looks eminently sound.

A SHORT GUIDE TO FURTHER READING AND STUDY

THE following guide to the study of the geography of peninsular Europe does not pretend to be comprehensive, but it contains most of those books which have been found of value in Sixth Form work. With a few minor exceptions in French, it is confined to books in English or translated from the original language. For some European countries, surprisingly little detailed information is published in textbook form; in these cases the official handbooks issued by their governments have proved useful. A list of the embassies and legations from which they may be obtained is given on page 597. For some of the volumes listed below, editions have been published at dates later than those given. Some of the older books are now out of print, but may be consulted at public libraries. Articles in geographical magazines and journals are kept to a minimum, as they are often beyond the scope of Sixth Form study or are ephemeral in nature. Much up-to-date information about population, production statistics, sources of raw materials, new developments in agriculture, engineering and communications, etc., is to be found in *Geographical Digest*, published annually by Philip (London).

THE CONTINENT OF EUROPE

Blanchard R. and Crist R. *A Geography of Europe.* Methuen, 1935.
Gottmann J. A. *A Geography of Europe.* Harrap, 1955.
Hoffman G. W. (Ed.). *A Geography of Europe.* (Methuen, 1953).
Houston, J. M. *A Social Geography.* Duckworth, 1953.
Manners, G. "The Pipeline Revolution," *Geography*, vol. XLVII, 1962.
Pound, N. J. G. *Europe and the Mediterranean.* McGraw-Hill, 1953.
Shackleton, M. R. *Europe: A Regional Geography.* Longmans, Green, 1958.
Unstead, J. F. *A Systematic Regional Geography*, vol. 2, "Europe." University of London Press, 1953.
Valkenburg, S. and Held, C. C. *Europe.* Chapman & Hall, 1952.

PHYSICAL BACKGROUND OF EUROPE

Collett, L. W. *The Structure of the Alps.* Arnold.
de Martonne, E. *A Shorter Physical Geography.* Christopher, 1927.
Hardy, M. E. *The Geography of Plants.* Oxford, 1925
Holmes, A. *Principles of Physical Geology.* Nelson, 1957.
Jacks, G. V. and Whyte, R. O. *The Rape of the Earth.* Faber & Faber, 1949. (A classic study of soil erosion)
Joly, J. *The Surface History of the Earth.* O.U.P., 1930.
Kendrew, W. G. *The Climates of the Continents.* O.U.P., 1961.
Miller, A. A. *Climatology.* Methuen, 1953.
Money, D. C. *Introduction to Human Geography.* University Tutorial Press, 1962.
Newbigin, M. I. *Plant and Animal Geography.* Methuen, 1950.
Robinson, G. W. *Soils.* Allen and Unwin, 1950. (The final chapter, "The geography of soils," is an excellent introduction to modern soil science)
Taylor, Griffith. *Urban Geography.* Methuen, 1961.

Tyrrell, G. W. *Volcanoes.* Butterworth, 1931.

Wills, L. J. *The Physiographical Evolution of Britain.* Arnold. (Contains material on continental Europe)

Wooldridge, S. W. and Morgan, R. S. *The Physical Basis of Geography.* Longmans, Green.

Wright, W. B. *The Quaternary Ice Age.* Macmillan, 1936.

NORTHERN EUROPE

Bjornsson, B. *Iceland: A Geographical, Political and Economic Survey.* Reykjavik, 1962. (Reprinted from *Viðskiptaskráin*; obtainable from the Icelandic Embassy)

Cundall, L. B. *Western Europe.* Harrap.

Denmark. Issued by the Royal Danish Ministry for Foreign Affairs, Copenhagen, 1956. (Obtainable from the Danish Embassy)

Facts about Iceland. Issued by the Publishing Department of the Cultural Fund, Reykjavik, 1962. (Obtainable from the Icelandic Embassy. NB: Many governments issue "Facts" books, which give a geographical summary and up-to-date trade statistics)

Facts about Norway. Issued by Aftenposten, Oslo, 1963. (Obtainable from the Norwegian Embassy)

Hille, E. A. *Swedish Life and Landscape.* Elek, 1947.

Jakobsson, G. (Ed.). *Iceland Today.* Landkynning, Reykjavik, 1961.

Karjalaiten, A. *A National Economy Based on Wood.* Tammi, Helsinki, 1957.

Knudsen, O. *Norway.* Issued by the Norwegian Ministry of Foreign Affairs, Oslo, 1961.

Kokko, Y. *The Way of the Four Winds.* Gollancz, 1954. (An excellent description of the Lapps in Finland)

Koljonen, J. "Finnish Wood," *Finnish Paper and Timber Trade Journal,* Helsinki, 1958.

Life in Denmark. Issued by the Royal Danish Ministry for Foreign Affairs, Copenhagen, 1957.

Mead, W. R. *An Economic Geography of the Scandinavian States and Finland,* University of London Press, 1958.

Miesma, J. (tr. P. Sjöblom). *Facts about Finland.* Otava, Helsinki, 1957. (Obtainable from the Finnish Embassy)

Norway's industries. Issued by the Federation of Norway's Industries, Oslo, 1958. (Obtainable from the Norwegian Embassy)

O'Dell, A. C. *The Scandinavian World.* Longmans, 1960.

Powrie, P. J. and Mansfield, A. J. *North-west Europe.* Harrap, 1959.

Somme, A. (Ed.). *The Geography of Norden: Denmark, Finland, Iceland, Norway, Sweden.* Heinemann, 1961.

Woods, E. G. *The Baltic Region.* Methuen, 1932. (Mainly physical)

WESTERN EUROPE

Belgique: terre de paix et de travail. Issued by the Belgian Office of Foreign Affairs, Brussels, 1958. Obtainable from the Belgian Embassy. (In French)

Bull, G. B. G. "The Netherlands Delta Plan," *Geography,* vol. XLVII, 1962.

"Changes in population in France," *Geography,* vol. XLVII, 1963.

Cundall, L. B. *Western Europe.* Harrap.

de la Blache, P. (tr. H. C. Brentnall) *The Personality of France.* Christophers, 1928.

de Martonne, E. (tr. H. C. Brentnall) *The Geographical Regions of France*. Heine-mann, 1952. (Does not cover all the regions but is excellent in the correlation of physical features and landscape)

Delta Plan, The. A booklet issued by the Information Department of the Nether-lands Ministry of Transport, 1958

Demangeon, A. "Belgique, Pays-Bas, Luxembourg," *Géographie universelle*, vol. 2. Armand Colin, 1927. (A classic, in French)

Desonay, F. *Belgium in a Nutshell*. Lumière Publishing Co., Brussels, 1955. (Obtainable from the Belgian Embassy)

Digest of the Netherlands, in 5 parts. Issued by the Netherlands Government In-formation Service, 1959.

Facts about Denmark. Issued by the Danish Ministry of Foreign Affairs, Copen-hagen, 1958. (Obtainable from the Danish Embassy)

Graftdijk, K. *Holland Rides the Sea*. World's Window, Baarn, Holland, 1960. (A first-hand account of land reclamation in the Netherlands)

Holland as a Trade Partner. Issued by the Netherlands Government Economic Information Service, The Hague.

Laborde, E. D. *Western Europe*. University of London Press.

Monkhouse, F. J. *The Belgian Kempenland*. University Press of Liverpool, 1949.

Monkhouse, F. J. *A Regional Geography of Western Europe*. Longmans.

Mutton, A. F. A. *Central Europe*. Longmans, Green. (Contains a section on the Benelux countries)

Ormsby, H. *France: A Regional and Economic Geography*. Methuen, 1950.

Powrie, P. J. and Mansfield, A. J. *North-west Europe*. Harrap, 1959.

Thompson, I. B. "Land reclamation in Eastern Corsica," *Geography*, vol. xlvii, 1962.

The French government, through its Secrétariat Général du Gouvernement, publishes a monthly series of *La documentation photographique:* photographs and notes dealing with French geography, history and sociology (in French).

CENTRAL EUROPE

Arntz, H. *Facts About Germany*. Issued by the Press and Information Office of the Federal German Government, 1960. (Obtainable from Federal German Em-bassy)

Bauer, H. *All About Switzerland: A Short Survey*. Issued by the Swiss National Tourist Office, Zürich, 1963.

de Martonne, E. "Europe centrale," *Géographie Universelle*, vol. 4. Armand Colin, 1931. (In French; covers Switzerland, Austria, Hungary, Czechoslovakia, Poland and Rumania. A classic)

Dickinson, R. W. *Germany*. Methuen, 1953.

Dickinson, R. W. *The Regions of Germany*. Routledge & Kegan Paul, 1945.

Egli, E. *Swiss Life and Landscape*. Elek, 1949.

Elkins, T. H. *Germany*. Christophers, 1960.

Elkins, T. H. "The Economic Background to Berlin." *Geography*, vol. xlvii, 1962.

Facts about Czechoslovakia. Orbis, Prague, 1962. (Obtainable from the Czecho-slovakian Embassy)

Germany reports: Land and People. Issued by the Press and Information Office of the Federal German Government, Bonn, 1961.

Lipski, W. *Agriculture in Poland*. Polonia Publishing House, Warsaw, 1962.

Mutton, A. F. A. *Central Europe*. Longmans, Green.
Poland: Facts and Figures. Polonia Publishing House, Warsaw, 1962. (Obtainable from the Polish Embassy)
Pounds, N. J. G. *The Economic Pattern of Modern Germany*. Murray, 1963.
Pounds, N. J. G. *The Ruhr: A Study in Historical and Economic Geography*. Faber, 1952.
Sinnhüber, K. A. *Germany: Its Geography and Its Growth*. Murray, 1961.
Votrubec, C. and Maxova, H. *Czechoslovakia: Its Geography*. Orbis, Prague, 1962.
Wanklyn, H. *Czechoslovakia*. Philip, 1954.

SOUTH CENTRAL EUROPE

de Martonne, E. *Europe centrale*. (In French: see above. Has sections on Hungary and Rumania)
Directives for the Development of the People's Republic of Bulgaria, 1961–80. Foreign Languages Press, Sofia, 1963. (Obtainable from the Bulgarian Legation)
Hamilton, F. E. I. "Yugoslavia's Hydro-electric Power Industry," *Geography*, vol. XLVIII, 1963.
Hutira, E. *The Development of the National Economy in the Rumanian People's Republic*. Meridiane, Bucharest, 1963. (Obtainable from the Rumanian Legation)
Lopandić, D. *Yugoslavia: Economic and Tourist Guide*. Privedni Pregled, Belgrade.
Marjanovic, P. (Ed.). *1000 Facts About Yugoslavia*. Yugoslavian Publishing House, Belgrade, 1963. (Obtainable from the Yugoslavian Embassy)
Rumanian Statistical Pocket Book. Central Statistical Board, Bucharest, 1963.
Statistical Pocket Book of Yugoslavia. Federal Institute for Statistics, Belgrade, 1963.
Vagács, A. *A Short Geography of Hungary*. Pannonia, Budapest, 1961.

SOUTHERN EUROPE

Buckley, P. *The Spanish Plateau*. Chatto & Windus, 1962.
Chantal, S. (tr. F. R. Holiday). *Portugal: The Land and Its People*. Shell Portuguesa in conjunction with the Portuguese Secretariat of Information, 1950. (Obtainable from the Portuguese Embassy)
"Factual Information on Greece," *National Economy*, series C. Prime Minister's Office, Foreign Press Division. Athens, 1958.
Itinerari del Sud. A series of seven booklets issued by the Cassa per il Mezzogiorno, 1962, through the Italian State Tourist Department, Rome. (An outline account of the proposed development and the completed projects in southern and insular Italy. Obtainable from the Italian Embassy)
Newbigin, M. I. *The Mediterranean Lands*. Christophers.
Newbigin, M. I. *Southern Europe*. Methuen, 1952.
Robinson, H. *The Mediterranean Lands*. University Tutorial Press, 1960.
Some Useful Facts About Greece. Prime Minister's Office, Foreign Press Division. Athens, 1963. (Obtainable from the Office of the Commercial Counsellor, London)
"Turkey," a *Guardian* survey. Reprinted from the *Guardian*, 8th August 1963.
Walker, D. S. *The Mediterranean Lands*. Methuen, 1960.
Walker, D. S. *A Geography of Italy*. Methuen.
Way, R. *A Geography of Spain and Portugal*. Methuen, 1960.

EMBASSIES AND LEGATIONS

Austrian Embassy, 18 Belgrave Square, S.W.1
Belgian Embassy, 103 Eaton Square, S.W.1
Bulgarian Legation, 12 Queens Gate Gardens, S.W.7
Czechoslovakian Embassy, 6–7 Kensington Palace Gardens, W.8
Danish Embassy, 29 Pont Street, S.W.1
Finnish Embassy, 66 Chester Square, S.W.1
French Embassy, 58 Knightsbridge, S.W.1
German Federal Republic: the Embassy, Chesham Place, S.W.1
Greece: Office of the Commercial Counsellor, 49 Upper Brook Street, W.1
Hungarian Legation, 35 Eaton Place, S.W.1
Icelandic Embassy, 1 Eaton Terrace, S.W.1
Italian Embassy, 14 Three Kings Yard, Davies Street, W.1
Luxembourg Embassy, 27 Wilton Crescent, S.W.1
Netherlands Embassy, 38 Hyde Park Gate, S.W.7
Norwegian Embassy, 25 Belgrave Square, S.W.1
Polish Embassy, 47 Portland Place, W.1
Portuguese Embassy, 11 Belgrave Square, S.W.1
Rumanian Legation, 4 Palace Green, W.8
San Marino Consulate-General, 19 St Peter's Road, Twickenham
Spanish Embassy, 24 Belgrave Square, S.W.1
Swedish Embassy, 29 Portland Place, W.1
Swiss National Tourist Office, 458 Strand, W.C.2
Turkish Embassy, 43 Belgrave Square, S.W.1.
Yugoslavian Embassy, 25 Kensington Gore, S.W.7
U.S.S.R. Embassy, 13 Kensington Palace Gardens, W.8

EXAMINATION QUESTIONS

1. Write a geographical appreciation of the difficulties at this time of any *one* continental European country. (O. & C.)

2. In what ways is the increasing use of hydro-electric power bringing about a new distribution of manufacturing industries? Give illustrations from Europe. (O. & C.)

3. "The political unity of a state can be greatly assisted by its physical geography but there are instances of political unity being achieved despite unfavourable physical conditions." Examine this statement with reference to Europe. (O. & C.)

4. Write an essay on "The interdependence of the European coal and steel industries."

5. "The chief reasons for the localisation of manufacturing industries in Europe are to be found in the distant past and under technological conditions very different from those of today." Examine this statement, quoting examples from at least *two* European countries. (O. & C.)

6. "Language is by no means an infallible guide to nationality." Examine this statement with particular reference to Europe.

7. Examine the importance of site in a consideration of any *three* capital cities of Europe. (O. & C.)

8. "Density of rural population bears no direct relation to soil fertility." Illustrate this statement from Europe. (O. & C.)

9. "A state has always a natural focus, but rarely a natural frontier." Illustrate this statement from the nation states of Europe. (O. & C.)

10. Comment on the significance in the development of the states of Europe of any *two* of the following: the Moors; the Vikings; the "Mark" states; the St Gotthard Pass; the Rhine; the Pyrenees. (O. & C.)

11. What qualities do you look for in a political capital? Illustrate your answer from *either* Paris *or* Berlin. (O. & C.)

12. Explain why the shipbuilding industry of continental Europe is concentrated in a few localities. (J.M.B.)

13. Compare the position and the functions of *one* major port on the Atlantic or North Sea coasts of mainland Europe with *one* major port on the Mediterranean coast of the same continent. (J.M.B.)

14. Throughout much of the main valley of the river Rhine the density of population is high, whereas in the valleys of the Elbe and Vistula it is much more variable. Discuss reasons for this contrast between the Rhine valley and the valley of *either* the Elbe *or* the Vistula. (J.M.B.)

15. Give a reasoned account of the distribution in Europe of developed hydro-electric power. (J.M.B.)

16. Discuss the distribution of the major coal resources of peninsular Europe. (J.M.B.)

17. Which countries of Europe do you consider to be under-developed? Explain the basis for your assessment and indicate the problems involved in the development of these countries. (J.M.B.)

18. Explain, and illustrate with specific examples in Europe, (a) entrepôt trade, (b) transhumance, (c) terrace cultivation, (d) international river. (J.M.B.)

19. Discuss the survival in contemporary Europe of regional groups of subsistence cultivators. (J.M.B.)

20. With reference to specific areas in Europe, examine the importance to human activities of water conservation and control. (J.M.B.)

INDEX

Main references are indicated by figures in **bold type**